THE GREAT BIG QUIZ BOOK

THE GREAT BIG QUIZ BOOK

MARTIN H. MANSER
GEORGE BEAL
CLIVE TROTT

Miles Kelly
PUBLISHING

Designer
Angela Ashton

Project Management
Ian Paulyn

Editorial Assistants
Liz Dalby and Helen Parker

Artwork Commissioning
Susanne Grant

Production
Jo Brewer

Editorial Director
Paula Borton

Art Director
Clare Sleven

Director
Jim Miles

First published in 2000 by Miles Kelly Publishing
Bardfield Centre, Great Bardfield, Essex, England CM7 4SL

24681097531

Copyright © Miles Kelly Publishing

Produced by Miles Kelly Publishing Ltd
Bardfield Centre, Great Bardfield, Essex, England CM7 4SL

ISBN 1-902947-80-0

Printed in Finland

The Great Big Quiz Book is divided into three sections: two adult sections and a children's section. Each of the quizzes is made up from one of the following categories.

- General Knowledge
- Natural History
- Geography
- English Language
- Cinema and TV
- Pop Music

- Literature
- History
- Famous People
- Sport and Leisure
- Science and Nature
- Entertainment

CONTENTS

Section 1

Section 2

Children's Section

HISTORY

1 Who was king of England in the year AD1000?

2 In which year was William Shakespeare born?

3 12 October, or the second Monday in October, is a public holiday in many states of the USA. What event of 1492 does it commemorate?

4 What event of 1453 is thought to have contributed substantially to the renaissance of learning and art in western Europe?

5 The composer Johann Sebastian Bach and George Frederick Handel were both born in the same year. What year was it?

6 Who compiled a book of words (published in 1852) that were arranged according to their meanings?

7 How many years after the Battle of Trafalgar did the Battle of Waterloo take place?

8 What was the number of the last King Louis to be king of France?

9 Who said 'When a man is tired of London, he is tired of life; for there is in London all that life can afford'?

10 When did Adolf Hitler come to power in Germany?

11 Who became president of the United States in 1929, the year of the Wall Street Crash?

12 In what year did Elvis Presley first enter the UK charts with 'Heartbreak Hotel'?

13 Which British politician won the Admiral's Cup in 1971 in his yacht 'Morning Cloud'?

14 In which year was a British task force sent to recover the Falkland Islands after an Argentinian invasion?

15 In which year did Tony Blair become leader of the British Labour Party?

ANSWERS

1. Ethelred II. 2. 1564. 3. Christopher Columbus's discovery of the New World. 4. The fall of Constantinople to the Turks. 5. 1685. 6. Peter Mark Roget. 7. 10 (1805–1815 – strictly 9 years and 8 months, Oct 1805–June 1815). 8. 18th (Louis XVIII 1814–24). 9. Samuel Johnson. 10. 1933. 11. President Hoover. 12. 1956. 13. Sir Edward Heath. 14. 1982. 15. 1994.

FAMOUS PEOPLE

1   David Ben Gurion became prime minister of which country in 1948?

2   Which film director once said of Brigitte Bardot, 'If she didn't exist, we'd have to invent her'?

3   By what name was the heavyweight fighter, Cassius Clay, better known?

4   In 1950 who made the allegation that 205 State Department officials were 'card carrying communists'?

5   Which US pop artist created '100 Campbells Soup Cans'?

6   Who killed John Lennon?

7   In 1961 which famous dancer sought political asylum in Paris?

8   Whose controversial radio broadcast of H. G. Wells *The War of The Worlds* (1938) caused widespread panic in the US?

9   For what crime was Al Capone finally convicted?

10 Who founded the state of Taiwan in 1949?

11 Which former Reuters' employee went on to create one of the world's most famous secret agents?

12 Who was known as the 'Sultan of Swat'?

13 Who wrote *The Common Sense Book of Child Care*?

14 Which Russian revolutionary died of head wounds on 21 August 1940?

15 Whose compositions included 'The Firebird' and 'Petrushka'?

SPORT & LEISURE

1 Was the first FA Cup Final held in: (a) 1868, (b) 1872 or (c) 1876?

2 In which month is the Ascot race meeting held?

3 In motor racing, what is the colour of flag to signify 'Danger, no overtaking': (a) red, (b) blue or (c) yellow?

4 What is the name of the international biennial yachting event coinciding with 'Cowes Week'?

5 How many pieces does each player have in Backgammon?

6 'Boston Crab' is a term used in which sport?

7 What is the name of Chicago's American Football team?

8 How many pegs or marbles are there in a Solitaire board game?

9 The author Dick Francis was formerly famous in which sport?

10 What is the name of Fulham's football ground?

11 'Lutz' is a term used in which sport?

12 How many squares are there on a traditional Snakes and Ladders board?

13 'The Curtis Cup' is awarded for which sport?

14 In ice hockey, how many players from each side are allowed on the ice at any one time?

15 In rowing, what is the name of the Oxford University reserve team?

ANSWERS

1. (b) 1872. 2. June. 3. (c) Yellow. 4. 'Admiral's Cup'. 5. 15. 6. Wrestling. 7. 'Bears'. 8. 33. 9. Horse racing. 10. 'Craven Cottage'. 11. Skating. 12. 100. 13. Golf. 14. 6. 15. Isis.

GENERAL KNOWLEDGE

1   What is 'mulligatawny'?

2   A 20th wedding anniversary is associated with gifts made of which material?

3   What is a 'filibuster'? Is it (a) a set of delaying tactics, (b) padding on upholstery or (c) a medieval weapon?

4   Why are 'red-letter days' so called?

5   What is the zip code for the US state of Maine?

6   What is the largest desert in the world?

7   What is a group of beavers called?

8   What is the last letter in the Greek alphabet?

9   During which months does Ramadan, the Muslim period of fasting, take place?

10 What does the international car index mark 'E' stand for?

11 What is the alternative name for the 'Pareto principle'?

12 What is 'lb' the abbreviation for?

13 In Cockney rhyming slang, what does 'frog and toad' refer to?

14 What is a samovar? Is it (a) a system of secret printing, (b) a metal urn for making tea or (c) a kind of sweater?

15 What is the former name of Myanmar?

ANSWERS

1. A kind of soup (a thick curry-flavoured meat soup). 2. China. 3. (a) A set of delaying tactics. 4. From the red letters used in church calendars to show saints' days and feasts. 5. ME. 6. The Sahara Desert. 7. Colony. 8. Omega. 9. May and June. 10. Spain. 11. The 80/20 rule. 12. Pounds (weight). 13. Road. 14. (b) A metal urn for making tea. 15. Burma.

SCIENCE & NATURE

1   What is the name of the unit that measures relative loudness?

2   What is the normal temperature of the human body?

3   What was the name of the British naturalist who developed a theory of evolutionary change?

4   By what vitamin letter and number is riboflavin also called?

5   Which law states that at a constant temperature, the pressure of a gas is inversely proportionate to its volume?

6   What is the chemical name for 'laughing gas'?

7   In what year was the 'Bunsen burner' invented: (a) 1855, (b) 1720 or (c) 1910?

8   What is the chemical symbol for iron?

9   What was 'Jodrell Bank' famous for?

10 'Cirrus' and 'altocumulus' are types of what?

11 What is 'rubella' the technical expression for?

12 What is the modern name for roentgen rays?

13 How many bytes are there in a kilobyte?

14 What is the ordinary name for acetylsalicylic acid?

15 What is the name of the space mission launched to fly past the planets Jupiter, Saturn, Uranus and Neptune?

ENTERTAINMENT

1 Who had a hit with 'The Sun Ain't Gonna Shine Anymore'?

2 *West Side Story* is based on which play by Shakespeare?

3 Which actress played the part of Angie in *EastEnders*?

4 Which TV policeman used to say 'Evenin' all'?

5 Who plays the US president in the film *Primary Colors*?

6 What is the name of the hospital in TV's *Casualty*?

7 Who played 'Gandhi' in the film of the same name?

8 'That's Living All Right' was the theme tune to which TV series?

9 BBC2 started in 1965. True or false?

10 Which disc jockey is known for saying 'Hi there pop-pickers'?

11 What tool did Peter Gabriel want to be in his single of April 1986?

12 What were The Police wrapped around in 1983?

13 The record 'I'd Like to Teach the World to Sing' was used to advertise which soft drink?

14 Which character did Harrison Ford play in the *Star Wars* films?

15 What was the name of the computer in *2001 – A Space Odyssey*?

HISTORY

1   In 1066, before the Battle of Hastings, King Harold fought a battle that shares its name with a famous football ground. What is it?

2   Who became king of England in the year AD1100?

3   In what year was the Magna Carta signed by King John?

4   In which century was the Ming dynasty in China conquered and succeeded by the Manchu dynasty?

5   What was the first book believed to have been printed by Johannes Gutenberg, the inventor of printing, around 1455?

6   In which year was the French king Louis XVI executed on the guillotine?

7   Who wrote *General Theory of Employment, Interest and Money*?

8   Where did the French emperor Napoleon Bonaparte die in 1821?

9   Which famous author of fairy tales was born in 1805?

10 In which year did the Charge of the Light Brigade take place at the Battle of Balaclava?

11 In which year was Mussolini appointed prime minister of Italy?

12 Who was Chancellor of the Exchequer at the time of the British General Strike of 1926?

13 In which year did Mikhail Gorbachov become general secretary of the Soviet Communist Party?

14 In which year was Nelson Mandela released from prison in South Africa?

15 Which former first secretary at the British Embassy in Washington died in 1988?

ANSWERS

1. Stamford Bridge. 2. King Henry I. 3. 1215. 4. The 17th century. 5. *The Bible*. 6. 1792. 7. John Maynard Keynes. 8. St Helena. 9. Hans Christian Andersen. 10. 1854. 11. 1922. 12. Winston Churchill. 13. 1985. 14. 1990. 15. Kim (Harold Adrian Russell) Philby.

FAMOUS PEOPLE

1   What was the name of the Scottish king killed by Macbeth?

2   Who was the first woman to fly solo from England to Australia?

3   Whose compositions include the *Messiah* and the *Water Music*?

4   In 1498, which Portuguese navigator sailed to India round the Cape of Good Hope?

5   Who wrote *Paradise Lost*?

6   Which fashion designer introduced the 'New Look' in 1947?

7   Who pioneered the use of antiseptics in surgery?

8   Which Scottish poet was also employed as an excise officer?

9   Who invented the revolver?

10 With the origins of what sport is William Webb Ellis associated?

11 Who was the daughter of William Godwin and Mary Woolstencraft?

12 Whose plays include *Uncle Vanya* and *The Three Sisters*?

13 Who founded the Christian Science Church?

14 Which writer created the character of 'Jeeves'?

15 Who was the second president of the USA?

ANSWERS

1. Duncan. 2. Amy Johnson. 3. George Frederick Handel. 4. Vasco da Gama.
5. John Milton. 6. Christian Dior. 7. Joseph Lister. 8. Robert Burns. 9. Samuel Colt.
10. Rugby football. 11. Mary Shelley. 12. Anton Chekhov. 13. Mary Baker Eddy.
14. P. G. Wodehouse. 15. John Adams.

SPORT & LEISURE

1 'Seasiders' is the nickname of which football team?

2 Who was declared the winner of the men's 100 metres at the 1988 Olympic Games after Ben Johnson was disqualified?

3 'Albatross' is a term used in which sport?

4 How many pieces are there in a chess game?

5 What is missing from this list of characters from *Cluedo*: 'Colonel Mustard', 'Professor Plum', 'Reverend Green', 'Miss Scarlet' and 'Mrs White'?

6 'Jib', 'Halyards' and 'Sheets' are terms used in which sport?

7 Is the marathon distance (a) 26 miles 350 yards, (b) 26 miles 375 yards or (c) 26 miles 385 yards?

8 How many balls are there in a game of snooker?

9 In athletics, what is a 'Fosbury Flop'?

10 'The Wightman Cup' is awarded in which sport?

11 In *Monopoly*, what colour is the set 'Trafalgar Square, Fleet Street and Strand'?

12 'The Derby' is held at which racecourse?

13 How many home bases are there in baseball?

14 'Eskimo Roll' is a term used in which sport?

15 What does 'TT' stand for in the Isle of Man motorcycle races?

1. Blackpool. 2. Carl Lewis. 3. Golf. 4. 32. 5. 'Mrs Peacock'. 6. Sailing. 7. (c) 26 miles 385 yards. 8. 21 + cue ball. 9. Backward style of High Jump. 10. Tennis. 11. Red. 12. Epsom. 13. Five. 14. Canoeing. 15. 'Tourist Trophy'.

GENERAL KNOWLEDGE

1. In which city is the famous 'Western Wall', or 'Wailing Wall'?

2. With what did Snow White's stepmother tempt her?

3. In the desert, what two things did the Israelites eat?

4. What substance forms the padding around the eyeball?

5. Who, in his speech in the House of Commons on 4 April 1940, said 'Hitler has missed the bus'?

6. Who is the French clothes designer born in 1936 particularly known for his efforts to bring fashionable clothes to ordinary people on a large scale?

7. What, in music, is a composition written as a setting of the Mass for the dead?

8. In which church are English monarchs usually crowned?

9. In which Oscar Wilde play is 'Jack' found in a handbag?

10. What do the words 'status quo' mean?

11. Cations have a net positive charge and anions a net negative charge. True or false?

12. What is the chief element used in hydrotherapy?

13. Into what two types of events is athletics divided?

14. What is the name of the stiff, felt hat with a rounded crown and narrow brim?

15. What is the name of the youth in Greek mythology who was renowned for his great beauty?

SCIENCE & NATURE

1 Jupiter and Uranus are either side of which planet?

2 What does the medical abbreviation 'OD' stand for?

3 From which plant is the drug quinine derived?

4 In computers, what do the initials HTTP stand for?

5 What is the gestation period of a rabbit?

6 Who is particularly known for his law of gravitation and his three laws of motion?

7 In the binary system of notation, which number represents '8'?

8 In the name of what kind of algebra do variables express logical statements and relationships, rather than numbers?

9 What is the name of the female reproduction organ of a flower?

10 How many sides does a nonagon have?

11 What is the name of the molten rock that is thrown up from a volcano?

12 What nationality was the astronomer Nicholas Copernicus?

13 What are caused by the gravitational pull of the Moon and Sun on the earth?

14 Where do crustaceans mainly live?

15 Which Swedish botanist established the system of naming living organisms?

ENTERTAINMENT

1   What was the name of the number one single from the album 'Scary Monsters' by David Bowie?

2   What was the name of the Human League's long-haired, lead singer?

3   What is the name of the café in TV's *'Allo 'Allo*?

4   Who loaded the crossbow in TV's *The Golden Shot*?

5   Which disc jockey was the first to be heard on Radio 1 in 1967?

6   What were the names of the brother and sister of The Carpenters?

7   Who played 'Ben Hur' in the film of the same name?

8   What was the address of Tony Hancock in *Hancock's Half Hour*?

9   'If I Were a Rich Man' is a song from which musical?

10 What was the name of the company that Reginald Perrin worked for in the TV series *The Fall and Rise of Reginald Perrin*?

11 Errol Flynn played 'Robin Hood' in 1938. Who played him in *Robin Hood, Prince of Thieves?*

12 Which character was played by Su Pollard in *Hi-de-Hi*?

13 Who sang the theme to the film *Goldfinger*?

14 Which newspaper did 'Superman' work for?

15 For which television comedy series was Souza's 'Liberty Bell' the theme music?

ANSWERS

1. 'Ashes to Ashes'. 2. Phil Oakey. 3. 'René's Café. 4. 'Bernie, The Bolt'. 5. Tony Blackburn. 6. Richard and Karen. 7. Charlton Heston. 8. 23 Railway Cuttings, East Cheam. 9. *Fiddler on the Roof*. 10. 'Sunshine Desserts'. 11. Kevin Costner. 12. 'Peggy'. 13. Shirley Bassey. 14. 'Daily Planet'. 15. *Monty Python's Flying Circus.*

HISTORY

1 In which year did William the Conqueror order the Domesday Book to be compiled?

2 Who, in 1497, discovered Newfoundland and claimed North America for England?

3 When did the Louvre in Paris first begin to be used as a museum?

4 In which year did Dutch settlers first land at the Cape of Good Hope and establish a trading post and settlement?

5 The British East India company was given its original charter in the reign of which English monarch?

6 What was the name of King Henry VIII's third wife who died in 1537?

7 What is significant about the words 'What hath God wrought?'?

8 Which famous Russian author was present at the siege of Sebastopol during the Crimean War?

9 In which year did the Battle of the Somme take place?

10 Sir John Anderson, after whom the Anderson shelter was named, held which office in the British government?

11 In which year did Joseph Stalin die?

12 Whom did Konstantin Chernenko succeed as general secretary of the Soviet Communist Party in 1984?

13 In which year did George Carey become Archbishop of Canterbury?

14 What was the maiden name of the First Lady, Hillary Clinton?

15 In which year did Margaret Thatcher resign as leader of the Conservative Party and Prime Minister?

FAMOUS PEOPLE

1 Who was the first premier of the Soviet Union?

2 According to Shakespeare, who cried out for 'A horse! A horse! My kingdom for a horse!'?

3 Whose novels first appeared under the name of Currer Bell?

4 Who invented the miners' safety lamp?

5 Which king was known as the 'Hammer of the Scots'?

6 Who composed the music for the ballets *Swan Lake*, *The Nutcracker Suite*, and *The Sleeping Beauty*?

7 Who in 1911 was the first man to reach the South Pole?

8 Which landscape painter's works include *The Haywain* and *The Cornfield*?

9 Who was the first socialist to be elected to the House of Commons?

10 Who discovered penicillin?

11 Which rider is famous for not winning the 1956 Grand National?

12 Who sailed round the world in the *Golden Hind*?

13 What did Valentina Tereshkova become famous for in 1963?

14 Who led the Protestant Reformation in 16th century Germany?

15 Who wrote the story of *The Ugly Duckling*?

SPORT & LEISURE

1 Who was the first to score 100 goals in football's Premier League?

2 The Westchester Cup is awarded for which sport?

3 What is another name for the sport of motocross?

4 How many players are there in a Gaelic Football team?

5 What is the highest grade awarded in judo?

6 In which year was the first football World Cup held?

7 On the four Jacks in a pack of standard playing cards, how many eyes appear in total?

8 Which sport was named after the home of the Duke of Beaufort?

9 In which year was Nigel Mansell Formula One World Champion?

10 What is the club song for West Ham United?

11 What is the diameter in metres of the circle from which a discus is thrown?

12 What is the name of a powered hang-glider?

13 How many players comprise a World Cup Squad?

14 How many points are scored when the goal-kicker converts a try in Rugby Union?

15 How many goals did Geoff Hurst score in the 1966 World Cup Final?

1. Alan Shearer. 2. Polo. 3. Scrambling. 4. 15. 5. 12th dan (white). 6. 1930 (In Uruguay). 7. 12. 8. Badminton. 9. 1992. 10. 'I'm Forever Blowing Bubbles'. 11. 2.5. 12. A microlight. 13. 22. 14. 2. 15. 3.

GENERAL KNOWLEDGE

1   What is the English term for the drink known in Scotland as 'Heavy'?

2   What kind of apes live on the Rock of Gibraltar?

3   What is the chief respiratory muscle called?

4   Which Scottish essayist is quoted as saying, 'History is the essence of innumerable biographies.'?

5   Which woman is holding up a torch in her right hand and represents freedom?

6   By what is SIDS more commonly known?

7   Who exclaimed 'Eureka' ('I've found it!') when noticing that his body displaced the water in his bath?

8   What is the name of a serpent, lizard or dragon reputed to kill by its breath or look?

9   What is the English title for the book of the Bible composed of 'sacred songs sung to Musical Accompaniment'?

10   Upon which instrument, played before or during a Church service, is a 'voluntary' played?

11   To what kind of person does the expression 'Walter Mitty' refer?

12   In which novel by George Orwell did 'Napolean' feature?

13   In 'Scrabble' what does the letter 'Z' score?

14   What is the name for a man's hat with a round, flat crown and a brim that can be turned down as well as up?

15   In which film did Henry Fonda play alongside his daughter as her father?

ANSWERS

1. Bitter. 2. Barbary Apes. 3. Diaphragm. 4. Thomas Carlyle. 5. Statue of Liberty. 6. Cot Death (Sudden Infant Death Syndrome). 7. Archimedes – Greek mathematician and scientist. 8. Basilisk. 9. Psalms. 10. Organ. 11. An ordinary person who indulges in extravagant daydreaming and fantasies to escape reality. 12. *Animal Farm* (the chief pig). 13. 10. 14. Pork-pie hat. 15. *On Golden Pond*.

SCIENCE & NATURE

1 What is the name of the largest moon in the Solar System?

2 In Einstein's famous equation $E = mc^2$ what does the letter 'c' represent?

3 What is petrology?

4 An insect's body is divided into three sections. What are they?

5 Which of these is the densest: ice, butter or oak?

6 What is the term for an animal that feeds on plants?

7 Which is the tallest breed of dog?

8 Which disease is transmitted to humans by the tsetse fly?

9 Parsley is a member of the carrot family. True or false?

10 In which part of your body would you find the bone called the metatarsus?

11 What is the term for a young kangaroo?

12 What is the junction between two nerve cells called?

13 What is the distinguishing characteristic of apterous insects?

14 Which planet was discovered by William Herschel in 1781?

15 What do the letters that make up the word 'laser' stand for?

ANSWERS

1. Ganymede. 2. The speed of light. 3. The study of rocks. 4. Head, thorax, abdomen. 5. Ice. 6. A herbivore. 7. Irish wolfhound. 8. Sleeping sickness. 9. True. 10. In your foot, between the ankle and the toes. 11. A joey. 12. A synapse. 13. They do not have wings. 14. Uranus. 15. Light amplification by stimulated emission of radiation.

ENTERTAINMENT

1 'Give us a twirl' is one of many catchphrases used by which entertainer?

2 Who played 'Rita' in the film *Educating Rita*?

3 Louise Lombard played a dress designer in which TV series?

4 What did 'Hickory', the Tin Man, want in *The Wizard of Oz*?

5 Arthur Negus first became famous for his appearances in which antiques programme?

6 'Mr Rigsby' was a character in which TV comedy series?

7 Which Beatles' album features a zebra crossing on its cover?

8 In TV's *Third Rock from the Sun* who plays 'Dick'?

9 Robert Allen Zimmerman was born in 1941. Who is this singer known as?

10 What character did Patrick Duffy play in *Dallas*?

11 Who is missing from this pop group name: Dave Dee, Dozy, Mick and Titch?

12 Who presents TV's *Police, Camera, Action?*

13 Who wrote the music for *West Side Story*?

14 How many number ones did Howard Jones have between 1983 and 1989: (a) 4, (b) 2 or (c) 0?

15 Who presents *Right to Reply* on Channel 4?

1. Bruce Forsyth. 2. Julie Walters. 3. *House of Elliott.* 4. A heart. 5. *Going For A Song.* 6. *Rising Damp.* 7. *Abbey Road.* 8. John Lithgow. 9. Bob Dylan. 10. Bobby Ewing. 11. Beaky. 12. Alastair Stewart. 13. Leonard Bernstein. 14. (c) 0. 15. Roger Bolton.

HISTORY

1 By what nickname was Sir Henry Percy, son of the Earl of Northumberland, who was killed at the battle of Shrewsbury in 1403, generally known?

2 Where was Joan of Arc burnt at the stake in 1431?

3 For what is Wynkyn de Worde (died about 1535) famous?

4 In which year did William Shakespeare die?

5 Who was appointed commander-in-chief of the Parliamentary forces in the English Civil War in 1645?

6 The composer Ludwig van Beethoven and the poet William Wordsworth were both born in the same year. Which year was it?

7 What position did King George I of Great Britain hold before he became king?

8 In which year did George I become king of Great Britain?

9 How old was Wolfgang Amadeus Mozart when he died in 1791?

10 What was the name of the ship that rescued most of the survivors from the sinking of the 'Titanic'?

11 In which year was Dr H. H. Crippen executed for the murder of his wife Cora Turner?

12 In which year did Israel fight the Six Day War against Egypt, Jordan and Syria?

13 Who was the prime minister of Rhodesia who declared its unilateral independence from Great Britain in 1965?

14 Whom did Idi Amin depose as prime minister of Uganda in a coup in 1971?

15 In which year did Lord Home renounce his peerage in order to become prime minister of Great Britain?

FAMOUS PEOPLE

1 Who was known as 'The Maid of Orleans'?

2 Which traveller first visited China in 1271?

3 Whose compositions include the operas *Tosca*, *Madame Butterfly* and *Turandot?*

4 Which Marquis gave his name to the rules that govern the sport of boxing?

5 What nationality is Christian Barnard, the surgeon who performed the first human heart transplant?

6 Which English explorer was imprisoned in the Tower of London and beheaded in 1618?

7 Who discovered the circulation of the blood?

8 What religious organization was founded by William Booth?

9 What kind of travel was pioneered by the Montgolfier brothers?

10 Which British impresario was noted for his productions of Gilbert and Sullivan operettas?

11 With which art form is Henri Cartier-Bresson associated?

12 Who became prime minister of India on its independence in 1947?

13 Which 19th century British explorer translated the *Arabian Nights* and has a famous 20th century namesake?

14 Who wrote *Don Quixote?*

15 Which astronomer first put forward the theory that the Earth and the planets revolve around the Sun?

ANSWERS

1. Joan of Arc. 2. Marco Polo. 3. Puccini. 4. Queensberry. 5. South African. 6. Sir Walter Raleigh. 7. William Harvey. 8. The Salvation Army. 9. Hot air balloon. 10. Richard D'Oyly Carte. 11. Photography. 12. (Jawaharlal) Nehru. 13. Richard Burton. 14. Miguel de Cervantes. 15. Nicolas Copernicus.

SPORT & LEISURE

1   'Old Trafford' is the ground of which football team?

2   In which sport would you use the term 'Dormie'?

3   Which horse won the 'Grand National' in 1973, 1974 and 1977?

4   The term 'Face-off' is used in which sport?

5   Who was America's 'Golden Girl' who fell in the 3,000 metres at the Los Angeles Olympics?

6   In which sport would you find a 'brakeman'?

7   What is the term for dwarf plant growing?

8   Lasse Viren was one of the world's greatest long-distance runners. From which country did he come?

9   With which sport do you associate John and Michael Whittaker?

10 Clive Lloyd captained which national cricket team?

11 How many players are there in each side of an Australian Rules football team?

12 Which team changes if there is a clash of colours in a football league match?

13 What kind of wrestling match is fought by more than two wrestlers?

14 What is the nickname of Newcastle United?

15 How many attempts is a pole-vaulter allowed to take at each height?

1. Manchester United. 2. Golf. 3. 'Red Rum'. 4. Ice Hockey. 5. Mary Decker. 6. Bobsleigh. 7. Bonsai. 8. Finland. 9. Show Jumping. 10. West Indies. 11. 18. 12. Away team. 13. A tag match. 14. 'The Magpies'. 15. Three.

GENERAL KNOWLEDGE

1 In Shakespeare's *Julius Caesar*, with which famous words did 'Julius Caesar' receive his wounds from 'Brutus'?

2 What is the sweetener used to make Greek baklava?

3 What kind of farming is arable farming?

4 Who was the first leader of the Soviet Union, from 1918–24?

5 On crossing the Rubicon in 49BC, which Roman general said: 'The die is cast'?

6 What dish is made up of the following ingredients; sheep's offal, suet, oats and spices?

7 In what part of the body are the bones, the tibia and fibula?

8 What does DAT stand for?

9 How did a 'cockatrice', the creature of classical mythology hatched from a cock's egg, supposedly kill?

10 'The Lord is my Shepherd, I shall not want'. Of which Psalm is this the first line?

11 In chemistry, what is the term for a particle of matter so small that it cannot be split?

12 Derived from Latin, the term 'caveat emptor' means we should ignore our hunger. True or false?

13 What is the name of a hat that has a shallow crown, a wide brim that is turned up at the back to hold decorative flowers?

14 What is found in the middle of a 'Sussex Pond Pudding'?

15 In music, what other term, apart from 'adagio', means slowly?

SCIENCE & NATURE

1 What is the study of earthquakes called?

2 A mule is the offspring of a female horse and a male ass. What is the offspring of a male horse and a female ass called?

3 What is the difference between the teeth of dolphins and those of porpoises?

4 What type of acid is found in rhubarb?

5 How is the disease varicella better known?

6 What is measured in pascals?

7 Phobos and Deimos are moons of which planet?

8 Which biologist described natural selection as the 'blind watchmaker'?

9 What is daltonism?

10 Which ape has a name that means 'man of the forest'?

11 Jackass, macaroni and emperor are all species of which bird?

12 Which element has the symbol W?

13 What is the name of the British scientist who is associated with the Gaia hypothesis, the theory that the Earth is a self-regulating organism?

14 Pure carbon can exist in two forms. What are they?

15 By what name is the root 'Zingiber officinale' better known?

1. Seismology. 2. A hinny. 3. Dolphins' teeth are pointed, porpoises' are squared. 4. Oxalic acid. 5. Chickenpox. 6. Pressure. 7. Mars. 8. Richard Dawkins. 9. Colour-blindness. 10. Orang-utan. 11. The penguin. 12. Tungsten. 13. James Lovelock. 14. Diamond and graphite. 15. Ginger.

ENTERTAINMENT

1 Who took over the role of 'Helen Herriot' from Carol Drinkwater in the TV series *All Creatures Great and Small*?

2 Where did The Bee Gees live before they emigrated to Australia?

3 Who starred as 'The Joker' in the 1989 film *Batman*?

4 What character does Joanna Lumley play in TV's *Absolutely Fabulous*?

5 Who wrote the musical *Oliver*! based on Charles Dickens' *Oliver Twist*?

6 Which musician narrated TV's *Thomas the Tank Engine and Friends*?

7 Who was the original presenter of TV's *Juke Box Jury*?

8 Which musical instrument does James Galway play?

9 Which group had a hit with 'Albatross'?

10 Who starred with Tony Curtis in the TV series *The Persuaders*?

11 On what road were the 'Talking Heads' in 1985?

12 Which film features the song 'Somewhere Over The Rainbow' sung by Judy Garland?

13 Who plays 'Alma Baldwin' in *Coronation Street*?

14 Which singer had hits with 'Catch a Falling Star' and 'Magic Moments'?

15 Who played the male lead in the film *Who Framed Roger Rabbit*?

ANSWERS

1. Lynda Bellingham. 2. Manchester. 3. Jack Nicholson. 4. 'Patsy'. 5. Lionel Bart. 6. Ringo Starr. 7. David Jacobs. 8. Flute. 9. Fleetwood Mac. 10. Roger Moore. 11. 'The Road To Nowhere'. 12. *The Wizard of Oz*. 13. Amanda Barrie. 14. Perry Como. 15. Bob Hoskins.

HISTORY

1   Who was king of England in the year 1200?

2   Before Switzerland became independent in 1499, which country was it ruled by?

3   How many wives did King Henry VIII of England divorce?

4   Who massacred whom during the Saint Bartholomew's Day Massacre of 1572?

5   Which country's territory was divided up between Russia, Prussia and Austria during the latter part of the 18th century so that it effectively vanished from the map of Europe until 1918?

6   In which English county was Lord Nelson born?

7   Which of Lord Nelson's famous victories took place in 1798?

8   What was the 19th century British prime minister Benjamin Disraeli's nickname?

9   Queen Victoria liked Disraeli, but disliked his great political rival – who was he?

10 When Lord Uxbridge exclaimed, 'By God, sir, I've lost my leg!', who replied, 'By God, sir, so you have!'?

11 How long did King Edward VII of Great Britain reign?

12 In which year did the United States enter World War I?

13 Who was prime minister of Great Britain during the abdication crisis of 1936?

14 In which year was John F. Kennedy elected president of the United States?

15 Whom did President Nelson Mandela marry in 1998?

FAMOUS PEOPLE

1 In 1301, who led the Peasants' Revolt?

2 Who was the first woman to fly the Atlantic?

3 Who wrote *The Pilgrim's Progress*?

4 What nationality was Nicolas Copernicus?

5 With what social reform is Elizabeth Fry associated?

6 Who composed the opera *Carmen*?

7 Which English king is sometimes referred to as 'The Unready'?

8 Who invented the lightning conductor in 1752?

9 Which admiral commanded the British fleet at the Battle of Jutland?

10 Who established the Presbyterian Church of Scotland in 1560?

11 Which artist is renowned for his paintings of his native city of Venice?

12 With what sporting pastime is Izaak Walton associated?

13 Who led an expedition to Africa in search of David Livingstone?

14 'Meg, Jo, Beth and Amy' are the four sisters created by which writer?

15 Which French physicist instigated the study of radioactivity and has a unit of radioactive activity named after him?

SPORT & LEISURE

1 In which Olympic Games were women's athletic events included for the first time?

2 Where was the first motor racing Grand Prix held in 1906?

3 Which two sports are played in a biathlon?

4 How long does a hockey match last?

5 In which hobby is the term 'French knot' used?

6 In which year was the London Marathon first held?

7 Who won both the 1989 and 1990 US Masters golf titles?

8 What was the name of the car in which Donald Campbell broke the land-speed record in 1964?

9 Which tennis player appeared in Wimbledon Men's Singles Finals at the ages of 19 and 39?

10 In what year did Mike Tyson beat Trevor Burbick to become Heavyweight World Champion?

11 Who was captain of the Great Britain Athletics team until his retirement in 1997?

12 What is the name of the ground at which the Scottish national soccer team plays its home matches?

13 'Canasta' is a card game. True or false?

14 In 110 metre high hurdles races, are the hurdles: (a) 110cm (43"), (b) 104cm (41") or (c) 106cm (42")?

15 Who was the manager of the England World Cup Winning Team in 1966?

ANSWERS

1. 1928. 2. Le Mans, France. 3. Cross Country Skiing and Rifle Shooting. 4. 70 minutes. 5. Embroidery. 6. 1981. 7. Nick Faldo. 8. 'Bluebird'. 9. Ken Rosewall. 10. 1986. 11. Linford Christie. 12. Hampden Park. 13. True. 14. (c) 106cm (42"). 15. Sir Alf Ramsey.

GENERAL KNOWLEDGE

1 What name do we give to a native or inhabitant of Manchester?

2 For which US state is KY the abbreviation?

3 In his poem *The Pied Piper of Hamelin*, who wrote: 'They fought the dogs and killed the cats, And bit the babies in the cradles'?

4 What is the Italian name for the pudding translated as 'Pick-me-up'?

5 What is the sour ingredient added to a 'Whiskey Sour'?

6 Which animal is associated with 'Paddy McGinty'?

7 How much does a magnum hold?

8 Who wrote *The Portrait of a Lady*?

9 What does 'ad hoc' mean?

10 To which sport does the 'butterfly' stroke belong?

11 Dermatology is the medical treatment of blood diseases. True or false?

12 What is the result of alpha decay, beta decay or gamma decay?

13 With how many letters does each player start in a game of 'Scrabble'?

14 In Norse mythology, who slayed the dragon, 'Fafnir'?

15 Which bear in A. A. Milne's books loves honey?

SCIENCE & NATURE

1   What is the science of very low temperatures called?

2   What bird is sometimes called a 'yaffle'?

3   Which scientist said: 'All science is either physics or stamp collecting'?

4   How many front toes does a parrot have?

5   What is the hardest substance in the human body?

6   Which is the only marsupial that is native to North America?

7   Which German physicist who founded the quantum theory won the Nobel Prize for Physics in 1918?

8   What does the word 'hippopotamus' mean?

9   Two types of mammal lay eggs. One is the platypus. What is the other?

10   How often does *Halley's Comet* orbit the Sun: (a) Every 56 years, (b) every 66 years or (c) every 76 years?

11   What metal is extracted from purified bauxite?

12   How is solid carbon dioxide commonly known?

13   Which planet has the shortest year?

14   On a plant, what is the name of the part of the stamen where pollen is produced?

15   Which is the largest member of the cat family?

ENTERTAINMENT

1 Which long-running TV comedy series features the married couple 'Howard and Pearl'?

2 Which singer had a hit in the 1960s with 'Puppet on a String'?

3 Who plays the TV detective 'Inspector Wexford'?

4 Which type of car featured strongly in the film *The Italian Job*?

5 Which TV presenter had a part in the film *The Color Purple*?

6 Which entertainer used the catchphrase 'I wanna tell you a story'?

7 In which Shakespeare play does the character 'Shylock' appear?

8 Which *Brimstone and Treacle* star wanted to 'Spread a Little Happiness' in 1982?

9 Who played the part of 'Simon Templar' in TV's *The Saint*?

10 Which actor had a hit with 'Grandad'?

11 On children's TV, who played the part of 'Worzel Gummidge'?

12 Art Garfunkel had a hit with a song from the film *Watership Down*. What was it called?

13 The cartoon character 'Sylvester' the cat is trying to catch which bird?

14 Who played the part of 'Peter' in the film *Peter's Friends*?

15 Who wrote the 'Moonlight Sonata'?

HISTORY

1 Which English king lost his only son when the 'White Ship' sank in the Channel in 1120?

2 Who founded Winchester College school and New College, Oxford?

3 Who or what were the Lollards?

4 In which year was Sir Thomas More executed for treason?

5 Captain John Smith was involved in the founding of which British colony in the 16th century?

6 In which year did the Battle of Naseby take place during the English Civil War?

7 What title was taken by Oliver Cromwell when he took over the government of England in 1653?

8 In which war did British forces fight in the battles of Dettingen and Fontenoy?

9 General Wolfe and his forces scaled the Heights of Abraham to attack the French forces guarding which city?

10 Who was Napoleon Bonaparte's first wife?

11 Zog I (ruled 1928–39) was king of which European country?

12 Whose record of 714 home runs in baseball was beaten by Hank Aaron in 1974?

13 The first volume of which former Labour cabinet minister's diaries were published in 1975?

14 Who was British Secretary of State for Education and Science from 1970–74?

15 In which year did Mikhail Gorbachev win the Nobel Peace Prize?

FAMOUS PEOPLE

1 How is the American writer Samuel Clemens better known?

2 Which archbishop was murdered in Canterbury cathedral in 1170?

3 To which royal house did Queen Victoria belong?

4 Who made the first flight across the English Channel?

5 Which family of Quaker manufacturers established the garden village of Bournville?

6 Whose sculpture of St Michael and the Devil can be seen outside Coventry Cathedral?

7 Who founded a medical mission at Lamberene in Gabon, Africa?

8 Who composed the music for the ballet *Coppelia*?

9 Which dancer met a tragic end when her scarf caught in the wheel of her car?

10 Who created the fictional detective 'Sergeant Cuff'?

11 Which Austrian doctor founded psychoanalysis?

12 With which 17th century political movement was John Lilburne associated?

13 Who invented a system of shorthand in 1837?

14 Which 19th century home secretary re-organized the London police force?

15 Whose expedition reached the South Pole on 17 January 1912 only to find that Amundsen had beaten them by a month?

SPORT & LEISURE

1 In athletics, how many events are there in a heptathlon?

2 How does a crown-green bowling green differ from an ordinary bowling green?

3 Johnny Weissmuller played the role of 'Tarzan'. Of which sport had he been a champion?

4 What is the name of the rubber disc used in ice hockey?

5 How many strikes per turn are allowed in a game of conkers?

6 What is the name of the ground which is the home of English Rugby Union?

7 The Formula One World Championship began in; (a) 1952, (b) 1950 or (c) 1955?

8 Is the maximum number of clubs that player may use in a round of golf; (a) 12, (b) 13 or (c) 14?

9 During a penalty shoot-out, where should non-participating players be?

10 In which year did the famous cricketer W. G. Grace die?

11 What are the first names of the motor-racing Schumacher brothers?

12 How many winks does each player have in the game of 'Tiddlywinks'?

13 'The Davis Cup' awarded for tennis was founded in: (a) 1905, (b) 1900 or (c) 1903?

14 Which London club plays in a red and blue striped jersey?

15 In which year did Damon Hill win the Formula One World Championship?

40

GENERAL KNOWLEDGE

1 How many lines does a limerick always have?

2 In one of his songs, who wrote 'Absence makes the heart grow fonder, Isle of Beauty, Fare thee well!'?

3 What do the initials of J. F. stand for in J. F. Kennedy, US president from 1961–63?

4 The cygnet is the young of which creature?

5 Pancreatic juice is strongly acidic. True or false?

6 In music, for what time of day is the performance of an 'aubade' originally intended?

7 What is the title of the novel by John Steinbeck about two itinerant farm labourers, one of huge strength and weak mind, exploited and protected by the other?

8 'In the beginning God created the heaven and the earth'. From which book of the Bible is this quoted?

9 Who rode the mythological 'hippocampus' – a sea horse, with a horse's forelegs and the tail of a fish or dolphin?

10 How many players are there in a hockey team?

11 What is the term we use, derived from Latin, which means 'note well or observe'?

12 What breed of cow with dark red or light brown colouring, famous for its rich milk was originally bred on the Channel Islands?

13 Where was 'Mr Orange' first shot in the film *Reservoir Dogs*?

14 To which area of medicine does paediatrics refer?

15 What is the name of the giants with a single eye in mid-forehead, encountered by Odysseus?

ANSWERS

1. Five. 2. Thomas Haynes Bayly. 3. John Fitzgerald. 4. Swan. 5. False. It is strongly alkaline. 6. Morning. 7. *Of Mice and Men*. 8. Genesis. 9. Neptune. 10. 11. 11. Nota bene. 12. Jersey cow. 13. In the stomach. 14. Treatment of children's diseases. 15. Cyclops.

SCIENCE & NATURE

1   The femur is another name for which bone?

2   Apart from the Sun, what is the nearest star to the Earth?

3   In geology, what is the term for the layer that comes between the Earth's crust and the core?

4   The uakari monkey has a brightly-coloured face. What colour is it?

5   Au is the chemical symbol for which element?

6   What is the name of the French scientist who invented the word 'biology' and attributed evolution to the inheritance of acquired characteristics?

7   What is a squirrel's nest called?

8   What is the smallest bird in the world?

9   What shape are ice crystals?

10   By what trade name is the plastic polytetraflouroethylene known?

11   What does a heliologist study?

12   Bronze is an alloy of what two metals smelted together?

13   Which scientist is depicted on the £20 note?

14   How does the rafflesia plant attract flies to pollinate it?

15   What is the liquid part of the blood called?

ENTERTAINMENT

1 Who had a hit with 'You Win Again'?

2 Who played the wheelchair-bound detective in TV's *Ironside*?

3 Who wrote the play *Under Milk Wood*?

4 The part of 'Bathsheba' was played by which actress in the 1967 film, *Far From the Madding Crowd*?

5 What was the first programme shown on Channel 4?

6 Who played 'The Kid' in the film *The Cincinnati Kid*?

7 In which year in the 1960s was the Woodstock music festival held?

8 Who had a hit with 'Ride on Time' in 1989?

9 In which soap does the character 'Jimmy Corkhill' feature?

10 The play, *The Mousetrap* opened in: (a) 1950, (b) 1952 or (c) 1954?

11 Who played the role of a disk jockey in the film *Good Morning Vietnam*?

12 In 1975, Pilot had a hit with a song named after a month. Which month?

13 Which gardening programme is featured on Radio 4?

14 The actor Lloyd Bridges had two sons who also became actors. What are their names?

15 Who wrote the lyrics for 'A Whole New World' featured in the cartoon film of *Aladdin*?

1. The Bee Gees. 2. Raymond Burr. 3. Dylan Thomas. 4. Julie Christie.
5. *Countdown*. 6. Steve McQueen. 7. 1969. 8. Black Box. 9. *Brookside*.
10. (b) 1952. 11. Robin Williams. 12. January. 13. *Gardeners' Question Time*.
14. Beau and Jeff. 15. Sir Tim Rice.

HISTORY

1   Who was accidentally killed by Sir William Tyrel in the New Forest in 1100?

2   Which saint died in 1226?

3   Who was the founder of the Society of Friends or 'Quakers'?

4   In which year did the Battle of Blenheim take place?

5   Who was the last king of Britain who personally led his troops into battle?

6   Where was the French revolutionary Jean Paul Marat assassinated?

7   Who assassinated him?

8   In which year was the Metropolitan Police Force founded?

9   Who was prime minister of Great Britain when Queen Victoria came to the throne in 1837?

10   In which year did the Battle of the Alamo take place?

11   Which famous American frontiersman was killed at the Battle of the Alamo?

12   The Alamo was part of a mission station near which Texas town?

13   Who was king of the Belgians during World War I?

14   In which year did the 'Dambusters' raid by the RAF on the Mohne and Eder dams in central Germany take place?

15   In which year did Emperor Hirohito of Japan die?

1. King William II (William Rufus) of England. 2. St Francis of Assisi. 3. George Fox (1624–91). 4. 1704. 5. King George II (at the Battle of Dettingen in 1743). 6. In his bath. 7. Charlotte Corday. 8. 1829. 9. Lord Melbourne. 10. 1836. 11. Davy Crockett (the slightly less famous Jim Bowie was also killed there). 12. San Antonio. 13. King Albert I. 14. 1943. 15. 1989.

FAMOUS PEOPLE

1   Who wrote the poem *The Tyger*?

2   Which American tennis player was known as 'Little Mo'?

3   Whose operatic compositions include *The Barber of Seville* and *William Tell*?

4   For what achievement is Mrs Sirimavo Bandarnaike noted?

5   What was the name of the Spanish conquistador who conquered Mexico in the 16th century?

6   Which ballerina became famous for the role of 'The Dying Swan'?

7   Who wrote *The Rights of Man*?

8   Who founded the Mormon Church?

9   Who invented the lift (or elevator)?

10 Which king of Great Britain and Ireland was married to Henrietta Maria?

11 Whose dictionary was published in America in 1828?

12 Who created the fictional hero 'Richard Hannay'?

13 Who painted the ceiling of the Sistine Chapel?

14 Who formulated the law of gravitation?

15 Which art historian and surveyor of the queen's pictures was also a Soviet spy?

ANSWERS

1. William Blake. 2. Maureen Connolly. 3. Rossini. 4. She was the world's first woman prime minister (of Ceylon, first in 1960–65). 5. Cortes (or Cortez). 6. Anna Pavlova. 7. Thomas Paine. 8. Joseph Smith. 9. Elisha Otis. 10. Charles I. 11. Noah Webster. 12. John Buchan. 13. Michelangelo. 14. Sir Isaac Newton. 15. Anthony Blunt.

SPORT & LEISURE

1 Which city's football supporters would you associate with the song 'You'll Never Walk Alone'?

2 A game of ice hockey is divided into three periods. How long does each period last?

3 In which game is the term 'Royal Flush' used?

4 How many gold medals did swimmer Mark Spitz win at the Munich Olympic Games in 1972?

5 In rowing, what is the name of the Cambridge University reserve team?

6 Pelé played three times for Brazil in football's World Cup. True or false?

7 How many players are there in a netball team?

8 Who won the 1998 Formula One World Championship?

9 What score do you get if you hit the 'bull's eye' at darts?

10 Which football team is nicknamed 'The Imps'?

11 In which year did Jayne Torvill and Christopher Dean win the 'BBC Sports Personality of the Year'?

12 Both boats sank in the University Boat Race in; (a) 1910, (b) 1911 or (c) 1912?

13 In which year did Emerson Fittipaldi become Formula One Racing Champion?

14 In which sport would the term 'scurry' be used?

15 Which soccer club became the first First Division champions to be promoted to the Premier League?

GENERAL KNOWLEDGE

1   What do we call a young frog?

2   When dried, what do we call plums?

3   What does the Latin term 'in extremis' mean?

4   From which country does acupuncture originate?

5   What do griffins, creatures of classical mythology, look like?

6   Who was the tyrannical prime minister of Kampuchea from 1975–79?

7   In music, when a concerto is played, what else, apart from the orchestra, is required?

8   What is the traditional name for the Wednesday on which Lent begins?

9   What term do we give to the hours when pubs are open for the sale of alcoholic drinks?

10 Who played 'James Bond' in the film, *Moonraker*?

11 In tennis, what is the score if each player has scored 40?

12 What is a CV?

13 Name the two most expensive properties in the game of 'Monopoly'?

14 What is your 'alter ego'?

15 What is the name of the highly ornate style of architecture and art that flourished in Europe from the late 16th century to the early 18th century?

1. Tadpole. 2. Prunes. 3. At the point of death, in extremity. 4. China. 5. They have an eagle's head and wings, and a lion's body and tail. 6. Pol Pot. 7. A solo instrument. 8. Ash Wednesday. 9. Licensing hours. 10. Roger Moore. 11. Deuce. 12. Curriculum Vitae (outline of a person's professional qualifications). 13. Park Lane and Mayfair. 14. Your other self. 15. Baroque.

SCIENCE & NATURE

1   The Sun is largely composed of which two gases?

2   What is the name of the hormone that diabetics are unable to produce?

3   What is a Geiger counter used to measure?

4   Which is the largest bird of prey in the world?

5   What are the names of the two scientists who established the molecular structure of DNA?

6   What is the term for a young elephant?

7   What is the common name for calcium oxide?

8   What is a vertebrate?

9   Which acid occurs in ant bites and nettle stings?

10   What are a mammal's vibrissae?

11   Which element derives its name from the Greek for 'bringer of light'?

12   What is the term for a negatively charged electrode?

13   What is a flight of geese called?

14   Protons and neutrons have been discovered to be composed of more fundamental particles. What are they called?

15   What kind of camel has two humps?

ENTERTAINMENT

1 Who composed the theme of the *Pink Panther* films?

2 'DCI Jane Tennison' is a character in which series of TV police thrillers?

3 What was 'Mickey Mouse's' original name?

4 With which children's TV programme would you associate 'Here's one I made earlier'?

5 Who had a hit with 'It's Over' and 'Only The Lonely'?

6 Lionel Blair and Una Stubbs were the team captains in which TV game show?

7 Which two actors played the parts of *The Likely Lads*?

8 What is the rest of this song title: 'Itsy Bitsy Teeny Weeny...'?

9 Who presented TV's *Crackerjack* and *This Is Your Life*?

10 'The Jets' and 'The Sharks' were the names of the gangs in which film?

11 What kind of an entertainer was Marcel Marceau?

12 'Tom and Jerry' was the original name for which performers?

13 'A Good Year For The Roses' was also good for which singer/songwriter?

14 Which comedian is famous for using the catchphrase 'It's the way I tell 'em'?

15 Which female singer won *Opportunity Knocks* in 1968?

1. Henry Mancini. 2. *Prime Suspect*. 3. 'Mortimer Mouse'. 4. *Blue Peter*. 5. Roy Orbison. 6. *Give Us A Clue*. 7. Rodney Bewes and James Bolam. 8. 'Yellow Polka Dot Bikini'. 9. Eamonn Andrews. 10. *West Side Story*. 11. A mime artist. 12. Simon and Garfunkel. 13. Elvis Costello. 14. Frank Carson. 15. Mary Hopkin.

HISTORY

1   What nationality was St Francis Xavier, one of the founders of the Jesuit order and the founder of a Christian mission in Japan?

2   Who led a rebellion against King James II of England in 1685?

3   In his speech on becoming prime minister in May 1940, Winston Churchill said that he had nothing to offer the British people but... what?

4   In which city was the conference held that resulted in the founding of the United Nations Organization in 1945?

5   In which year did the Berlin airlift begin after Soviet forces blocked land access by America, Britain, and France to West Berlin?

6   Who famously said 'Ich bin ein Berliner' (I am a Berliner)?

7   In which year was the Berlin wall erected by the East German regime?

8   In which year, according to the British poet Philip Larkin, was 'sexual intercourse invented'?

9   Who won the US presidential election of 1968?

10 What did Jan Palach, a Czech student, do in 1969 to protest against the Soviet occupation of Czechoslovakia?

11 In which year did Great Britain and Ireland formally join the European Common Market?

12 In which year did passenger services on the Concorde supersonic jet between London and New York begin?

13 Who became prime minister of the Republic of Ireland in 1981?

14 In which year did IRA bombers attempt to assassinate Prime Minister Margaret Thatcher and other members of the British government and Conservative party at the Grand Hotel in Brighton?

15 Which country, after leaving the British Commonwealth in 1972, rejoined it in 1989?

ANSWERS

1. Spanish. 2. The Duke of Monmouth. 3. 'Blood, toil, tears and sweat'.
4. San Francisco. 5. 1948. 6. US President John F. Kennedy. 7. 1963. 8. 1961.
9. Richard M. Nixon. 10. He publicly burnt himself to death in Prague. 11. 1973.
12. 1977. 13. Dr Garret Fitzgerald. 14. 1984. 15. Pakistan.

FAMOUS PEOPLE

1 Who was the first man in space?

2 Who was exiled to the island of St Helena in 1815?

3 How is Charles Lutwidge Dodgson better known?

4 Which queen was executed at Fotheringay Castle?

5 For what category of painting was Sir Joshua Reynolds famous?

6 Who, in 1865, became the first English woman to qualify as a medical doctor?

7 Who invented the safety razor?

8 Who was the founder of Methodism?

9 Which American artist did not begin painting until she was 75 years old?

10 Who wrote *The Three Musketeers*?

11 Who was the first man to swim the English Channel?

12 Who commanded the light brigade at the battle of Balaclava?

13 What did William Wilberforce campaign against?

14 Who invented the seed drill in the 18th century, and had a pop group named after him in the 20th century?

15 Who was King Stephen's rival claimant for the English crown following the death of Henry I?

SPORT & LEISURE

1 In *Monopoly*, with how much money does each player start?

2 Which TV celebrity is on the Board of Directors of Norwich City?

3 What was the original name of 'Bingo'?

4 Who was the captain of the 1966 England World Cup team?

5 In which sport was Betty Calloway a coach?

6 What nationality was the racing driver Emerson Fittipaldi?

7 How many pieces are there in a game of draughts?

8 In diving, the word 'scuba' is made up from the initials of which words?

9 Who sailed single-handedly round the world in 1967?

10 A game of polo is divided into periods. What are they called?

11 Hammersmith Bridge is the first bridge that is passed under in the University Boat Race. True or false?

12 How many holes does a ten-pin bowling ball have?

13 How many players are there in a water polo team?

14 'Whitechapel' is a term used in which sport?

15 Which football team plays at 'The Dell'?

ANSWERS

1. £1,500. 2. Delia Smith. 3. 'Housey-Housey'. 4. Bobby Moore. 5. Ice dance (for Torvill and Dean). 6. Brazilian. 7. 24. 8. Self-Contained Underwater Breathing Apparatus. 9. Francis Chichester. 10. Chukkers (or Chukkas). 11. True. 12. Three. 13. Seven. 14. Billiards. 15. Southampton.

GENERAL KNOWLEDGE

1 On which main river is Bristol situated?

2 Java, Columbian and Kenyan are types of what?

3 Named after a famous British statesman, what do we call a rubber boot without fastenings that reaches the knee?

4 Which smoked fish is called a kipper?

5 To which Roman general are the words 'Veni, vidi, vici', 'I came, I saw, I conquered', attributed?

6 In musical terms, a 'humoresque' is a playful or humorous composition. True or false?

7 In which English town is the traditional Goose Fair held, taking place on the first Thursday, Friday and Saturday in October?

8 Who wrote *Three Men In a Boat*?

9 What does 'per annum' mean?

10 When we want something 'quid pro quo', do we want something for nothing?

11 What does a sphygmomanometer measure?

12 In golf, what term means a score of one stroke under par for the hole?

13 In Greek mythology, what is the name of the creature having the head, trunk and arms of a man, and the legs of a horse?

14 What is banting?

15 What does WYSIWYG stand for?

1. Avon. 2. Coffee. 3. Wellington boot. 4. Herring. 5. Julius Caesar. 6. True. 7. Nottingham. 8. Jerome K. Jerome. 9. Annually. 10. No, we want something for something, an equal value exchange. 11. Blood pressure. 12. Birdie. 13. Centaur. 14. A method of slimming by eating high amounts of protein and avoiding sugar, starch and fat. 15. What you see is what you get.

SCIENCE & NATURE

1 Which has more bones in its neck, a giraffe or a mouse?

2 Of what field of science was Gregor Mendel the founder?

3 What is the name of the sugar that occurs naturally in honey and many sweet fruits?

4 What is the largest type of owl?

5 What gas forms about 78 percent of the Earth's atmosphere?

6 What is the term for a substance that causes cancer?

7 Which mammal has the longest pregnancy (20 months)?

8 What does the Kelvin scale measure?

9 What is the name of the tiny cell fragments in the blood that help it to clot?

10 What is unusual about the beak of the New Zealand wrybill?

11 What were formerly known as Röntgen rays, after their discoverer?

12 What is magma?

13 What plant does opium come from?

14 What is the term for the process by which a chrysalis changes into a butterfly or a tadpole changes into a frog?

15 Sufferers of haemophilia are almost always female. True or false?

ANSWERS

14. Metamorphosis. 15. False.
sideways. 11. X-rays. 12. Molten rock within the earth. 13. The opium poppy.
6. A carcinogen. 7. The Asian elephant. 8. Temperature. 9. Platelets. 10. It curves
1. They both have seven. 2. Genetics. 3. Fructose. 4. The eagle owl. 5. Nitrogen.

ENTERTAINMENT

1 The phrase 'Book 'em, Danno' was associated with which TV show?

2 How many 'Von Trapp' children were there in the film *The Sound of Music*?

3 In which London Park is there an open-air theatre?

4 Elvis Presley died in 1977. True or false?

5 In which town is *Postman Pat* set?

6 'Why Can't This Be Love?' was a number eight hit for whom in 1986?

7 In what kind of building was the soap *Crossroads* based?

8 Celia Johnson starred with which actor in the film *Brief Encounter*?

9 What is the connection between the singers Dionne Warwick and Whitney Houston?

10 Who wrote the musical *Blood Brothers*?

11 June Brown plays which character in *EastEnders*?

12 Who starred as 'Dr Dolittle' in the original film of the same name?

13 Who had hits in the 1960s with 'Don't Sleep in the Subway', 'Downtown', and 'The Other Man's Grass'?

14 Who was the first presenter of TV's *Gardeners' World*?

15 What was the full name of the character played by Ronnie Barker in the TV programme *Porridge*?

HISTORY

1   In which year was the first Olympic games of the modern era held in Athens?

2   Which famous long-distance race was first held in France in 1903?

3   Which survival device for people travelling in aircraft was first successfully used in 1912?

4   In which year was summer time or daylight-saving time first introduced in Britain?

5   Whose career in first-class cricket lasted from 1864 to 1908?

6   In which year were the Olympic Games held in Berlin?

7   Who annoyed Adolf Hitler by winning four gold medals at the Berlin Olympics?

8   In which year did the Agatha Christie play *The Mousetrap* open in London's West End?

9   Who won the women's tennis Grand Slam in 1953?

10 In which year did the British newspaper 'The Sunday Times' issue its first colour supplement?

11 Where were the Olympic Games held in 1968?

12 In which country did Muhammad Ali regain the world heavyweight boxing championship by defeating George Foreman in 1973?

13 What British honour did both film comedian Charlie Chaplin and author P. G. Wodehouse receive in 1975?

14 What nationality were both the men's and women's singles tennis champions at Wimbledon in 1989?

15 What, also in 1989, was controversially erected outside the Louvre museum in Paris?

FAMOUS PEOPLE

1 Which English poet died fighting for Greek independence?

2 Who discovered the tomb of Tutankhamun in 1922?

3 During which war did Florence Nightingale pioneer a nursing service for the British troops?

4 Which king succeeded Edward the Confessor to the English throne?

5 Whose painting of *The Birth of Venus* hangs in the Uffizi Gallery in Florence?

6 Who wrote the music for *The Threepenny Opera*?

7 Which Scottish missionary was the first European to discover the Victoria Falls?

8 Who was the architect of St Paul's Cathedral?

9 Who wrote *Gone with the Wind*?

10 Which scientist formulated the theory of relativity?

11 Who commanded the British capture of Quebec in 1759?

12 Who invented the gramophone?

13 Whose poems include the *Sonnets from the Portuguese*?

14 Which English king ordered the compilation of the Domesday Book?

15 By the time he died in 1227, whose empire stretched from the Black Sea to the Pacific?

ANSWERS

1. Lord Byron. 2. Howard Carter. 3. The Crimean War. 4. Harold. 5. Botticelli. 6. Kurt Weill. 7. David Livingstone. 8. Sir Christopher Wren. 9. Margaret Mitchell. 10. Albert Einstein. 11. General Wolfe. 12. Thomas Edison. 13. Elizabeth Barrett Browning. 14. William I ('The Conqueror'). 15. Genghis Khan.

SPORT & LEISURE

1 The motorcycle road race held on the Isle of Man is called the TT. What does TT stand for?

2 Who won the UEFA Cup in 1973?

3 On which golf course is the US masters always played?

4 What type of game is euchre?

5 How many players are on each side in a game of polo?

6 In the dice game craps, what number is designated 'snake eyes'?

7 Which American racing driver won the world Grand Prix championship in 1978?

8 Who was the first gymnast to score a perfect 10 in an Olympic gymnastics competition?

9 Which cricketer ended his career with a test batting average of 99.94?

10 What is the game resembling hurling played in the Scottish Highlands?

11 In what sport is the NBA Championship played in the US?

12 Which city was the site of the Olympic Games in 1988?

13 Which European football club plays at the Nou Camp stadium?

14 In tennis, what is the women's equivalent of the Davis Cup called?

15 How is the game called tick-tack-toe in the US better known in Britain?

GENERAL KNOWLEDGE

1 What is the traditional name of the dish made of sausages in batter?

2 What type of fish are plaice, sole and halibut?

3 Which capital city stands on the River Liffey?

4 Which Greek philosopher is quoted as saying, 'What we have to learn to do, we learn by doing'?

5 Founded in 1934, what is the name of the public school which became co-educational in 1972, near the coast in north-east Scotland?

6 On what day does Lent finish?

7 Who played the young 'John Connor' in the film *Terminator 2*?

8 In golf, what is an 'eagle'?

9 What are the three green coloured properties in the game of 'Monopoly'?

10 With which disease is the drug L-dopa originally associated?

11 What does 'vice versa' mean?

12 What is the chemical formula for water?

13 What is a baud?

14 From which mythology does afreet, the powerful evil demon, come?

15 What is the name of Socrates' wife who gave her name to mean an ill-tempered or irritable woman or wife?

ANSWERS

1. 'Toad in the Hole'. 2. Flat fish, salt water fish. 3. Dublin. 4. Aristotle. 5. Gordonstoun. 6. The day before Easter. 7. Edward Furlong. 8. Score of two strokes under par for the hole. 9. Bond Street, Regent Street and Oxford Street. 10. Parkinson's disease. 11. The other way round. 12. H_2O. 13. A unit of measuring the speed of electronic data transmission. 14. Arab mythology. 15. Xanthippe.

SCIENCE & NATURE

1   In what decade was the first photograph taken?

2   In addition to neutrons, what two other particles make up atoms?

3   What is particularly lacking in the body of an albino?

4   What do the initials TNT stand for?

5   For what was *Apollo II* space mission most famous?

6   What is the substance that makes plants green?

7   How many feet are there in one fathom?

8   As what are iron pyrites commonly known?

9   What does an anemometer measure?

10 What is a CAT scanner usually used to detect?

11 What was the Earth's first artificial satellite?

12 What is the study of poisons called?

13 Which planet orbits nearest to Earth?

14 Where is the Sea of Tranquillity?

15 How did the QWERTY keyboard get its name?

ANSWERS

1. 1820s. 2. Protons and electrons. 3. Melanin. 4. Trinitrotoluene. 5. Putting the first men on the Moon. 6. Chlorophyll. 7. Six feet. 8. Fool's gold. 9. Wind speed. 10. Cancers in the body. 11. *Sputnik 1.* 12. Toxicology. 13. Venus. 14. On the Moon. 15. From its first six letter keys.

ENTERTAINMENT

1   TV's *London's Burning* features which fire station and watch?

2   In the 1950s, which British 'skiffle' star had a hit with 'Putting on the Style'?

3   In which year was the film *Crocodile Dundee* released?

4   Who plays 'Ricky Butcher' in *EastEnders*?

5   Which couple had a hit with 'I Got You Babe' in 1965?

6   *The Archers* is set in which fictional county?

7   Who played the part of the landlord in TV's *Rising Damp*?

8   What was the name of the club in Liverpool where the 'Beatles' performed in the early sixties?

9   Marion Morrison was the real name of which American film star?

10 What is the name of René's wife in TV's *'Allo 'Allo*?

11 Who wrote the comedy play *Noises Off*?

12 Who plays 'Axel Foley' in the *Beverly Hills Cop* films?

13 How many times did 'Blue Monday' by 'New Order' enter the charts between 1983 and 1988?

14 Who had a hit with 'The House of the Rising Sun'?

15 Which actor/entertainer plays the part of 'Les Patterson'?

HISTORY

1 Who was king of England in the year 1300?

2 In which century did Marco Polo travel overland from Italy to China?

3 In 1517 Martin Luther wrote 95 theses condemning the practices of the church with regard to the sale of indulgences and questioning papal authority. What did he do with them?

4 What was an indulgence?

5 Who besieged Vienna in 1683?

6 Who raised the siege of Vienna in 1683 by defeating the army that was besieging it?

7 In which year did the Great Fire of London take place?

8 Did the severe outbreak of plague in London described in Daniel Defoe's *Journal of the Plague Year* take place before or after the Great Fire?

9 What church was King Charles II of England a member of when he died?

10 What event was the French marshal Pierre Bosquet observing when he remarked 'C'est magnifique, mais ce n'est pas la guerre' (It's magnificent, but it is not war)?

11 British prime ministers Harold Wilson and Edward Heath were both born in the same year. Which year was it?

12 What was the 'Polish Corridor'?

13 In which year did Princess Margaret marry Anthony Armstrong-Jones (Lord Snowdon)?

14 For how long did Pope John Paul I hold office?

15 Which Chancellor of the Exchequer introduced Personal Equity Plans (PEPs)?

FAMOUS PEOPLE

1 Who wrote *Wuthering Heights*?

2 During the reign of which British king did the American colonies achieve independence?

3 Whose musical compositions include *The Rite of Spring* and the ballet music for *The Firebird*?

4 What was the name of the Nepalese mountaineer who reached the summit of Everest in 1953?

5 Who famously kept a diary from 1660 to 1669?

6 Who was the first woman to take her seat in the House of Commons?

7 Which German scientist discovered X-rays in 1895?

8 What was the name of the Indian warrior who defeated Custer at the Little Big Horn?

9 Which American writer created the tough-guy detective 'Philip Marlow'?

10 Who painted the *Laughing Cavalier*?

11 Who founded the Society of Jesus (also called the Jesuits)?

12 Which 19th century naturalist made a voyage on the 'Beagle'?

13 Who was the mother of Queen Elizabeth I?

14 Which sculptor's works include *The Kiss* and *The Thinker*?

15 Who was the first man to run a mile in under four minutes?

ANSWERS

1. Emily Brontë. 2. George III. 3. Stravinsky. 4. (Sherpa) Norgay Tenzing. 5. Samuel Pepys. 6. Viscountess Nancy Astor. 7. Röntgen. 8. Sitting Bull. 9. Raymond Chandler. 10. Franz Hals. 11. Saint Ignatius Loyola. 12. Charles Darwin. 13. Anne Boleyn. 14. Auguste Rodin. 15. Roger Bannister.

SPORT & LEISURE

1. How many properties are there on a Monopoly board?

2. Which female US tennis player was known as 'Little Mo'?

3. What are the periods into which a game of polo is divided called?

4. In poker, what is a 'blaze'?

5. Which Australian golfer is known as the 'Great White Shark'?

6. Which game derives its name from the Persian word *shah* meaning 'a king'?

7. Who is the only world heavyweight boxing champion to retire without ever being defeated?

8. In golf what is an 'albatross'?

9. The footballer Tom Finney played for only one Football League club, his home-town team. What was the club?

10. What is the longest athletics race in the Olympic Games?

11. Three South American teams have won the football World Cup. Brazil and Argentina are two of them; who is the third?

12. What colour is the five-point ring on an archery target?

13. Which football team is known as 'The Owls'?

14. What is the height of the wicket in a game of cricket?

15. In a pack of playing cards, only one of the kings is shown in profile. Which one?

1. 28. 2. Maureen Connolly. 3. Chukkas. 4. A hand containing only court-cards. 5. Greg Norman. 6. Chess. 7. Rocky Marciano. 8. A score of three strokes under par for a hole. 9. Preston North End. 10. The 50km (31.5 miles) walk. 11. Uruguay. 12. Blue. 13. Sheffield Wednesday. 14. 71.1cm (28"). 15. The King of diamonds.

GENERAL KNOWLEDGE

1 Which fruit was traditionally eaten on Mothering and Palm Sundays?

2 What is a cliché?

3 On which foodstuff does the enzyme amylase found in the pancreas specifically act?

4 Who do we call the young of a deer?

5 From which book does the quotation 'Open Sesame!' come?

6 From which country comes the paso doble?

7 What is the name of the last book of the Bible?

8 What is the name of the racecourse near Chichester in West Sussex?

9 Who walks in a dream through the looking-glass in a book by Lewis Carroll?

10 What is the target number in the card game 'Pontoon'?

11 What is a 'post mortem'?

12 In which sport was a 'mashie' used for lifting the ball high?

13 What activity do electromyographs record?

14 What is the full name for CO_2?

15 What is the name of the fine, soft, sheer fabric of plain weave used especially in shirts, lingerie, dresses and handkerchiefs?

ANSWERS

1. Figs. 2. A phrase that has become worn out and emptied of meaning by over-frequent and careless use. 3. Starch. 4. Fawn. 5. *The History of Ali Baba*. 6. Spain. 7. Revelation. 8. Goodwood. 9. 'Alice'. 10. 21. 11. An examination of a corpse to discover the cause of death. 12. Golf. 13. Muscle activity. 14. Carbon dioxide. 15. Batiste.

SCIENCE & NATURE

1 When was the planet Pluto discovered?

2 Of which element is 'ozone' a form?

3 What is the lowest layer of the atmosphere called?

4 What is the common name for the part of the body called the 'epidermis'?

5 What type of creature is a gastropod?

6 Which conifer is deciduous?

7 'Green Hairstreak', 'Wall' and 'Gatekeeper' are types of what?

8 What coastal bird with a brightly coloured beak lives in burrows?

9 Which gas do plants absorb during the day?

10 What is the technical name for the collarbone?

11 Which two elements combine to form common salt?

12 Bronze is an alloy of which two metals?

13 What blocks out the Sun's rays in a lunar eclipse?

14 Excluding wisdom teeth, how many teeth should an adult human have?

15 What is a 'shrike'?

1. 1930. 2. Oxygen. 3. Troposphere. 4. The skin. 5. A snail or slug. 6. Larch. 7. Butterflies. 8. Puffin. 9. Carbon dioxide. 10. Clavicle. 11. Sodium and chlorine. 12. Copper and tin. 13. The Earth. 14. 32. 15. A bird.

ENTERTAINMENT

1. Who performed 'I Won't Let the Show Go On' wearing a clown's costume?

2. Which actor played the part of 'Hazell' in the TV series of the same name?

3. Who was the first presenter of TV's *Blankety Blank*?

4. Who plays the part of 'Brian Quigley' in *Ballykissangel*?

5. Which was the only 'James Bond' film in which George Lazenby appeared as '007'?

6. Who wrote the lyrics for the musical *Starlight Express*?

7. John Alderton played 'Bernard Hedges' in which TV comedy series?

8. In which film were the 'Blue Meanies' featured?

9. In the 1930s, which character was played by Buster Crabbe?

10. Colonel Tom Parker was the manager of which singer?

11. Which two people wrote the TV comedy series *Fawlty Towers*?

12. What collaboration had a number two hit with 'Fairytale of New York' in 1987?

13. Which character did Burt Kwouk play in the *Pink Panther* films?

14. Who was famous for singing 'Sally' and 'The Biggest Aspidistra in the World'?

15. Which disc jockey is famous for 'Our Tune'?

HISTORY

1   In what movement of the 15th century did Philipp Melanchthon and Ulrich Zwingli play prominent parts?

2   Who organized the dissolution of the monasteries for King Henry VIII of England?

3   Who was queen of England for nine days in 1553?

4   In which year did the Spanish Armada sail up the English Channel in order to carry an invasion force into England?

5   Which king of Spain ordered the Armada to set sail?

6   Who commanded the Spanish Armada?

7   Who, when Britain declared war against Spain in 1739, said 'They now ring the bells, but they will soon wring their hands'?

8   Which seven years were the years of the Seven Years War in Europe?

9   Which other country was Britain's main ally during the Seven Years War?

10 In which year did George Stephenson's 'Rocket' win a contest between different locomotives at Rainhill?

11 Who was appointed engineer to the Great Western Railway in 1833?

12 Who, in the 19th century, was a lord mayor of York and MP for Sunderland, but is best-known as the 'Railway King'?

13 How did William Huskisson, a former president of the Board of Trade, meet his death in 1830?

14 In which year was the *Communist Manifesto* published?

15 Who were the joint authors of the *Communist Manifesto*?

FAMOUS PEOPLE

1   What was the name of the British prime minister assassinated in 1812?

2   Which French artist spent most of his later years living on the South Sea islands of Tahiti and the Marquesas?

3   Who wrote *King Solomon's Mines*?

4   What was the nickname of the American Confederate General Thomas Jonathan Jackson?

5   Which Italian-born explorer sailed from Bristol and landed in Newfoundland in 1497?

6   With what artistic movement is Holman Hunt associated?

7   Who was the mother of Richard the Lionheart?

8   Who was the chief conspirator in the Gunpowder Plot?

9   Which Polish composer is best known for his compositions for the piano?

10 Which English bookseller gave his name to the London institution which he founded in 1722?

11 Whose plays include *Lady Windermere's Fan* and *A Woman of No Importance*?

12 Who founded the Women's Franchise League in 1889?

13 Who invented the spinning frame in 1768?

14 Which king founded the Order of the Garter?

15 Which famous English lady was married to Leofric, Earl of Chester?

SPORT & LEISURE

1 Which cricketer became the first professional captain of the England team in 1953?

2 How many domino tiles are there in a standard set?

3 Which horse won the Grand National in 1973, 1974 and 1977?

4 Who did Muhammad Ali defeat to become the world heavyweight boxing champion in 1964?

5 How is Edson Arantes do Nascimento better known?

6 Who is the only racing driver to win the world championship driving his own car?

7 What is the name of the heroine of the *Tomb Raider* video games?

8 Where were the Olympic Games held in 1964?

9 Which football club is the object of Nick Hornby's obsession in his book *Fever Pitch*?

10 Which US golfer was known as 'the Golden Bear'?

11 Which game was invented in 1931 by the architect Alfred Butts?

12 Who was the first woman tennis player to win one million dollars in prize money?

13 In which sport was Ty Cobb an outstanding player?

14 Which batsman scored six 6s in one over in a match between Nottinghamshire and Glamorgan in 1968?

15 After whom was the first football World Cup trophy named?

GENERAL KNOWLEDGE

1 What do we call a young horse?

2 Which town is the capital of Jamaica?

3 What is the most frequently used letter in English?

4 In his play *The Rehearsal*, who wrote; 'The object of art is to give life a shape'?

5 On Easter Sunday, what cake is traditionally eaten?

6 In the card games bridge or whist, what is the name for a hand in which none of the cards is higher than nine?

7 What is the musical term for a composition, usually on a religious theme, for voices and orchestra?

8 Who are 'Athos, Porthos and Aramis' in a novel by Dumas?

9 What is the square diagonally opposite 'Go' in the game of 'Monopoly'?

10 In the game 'Triominoes', what shape are all the pieces?

11 What do electroencephalographs record?

12 In which book of the Bible is the hippopotamus-like beast, the behemoth, described?

13 In which town can you see the 'Bayeux Tapestry'?

14 What are 'hash browns'?

15 In music, what sort of scene is a 'pastorale' suggesting?

71

SCIENCE & NATURE

1   What took place in Alamogordo, Northern Mexico on 16 July 1945?

2   Which is the highest level of the atmosphere that Concorde reaches in flight?

3   Many aerosols used to use CFCs as propellants. What do the letters CFC stand for?

4   Is a magnifying glass made with a concave or a convex lens?

5   Which planet has a moon called Europa?

6   What is the name for the pupa of a butterfly?

7   Which scientist devised the three laws of motion?

8   Which two elements make up sand?

9   What is the common name of the plant with the Latin name *Hedera helix*?

10 Which slow growing conifer has red berries which are poisonous to humans?

11 What is the 'Jersey Tiger' that can be found in Devon?

12 In a bee-hive, which are there more of: (a) Queens, (b) drones or (c) workers?

13 What was bubonic plague called in the 14th century?

14 How many humps does a Bactrian or Asian camel have?

15 What type of rock is Ayer's Rock in Australia made of?

ANSWERS

1. The first atomic bomb was detonated. 2. Stratosphere. 3. Chlorofluorocarbon.
4. Convex. 5. Jupiter. 6. Chrysalis. 7. Sir Isaac Newton. 8. Oxygen and silicon.
9. Ivy. 10. Yew. 11. A moth. 12. (c) Workers. 13. The Black Death. 14. Two.
15. Sandstone.

ENTERTAINMENT

1 Who wrote the play *A Man For All Seasons*?

2 Which instrument did the jazz musician Acker Bilk play?

3 Who presented the TV series *The Big Time*?

4 The film *Bonnie and Clyde* starred which two actors?

5 Who performed the song 'Chirpy Chirpy Cheep Cheep'?

6 Rodney Bewes, Derek Fowlds and Roy North all appeared with which TV puppet?

7 What was The Animals' only number one hit record?

8 Sue Nicholls plays which character in *Coronation Street*?

9 What nationality was the composer Chopin?

10 Who played the part of 'Scarlet O'Hara' in the film *Gone With The Wind*?

11 What was the international name of TV's *It's a Knockout*?

12 Which pop programme in the 1960s was presented by Cathy McGowan and Keith Fordyce?

13 Which actors played the husband and wife in the film *Kramer versus Kramer*?

14 What was the name of the 1988 number one hit by U2?

15 In which country was the TV police series *Van Der Valk* set?

SESSION 11   QUIZ 6

73

ANSWERS

1. Robert Bolt. 2. Clarinet. 3. Esther Rantzen. 4. Faye Dunaway and Warren Beatty. 5. 'Middle of the Road'. 6. 'Basil Brush'. 7. 'House of the Rising Sun'. 8. Audrey Roberts'. 9. Polish. 10. Vivien Leigh. 11. *Jeux Sans Frontieres*. 12. *Ready, Steady, Go*. 13. Meryl Streep and Dustin Hoffman. 14. 'Desire'. 15. Holland.

HISTORY

1 In which country was the Pale?

2 What was the Pale?

3 Which favourite of Queen Elizabeth I of England was made lord-lieutenant of Ireland in 1599?

4 Which Irish towns did Oliver Cromwell and his forces sack, massacring many of the inhabitants, in 1649?

5 Of which cathedral was the author of *Gulliver's Travels*, Jonathan Swift, dean from 1713 to 1745?

6 The playwrights William Congreve, Oliver Goldsmith, Richard Brinsley Sheridan, Oscar Wilde and George Bernard Shaw all had strong Irish connections. Who was the only one of them not born in Ireland?

7 In which year did Wolfe Tone lead a small French expeditionary force into Ireland in an attempt to spark a rebellion against British rule?

8 Which 19th century Irish member of the British House of Commons was known as the 'uncrowned king of Ireland'?

9 Which 19th century British prime minister twice tried unsuccessfully to have a bill for Home Rule for Ireland passed by parliament?

10 In which year did the Easter Uprising in Dublin take place?

11 Which Irish nationalist politician, one of the early leaders of Sinn Fein, was gunned down in an ambush in 1922?

12 Where was Éamon de Valera, Irish nationalist leader, prime minister and president of the Republic of Ireland born?

13 In which year did the partition of Ireland take place?

14 Who became the Irish Republic's first female president in 1990?

15 On which day of 1998 was a peace agreement signed between the Unionist and Nationalist groups in Northern Ireland?

FAMOUS PEOPLE

1   Who was the first director-general of the BBC?

2   What nationality were the Brothers Grimm?

3   Which American astronaut flew in the space shuttle 36 years after he flew in orbit around the earth?

4   Who wrote *Das Kapital*?

5   Who landed at Botany Bay in 1770?

6   What was the name of Queen Victoria's husband?

7   Who gave the title of *An Arrangement in Grey and Black* to a portrait of his mother?

8   Which composer wrote *Rule, Britannia*?

9   Who created the fictional character 'Long John Silver'?

10 Which English astronomer is renowned for his studies of comets?

11 Which operatic singer has given her name to a sweet sauce, often served with peaches?

12 Who wrote under the pseudonym 'Saki'?

13 Who instigated the penny post in 1840?

14 Which Scottish explorer undertook expeditions to the River Niger area?

15 Who has given his name to the loading line marked around the hull of ships?

1. Lord Reith. 2. German. 3. John Glenn. 4. Karl Marx. 5. James Cook. 6. (Prince) Albert. 7. James Whistler. 8. Thomas Arne. 9. Robert Louis Stevenson (in *Treasure Island*). 10. Edmund Halley. 11. Dame Nellie Melba (Melba sauce). 12. H. H. Munro. 13. Rowland Hill. 14. Mungo Park. 15. Samuel Plimsoll.

SPORT & LEISURE

1 Which boxer was world heavyweight champion between 1937 and 1949?

2 How many holes does a cribbage board have?

3 In baseball, what is a 'switch-hitter'?

4 Who did Bobby Fischer defeat in the world chess championship in 1972?

5 What was burned in 1883 to produce 'The Ashes', kept in an urn, for which the England and Australia cricket teams regularly compete?

6 In which game are various parts of the playing areas called 'penthouse', 'dedan' and 'tambour'?

7 Which athlete won four gold medals at the 1936 Berlin Olympics?

8 Who was the British snooker player who won the world championship fifteen times between 1927 and 1946?

9 What is the name of the blue piece in the game of Cluedo?

10 What is the name of the golf tournament played between teams of male amateurs representing the US and Great Britain and Ireland?

11 What is the value of the outer central ring on a dartboard?

12 What is the term for the main group of cyclists in a race?

13 Which football manager said: 'Some people think football is a matter of life and death. I can assure them it is much more serious than that'?

14 Which is the oldest of the English classic horse races?

15 How many players are there in an indoor handball team?

ANSWERS

1. Joe Louis. 2. 120 – four rows of 30 holes each. 3. A batter who can bat either right-handed or left-handed. 4. Boris Spassky. 5. A bail. 6. Real tennis. 7. Jesse Owens. 8. Joe Davis. 9. Mrs Peacock. 10. The Walker Cup. 11. 25. 12. The peloton. 13. Bill Shankly. 14. The St Leger. 15. Seven.

GENERAL KNOWLEDGE

1 What is the fifth letter of the Greek alphabet?

2 What three layers make up 'Millionaire's Shortcake'?

3 What is a person's 'alma mater'?

4 What fruit is used to flavour Aurum liqueur?

5 The finger and toe nails of the human body have nerves and blood vessels. True or false?

6 What, in musical terms, is a rhapsody?

7 What, in Britain, are traditionally eaten on Good Friday?

8 Who plays the part of 'Ed Wood' in the film of the same name?

9 How many squares are there in total on a chess board?

10 What is a 'non sequitur'?

11 What do electrocardiographs record?

12 What, in gardening, is bolting?

13 From whom do these words originally come: 'Don't count your chickens before they are hatched'?

14 What kind of 'ship' is a 'zeppelin'?

15 In the film *Schindler's List*, what was the colour of the little girl's coat shown in colour in the black and white scenes?

ANSWERS

1. Epsilon. 2. Shortcake, caramel, chocolate. 3. One's school, college, university, etc. 4. Orange. 5. False. 6. A work with no set form, often based on folk tunes. 7. Hot Cross Buns. 8. Johnny Depp. 9. 64. 10. Something that does not logically follow from what has gone before. 11. Heartbeats. 12. Premature running to seed. 13. Aesop, in his fable *The Milkmaid and her Pail*. 14. Airship. 15. Red.

SCIENCE & NATURE

1 Is a 'sea cucumber' a plant or an animal?

2 What is the largest invertebrate creature in the world?

3 How far is the Sun from the Earth?

4 What is the name for moving energy?

5 In 1712 Thomas Newcomen built the first real engine. What was it for?

6 What is a 'sand tiger'?

7 Who invented the first camera to use film rather than plates?

8 In 1938, what did German physicists Otto Hahn and Fritz Strassman achieve?

9 Which is the brightest planet, as seen from Earth?

10 Which volcano has been erupting continuously since 1983?

11 What is a male seal called?

12 Which two gases are liquified to make rocket fuel?

13 When did the last Ice Age end? Was it (a) 1 million years ago, (b) 100,000 years ago or (c) 10,000 years ago?

14 What are the two types of light sensitive cells on the retina?

15 Why is helium now used to fill airships instead of hydrogen?

ENTERTAINMENT

1 On which radio programme did the characters 'Major Bloodnok' and 'Henry Crum' appear?

2 The song 'How Deep Is Your Love' is featured in which film?

3 J. M. Barrie's play *Peter Pan* had its first performance in Britain in: (a) 1904, (b) 1908 or (c) 1910?

4 In the TV series *Perry Mason*, what was the name of 'Perry Mason's' female assistant?

5 Which instrument did the bandleader Count Basie play?

6 'Huey', 'Dewey' and 'Louie' were the nephews of which cartoon character?

7 Trudie Goodwin plays which character in *The Bill*?

8 In the 1960s, which group performed with Billy J. Kramer?

9 Which female comedian won ITV's *New Faces* talent show in 1973?

10 Who played 'Mary Poppins' in the film of that name?

11 In the series *Are You Being Served?*, what character does John Inman play?

12 According to *My Fair Lady*, in which three places do 'Hurricanes hardly ever happen'?

13 Which godfather was 'Living in America' in 1986?

14 Who performed the hit song 'Bridge Over Troubled Water'?

15 What is 'Fred Flintstone's' wife called in the cartoon series *The Flintstones*?

79

HISTORY

1 Who commanded the Spanish and Papal forces which defeated the Turks at the Battle of Lepanto in 1571?

2 What sort of battle was the Battle of Lepanto?

3 Who was called 'the wisest fool in Christendom'?

4 What nationality was King Charles I of England's queen?

5 Who was Catherine of Braganza?

6 At which battle did the forces of King James II finally defeat the rebel forces of the Duke of Monmouth in 1685?

7 Where were the 'Bloody Assizes' held following the defeat of Monmouth's rebels?

8 Which judge presided at the 'Bloody Assizes'?

9 Captain William Coram was a noted English philanthropist. What did he found in 1741?

10 August Gneisenau was a German commander during which wars?

11 What, in the context of World War II, were the Scharnhorst and the Gneisenau?

12 Who was the first post-war Labour prime minister of Great Britain?

13 Which leader of the British Labour Party promised to 'fight, fight, fight, and fight again' to save the party after being defeated in conference debate on nuclear disarmament?

14 In which year was American pilot Francis Gary Powers shot down while on a U2 spy plane mission over the USSR?

15 The United Kingdom and six other nations founded what in 1960 as a rival to the European Economic Community?

FAMOUS PEOPLE

1   Who in 1791 built the first cast iron bridge over the river Severn at Coalbrookdale?

2   Which king of Spain financed Columbus's voyage to America?

3   Whose paintings include *Blue Boy* and *Mrs Siddons*?

4   Which American president was assassinated in 1901?

5   Who wrote *Vindication of the Rights of Women*?

6   What was the stage name of Margaret Hookham?

7   Whose operatic compositions include *Orpheus in the Underworld* and *Tales of Hoffman*?

8   Who commanded the British at the Battle of Waterloo?

9   Who wrote *Vanity Fair*?

10   With what area of social reform is Octavia Hill associated?

11   Which jazz musician had the nickname 'Satchmo'?

12   Which Elizabethan painter was famous for his miniature portraits?

13   Which Scottish chemist patented a method for waterproofing cloth?

14   Which Italian patriot was the leader of the 'Red Shirts'?

15   Who led the 1953 British expedition to climb Mount Everest?

ANSWERS

1. Abraham Darby. 2. Ferdinand. 3. Thomas Gainsborough. 4. William McKinley. 5. Mary Wollstonecraft. 6. Margot Fonteyn. 7. Offenbach. 8. Duke of Wellington. 9. William Makepeace Thackeray. 10. Housing conditions. 11. Louis Armstrong. 12. Nicholas Hilliard. 13. Charles Macintosh. 14. Garibaldi. 15. Sir John Hunt.

SPORT & LEISURE

1   Geoff Hurst scored a hat-trick for England in the 1966 World Cup final. Who scored England's other goal?

2   In card games such as solo whist, what does 'misère' mean?

3   What nationality was the racing driver Ayrton Senna?

4   What game was invented by Charles Darrow in 1929, the year of the Wall Street crash?

5   In ice hockey, what is the name of the end-of-season playoff tournament between the top Canadian and US teams?

6   Who were the first British football club to win the European Cup?

7   Which Olympic champion was known as the 'Flying Finn'?

8   Tennis's Grand Slam is made up of Wimbledon, the US Open, the French Open and which other tournament?

9   Which sport features snatches and clean jerks?

10   In what city did Roger Bannister run the first four-minute mile?

11   Which darts player was nicknamed 'the Crafty Cockney'?

12   In which Olympic swimming races do competitors start in the water?

13   What is the American equivalent of the card game pontoon?

14   What Chinese game has a name that means 'the sparrows'?

15   Which boxer was world heavyweight champion between 1919 and 1926?

1. Martin Peters. 2. A declaration that a player will win no tricks in a hand.
3. Brazilian. 4. Monopoly. 5. The Stanley Cup. 6. Celtic. 7. Paavo Nurmi.
8. The Australian Open. 9. Weightlifting. 10. Oxford. 11. Eric Bristow.
12. Backstroke. 13. Blackjack. 14. Mahjong. 15. Jack Dempsey.

GENERAL KNOWLEDGE

1 Who wrote *The Mayor of Casterbridge*?

2 Ozone is a highly toxic, unstable, colourless gas. True or false?

3 Which are generally hotter, green or red chillies?

4 In one of his essays, who is quoted as writing, 'The remedy is worse than the disease'?

5 What musical term means a composition in which a refrain is repeated between separate sections?

6 As opposed to a 'tied house', what is the name given to a pub that is free to receive its supplies from a number of brewers?

7 In Dickens' novel, what is the hero, Chuzzlewit's, first name?

8 What does the abbreviation p.m. stand for?

9 How many pawns does each player have in the game of 'Chess'?

10 What does it mean to 'bowdlerize a book'?

11 What does IVF stand for?

12 What is the capital of Austria?

13 What is the name used to describe pig-offal loaf?

14 What is the name of the outer skin layer of the body?

15 In what script is the Russian alphabet written?

SCIENCE & NATURE

1   Which sand-burrowing amphibian is legally protected in Britain?

2   Which force opposes motion, wastes energy and produces heat?

3   What is the function of the stoma on the leaves of plants?

4   What was the name of the first artificial satellite launched by the Soviet Union in October 1957?

5   The symbol Ag is used to represent which chemical element?

6   Which is the biggest fish in the world?

7   The core of the Earth is made of nickel and which other element?

8   What is a young spider called?

9   A 'supernova' is the birth of a star. True or false?

10 Cirrus clouds are made of: (a) Ice crystals, (b) water droplets or (c) water vapour?

11 Which animal has the largest brain?

12 What is the hardest substance in the human body?

13 What is the name of the structure a beaver builds to live in?

14 Chalk, shale and sandstone are what type of rocks?

15 In which year did Yuri Gagarin make the first manned space flight: (a) 1959, (b) 1961 or (c) 1963?

ANSWERS

1. The natterjack toad. 2. Friction. 3. To allow oxygen and carbon dioxide in and out of the leaf. 4. Sputnik 1. 5. Silver. 6. The whale shark. 7. Iron. 8. A spiderling. 9. False – it is the death of a star. 10. (a) Ice crystals. 11. The sperm whale. 12. Tooth enamel. 13. A lodge. 14. Sedimentary rocks. 15. (b) 1961.

ENTERTAINMENT

1   Who wrote the musical *Oklahoma*?

2   Which children's radio programme began with these words 'Are you sitting comfortably, then I'll begin'?

3   Who played 'Queen Elizabeth' in TV's *Blackadder II*?

4   In which year was the film *E.T.* released?

5   Roger Daltrey was the lead singer with which group?

6   Tim Brooke-Taylor was one of TV's *The Goodies*. Who were the other two?

7   In which year did *Euro Disney* open in France?

8   Who played the title role in TV's *Bergerac*?

9   Which war-time singer had a hit with 'We'll Meet Again'?

10 Who played 'Lara' in the film *Dr Zhivago*?

11 Which band, fronted by Peter Murphy, got to number fifteen with a cover of Bowie's 'Ziggy Stardust'?

12 Who starred with Bruce Willis in the TV series *Moonlighting*?

13 Who was famous for the catchphrase 'Here's another fine mess you've gotten me into'?

14 Who had a hit with 'The Land of Make Believe'?

15 In the film *Butch Cassidy and The Sundance Kid*, who played the part of 'The Sundance Kid'?

ANSWERS

1. Rodgers and Hammerstein. 2. *Listen With Mother*. 3. Miranda Richardson.
4. 1982. 5. The Who. 6. Graeme Garden and Bill Oddie. 7. 1992. 8. John Nettles.
9. Vera Lynn. 10. Julie Christie. 11. Bauhaus. 12. Cybill Shepherd. 13. Oliver Hardy.
14. Bucks Fizz. 15. Robert Redford.

HISTORY

1 In memory of what was Battle Abbey in Sussex founded?

2 Who was Hereward the Wake?

3 Which English poet was born around 1345 and died in 1400?

4 The Battles of Wakefield, Barnet and St Albans all took place during which civil conflict?

5 Which English king married Margaret of Anjou in 1445?

6 In which year did King Henry VII of England come to the throne?

7 Thomas Cranmer was appointed Archbishop of Canterbury under which English king?

8 Whom did Queen Mary Tudor (Mary I) of England marry in 1554?

9 How many children did Queen Mary Tudor have?

10 What relation was Queen Elizabeth I of England to Queen Mary Tudor?

11 Who was Queen Mary Tudor's mother?

12 Who was Queen Elizabeth's mother?

13 Sir Francis Walsingham was secretary of state to Queen Elizabeth I of England. What did he create that was extremely useful to her?

14 Whom did the Babington plot intend to install on the English throne?

15 The 'Rye House plot' of 1683 was a plot to assassinate which English king?

1. The Battle of Hastings in 1066. 2. A leader of Anglo-Saxon resistance against William the Conqueror and the spread of Norman power, especially in the fen country of eastern England. 3. Geoffrey Chaucer. 4. The Wars of the Roses. 5. King Henry VI. 6. 1485. 7. Henry VIII. 8. King Philip II of Spain. 9. None. 10. Half-sister. 11. Catherine of Aragon. 12. Anne Boleyn. 13. A spy network or system of espionage, at home and abroad, that uncovered several plots against the Queen. 14. Mary Queen of Scots. 15. King Charles II.

FAMOUS PEOPLE

1 Which Scottish king led his troops to victory over the English at Bannockburn?

2 Who wrote the symphonies known as the *Pastoral* and the *Choral*?

3 Which American athlete won four gold medals at the 1936 Olympics?

4 Which brothers invented a cinematograph in 1894?

5 Who was the British minister of health who introduced the National Health Service?

6 Who wrote *Tarzan of the Apes*?

7 Which Welsh buccaneer later became a deputy-governor of Jamaica?

8 Who invented a method of constructing road surfaces by compressing layers of crushed stone together and binding them together with tar or asphalt?

9 Who created the fictional character 'The Scarlet Pimpernel'?

10 Which English king went on the Third Crusade?

11 Who was the music hall singer whose famous songs included: 'My Old Man Said Follow the Van' and 'I'm One of the Ruins that Cromwell Knocked About a Bit'?

12 Which French general was defeated by General Wolfe on the plains of Abraham?

13 What was Gertrude Jekyll famous for?

14 Who was the writer of hymns including 'Hark the Herald Angels Sing' and 'Love Divine All Loves Excelling'?

15 Who invented the 'Kodak' box camera?

ANSWERS

1. Robert the Bruce (Robert I). 2. Beethoven. 3. Jesse Owens. 4. (Auguste & Louis) Lumiere. 5. Aneurin Bevan. 6. Edgar Rice Burroughs. 7. Sir Henry Morgan. 8. John McAdam. 9. Baroness Orczy. 10. Richard I (Lionheart). 11. Marie Lloyd. 12. General Louis Montcalm. 13. Garden design. 14. Charles Wesley. 15. George Eastman.

SPORT & LEISURE

1 Which swimmer won seven gold medals at the 1972 Olympic Games?

2 In card games, what is a 'prial'?

3 How many different colours are the spaces on a Scrabble board?

4 What sporting event takes place between Putney and Mortlake?

5 In which sport was Jahangir Khan a dominant figure in the 1980s?

6 Who was the first European Footballer of the Year, in 1956?

7 Of which sport are *glima*, *kushti* and *schwingen* all forms?

8 In what year were the Winter Olympics first held?

9 On which US city was the game of Monopoly originally based?

10 Which football club plays at The Dell?

11 What is the usual term for a golf course by the sea?

12 In which city is the Waca cricket ground?

13 What was the name of the US high jumper who originated the technique of jumping over the bar headfirst and backwards?

14 What sport do the Chicago Bulls play?

15 What nationality was the figure skater Sonja Henie?

1. Mark Spitz. 2. Three cards of the same rank in a hand. 3. Five. 4. The Oxford–Cambridge boat race. 5. Squash. 6. Stanley Matthews. 7. Wrestling. 8. 1924. 9. Atlantic City. 10. Southampton. 11. A golf links. 12. Perth, Australia. 13. Dick Fosbury. 14. Basketball. 15. Norwegian.

GENERAL KNOWLEDGE

1 According to some alchemists, into what was the 'philosopher's stone' thought to be capable of transmuting base metals?

2 In which country is the port of Antwerp?

3 What spirit is made from potatoes?

4 From which country did chocolate originate?

5 In the Bible, who was thrown into the lion's den?

6 What was the name of the spoilt ill-tempered orphan in Frances Hodgson Burnett's *The Secret Garden*?

7 How many rooks are there on the board at the start of a game of chess?

8 Where are the Crown Jewels displayed when not being used?

9 What is a 'modus operandi'?

10 In which film did Rhett Butler fall in love with Vivienne Leigh?

11 What is the term given to philosophical discussion and logical disputing?

12 From which animal do we get 'vellum'?

13 What is the name of the branches of the windpipe running into the lungs?

14 Traditionally, to whom is the first toast made at a wedding?

15 What is the title of the operetta that Sullivan composed without Gilbert to a libretto by F. C. Burnand?

SCIENCE & NATURE

1 What is an LED?

2 Where in the UK is an extinct volcano with a famous castle on its summit?

3 What are the membranes enveloping the brain and spinal cord called?

4 What commonly used chemical is known as MSG and is used as a flavour enhancer?

5 What disease can humans catch from parrots and pigeons?

6 Who invented the first battery?

7 Who discovered the first safe smallpox vaccine?

8 What chemical is released in the body of a hayfever sufferer which generates the runny nose and other allergy symptoms?

9 What spice comes from the seed pod of a 'Mexican Orchid'?

10 What is the temperature of Absolute Zero in degrees Celsius? Is it (a) −403.10 degrees Celsius, (b) −273.16 degrees Celsius or (c) −100.67 degrees Celsius?

11 Where are the Islets of Langerhans?

12 Which metallic element exists in the liquid state at room temperature?

13. Who was the doctor who discovered the principles of homeopathy in 1796?

14 Where is the smallest muscle in the body?

15 What tree produces yellow flowers in the spring, is poisonous and belongs to the *Leguminosae*?

ANSWERS

1. A Light Emitting Diode. 2. Edinburgh. 3. Meninges. 4. Mono-sodium glutamate. 5. Psittacosis. 6. Alessandro Volta in 1800. 7. Edward Jenner. 8. Histamine. 9. Vanilla. 10. (b) −273.16 degrees Celsius. 11. In the pancreas. 12. Mercury. 13. Dr Samuel Hahnemann. 14. In the ear. It is the stapedius muscle. 15. Laburnum.

ENTERTAINMENT

1   What was the name of the horse in the TV series
    Steptoe and Son?

2   What instrument did Dave Clark of the 'Dave Clark Five' play?

3   What was the occupation of 'Captain Mainwaring' in *Dad's Army*?

4   Which film and TV series featured the character 'Hotlips
    Hoolihan'?

5   In 1966, which TV play featured a homeless young mother?

6   Which radio and television series had as its title the name of a
    book, with the useful words inside, 'Don't Panic'?

7   With which pop group did Phil Collins originally play?

8   Who plays 'Charlie Fairhead' in TV's *Casualty*?

9   Who presented TV's music hall programme *The Good Old Days*?

10 Judith Durham was the singer with which Australian group?

11 Who presents the TV quiz programme *Fifteen-to-One*?

12 Who composed 'The Planets'?

13 Which singer changed his name to Yusef Islam?

14 Who sang 'Hopelessly Devoted To You' in the film *Grease*?

15 Who performed the song 'Combine Harvester'?

HISTORY

1 Elizabeth of Hungary lived from 1207 to 1231 and married to the Landgrave of Thuringia. What happened to her in 1235?

2 Which English king married Elizabeth Woodville in 1464?

3 When did Queen Elizabeth I of England come to the throne?

4 What did Robert Dudley, Earl of Leicester, hope to get from Queen Elizabeth I?

5 Elizabeth, the daughter of King James I of England, also known as 'the Winter Queen' and the 'Queen of Hearts' was queen of which country?

6 Elizabeth 'the Winter Queen' died while on a visit to King Charles II of England in 1662. What relation was she to him?

7 The Empress Elizabeth of Russia (1709–62) was the daughter of whom?

8 The Empress Elizabeth of Russia is said to have entered the Seven Years War because of her hatred for which Prussian monarch?

9 Whose sister Elizabeth was guillotined in 1794?

10 Who lived at 50 Wimpole St in London from 1837 until her marriage in 1846?

11 Who in 1892 was acquitted of murdering her parents with an axe in Fall River, Massachusetts?

12 How did Elizabeth of Bavaria, the wife of the Austrian Emperor Franz Joseph I meet her death in 1898?

13 In which year was Queen Elizabeth the Queen Mother (wife of King George VI of Great Britain) born?

14 In which year did Princess Elizabeth (the future Queen Elizabeth II) of Great Britain marry Philip Mountbatten, Duke of Edinburgh?

15 For what is Betty Boothroyd chiefly famous?

ANSWERS

1. She was canonized (made a saint). 2. King Edward IV. 3. 1558. 4. Her hand in marriage. 5. Bohemia. 6. She was his aunt. 7. Emperor Peter the Great. 8. Frederick the Great (Frederick II). 9. King Louis XVI of France. 10. Elizabeth Barrett (Browning), the poet. 11. Lizzie Borden. 12. She was assassinated (stabbed to death) by an anarchist in Geneva. 13. 1900. 14. 1947. 15. For becoming the first woman Speaker of the British House of Commons.

FAMOUS PEOPLE

1 In 1901, who successfully transmitted the first radio signal across the Atlantic?

2 Which Lady became Lord Nelson's mistress?

3 Who was the first person to print a book in English?

4 Who commanded the New Model Army?

5 To which king of France was Marie Antoinette married?

6 By what name is the writer Mary Ann (or Marian) Evans better known?

7 Which Russian jeweller is famous for creating ornate eggs?

8 Which Mongol emperor did Marco Polo serve for 17 years?

9 Who composed *The Bartered Bride*?

10 What kind of buildings was the architect Nicholas Hawksmoor particularly noted for?

11 Which English king signed *Magna Carta*?

12 Who wrote a number of novels set in his own home area of 'the Potteries'?

13 Who invented the first electric telegraph, and also the code which bears his name?

14 Which English queen was known as 'Bloody Mary'?

15 Who was the author of *Candide*?

ANSWERS

1. Marconi. 2. Emma Hamilton. 3. William Caxton. 4. Oliver Cromwell. 5. Louis XVI. 6. George Eliot. 7. Peter Faberge. 8. Kublai Khan. 9. Smetana. 10. Churches. 11. King John. 12. Arnold Bennet. 13. Samuel Morse. 14. Mary I (Tudor). 15. Voltaire.

SPORT & LEISURE

1. With which sports are Wayne Gretzky and Gordie Howe associated?

2. According to the rules of cricket, how many forms of dismissal are there?

3. Why was the Italian athlete Dorando Pietri disqualified from the marathon in the 1908 Olympics?

4. Who became Britain's first one million pounds footballer in 1979?

5. What is the name of the Dallas American football team?

6. What have these five sports in common: cycling, fencing, gymnastics, swimming and track and field athletics?

7. Which football team do the 'Toon Army' support?

8. Which playing card is the symbol of love?

9. Who was said to 'float like a butterfly, sting like a bee'?

10. In American football, how many points does a touchdown score?

11. What is the first name of the jockey Dunwoody?

12. In which sport would the term 'Shortstop' be used?

13. How many times did Jackie Steward win the Formula 1 World Championship?

14. In boxing, who drew up a set of rules in 1867?

15. What colour jacket is awarded to the winner of the US Masters golf tournament?

1. Ice Hockey. 2. Ten. 3. He had to be assisted by officials on the last lap of the track. 4. Trevor Francis. 5. The Dallas Cowboys. 6. They are the only sports to appear in every modern Olympic Games since 1896. 7. Newcastle United. 8. The nine of hearts. 9. Muhammad Ali. 10. Six. 11. Richard. 12. Baseball. 13. 3. 14. The Marquess of Queensberry (John Shotto Douglas). 15. Green.

GENERAL KNOWLEDGE

1   Into which sea does the River Mersey flow?

2   In what part of the body is the tibia found?

3   In which group of islands is Tenerife?

4   What is frangipane?

5   Who said 'That's one small step for man, one giant leap for mankind'?

6   Which type of tree is a traditional Christmas tree?

7   Which of George Eliot's heros was a single, adopted father?

8   What do we mean when we use the term 'et al'?

9   What alcoholic beverage is commonly associated with a variety of the card game 'Rummy'?

10 What is the character name of the waitress in the original *Fawlty Towers* TV series?

11 What is the name given to the voluntary bureau organization giving advice to people who are uncertain about their rights or who seek special state or voluntary aid but do not know where to find it?

12 What were commissioned by C. Ludwig in 1721?

13 Which British prime minister said 'An iron curtain has descended across the continent'?

14 Of which country is Ottawa the capital?

15 From which fruit is the West Country 'Scrumpy' made?

ANSWERS

1. Irish Sea. 2. Leg (thigh). 3. Canary Islands. 4. Almond-flavoured paste (for cakes). 5. Neil Armstrong (of his first step onto the moon). 6. Fir tree. 7. Silas Marner'. 8. And others. 9. Gin. 10. 'Polly'. 11. Citizens' Advice Bureau. 12. Bach's Brandenburg Concertos. 13. Winston Churchill. 14. Canada. 15. Apples.

SCIENCE & NATURE

1 Which alloy consists of copper and tin and sometimes zinc and lead?

2 What is the chemical symbol for potassium?

3 What drink is produced by the fermentation of honey?

4 What disease is caused by a deficiency of vitamin D?

5 Which chemist was the first to use the term 'atom' to describe the smallest particle of an element?

6 Which gas has a smell of rotten eggs?

7 What is the name of the comet, visible every 33 years, which causes meteorite showers known as the 'Leonid showers'?

8 What pigment is missing in the skin of human albinos?

9 What is the ore from which lead is extracted?

10 Which birds are capable of rotating their neck through 270 degrees?

11 If a substance has a pH of 3.5 is it: (a) Acidic, (b) alkaline or (c) neutral?

12 What is a 'Red Giant'?

13 What is the position of the Sun and Moon relative to each other when a spring tide occurs on the water on the Earth?

14 What kind of rock is sandstone?

15 What acid is produced in the stomach?

1. Bronze. 2. K. 3. Mead. 4. Rickets. 5. John Dalton. 6. Hydrogen Sulphine. 7. Tempel-Tuttle. 8. Melanin. 9. Galena. 10. Owls. 11. (a) Acidic. 12. It is a stage in the life of a star when the star starts to expand. 13. They are in line with each other. 14. Sedimentary rock. 15. Hydrochloric acid.

ENTERTAINMENT

1   In which TV programme did the characters 'Frank and Betty Spencer' appear?

2   Which soap was broadcast on Radio 2 from 1969 to 1980?

3   Who is Michael Douglas' co-star in the 1984 film *Romancing The Stone*?

4   In 1962, B Bumble and The Stingers had a one-hit wonder. What was it called?

5   Who presented the children's TV programme *Animal Magic*?

6   Which film, starring Kevin Costner, describes the story of a Civil War hero befriending the Sioux?

7   Which girls' group regularly appeared in the late 1950s and early 1960s on pop television shows like *Oh Boy*?

8   Who had a hit in 1964 with 'Needles and Pins'?

9   William Shatner is famous for playing 'Captain Kirk' but what part did he play in a police series?

10 Which two people presented Radio 4's *Today* between 1975 and 1986?

11 Which singer originally sang with 'The Tremeloes'?

12 Who presented the TV programme *Civilisation*?

13 Who plays the lead role of 'Johnny Castle' in the film *Dirty Dancing*?

14 Which members from the original line-up were missing from the reformed Pink Floyd in 1987?

15 Who was adamant, 'This Is Not a Love Song'?

ANSWERS

1. *Some Mothers Do 'Ave 'Em*. 2. *Waggoners' Walk*. 3. Kathleen Turner. 4. 'Nut Rocker'. 5. Johnny Morris. 6. *Dances With Wolves*. 7. The Vernons Girls. 8. The Searchers. 9. 'T. J. Hooker'. 10. John Timpson and Brian Redhead. 11. Brian Poole. 12. Kenneth Clark. 13. Patrick Swayze. 14. *Syd Barrett and Roger Waters*. 15. Public Image Limited.

HISTORY

1　In which year did the Battle of Agincourt take place?

2　Which English king led his forces to victory at Agincourt?

3　Why was Richard Duke of York named Protector of England in 1454?

4　In which year did King Henry VIII of England meet King Francis I of France at the 'Field of the Cloth of Gold'?

5　The site of the 'Field of the Cloth of Gold' is near which French port?

6　For whom was Hampton Court Palace near London originally built?

7　How old was King Edward VI when he succeeded to the throne?

8　The French King Henri IV signed the Edict of Nantes in 1598. What did that edict guarantee?

9　Which French king revoked the Edict of Nantes?

10　Jeanne Antoinette Poisson (1721–64), a mistress of the French king Louis XV, is better known by what title?

11　'Bliss was it in that dawn to be alive/But to be young was very heaven' – what event was the poet William Wordsworth referring to and celebrating in those lines?

12　In which year did the Battle of Austerlitz take place?

13　How many emperors were involved in the Battle of Austerlitz?

14　Simon Bolivar was proclaimed emperor of which country in 1824?

15　Thomas Arnold was headmaster of which famous English public school?

1. 1415. 2. Henry V. 3. Because the reigning king, Henry VI, was declared (temporarily) insane. 4. 1520. 5. Calais. 6. Cardinal Wolsey. 7. 10. 8. The rights of and freedom of worship for the Huguenots (French Protestants). 9. King Louis XIV. 10. Madame de Pompadour. 11. The French Revolution. 12. 1805. 13. Three (The French Emperor Napoleon, and the Austrian and Russian Emperors). 14. Peru. 15. Rugby.

FAMOUS PEOPLE

1   Which English missionary founded the 'Inn of the Sixth Happiness' in China?

2   Who devised a method of map projection which is named after him?

3   Which American car manufacturer pioneered the use of assembly-line production methods?

4   Who wrote the radio play *Under Milk Wood*?

5   Who was noted for pioneering agricultural improvements on his estate at Holkham, Norfolk?

6   Which 18th century canal builder designed and built the Bridgewater Canal?

7   Which Norwegian explorer crossed Greenland from east to west in 1888?

8   Who was queen of England for only ten days?

9   Which artist was famous for his stylized black-and-white drawings, including the illustrations for Oscar Wilde's *Salome*?

10 Who composed the opera *Cosi fan tutte*?

11 Which poet was noted for his nonsense rhymes and limericks, including 'The Owl and The Pussy-Cat'?

12 What is the American librarian Melvil Dewey especially famous for?

13 Who built the first iron-hulled steam ship, the 'Great Britain'?

14 Who was the last British king to lead his troops in battle?

15 Who created the fictional detective 'Father Brown'?

1. Gladys Aylward. 2. (Gerhardus) Mercator. 3. Henry Ford. 4. Dylan Thomas. 5. Thomas Coke (Coke of Holkham). 6. James Brindley. 7. Nansen. 8. Lady Jane Grey. 9. Aubrey Beardsley. 10. Mozart. 11. Edward Lear. 12. Devising a book classification scheme, the Dewey Decimal System. 13. Isambard Kingdom Brunel. 14. George II (at the battle of Dettingen, 1743). 15. G. K. Chesterton.

SPORT & LEISURE

1 In which year was the first Soccer World Cup competition organized?

2 In which sport is the Stanley Cup played for?

3 The longest golf hole in the world is the seventh of Satsuki GU, Sano, Japan, which measures 964 yards/881 metres. What par is it?

4 How many gold medals did swimmer Mark Spitz win at the 1972 Olympics?

5 How many runs did Victoria score in 10.5 hours in a cricket match against New South Wales in 1926?

6 Who was the shamed 1987 World 100 metre sprint champion?

7 How many players are in a male lacrosse team?

8 How many times has Jaques Anquetil won the Tour de France?

9 How long does the Le Mans Motor Race last for?

10 Who is the most successful tennis player in the history of the game (male or female)?

11 What is the height of the biggest competition ski-jump hill?

12 Which city hosts the Grand National?

13 How old was Jonah Lomu when he played in his first Rugby World Cup?

14 How many rowers are in an International Dragon Boat team?

15 In judo, which belt follows the Yellow Belt?

ANSWERS

1. 1930. 2. Ice hockey. 3. Par seven. 4. Seven. 5. 1,107 runs. 6. Ben Johnson. 7. Ten. 8. Five. 9. 24 hours. 10. Martina Navratilova. 11. 90 metres. 12. Liverpool. 13. 20 years old. 14. 26 rowers. 15. Orange.

GENERAL KNOWLEDGE

1 What musical term means 'notes of a chord played in quick succession'?

2 The term National Debt was first used in 1694. How much was it then?

3 Who provides the voice for the starring child in *Look Who's Talking*?

4 What is the name of the Scottish ball game similar to hockey?

5 What do the letters RSVP stand for?

6 What do 'gorgons', in classical mythology, have for hair?

7 What is a Bailey bridge?

8 What name do we give to a marinated herring?

9 What is the name of the American comic strip orphan character who gets into a lot of trouble especially when 'Daddy Warbucks' is away?

10 Which bird was the emblem of the Roman Empire?

11 What is the capital city of Sudan, known to many British people as the place where General Gordon was killed in the 1880s?

12 What does E-mail stand for?

13 From what is 'scampi' made?

14 For which street is 'Millionaires' Row' a nickname?

15 Which sport is being described by the term 'natation'?

1. Arpeggio. 2. £49 million. 3. Bruce Willis. 4. Shinty. 5. Répondez s'il vous plaît (please reply, used at the end of an invitation). 6. Serpents. 7. A kind of temporary military bridge. 8. Rollmop. 9. 'Little Orphan Annie'. 10. Eagle. 11. Khartoum. 12. Electronic mail. 13. Prawns. 14. Kensington Palace Gardens. 15. Swimming.

SCIENCE & NATURE

1 How do pythons kill their prey?

2 What is the name of fossilized resin which is used to make jewellery?

3 What is the largest whale in the world?

4 What is the name of a cold dry wind which blows southward over the south coast of France?

5 What is the hardest substance in the human body?

6 Which parasite plant commonly grows on apple trees in this country?

7 What is trepanning?

8 What is the name of the nearest star to Earth?

9 Which member of the legume family is a widely used laxative?

10 Which monk is credited with being the founder of the science of genetics?

11 What is the term for atoms which have the same atomic number but a different atomic mass?

12 Why do pigs wallow in mud?

13 What is SAD?

14 What is the name for the giant wave produced by the effects of an earthquake on the sea?

15 How long does it take for the planet Jupiter to rotate once on its axis: (a) 36.5 hours, (b) 12.8 hours or (c) 9.9 hours?

1. By squeezing or constricting until they suffocate. 2. Amber. 3. The blue whale. 4. *The Mistral*. 5. Enamel. 6. Mistletoe. 7. It is a surgical technique to remove a disc of bone from the skull. 8. *Proxima Centauri*. 9. Senna. 10. Father Gregor Johann Mendel, who published his works in 1866. 11. Isotopes. 12. They do not have any sweat glands and therefore wallow in the mud to keep cool. 13. Seasonal Affective Disorder, a form of depression brought on by lack of daylight in the winter months. 14. 'A tsunami'. 15. (c) 9.9 hours.

ENTERTAINMENT

1. What does the 'T' stand for in 'James T. Kirk' of TV's *Star Trek*?

2. *The Misfits* was the last completed film of which actress?

3. Phil Collins had a hit with 'A Groovy Kind of Love'. Who sang the original version in the 1960s?

4. Did *Bill and Ben* first appear on children's TV in (a) 1950, (b) 1951 or (c) 1952?

5. Which film was based on the life of Dian Fossey's work with mountain gorillas?

6. The song 'I'm Gonna Wash That Man Right Out Of My Hair' comes from which musical?

7. Which musical instrument does Lisa play in TV's *The Simpsons*?

8. Was the film *Ghostbusters* released in (a) 1981, (b) 1984 or (c) 1986?

9. Which composer wrote 'Eine Kleine Nachtmusik'?

10. In the TV comedy series *Red Dwarf*, which role does Chris Barrie play?

11. Who was the first female disc jockey on Radio 1?

12. Which popular singer died in 1977 after a game of golf?

13. Who played the title role in TV's *The Singing Detective*?

14. Who wanted to 'Make It With You' in June 1996?

15. Who was telling 'A Winter's Tale' in December 1982?

103

HISTORY

1 By what nickname is Richard Neville, Earl of Warwick (1428–71) often known?

2 The Sforzas were, from 1450, the ruling family in which Italian city?

3 Lodovico Sforza (1451–1508) was a patron of which famous Renaissance artist?

4 In which year did Joan of Arc defeat the English to raise the siege of Orleans?

5 What nationality was the great Protestant reformer and theologian John Calvin?

6 What happened to Bishops Hugh Latimer and Nicholas Ridley in Oxford in October 1555?

7 In which year did the Battle of Marston Moor take place?

8 What were 'the Fifteen' and 'the Forty-five'?

9 The English statesman the Earl of Chatham (1708–78) is better known as what?

10 Of which British political party was Charles James Fox a leader?

11 Who was elected the fourth president of the United States in 1809?

12 Queen Victoria and her husband Prince Albert were both born in the same year. Which year was it?

13 Who invented the first automatic machine gun in the early 1880s?

14 War broke out between Russia and which other country in 1904?

15 The Russian Social Democratic Party split into Mensheviks and Bolsheviks at its congress of 1903 in which city?

ANSWERS

15. London.
10. The Whigs. 11. James Madison. 12. 1819. 13. (Hiram) Maxim. 14. Japan.
rebellions against the Hanoverians of 1715 and 1745. 9. (William) Pitt the Elder.
6. They were burnt at the stake (for being Protestants). 7. 1644. 8. The two Jacobite
1. Warwick the Kingmaker. 2. Milan. 3. Leonardo da Vinci. 4. 1429. 5. French.

FAMOUS PEOPLE

1 Which Russian writer's works include *Eugene Onegin* and *Boris Godunov*?

2 With which European city is the architect Antonio Gaudi chiefly associated?

3 Who led the 'Kon-Tiki' expedition in 1947?

4 Which US president was assassinated in 1881 after only four months in office?

5 Who was the second person to walk on the Moon?

6 What feat did Amy Johnson achieve in 1930?

7 How was William H. Bonney better known?

8 What nationality was Karen Blixen, author of *Out of Africa*?

9 Who founded the Christian Science movement?

10 Who said: 'In the future everybody will be world famous for fifteen minutes'?

11 Who wrote *The Female Eunuch*?

12 Which French painter is associated with the technique known as 'pointillism'?

13 John Lennon and Denis Healey shared the same middle name. What is it?

14 Who in 1895 was the first actor to be knighted?

15 Who invented the hovercraft?

1. Aleksander Pushkin. 2. Barcelona. 3. Thor Heyerdahl. 4. James Garfield. 5. Edwin 'Buzz' Aldrin. 6. She became the first woman to fly solo from England to Australia. 7. Billy the Kid. 8. Danish. 9. Mary Baker Eddy. 10. Andy Warhol. 11. Germaine Greer. 12. Georges Seurat. 13. Winston. 14. Henry Irving. 15. Christopher Cockerell.

SPORT & LEISURE

1 In which Scottish town do the two top football teams have grounds on the same street, 100 yards apart?

2 How many players are playing in a team of Australian Rules football at any one time.

3 What is the maximum number of clubs a golfer may carry during a round of Golf?

4 Which Scottish sprinter won Gold in the 100 metres in Moscow, 1980?

5 Which Warwickshire batsman, scored the following successive scores in 1994: 147/106/120 not out /136/26/140/501 not out?

6 In athletics, which track race is called the Metric Mile?

7 Who won nine Gold Medals for swimming during the 1968 and 1972 Olympics?

8 What is the shortest distance raced, in cycling, on the track in the Olympics?

9 Silverstone, Aintree, Brooklands and Donnington have all been used for Formula 1. Which other British circuit was also used?

10 In which town are the oldest surviving 'real' tennis courts, built in 1539 in a Scottish palace grounds?

11 Where were the 1994 Winter Olympic Games held?

12 Which darts player has won the World Masters Championship five times, the World Professional Championship five times and the World Cup Singles four times?

13 Which Rugby League player has won 33 winner or runner-up medals in his career?

14 Which rowing regatta has been an annual event since 1839?

15 How many balls are used in a game of pool?

1. Dundee. 2. 18. 3. 14. 4. Alan Wells. 5. Brian Lara. 6. 1,500 metres. 7. Mark Spitz. 8. 1,000 metre sprint. 9. Brands Hatch. 10. Falkirk. 11. Lillehammer, Norway. 12. Eric Bristow. 13. Shaun Edwards. 14. Henley. 15. 16, including white.

GENERAL KNOWLEDGE

1 Which French writer in his book *The Fall* is quoted 'Style, like sheer silk, too often hides eczema'?

2 What is a 'chihuahua'?

3 What is the more common name given to 'Silver Darlings' which live in British waters?

4 Taken from Dickens' novel *A Christmas Carol,* what term have we coined to mean a miser?

5 What is a 'golden handshake'?

6 What nationality was the musician 'Liberace'?

7 What, in music, is a prelude?

8 By what military display is the official birthday of the sovereign marked?

9 To what did Tom Hanks liken life in the film *Forrest Gump*?

10 Name the sport played between two teams of players on horseback?

11 In 'Scrabble' what does the letter 'W' score?

12 What is the name of the therapy which uses massage and infra-red or ultra-violet rays in its treatment?

13 Who, in one of Jane Austen's novels, was known as a 'match-maker'?

14 What is the Latin phrase we use to say 'by virtue or office or because of one's position'?

15 In which decade were 'Teddy boys' particularly fashionable in Britain?

1. Albert Camus. 2. Dog (Mexican dwarf dog). 3. Herring. 4. Scrooge. 5. A large sum of money given to certain employees when they leave a company after a long period of service. 6. American. 7. A piece introducing a larger work; a show-piece for piano and orchestra. 8. Trooping the colour. 9. 'A box of chocolates'. 10. 'Polo'. 11. Four. 12. Physiotherapy. 13. 'Emma'. 14. Ex officio. 15. The 1950s.

SCIENCE & NATURE

1   Which British physicist discovered that an electric current could be made to flow in a wire, without a battery, by a magnet nearby?

2   What metal is used to galvanize steel or iron?

3   What is the name of the shallow glass dishes used in laboratories to grow bacterial cultures?

4   What is an isthmus?

5   What name is given to trees that shed all their leaves, especially in the autumn?

6   What primitive group of mammals does the platypus belong to?

7   Neon and Argon are examples of what group of gases?

8   How many moons does Neptune have?

9   How long does it take for a frog to develop from spawn to adult? Is it (a) 6 weeks, (b) 26 weeks or (c) 16 weeks?

10   What is ADD?

11   'Deadly Nightshade' belongs to the plant family *Solanacae*. What common member of the same family is grown in greenhouses in this country?

12   Who developed the periodic table of the elements?

13   What is the voltage of electricity transmitted from a power station? Is it (a) 400,000 volts, (b) 40,000 volts or (c) 4,000 volts?

14   Which 18th century chemist was viewed as the father of modern chemistry for his experiments into combustion and respiration?

15   What mineral can be obtained from seaweed?

1. Michael Faraday. He discovered electro-magnetic conduction. 2. Zinc.
3. Petri dishes. 4. It is a narrow strip of land connecting two larger land areas.
5. Deciduous. 6. Monotremes. 7. Inert gases. 8. Eight, two of which are visible
from Earth. 9. (c) 16 weeks. 10. Attention Deficit Disorder, sometimes known as
hyperactivity. 11. Tomatoes. 12. Dmitry Ivanovitch Mendeleyev in 1869.
13. (a) 400,000 volts. 14. Antoine Lavoisier (1743–94). 15. Iodine.

ENTERTAINMENT

1 Which plumber features in a popular video game?

2 Which entertainer had a hit with 'Jake the Peg'?

3 Which character was played by Sir Alec Guinness in TV's *Tinker, Tailor, Soldier, Spy?*

4 Who wrote and starred in the film *Roxanne*, a modern version of *Cyrano de Bergerac?*

5 Which singer in the 1960s had hits with 'I'm Gonna Be Strong' and 'Somethin's Gotten Hold of My Heart'?

6 In which city is the TV soap *Brookside* set?

7 Who presents the radio programme *In the Psychiatrist's Chair?*

8 Who had a hit in 1962 with 'Bobby's Girl'?

9 The TV series *Voyager* is a spin-off from which programme?

10 Brenda Fricker and Daniel Day-Lewis both won Oscars in which film about a writer with cerebral palsy?

11 Which Australian singer had hits with 'I Remember You' and 'Lovesick Blues'?

12 Who presents the TV quiz show *Strike It Rich?*

13 In a film released in 1989, two people had an *Excellent Adventure* – who were they?

14 'The Final Countdown' reached number one for whom?

15 The lead singer of Japan went on to forge a solo career of his own. What was his name?

1. 'Mario', 2. Rolf Harris. 3. George Smiley. 4. Steve Martin. 5. Gene Pitney.
6. Liverpool. 7. Dr Anthony Clare. 8. Susan Maughan. 9. *Star Trek.*
10. *My Left Foot.* 11. Frank Ifield. 12. Michael Barrymore. 13. 'Bill and Ted'.
14. Europe. 15. David Sylvian.

HISTORY

1 Who was king of England in the year 1400?

2 In which year did the Battle of Shrewsbury take place?

3 As what was Girolamo Savonarola (1452–98) famous?

4 Christopher Columbus and Amerigo Vespucci (the explorer after whom America was named) were both born in the same year. What year was it?

5 What was the original name of the ship in which Francis Drake, the English explorer, set out to sail around the world in 1577?

6 Drake changed the name of his ship in mid-voyage. To what?

7 What did Drake describe as the 'fairest cape' that he saw in the course of his voyage?

8 The days 3 to 13 September were omitted from the calendar in Britain in 1752. Why?

9 In which year did the 'Boston Tea Party' take place?

10 What was the 'Boston Tea Party' a protest against?

11 As what did the people who took part in the 'Boston Tea Party' disguise themselves?

12 Maximilian, the younger brother of the Austrian emperor Franz-Joseph I, was proclaimed emperor of which country in 1863?

13 How did the Emperor Maximilian meet his death in 1867?

14 Which country did the United States declare war on in 1898 over Cuba?

15 In which year did Fidel Castro come to power as prime minister in Cuba?

1. King Henry IV. 2. 1403. 3. He was an Italian preacher and religious reformer. 4. 1451. 5. *The Pelican*. 6. *The Golden Hind*. 7. The Cape of Good Hope. 8. Because of the changeover from the Julian to the Gregorian calendar. 9. 1773. 10. The tax on tea imposed by the British government on the American colonies and the tea monopoly of the East India Company. 11. (Red) Indians. 12. Mexico. 13. He was executed by firing squad. 14. Spain. 15. 1959.

ANSWERS

FAMOUS PEOPLE

1 With which style of music is the American composer Scott Joplin associated?

2 Which US newspaper tycoon was the model for the central character of Orson Welles' film *Citizen Kane*?

3 Who was the first person to reach the South Pole?

4 What organization did William Booth found in 1878?

5 How did T. E. Lawrence, Lawrence of Arabia, die?

6 Which rock musician said: 'Rock journalism is people who can't write interviewing people who can't talk for people who can't read'?

7 Who wrote *The Interpretation of Dreams* (1900)?

8 What was the name of the plane in which the US aviator Charles Lindbergh made the first solo non-stop flight across the Atlantic in 1927?

9 How many of Henry VIII's wives were beheaded?

10 Which US president was the principal author of the Declaration of Independence in 1776?

11 What nationality was the painter Edvard Munch?

12 Who headed the FBI from 1924 to 1972?

13 How was the Swiss architect Charles-Édouard Jeanneret better known?

14 Which English biologist and humanist coined the word 'agnostic' to describe his own beliefs?

15 What did the German archaeologist Heinrich Schliemann discover in the early 1870s?

1. Ragtime. 2. William Randolph Hearst. 3. Roald Amundsen.
4. The Salvation Army. 5. In a motorcycle accident. 6. Frank Zappa.
7. Sigmund Freud. 8. 'Spirit of St Louis'. 9. Two. 10. Thomas Jefferson.
11. Norwegian. 12. J. Edgar Hoover. 13. Le Corbusier. 14. Thomas Huxley.
15. The remains of the city of Troy.

SPORT & LEISURE

1 Spurs lost against Chelsea three-two on 1 December 1990 and were fined for being late. Why?

2 In American football how many teams does each side have at a match?

3 What is the Ryder Cup?

4 Who was the first European Olympic Champion who won the 100m in 1924 and was immortalized in the film *Chariots of Fire*?

5 Which cricketer made 18 centuries in 50 innings in 1947?

6 The Athlete Sergey Bubka dominated which Field event in the 1980s and 1990s?

7 How many players play at any one time in a water polo team?

8 How many one-day stages does the Tour de France have?

9 When was the last Grand Prix held in the USA?

10 In table tennis, how many points (minimum) must you score to win a game?

11 What is the maximum height difference (between start and finish lines) in any Nordic Cross Country Ski event?

12 Which Argentinean did David Beckham 'kick out at' in St Etienne during the 1998 World Cup?

13 The now notorious Will Carling, captained England a world record 42 times. In that time how many games did England win?

14 In what sport would you be competing if you had to perform the 'Volte', 'Piroutte' and 'Serpentine'?

15 Anthony Hembrick, USA, was the Boxing Gold Medal favourite in Seoul, 1988. Why did he not win any medals?

GENERAL KNOWLEDGE

1   In music, 'nocturne' suggests the qualities of what time of day?

2   Which Spanish writer in his novel *Don Quixote*, is quoted as saying, 'Tell me what company thou keepest, and I'll tell thee what thou art'?

3   What type of food is Brin D'Affinois?

4   By what name was Sri Lanka formerly known?

5   What is the ingredient that is usually used to turn rice or curry yellow?

6   Who wrote the play *The Merry Wives of Windsor*?

7   What does the abbreviation a.m. stand for?

8   What parts of the body do orthopaedics treat?

9   What drink named after a bartender consists of gin, lime (or lemon) juice, sugar and soda water?

10 What is the name of the winged horse, offspring of Gorgon Medusa, and the mount of Perseus and Bellerophon?

11 In which US state is Hollywood situated?

12 What is the name of the alphabet used to clarify individual letters in radio communications?

13 In Lewis Carroll's book *Alice's Adventures in Wonderland*, who said, 'The Queen of Hearts, she made some tarts, All on a summer day: The Knave of Hearts, he stole those tarts, And took them quite away!'?

14 What species is 'Bombay duck'?

15 Which muscles fill the spaces between the ribs to prevent them being sucked in or blown out during respiration?

ANSWERS

1. Night. 2. Miguel de Cervantes. 3. Cheese. 4. Ceylon. 5. Turmeric. 6. William Shakespeare. 7. Ante meridiem (in the morning). 8. Bone and muscles. 9. Tom Collins. 10. 'Pegasus'. 11. California. 12. Phonetic alphabet. 13. 'White Rabbit'. 14. Fish. 15. Intercostal muscles.

SCIENCE & NATURE

1 Where are rods and cones found together?

2 What name is given to the study of plants?

3 How many men have walked on the Moon?

4 What is the unit of measurement of frequency?

5 What is the common name of the flower *Bellis Perennis*?

6 If you suffered from prosopagnosia, what would you have difficulty in remembering?

7 What do the initials MRI stand for?

8 Who developed the first calculator?

9 Which law states that voltage = current x resistance?

10 What is the group name for chemical elements which include Fluorine, Chlorine and Bromine?

11 What is REM sleep?

12 What is the process whereby plants turn carbon dioxide and water into carbohydrates?

13 Which gland in the human body requires the mineral iodine to work properly?

14 What is the Ishihara test?

15 When was Morse Code developed? Was it (a) 1836, (b) 1866 or (c) 1906?

ENTERTAINMENT

1   Which singer was originally known as Gerry Dorsey?

2   Who plays 'Edina's mother in TV's *Absolutely Fabulous*?

3   Matt Damon and Ben Affleck won joint Oscars for the screenplay of which film?

4   Who had hits in the 1960s and later became an actor starring in the TV series *Budgie*?

5   Who is the regular contributor on wine on TV's *Food and Drink* programme?

6   Who directed the 1987 film *Empire of the Sun*?

7   Who founded London's 'Promenade Concerts'?

8   Who plays 'Bianca' in *EastEnders*?

9   In which year was *Jazz FM* first broadcast?

10 Which group had a hit with 'Good Vibrations'?

11 'Dick Dastardly' and 'Muttley' featured in which children's cartoon?

12 Who played Charlie Chaplin in the 1992 film *Chaplin*?

13 Which singer presented his own television shows and was associated with a rocking chair?

14 Who saw 'The Whole of the Moon'?

15 What was the number two hit by Crystal Waters? Was it
(a) 'Gypsy Woman (La Dee Da)', (b) 'Gypsy Woman (La Lee La)'
or (c) 'Gypsy Woman (La Da Dee)'?

ANSWERS

1. Engelbert Humperdinck. 2. June Whitfield. 3. *Good Will Hunting*. 4. Adam Faith.
5. Jilly Goolden. 6. Steven Spielberg. 7. Sir Henry Wood. 8. Patsy Palmer. 9. 1990.
10. The Beach Boys. 11. *Wacky Races*. 12. Robert Downey, Jnr. 13. Val Doonican.
14. The Waterboys. 15. (c) 'Gypsy Woman (La Da Dee)'.

HISTORY

1 The Italian dictator Benito Mussolini and the British prime minister Clement Attlee were both born in the same year. What year was it?

2 In which year was British general Charles Gordon killed at Khartoum?

3 General Gordon was known as 'Chinese Gordon' because of his exploits in China, including taking part in the capture of which city in 1860?

4 The young Winston Churchill took part in a cavalry charge in which battle?

5 Alfred Milner was appointed governor of which British colony in 1897?

6 In which year did Theodore Roosevelt become president of the United States?

7 Under what circumstances did he become president?

8 In which year did the Panama Canal open?

9 Who was in charge of a previous unsuccessful French attempt to build a canal across the isthmus of Panama?

10 In which year was federal income tax first introduced in the United States?

11 Who was the first woman to be elected to the British House of Commons?

12 Who was the first woman to sit in the British House of Commons?

13 Canadian private George Price had the unfortunate distinction of being what in November 1918?

14 In which year was the first two minutes' silence held to honour war dead in Great Britain?

15 In which country did the German Kaiser Wilhelm II go into exile after World War I?

ANSWERS

1. 1883. 2. 1885. 3. Peking (Beijing). 4. The battle of Omdurman in 1898. 5. The Cape Colony. 6. 1901. 7. He was vice-president and assumed office when the President William McKinley was assassinated. 8. 1914. 9. Ferdinand de Lesseps (the builder of the Suez Canal). 10. 1913. 11. Constance Markiewicz (she was elected as a Sinn Féin MP in 1918 but refused to take her seat). 12. Lady Nancy Astor. 13. The last Allied soldier (or one of the last Allied soldiers) to be killed on the western front in World War I (he was shot by a sniper two minutes before the time at which the armistice came into force). 14. 1919. 15. The Netherlands.

FAMOUS PEOPLE

1 Who succeeded Anthony Eden as prime minister in 1957?

2 Which king did Henry Tudor defeat at Bosworth to become King Henry VII?

3 Which queen of France was executed in 1793?

4 Which brothers were the first to fly a powered airplane in 1903?

5 Who invented the ballpoint pen in 1938?

6 Which 19th century politician was the author of the novels *Coningsby* and *Sybil*?

7 Who patented his invention of a burglar proof safe in 1835?

8 Which queen made the use of chloroform in childbirth popular?

9 In 1947 who sailed on a raft from Peru to Polynesia?

10 Which kidnapped newspaper heiress joined her captors, the Symbionese Liberation Army, in 1974?

11 Which Spanish artist painted *Guernica* in 1937?

12 What was the job of Grace Darling's father?

13 Which Minister of Transport introduced the 70 mph speed limit and the breathalyser test?

14 Who was the American president, elected in 1968, who promised to end the Vietnam War?

15 Which English Egyptologist discovered the tomb of King Tutankhamun?

ANSWERS

1. Harold Macmillan. 2. Richard III. 3. Queen Marie Antoinette. 4. Orville and Wilbur Wright. 5. Laszlo Biró. 6. Benjamin Disraeli. 7. Charles Chubb. 8. Queen Victoria (during the birth of her seventh child). 9. Thor Heyerdahl. 10. Patricia Hearst. 11. Pablo Picasso. 12. Lighthouse keeper. 13. Barbara Castle. 14. Richard Nixon. 15. Howard Carter.

SPORT & LEISURE

1 How many seconds did it take Vinny Jones to be booked in his match on 19 January 1991?

2 Michael Jordan played basketball for whom?

3 Who has finished highest in the European 'Order of Merit' Golf Tour for six consecutive years?

4 British Women Heptathlon champion, Denise Lewis, competes in how many events to make up the Heptathlon?

5 Ian Botham made 5,200 runs in 102 test matches but how many catches did he make?

6 How many Gold Medals did Daley Thompson win at the Olympics?

7 Which sport would you be performing if you were doing a 'ballet leg double', a 'knight' or 'castle', a 'tuck', a 'front pike' or a 'split'?

8 How many 'Chukkers' make up a game of polo?

9 In a career of ten years in Formula One, which driver achieved pole position in over 40% of races entered and won one in every four?

10 Which squash player was not defeated between 1981 and 1986?

11 In all Alpine Skiing races, skiers race between gates consisting of two coloured flags. What are the two colours?

12 How many metres is a furlong?

13 The world's prestigious Rugby Seven's tournament was first hosted in 1976. In which country?

14 In which sport did Sean Currly compete for Great Britain in the 1992 and 1996 Olympics?

15 How many press-ups did Charles Servizio complete during 24 hours in California, April 1993?

GENERAL KNOWLEDGE

1 When was Braille invented? (a) 1824, (b) 1799 or (c) 1856?

2 What name is given to the chief muscle of the hip forming the curve of the buttocks?

3 Which French president who came to power in 1969 has a museum in Paris named after him?

4 What, in the Arabian legend, is a 'roc'?

5 In 'Scrabble' what does the letter 'B' score?

6 For what does the abbreviation AD stand?

7 What is the term for the treatment of women's diseases?

8 What is the full name given to the arrangement of the chemical elements?

9 What is the eponymic name of the visible projection at the front of the neck, formed by the thyroid cartilage?

10 Which shrub-like plant produces the berries to make gin?

11 What do we call a group of whales?

12 What is the common name for the patella?

13 Jack Sprat refused to eat what type of food?

14 What is the fifth book of the Bible?

15 What happened to a 'phoenix', the fabulous bird of classical mythology, when it destroyed itself on a burning altar?

ANSWERS

1. (a) 1824. 2. Gluteus maximus. 3. Georges Pompidou. 4. A bird of enormous size. 5. Three. 6. Anno Domini: in the year of our Lord. 7. Gynaecology. 8. The Periodic Table of Elements. 9. Adam's apple. 10. Juniper. 11. A school (or gam). 12. Knee-cap. 13. Fat. 14. Deuteronomy. 15. A new bird emerged from the ashes.

SCIENCE & NATURE

1 Who was the first woman in space?

2 What is the name of the cataract of water on the Canadian side of Niagara Falls?

3 Which armoured dinosaur had a double row of bony plates on its back?

4 Which ethologist is famous for his studies of the 'imprinting' behaviour of geese?

5 What is the name for the lowest layer of the Earth's atmosphere?

6 What is the name of the first part of the small intestine?

7 Which precious metal is used in injections to treat arthritis?

8 What is the name for the process of water loss through evaporation from the leaves of plants?

9 What does a mycologist study?

10 What is the name of the largest cut diamond in the world?

11 What is panphobia?

12 Which cells in the human body do not have a nucleus?

13 Who invented the first carpet sweeper?

14 What are the two upper chambers of the heart called?

15 What is pyelitis?

1. Valentino Tereshkova. 2. 'The Horseshoe Falls'. 3. Stegosaurus. 4. Konrad Lorenz. 5. The troposphere. 6. The duodenum. 7. Gold. 8. Transpiration. 9. Fungi. 10. The Star of Africa'. 11. A fear of everything. 12. Red blood cells. 13. Thomas Ewbank in 1889. 14. The atria. 15. Inflamation of the lining of the pelvis of the kidney.

ENTERTAINMENT

1 Which singer had hits with 'Calendar Girl' and 'Breaking Up Is Hard To Do'?

2 In which city is the TV soap *Neighbours* set?

3 The 1984 film *The Killing Fields* was set in which country?

4 The song 'The Lambeth Walk' comes from which musical?

5 Who played the title role in TV's *Boon*?

6 Who played the station master in the film *The Railway Children*?

7 Which group had a hit in 1964 with 'Have I The Right'?

8 Who played the title role in TV's *Yes, Minister*?

9 Which quiz show began on Radio 4 in 1967?

10 Con and Declan Clusky formed which group?

11 Who presents TV's *Antiques Roadshow*?

12 Who stars in the 1989 film *Field of Dreams*?

13 In music, what does the abbreviation 'ff' mean?

14 'The Simpsons' got to number one by doing which dance?

15 In 1982 a selection of sheep noises known as 'The Singing Sheep' got to number 42 in the UK charts. With what song did it chart?

HISTORY

1 Which decade did the poet W. H. Auden describe as 'a low dishonest decade'?

2 Who was the first Labour prime minister of Great Britain?

3 Who was prime minister and leader of the National Government from 1931 to 1935?

4 Who was elected president of Germany in 1932?

5 Fiorello La Guardia was elected mayor of which city in 1933?

6 John Dillinger, shot by the FBI in 1934, was known as what?

7 In which year were Italian forces ordered to invade Abyssinia by Mussolini?

8 Where did the Abyssinian Emperor Haile Selassie go into exile after Abyssinia was annexed by Italy?

9 The International Brigade was formed to fight in which war?

10 Who was Archbishop of Canterbury during the British abdication crisis of 1936?

11 Whom did the former King Edward VIII of Great Britain marry in 1937?

12 Who disappeared during a flight across the Pacific in 1937?

13 Which part of Czechoslovakia did Hitler's German forces occupy in October 1938?

14 In which year did Orson Welles' radio production of H. G. Wells *The War of the Worlds* cause panic in some areas of the United States?

15 On which day in 1939 did Great Britain and France declare war on Germany?

1. The 1930s (in his poem *September 1st 1939*). 2. (James) Ramsay MacDonald during 1924. 3. Ramsay MacDonald. 4. General Hindenburg. 5. New York City. 6. Public Enemy Number One. 7. 1935. 8. In England (Great Britain). 9. The Spanish Civil War. 10. Cosmo Lang. 11. Mrs Wallis Simpson. 12. Amelia Earhart. 13. The Sudetenland. 14. 1938. 15. 3 September.

ANSWERS

FAMOUS PEOPLE

1   Who was the first wife of King Henry VIII?

2   In 1796, who introduced vaccination against smallpox?

3   What title was Arthur Wellesley given in recognition of his military victories?

4   Which American president was assassinated in 1881?

5   Who invented the electric telegraph in 1837?

6   Which music producer's recording techniques became known as his 'wall of sound'?

7   Who was the first woman Member of Parliament?

8   Which Polish trade union leader became Polish president in 1990?

9   Which British writer of short stories, plays and novels worked as a secret agent in both World Wars?

10   Who became the Republic of Ireland's president in 1990?

11   How did 19-year-old Matthias Rust make an entrance into Moscow's Red Square in 1987?

12   Which explorer discovered the Victoria Falls of the Zambezi River?

13   What year was Queen Victoria crowned?

14   Which English teacher published a manual *Stenographic Sound Hand* in 1837?

15   Who walked across the Niagara Falls on a tightrope in 1859?

ANSWERS

1. Catherine of Aragon. 2. Edward Jenner. 3. The Duke of Wellington. 4. James Garfield. 5. Samuel Morse. 6. Phil Spector. 7. Nancy Astor. 8. Lech Walesa. 9. William Somerset Maugham. 10. Mary Robinson. 11. He flew a small plane from Helsinki and landed it in Red Square. 12. David Livingstone. 13. 1838. 14. Isaac Pitman. 15. Charles Blondin.

SPORT & LEISURE

1   Which football club were the first in Great Britain to introduce a stripe down the seam of their shorts?

2   Which baseball team play in New York?

3   The oldest golf player to score his age was Arthur Thompson in 1973. How old was he?

4   What is the longest race in men's athletics?

5   Who took 434 wickets in 131 Tests by early 1994?

6   Over what distance are the men's athletics High Hurdles?

7   What is the length of an Olympic size swimming pool?

8   Where is the oldest annually contested motorcycle race held?

9   How many laps is the Indianapolis 500?

10 Who became the youngest ever international footballer to play for Wales?

11 How many times have Jayne Torvill and Christopher Dean won the British Ice Dance Championships?

12 White City in London was famous for athletics and which other track sport?

13 Philippe Sella appeared over 100 times for France between 1982 and 1994. How many times did he appear?

14 Boxer, Mike Tyson was jailed for what offence in the early 1990s?

15. Name the first, male British gymnast to win a medal at the World Championships in 1993.

GENERAL KNOWLEDGE

1   Where is the Scottish Football Cup Final played?

2   Which vegetable did Mark Twain call 'cabbage with a college education'?

3   Of what are 'venules' the smallest branches?

4   What is the name for the under layer of skin (beneath the epidermis)?

5   From which animal do we get 'cat gut'?

6   What is the musical term for a study, a piece designed as an exercise?

7   Who said of Prime Minister Gladstone, 'He speaks to me as if I was a public meeting'?

8   What food was originally used by the Aztecs as currency?

9   What shape is farfale pasta?

10   Who was the British General who began the Scouts Association?

11   What does the Beaufort Scale measure?

12   How many pints of beer are there in a 'hogshead'?

13   What is the name for a plant that has resulted from crossing two different species?

14   Who, in 1882, said 'Our market is the world'?

15   What is the capital of Luxembourg?

SCIENCE & NATURE

1 The circumference of the Earth at the equator is approximately:
(a) 30,000km (18,642 miles), (b) 40,000km (24,856 miles) or
(c) 50,000km (31,069 miles)?

2 Where in the body is the pituitary gland?

3 Which two elements make up ammonia?

4 Pyrophobia is a fear of what?

5 Which vitamin can help to prevent rickets?

6 What is the square root of 64?

7 What is the name for a group of partridges?

8 What do 'pumice' and 'basalt' have in common?

9 Is a 'lady's slipper' a type of: (a) shell, (b) mushroom or
(c) orchid?

10 What do the initials of BASIC, the computer programming
language, stand for?

11 What is the larva of the crane fly called?

12 Which acid is found in apples?

13 Which is the largest British newt?

14 Tendons join bones together. True or false?

15 What is the name for the type of plant that takes
two years to come into flower?

1. (b) 40,000km (24,856 miles). 2. At the base of the brain. 3. Hydrogen and
nitrogen. 4. Fire. 5. Vitamin D. 6. 8. 7. A covey. 8. Both types of rock are formed
in volcanoes. 9. (c) Orchid. 10. Beginner's All-purpose Symbolic Instruction Code.
11. Leatherjacket. 12. Malic acid. 13. Great crested newt. 14. False, they join
muscles to bone or other structures. 15. Biennial.

ENTERTAINMENT

1 Which singer's trademarks were a top hat and cane, and an athletic side kick?

2 Who were the original presenters of TV's *The Clothes Show?*

3 Harrison Ford and Kelly McGillis star in which 1985 film set in an Amish community?

4 In the 1960s, which group appeared with Wayne Fontana?

5 In which year did Frank Sinatra die?

6 Which radio presenter had the nickname 'Cheerful Charlie'?

7 Which group appeared with Smokey Robinson?

8 'Spock' in *Star Trek* came from which planet?

9 The musical *Kiss Me, Kate* is based on which Shakespeare play?

10 Who was the quiz master of TV's *Take Your Pick*?

11 Who plays 'Hannah' in the film *Hannah and Her Sisters*, directed by Woody Allen?

12 Which Frenchman had a hit with 'Thank Heaven For Little Girls'?

13 Which 1960s children's TV programme featured the 'Soup Dragon' and the 'Froglets'?

14 Who did Lulu 'Relight My Fire' with?

15 Whose 1991 album features a naked baby swimming after a dollar bill?

127

ANSWERS

1. Frankie Vaughan. 2. Jeff Banks and Selina Scott. 3. *Witness*.
4. The Mindbenders. 5. 1998. 6. Charlie Chester. 7. The Miracles.
8. 'Vulcan'. 9. *The Taming of the Shrew*. 10. Michael Miles. 11. Mia Farrow.
12. Maurice Chevalier. 13. The Klangers. 14. Take That. 15. Nirvana, the album was 'Nevermind'.

HISTORY

1   Philip the Bold, John the Fearless and Philip the Good were all dukes of what?

2   Henry IV, king of France, was the first king of which dynasty?

3   What, in French history, were the two Frondes of 1648–49 and 1650–53?

4   In which year did the 'Glorious Revolution' take place overthrowing King James II of England?

5   In which war did the battles of Oudenarde and Malplaquet take place?

6   Whom did Sarah Churchill, the wife of the Duke of Marlborough, correspond with privately under the name of 'Mrs Freeman'?

7   In which year did the Union of England and Scotland take place forming the kingdom of Great Britain?

8   Charlotte of Mecklenburg(-Strelitz) was the wife of which British king?

9   Which British commander surrendered to American forces after the Battle of Yorktown in 1781?

10 Thaddeus Kosciusko was a nationalist leader in which country in the late 18th century?

11 Which sport originated at an English public school in or around 1823?

12 William B. Burt of Detroit took out the first US patent on what in 1829?

13 Where did Florence Nightingale take over and run a hospital during the Crimean War?

14 In which year did three German emperors in succession reign?

15 Who was president of the United States in the year 1900?

FAMOUS PEOPLE

1   Aboard which ship did Darwin's revolutionary theories evolve?

2   Who took 24 years to get from Italy to China and back again?

3   Which king of France was known as 'the Sun King'?

4   What unusual career did Anne Bonny and Mary Read follow?

5   Who was known as 'The Shrimp'?

6   Which English doctor first discovered that blood constantly circulates around the body?

7   Who was the first person to reach the South Pole in 1911?

8   Who was the American vice president when George Bush was president?

9   Which actor and dancer died in 1987 aged 88?

10 Who performed the world's first human heart transplant in Capetown in 1967?

11 Under her married name Marie Sklodowska won two Nobel prizes. Whom did she marry?

12 Which General died at Khartoum in 1885?

13 In which film did David Bowie play an alien?

14 Who was the first person to send radio signals across the Atlantic Ocean in 1901?

15 Who was the English architect responsible for the Lloyds of London building?

1. 'The Beagle'. 2. Marco Polo. 3. Louis XIV. 4. Piracy. 5. Jean Shrimpton. 6. William Harvey. 7. Roald Amundsen. 8. Dan Quayle. 9. Fred Astaire. 10. Dr Christiaan Barnard. 11. Pierre Curie. 12. Charles George Gordon. 13. *The Man Who Fell To Earth*. 14. Guglielmo Marconi. 15. Richard Rogers.

SPORT & LEISURE

1   How many games did it take Jimmy Greaves to score his 351st goal?

2   What sport is Wayne Gretzky famous for?

3   How many golf courses are there at St Andrew's on the Links?

4   There are two courses at Newmarket. One is the Rowley mile, what is the other one called?

5   How many times did Wilfred Rhodes complete the 'Cricket Double' of 1,000 runs and 100 wickets in a season between 1903 and 1926?

6   Who set six world records for athletics within 45 minutes on 25 August 1935 in Michigan, USA?

7   How many dives is the men's Olympic high board diving scored out of?

8   What sport was Greg Le Mond famous for?

9   The 'Network Q' Rally of Great Britain was formerly sponsored by whom?

10   Two British men finished in the top ten of the ATP World Tennis Rankings at the end of 1998. One was Tim Henman, who was the other?

11   Which British skater jumped 19' 1" in an axel jump in November 1983?

12   In a 1990 Gallup Poll, which famous race horse achieved higher public recognition than Norman Lamont, the Chancellor?

13   Which Rugby League player broke the transfer record in 1992 when transferring from Widnes to Wigan for £440,000?

14   In which sport would you be taking part if you were 'Luffing', 'Gybing' and 'Bearing Away'?

15   In Rugby Union what number does the hooker have?

1. 500. 2. Ice Hockey. 3. Four (Old/New/Eden/Jubilee). 4. The July Course. 5. 16. 6. Jesse Owens. 7. Ten. 8. Cycling. 9. RAC. 10 Greg Rusedski. 11. Robin Cousins. 12. Desert Orchid 84% (Norman Lamont 77%). 13. Martin Offiah. 14. Yachting. 15. Two.

GENERAL KNOWLEDGE

1　What is the term for the type of tree which annually sheds its leaves?

2　What are sturgeon's eggs also known as?

3　Which character said 'I am a bear of very little brain, and long words bother me'?

4　Which salary scale for teachers was established in 1924 and abolished in 1987?

5　From which fruit is calvados made?

6　Which 19th century author said 'There are three kinds of lies: lies, damned lies, and statistics'?

7　Which forgotten composer had his music re-introduced to the public by Mendelssohn?

8　Which moustache which was especially popular with men in the British Air Force in World War II, is long and heavy and curves upwards at both ends?

9　What is the name given to the undeveloped, slightly sunken growth buds on potatoes?

10　In which country is Lake Como?

11　Which American president coined the phrase, 'The buck stops here'?

12　What does 'ad infinitum' mean?

13　'Sub rosa' is Latin for beautifully. True or false?

14　What mark is used to show that a product meets the traditional safety standards of the British Standards Institution?

15　To which genus do cabbages belong?

1. Deciduous. 2. Caviar. 3. 'Winnie the Pooh'. 4. Burnham Scale. 5. Apples.
6. Mark Twain. 7. J. S. Bach. 8. Handlebar moustache. 9. Eye. 10. Italy.
11. Harry S. Truman. 12. Endlessly. 13. False. It means secretly or confidentially.
14. Kite-mark. 15. Brassica.

SCIENCE & NATURE

1   What is another name for the rowan tree?

2   What speed must a rocket achieve to reach escape velocity and break free from Earth's gravity? Is it: (a) 40,000 kph (24,856 mph), (b) 50,000 kph (31,069 mph) or (c) 60,000 kph (37,283 mph)?

3   Which common childhood disease is also called 'varicella'?

4   How many hours are there in a week?

5   Where in the body is the 'maxilla'?

6   What are 'laver', 'dulse' and 'carrageen' types of?

7   Which British snake gives birth to live young?

8   Which chemical element has the symbol 'Kr'?

9   Which sense does 'olfactory' relate to?

10   Wall flowers are members of the cabbage family of plants. True or false?

11   Of which element is 'graphite' a form?

12   Which protein forms horn, nails and hair?

13   What is the function of 'chloroplasts' in plant cells?

14   Which British woodpecker is black, white and red?

15   In 1782 which French brothers made a flight in a hot air balloon?

ENTERTAINMENT

1   In the TV comedy series *Roseanne*, what is the name of Roseanne's sister?

2   Who had a hit in the 1960s with 'My Boy Lollipop'?

3   Who presented the TV programme *Blockbusters*?

4   Which disc jockey had the nickname 'Kid'?

5   Who won an Oscar for his role in the 1970 film *Ryan's Daughter*?

6   What are the names of the Everly Brothers?

7   Who played the title role in the TV series *Magnum P.I.*?

8   Which composer wrote 'Music for the Royal Fireworks'?

9   Who presented *Junior Choice* on Radio 1 and 2 between 1968 and 1979?

10 Who played the role of Reginald Perrin's wife in *The Fall and Rise of Reginald Perrin*?

11 Which two actors had a hit with 'Whispering Grass'?

12 Which radio presenter was known as 'The Voice of London' during World War II?

13 Who won an Oscar for the 1969 film *True Grit*?

14 Which French female vocalist had a hit with 'Joe Le Taxi'?

15 Whose lips were sealed in April 1983?

133

1. 'Jackie'. 2. Millie. 3. Bob Holness. 4. David Jenson. 5. Sir John Mills.
6. Don and Phil. 7. Tom Selleck. 8. Handel. 9. Ed Stewart ('Stewpot').
10. Pauline Yates. 11. Windsor Davies and Don Estelle. 12. John Snagge.
13. John Wayne. 14. Venessa Paradis. 15. Fun Boy Three.

HISTORY

1 In which year was the Festival of Britain held?

2 Who was prime minister of Australia from 1949 to 1966?

3 Which year saw the election of a Nationalist government and the beginning of the apartheid era in South Africa?

4 Theodor Heuss was the first post-war president of which country?

5 Who escaped to the USSR in 1951?

6 In which year did an uprising take place in Hungary against the Communist system and domination by the USSR?

7 Which former high-ranking Nazi was seized in Argentina in 1960?

8 Sir Robert Boothby had a long-running affair with the wife of which British prime minister?

9 In which year did the 'Bay of Pigs' landing take place in an attempt to topple the Cuban leader Fidel Castro?

10 Which world figure was killed in an air crash in Zambia in 1961?

11 Who led the commission appointed to investigate the assassination of President J. F. Kennedy?

12 John Dean, John Ehrlichmann and H. R. Haldemann were all implicated in what?

13 In which year did Harold Wilson resign as British prime minister to be succeeded by James Callaghan?

14 Which winter in Britain was 'the Winter of Discontent'?

15 In which year was the first women's professional boxing match held in Britain?

FAMOUS PEOPLE

1   Which English conductor founded the Promenade Concerts?

2   Which black American general became famous during the Gulf War?

3   Which Swiss psychiatrist introduced the concepts of 'introvert' and 'extrovert' personalities?

4   Who is famous for his portrait of *The Laughing Cavalier*?

5   Which of King Henry VIII's wives survived him?

6   In 1932 Amelia Earhart flew alone over which ocean?

7   In the American Civil War, who was the Confederate general who surrendered to General Ulysses S. Grant?

8   Which English physicist wrote *A Brief History of Time*?

9   In 1770 which English captain claimed the east coast of Australia for Britain?

10   Isadora Duncan was a famous opera singer. True or false?

11   What was the first name of the Regency man of fashion 'Beau' Brummell?

12   Which photography pioneer published the first photographically illustrated book called *Pencil of Nature* in 1844?

13   Which French physicist discovered radioactivity?

14   Who opened his circus 'The Greatest Show on Earth' in Brooklyn in 1871?

15   Where did Churchill, Roosevelt and Stalin meet in 1945 to discuss the final defeat of Germany and the post-war world?

ANSWERS

1. Sir Henry Wood. 2. General Colin Powell. 3. Carl Gustav Jung. 4. Frans Hals. 5. Catherine Parr. 6. Atlantic Ocean. 7. General Robert E. Lee. 8. Stephen Hawking. 9. Captain James Cook. 10. False, she was a dancer. 11. George. 12. William Henry Fox Talbot. 13. A. H. Becquerel. 14. Phineas T. Barnum. 15. Yalta in the Crimea.

SPORT & LEISURE

1 Why did Doncaster Rovers' goalkeeper, Ken Hardwick, not get to play in the England Under 23's trial in January 1955 after being asked to?

2 Which Pro American football team play in San Francisco?

3 Sam Snead recorded the lowest score ever for 36 holes in 1959. What was his score?

4 Women's gymnastics is made up of Vault, Floor, Uneven Bars and what other event?

5 In 1990 at Victoria, Australian cricketer Gary Chapman scored a record number of runs from one ball with no overthrows. What was his score?

6 In which city was the first Athletics World Championship held in 1983?

7 How many strokes would you do if you swam in the Individual Medley Race?

8 There are three weapons used in fencing: the Foil, the Épée and which other?

9 Who won the Formula 1 Grand Prix from Nigel Mansell by 0.014 seconds in Spain on 13 April 1986?

10 Which famous tennis player now hosts *A Question of Sport*?

11 In what sport did Alberto Tomba compete for Italy at Olympics and World Championships?

12 In horse racing betting circles, how much is a bet of a 'monkey' worth?

13 Which Scottish Rugby Union Captain also plays American football?

14 In ten pin bowling, what is a 'spare'?

15 What is the value in points of a pink ball in snooker?

ANSWERS

1. He was 30 years old! 2. Forty Niners. 3. 122. 4. Beam. 5. 17. 6. Helsinki. 7. Four. 8. Saber. 9. Ayrton Senna. 10. Sue Barker. 11. Skiing. 12. £500. 13. Gavin Hastings. 14. Two consecutive bowls which, combined, knock ten pins down. 15. Six.

GENERAL KNOWLEDGE

1   To which college in Cambridge does the Bridge of Sighs belong?

2   What does 'persona non grata' mean?

3   In the nursery rhyme, who sat in a corner eating Christmas pie?

4   What does the term 'heeling in' mean, in gardening?

5   Which famous Christian preacher said, 'I look upon the world as my parish'?

6   What is the gelling agent in jelly?

7   In which city was the first public performance of Handel's *Messiah*?

8   What are Dr Martens?

9   What is the capital of Lebanon?

10 According to tradition, where must a true Cockney be born to be so called?

11 What is 'terra firma'?

12 Which ingredient gives the flavour to Amaretto liqueurs and biscuits?

13 Who, in the play *The Importance of Being Earnest*, said 'to lose one parent, Mr Worthing, may be regarded as a misfortune; to lose both looks like carelessness'?

14 On which bird is a parson's nose found?

15 Where is the Derby horse race held?

ANSWERS

1. St John's College. 2. A person unacceptable or not welcome. 3. 'Little Jack Horner'. 4. Temporary planting (especially fruit trees). 5. John Wesley. 6. Gelatine. 7. Dublin. 8. A make of strong, heavy boots with laces. 9. Beirut. 10. Within the sound of the Bow Bells. 11. Solid ground. 12. Almond. 13. 'Lady Bracknell'. 14. Chicken. 15. Epsom.

SCIENCE & NATURE

1 Which member of the crow family has the Latin name *Pica pica*?

2 Which planet is nearest to the Sun?

3 Where would you find the 'cornea'?

4 Which native tree has seeds called 'keys'?

5 What is 'pertussis' also known as?

6 Which is the most common British bat?

7 Only two deer species are native to Britain. One is the roe deer, what is the other?

8 What type of plant is a 'fescue'?

9 By what other name is the group of inert gases which includes neon and helium known?

10 From which plant is the heart drug 'digitalis' obtained?

11 What is the term for the dating of past events by studying the annual growth rings of trees?

12 Which acid forms in muscles during exercise?

13 In which branch of science did Edwin Hubble specialize?

14 If a chemical is 'anhydrous', what does it not contain?

15 What is the common name for 'calcium sulphate'?

ENTERTAINMENT

SESSION 22 QUIZ 6

1 Two of the actors who played 'Doctor Who' on TV have something in common. What is it?

2 Who plays the title role in the 1969 film *The Prime of Miss Jean Brodie*?

3 Who was a founder member of The Beatles but left before they became famous?

4 In which year did Radio 1 begin broadcasting?

5 Who won an Oscar in 1988 for his role in the film *Wall Street*?

6 Which singer had hits in the early 1960s including 'The Night Has A Thousand Eyes'?

7 Which radio presenter had hits in the 1950s with 'Unchained Melody' and 'The Man From Laramie'?

8 Brian Rix performed at London's Whitehall Theatre in the 1950s and 1960s in which kind of plays?

9 With which group did Diana Ross originally sing?

10 In which American TV series do 'Medavoy' and 'Martinez' appear?

11 Which actress starred in the 1961 film *Breakfast at Tiffany's*?

12 Which singer, born in Dagenham in 1947, was originally known as Sandra Goodrich?

13 'The Swan' is the name of the pub in which TV soap?

14 What did 'Frankie' say in 1983?

15 'Me Myself I' was a top 30 hit for which, comic loving, singer/songwriter?

139

ANSWERS

1. The surname Baker (Tom and Colin). 2. Maggie Smith. 3. Pete Best. 4. 1967. 5. Michael Douglas. 6. Bobby Vee. 7. Jimmy Young. 8. Farce. 9. The Supremes. 10. *NYPD Blue*. 11. Audrey Hepburn. 12. Sandie Shaw. 13. *Brookside*. 14. 'Relax'. 15. Joan Armatrading.

HISTORY

1   Who became king of Scotland in 1040?

2   Who became king of England in 1042?

3   Which Spanish national hero was born in or around 1043?

4   How is King Louis IX of France (1215–70) also known?

5   King Louis IX of France recognized King Henry III of England as Duke of which part of France in 1259?

6   In which century did the Black Death decimate the population of Europe?

7   Whose chronicles, written at the time, are a major source of information about the early stages of the Hundred Years War between England and France?

8   Anne of Bohemia was queen to which English king?

9   Who, on the basis of a prophecy, thought he was destined to die in Jerusalem on a crusade, and in fact died in the Jerusalem Chamber of the palace of Westminster?

10 What is remarkable about the book *Recuyell of the Historyes of Troye*?

11 In which country did the Vasa dynasty rule, beginning in 1523?

12 In which German city did Anabaptists set up a quasi-communist state in 1534?

13 Cardinal Wolsey was the founder of which Oxford college?

14 Who wrote the *A Defense of the Seven Sacrements*, printed in 1521, which was directed against Martin Luther's teaching?

15 What was the Scottish title of King James I of England?

ANSWERS

1. Macbeth. 2. Edward the Confessor. 3. El Cid (Rodrigo Diaz de Vivar). 4. Saint Louis. 5. Aquitaine. 6. The 14th century. 7. Froissart's (Jean Froissart c.1333 – c.1404). 8. Richard II. 9. King Henry IV of England. 10. It was the first book in English to be printed (by William Caxton). 11. Sweden. 12. Münster in Westphalia. 13. Christ Church. 14. Henry VIII. 15. King James VI.

FAMOUS PEOPLE

1   Whose works include the *Primavera* and *The Birth of Venus*?

2   In which city did the poet Keats die?

3   Which Rhodesian prime minister declared Unilateral Declaration of Independence in 1965?

4   Who wrote *Zorba the Greek*?

5   Name the famous Kansas marshal who was shot from behind in Deadwood, South Dakota.

6   Who was the first Japanese crown prince to visit Europe?

7   Who invented the vacuum flask in 1872?

8   Which sport is Steve Cauthen famous for?

9   What nationality was the artist Paul Klee?

10 Who was Eric Arthur Blair better known as?

11 Which 17th century priest is credited as the inventor of the slide rule?

12 Which Gandhi was assassinated in 1991?

13 Who was vice-president to Gerald Ford?

14 Before his death in 1805, who had constructed over 1,000 miles of road and 1,200 bridges, churches and harbours in Scotland?

15 Where was the body of William Pitt the Younger buried?

ANSWERS

1. Sandro Botticelli. 2. Rome. 3. Ian Smith. 4. Nikos Kazantzakis. 5. 'Wild Bill' Hickok (James Butler Hickok). 6. Hirohito. 7. James Dewar. 8. Horse racing. 9. Swiss. 10. George Orwell. 11. William Oughtred. 12. Rajiv. 13. Nelson A. Rockefeller. 14. Thomas Telford. 15. Westminster Abbey.

SPORT & LEISURE

1. Who won the 1970 football World Cup Final?

2. What is the name of the Dallas American football team?

3. Kriss Akabusi moved from running the 400m to competing in what event?

4. What sport do the New York Mets play?

5. How wide is a basketball court?

6. What is the name of the world governing body of football?

7. Which woman won the Wimbledon singles title in 1981?

8. What golf shot is John Daly famous for?

9. What is the name of Chelsea Football Club's ground?

10. In cricket what does LBW stand for?

11. How many times did Nelson Piquet win the Formula 1 World Championships?

12. What piece in chess can only be moved diagonally?

13. Who said 'You cannot be serious'?

14. Who are 'The Cottagers' in football?

15. William Webb Ellis is responsible for giving us which sport?

GENERAL KNOWLEDGE

SESSION 23   QUIZ 4

1   What is the English name for the American game of 'checkers'?

2   In 'loco parentis' means that one has eccentric parents.
    True or false?

3   Which 20th century author, in one of his novels, wrote 'All
    animals are equal, but some animals are more equal than
    others'?

4   What is the raising agent used in soda bread?

5   Traditionally, on which day are pancakes eaten?

6   What is the name for a shirt with short sleeves and a collar,
    made out of soft, knitted cotton material?

7   What is the name of the joint on a stem from which leaves arise?

8   What scale of values measures soil alkalinity or acidity?

9   Of which country is Tripoli the capital?

10 What is the name for the bells of the London church
    St Mary-le-Bow?

11 What is the traditional name for the day after Christmas Day?

12 In what script is the English alphabet written?

13 Traditionally, who proposes a toast to the parents of the bride
    and groom at a wedding?

14 What is the grammatical term used to say a roundabout way of
    expressing something?

15 Where did Weber establish a theatre for the performance of
    opera in German?

1. Draughts. 2. False. It means in the place or role of a parent. 3. George Orwell.
4. Bicarbonate of Soda. 5. Shrove Tuesday. 6. Polo shirt. 7. Node. 8. pH level.
9. Libya. 10. Bow Bells. 11. Boxing Day. 12. Roman. 13. The best man.
14. Periphrasis. 15. Dresden.

SCIENCE & NATURE

1 How many sides does a snowflake have?

2 How many bones are there in the human body?

3 What is a 'mermaid's purse'?

4 Which drug comes from the coca plant?

5 Which bird lays the world's largest egg?

6 What is the one kind of rock that can float on water?

7 Where does spermaceti oil come from?

8 Who developed a rudimentary submarine in 1620, which was successfully tested in the River Thames?

9 What are the primary colours of white light?

10 Through which part of the eye does light enter the body?

11 What is the noticeable difference between an alligator and a crocodile?

12 In which year was the far side of the Moon first shown?

13 Which is the largest animal that has ever lived?

14 Which two planets are furthest from the Sun?

15 What is the difference between African and Indian elephants?

144

ENTERTAINMENT

1 Who played the parts of the con men in the film *The Sting*?

2 Who plays 'Madge' in *Neighbours*?

3 What is the name of the holiday camp in TV's *Hi-de-Hi*?

4 The children's TV character 'Ivor The Engine' lived in which country?

5 Who was the first presenter of TV's *Tomorrow's World*?

6 Who played the headmistress in the film *The Belle of St Trinian's*?

7 Who was the creator of the TV soap *Brookside*?

8 Brotherhood of Man won the Eurovision Song Contest in 1976 with which song?

9 Who directed the film *Star Wars*?

10 Who presented *The Generation Game* after Bruce Forsyth and Anthea Turner?

11 Who played the role of 'Topper Harley' in the comedy film *Hot Shots*?

12 Dennis Waterman and John Thaw starred in which TV police series?

13 Who played the Russian submarine commander in the 1990 film *The Hunt For Red October*?

14 Which famous street is on the cover of Paul McCartney's 'Paul is Live' album?

15 Fill in the blanks: Portis _____, Motor _____ and Radio _____?

1. Robert Redford and Paul Newman. 2. Anne Charleston. 3. 'Maplins'. 4. Wales. 5. Raymond Baxter. 6. Alastair Sim. 7. Phil Redmond. 8. 'Save Your Kisses For Me'. 9. George Lucas. 10. Larry Grayson and Isla St Clair. 11. Charlie Sheen. 12. *The Sweeney*. 13. Sean Connery. 14. Abbey Road, London. 15. Head.

HISTORY

1 In which year was the House of Commons established in England?

2 Which English king is known as the 'Hammer of the Scots'?

3 In which year did the future King Henry VII of England defeat King Richard III at the Battle of Bosworth?

4 To what was Oliver Cromwell referring when he said 'What shall we do with this bauble? There, take it away' (or 'take away this bauble')?

5 In which year did Samuel Pepys begin his diary?

6 Christopher Wren, Robert Boyle and John Wilkins were prominently members of which association founded in 1660?

7 The Bourbon dynasty began to rule which country from 1700?

8 The naval battles of Lagos and Quiberon Bay took place during which war?

9 Who saw off a mob intent on overthrowing the government of the Directory in France in 1795 with 'a whiff of grapeshot'?

10 Who was chancellor of Austria from 1821 to 1848?

11 In which year did Queen Victoria's husband Prince Albert die?

12 What did Prince Albert die of?

13 Who defeated whom at the Battle of Isandhlwana in 1879?

14 The son of which former European ruler was killed at the Battle of Isandhlwana?

15 In which year did David Lloyd George become prime minister of Great Britain?

1. 1258. 2. King Edward I. 3. 1485. 4. The Mace in the House of Commons. 5. 1660. 6. The Royal Society. 7. Spain. 8. The Seven Years War. 9. Napoleon Bonaparte. 10. (Prince Clemens) Metternich. 11. 1861. 12. Typhoid. 13. The Zulus defeated the British. 14. The Emperor Napoleon III (Louis Napoleon) of France. 15. 1916.

FAMOUS PEOPLE

1 Which 19th century medical scientist pioneered effective treatments against anthrax and rabies?

2 Who was known as 'Bird'?

3 Whose attempt to impose the use of the Prayer Book on the Scots provoked a revolt which lead to the English civil war?

4 What was Malcolm X's surname?

5 Who won an Academy Award for his 1933 performance in the film *The Private Life of Henry VIII*?

6 Whose *Requiem* was unfinished at his death, and completed by a pupil?

7 Which Spanish soldier became conqueror and governor of Mexico?

8 Who succeeded Herbert Clark Hoover as American president?

9 Name the Italian pioneer in the invention and development of wireless telegraphy.

10 Who was known as the 'Iron Duke'?

11 Who succeeded Neville Chamberlain as prime minister in 1940?

12 Name the German dramatist and poet who first made a name with his adaption of John Gay's *Beggar's Opera* as *The Threepenny Opera*?

13 Who organized the New Model Army and lead them to victory at Naseby?

14 Whose works include the unfinished *The Mystery of Edward Drood*?

15 Which English physician discovered the circulation of blood and whose theory of circulation was published in 1628?

SPORT & LEISURE

1   Who missed the final penalty for England in the 1990 World Cup semi-final?

2   What is the name of the main trophy in American football?

3   Backley and Hill compete for Great Britain in which sport?

4   Kristen Otto won six gold medals in the 1988 Olympic Games, but in what sport?

5   What is the real name of 'Dickie' Bird?

6   How many Formula 1 World Championships did Jackie Stewart win?

7   Angus Fraser is famous for playing what sport?

8   One hundred and ten feet is the longest putt ever holed. Two people have achieved it. Nick Price is one, who is the other?

9   Arthur Ashe is famous for which sport?

10 Which basketball player starred alongside cartoon characters in the film *Space Jam*?

11 What football team play at Maine Road?

12 What country are the 'All Black' Rugby team from?

13 From which country do ex-Tottenham footballers Ossie Ardiles and Ricky Villa come?

14 Who rode West Tip to Grand National victory in 1986?

15 On what island did bungee jumping originate?

GENERAL KNOWLEDGE

1 Which British statesman is quoted in various speeches as saying: 'Wait and see'?

2 For what is arrowroot most commonly used?

3 What is the American word for English 'crisps'?

4 How many letters are there in the Greek alphabet?

5 From what region of France does Claret come?

6 Which British statesman said, 'A Conservative government is an organized hypocrisy'?

7 In one of his essays, who is quoted as saying, 'Money is like muck, not good except it be spread'?

8 What is the English word for the American 'fall'?

9 Who composed the songs 'The Old Folks at Home' and 'Camptown Races'?

10 What colour does beta carotene turn food?

11 By what other name was Richard I known?

12 What is the name of the thin, curling outgrowths by which certain climbing plants cling to supports?

13 In which country is Lake Bala found?

14 What do we play with two fingers on the piano, but Borodin, Rimsky-Korskov and Liszt composed variations of?

15 What is the name for the chest cavity?

SCIENCE & NATURE

1   Where is the Prime Meridian?

2   Which is the human body's largest organ?

3   What is the dye that turns pink in the presence of acid and blue in the presence of alkali?

4   Where is the world's largest rainforest?

5   What element makes up the gas ozone?

6   Where was the world's biggest gold nugget found?

7   Which gas makes up most of the world's atmosphere?

8   How fast does the heart beat?

9   Cirrus, stratus and cumulus are types of what?

10 Is the point directly below the observer called the nadir or the zenith?

11 When was the microwave cooker invented?

12 Where would you find haemoglobin?

13 What was the name of the first artificial satellite?

14 When was the first artificial satellite launched?

15 Which was the first antibiotic?

ENTERTAINMENT

1. Were the Oscars first awarded in (a) 1928, (b) 1929 or (c) 1930?

2. Which actress played 'Ena Sharples', one of the original characters in *Coronation Street*?

3. Kate Bush had a hit with 'Wuthering Heights'. Who wrote the novel with the same name?

4. Who plays 'Indiana Jones' in the film *Raiders of the Lost Ark*?

5. Which character in the TV comedy series *The Rise and Fall of Reginald Perrin* had the catchphrase 'I didn't get where I am today...'?

6. Who had a hit with 'Nights in White Satin'?

7. Who plays the part of 'Karen Blixen' in the film *Out of Africa*?

8. Who replaced Roy Plumley as the host of *Desert Island Discs*?

9. Which group appeared with Buddy Holly?

10. Where does the cartoon character 'Snoopy' sleep?

11. Which singer was born Marie MacDonald McLaughlin Lawrie?

12. Which actor played the character 'David Starksy' in *Starsky and Hutch*?

13. The 1960s folk duo, 'Nina and Frederick', were from which country?

14. Which former Take That star wanted to entertain you?

15. Boyzone had a hit with 'Words' in October 1996. Who else had this been a top ten hit for in 1968?

HISTORY

1 Edward Hawke, George Rodney and John Jervis all achieved distinction as what?

2 General John Burgoyne is best-known as a commander of British forces in which war?

3 In which year was Napoleon proclaimed emperor of France?

4 Who crowned Napoleon as emperor?

5 Jean Bernadotte, a former marshal of France, became king of which country in 1818?

6 In which year did the Congress of Vienna begin?

7 Who succeeded Louis XVIII as king of France in 1824?

8 Which migration of Dutch-speaking settlers out of the Cape Colony began in the mid 1830s?

9 Which states did these Dutch-speaking migrants eventually found?

10 Which Australian outlaw and folk hero was hanged in Melbourne in 1880?

11 Lyndon B. Johnson, the future president of the United States, and Ian Fleming, author of the James Bond novels were both born in the same year. Which year was it?

12 Who was president of the United States in the year 1910?

13 In which year did the Battle of Mons take place?

14 In which year did Oswald Mosley leave the Labour Party to form the British Union of Fascists?

15 Who said 'a week is a long time in politics'?

ANSWERS

1. British admirals. 2. The American War of Independence. 3. 1804. 4. He crowned himself (in the presence of the Pope). 5. Sweden. 6. 1814. 7. Charles X. 8. The Great Trek. 9. The Orange Free State and the Transvaal. 10. Ned Kelly. 11. 1908. 12. William Howard Taft. 13. 1914. 14. 1931. 15. Harold Wilson, British prime minister.

FAMOUS PEOPLE

1. Who was awarded an honorary KBE in 1985 for his promotion of charities through popular music?

2. Whose largely fictitious 'popish plot' led to the execution of many innocent Roman Catholics between 1678 and 1680?

3. Which Lancashire comedian was famous for his ukulele?

4. Who was the rock guitarist James Marshall better known as?

5. What was the US Confederate general, Thomas Jonathan Jackson better known as?

6. Which French philosopher became the most prominent exponent of atheistic existentialism and refused a Nobel prize for literature in 1964?

7. Which saint was born at Domrémy in 1412?

8. Name the French army officer wrongly convicted of treason in 1894.

9. Who engraved 'A Harlot's Progress' in 1731?

10. What was T. E. Lawrence better known as?

11. Which country was Archbishop Makarios president of between 1960 and 1977?

12. Whose novels include *Tropic of Cancer* and *Tropic of Capricorn*?

13. Who hoped 'to justify the ways of God to man'?

14. Who, in 1970, committed hara-kiri as a demonstration against the corruption of the nation and the loss of the samurai warrior tradition?

15. Which Italian saint is said to have had the ability to charm wild animals and influence people in all walks of life?

ANSWERS

1. Bob Geldof. 2. Titus Oates. 3. George Formby. 4. Jimi Hendrix. 5. 'Stonewall' Jackson. 6. Jean Paul Sartre. 7. Joan of Arc. 8. Alfred Dreyfus. 9. William Hogarth. 10. Lawrence of Arabia. 11. Cyprus. 12. Henry Miller. 13 Milton, in the poem *Paradise Lost*. 14. The Japanese novelist Yukio Mishima. 15. Saint Francis of Assisi.

SPORT & LEISURE

1 In which country was the 1982 football World Cup held?

2 Complete the name of the American football team 'The Washington...'?

3 What nationality is the former 2000m and 5000m world record holder Said Aouita?

4 Who trained Corbiere, the winner of the 1983 Grand National?

5 If you were watching the football team River Plate, what country would you be in?

6 How many basketball players, from one team, are allowed on court at any one time?

7 Where is the American Open Tennis Championships held?

8 Shaq and Magic are associated with which sport?

9 The Buccaneers, Cowboys and Steelers all play what sport?

10 Who won the 1970 FA Cup Final?

11 Who is the oldest ever US Open Golf Champion?

12 What do the initials MCC stand for?

13 Mario Andretti won the Formula 1 World Championship in 1977. True or false?

14 Where do Newcastle United FC play their home games?

15 The Baseball World Series is out of the best of how many games?

GENERAL KNOWLEDGE

1 What kind of plant is marjoram?

2 The people of which religion follow the teaching of Siddhartha Gantama?

3 In which country is Sevastapol?

4 'Little Jack Horner sat in the corner, eating...' Finish this line of the nursery rhyme.

5 What drink is made from molasses?

6 Who is said to have confessed, 'Give me chastity and continence, but not yet'?

7 In music, what is 'The 48'?

8 In which play by Oscar Wilde did 'Lord Darlington' say, 'I can resist everything except temptation'?

9 In the world of pop music, which brothers 'Walked Right Back'?

10 In one of Jane Austen's novels, who is quoted as saying, 'One half of the world cannot understand the pleasures of the other'?

11 Who was the drummer in The Beatles?

12 What is the English word for the American 'half note'?

13 How many characters are there in the Russian alphabet?

14 What is the name of the channel leading to the eardrum?

15 What is the American word for grilling (food)?

155

SCIENCE & NATURE

1 Which was the largest dinosaur?

2 Which is the fastest flying insect?

3 What is a googol?

4 What is the instrument that measures blood pressure called?

5 For what is 'Y' the chemical symbol?

6 What is the name of the naturalist who originated the concept that living things evolve by natural selection?

7 What is the temperature scale with freezing point of water as 0° and boiling point as 100°?

8 What is the technical name of the skin disease that results in inflammation and a scaly rash?

9 What are the sound frequencies that are too high for the human ear to hear?

10 What is a quasar?

11 For what achievement was Otto Hahn awarded the Nobel Prize for Chemistry (1944)?

12 What are springtails?

13 Name the process of separating mixtures of liquids through a semi-permeable membrane?

14 What is pepsin?

15 What name is given to the long spikes of flowers found hanging on trees such as the hazel or willow?

ANSWERS

1. *Seismosaurus* – 35m (38.3yds) from nose to tail. 2. A type of dragonfly found in Australia. 3. A very high number (one followed by a hundred zeros). 4. Sphygmomanometer. 5. Yttrium. 6. Charles Darwin. 7. Celsius (formerly Centigrade). 8. Dermatitis. 9. Ultrasound. 10. A quasi-stellar object (usually a source of radio waves). 11. Splitting of the uranium atom. 12. Small wingless insects. 13. Dialysis. 14. An enzyme in the stomach that digests proteins. 15. Catkins.

ENTERTAINMENT

1 The song 'Somewhere My Love' is the theme tune of which film?

2 Who plays the title role in the film *Edward Scissorhands*?

3 Polly James and Nerys Hughes starred in which TV comedy series?

4 Which musical features the song 'Oh, What A Beautiful Morning'?

5 Who plays 'John McClane' in the *Die Hard* films?

6 Who presented the TV programme *Winner Takes All*?

7 The skaters Torvill and Dean made the music 'Bolero' famous: Who composed it?

8 Which singer starred in the American TV series *The Partridge Family*?

9 Which group had a hit with 'Jumpin' Jack Flash'?

10 'Sonny Crockett' was a character in which TV series?

11 The catchphrase 'Left hand down a bit!' was associated with which radio comedy programme?

12 Who featured on television demolishing chimneys?

13 Which puppet 'attacked' Michael Parkinson on his TV chat show?

14 The film version of *Evita* meant two top ten hits for Madonna. Name them.

15 The director Mel Brooks was goose-stepping around the top 20 in February 1984. With what song did he get to number 12?

HISTORY

1   Charles the Bald, Charles the Wise and Charles the Affable were all kings of which European country?

2   Who succeeded Ethelred the Unready as king of England in 1016?

3   In which year was the First Crusade launched?

4   What was the name of the daughter of King Henry I of England who was proclaimed queen in 1141?

5   Which family dynasty ruled England from 1154 to 1485?

6   Who was the first king of all Spain?

7   In which year did King Henry IV come to the English throne?

8   Which king did Henry IV of England depose in order to become king?

9   In which century were the artists Leonardo da Vinci, Michelangelo and Raphael born?

10   Which pope commissioned Michelangelo to paint the ceiling of the Sistine chapel?

11   From what office did Sir Thomas More resign in 1532?

12   Sir Thomas More wrote a historical account of which English king?

13   Where was the Princess Elizabeth living, in exile from the court, when she was told she was to become Queen Elizabeth I of England?

14   Which famous Elizabethan dramatist was killed in a brawl in 1593?

15   In which year did Queen Elizabeth I of England die?

FAMOUS PEOPLE

1   Which Scottish author became 1st Baron Tweedsmuir?

2   Which young English poet, perhaps more famous for his unconventional behaviour, drowned off the coast of Italy in 1822?

3   The singer/songwriter, born David Robert Jones, had a hit with a song inspired by Stanley Kubrik's *2001: A Space Odyssey*. Name the song and the artist's stage name.

4   Whose *Confessions of an English Opium Eater* tell of his companionship with a young orphan called 'Ann'?

5   Who wrote 'Mein Kampf'?

6   Which Austrian 19th century composer was often persuaded to abridge and modify his lengthy orchestral compositions?

7   Using the chains from his own Hungerford Suspension Bridge, what did Isambard Kingdom Brunel complete in 1864?

8   *Finnigan's Wake* was the last novel of which author?

9   Which Canadian ship owner formed a shipping line which eventually bore his name?

10 Who composed scores for the films, *Gone With The Wind* and *Casablanca*?

11 In 1581, who did Ivan The Terrible accidentally kill in a fit of anger?

12 Who was queen of England from 9 July to 19 July in 1553?

13 Which Scottish patriot led a revolt against English rule in 1297?

14 Who was founder of the Nationalist Guomindang Party and guiding force behind the Chinese Revolution in 1911?

15 Who was appointed bishop of Durham in 1984, amidst controversy over his interpretation of the Virgin Birth?

ANSWERS

1. John Buchan. 2. Percy Shelley. 3. 'Space Oddity' by David Bowie. 4. Thomas De Quincey. 5. Adolf Hitler. 6. Anton Bruckner. 7. The Clifton Suspension Bridge. 8. James Joyce. 9. Sir Samuel Cunard. 10. Max Steiner. 11. His own son. 12. Lady Jane Grey. 13. William Wallace. 14. Sun Yat-sen. 15. David Jenkins.

SPORT & LEISURE

1 In what sport were Flach and Seguso a famous partnership?

2 What country did Niki Lauda drive for?

3 In which year was the Football Association founded?

4 Sergi Bubka is famous for competing in what sporting event?

5 What is the name given to the player who throws the ball in American football?

6 Who are the 'Toffee Men' in football?

7 How many players do you find in a baseball team?

8 What do the initials TCCB stand for?

9 What country won the first Rugby Union World Cup?

10 Who was the top scorer in the 1982 football World Cup Final?

11 Who became the youngest golfer to win the US Masters, in 1997?

12 Name the four tennis tournaments that make up the Grand Slam?

13 Where do Watford Football Club play their home fixtures?

14 Pirmin Zurbriggen is a World Cup winner in which sport?

15 How many points is an 'H' worth in Scrabble?

GENERAL KNOWLEDGE

1 From whom does the teddy bear take its name?

2 In which George Orwell novel is 'Big Brother' said to be watching you?

3 On which musical instrument would you be most likely to play a pibroch?

4 What is the name of the brimless Scottish cap, which usually has a pom-pom on top?

5 In the song which line follows 'Rule Britannia, Britannia rules the waves'?

6 Who lost her sheep in the traditional nursery rhyme?

7 In which country is Marrakesh?

8 To which religion do 'Sangha' monks and nuns belong?

9 In the song, who stuck a feather in his cap and called it macaroni?

10 What do we call the drink which is made from the roots of the Smilax plant?

11 What is the fruit of a certain type of Rose?

12 From which Jane Austen novel is 'Let other pens dwell on guilt and misery' quoted?

13 What is the American word for 'nappy'?

14 With which country do you associate the drink Pernod?

15 Which song begins, 'Dashing through the snow, in a one horse open sleigh'?

ANSWERS

1. Theodore Roosevelt (US president). 2. 1984. 3. Bagpipes. 4. Tam-o'-shanter. 5. 'Britons never, never, never shall be slaves'. 6. Little Bo-Peep'. 7. Morocco. 8. Buddhism. 9. 'Yankee Doodle'. 10. Sarsaparilla. 11. Hips. 12. *Mansfield Park*. 13. Diaper. 14. France. 15. 'Jingle Bells'.

SCIENCE & NATURE

1   What is the brightest artificial light?

2   Which animal has musth glands?

3   In which year did the American astronomer Clyde William Tombaugh discover the planet Pluto?

4   Which is the fastest swimming whale?

5   Where in the human body is the pituitary gland?

6   What is the average area of the human lungs?

7   Who invented the revolver?

8   By which process do liquids pass through a porous membrane?

9   What was archaeopteryx?

10 What is oakum?

11 What breed of animal is a duroc?

12 What is crocidolite and why is it dangerous?

13 What is bird's nest soup?

14 What does an otorhinolaryngologist treat?

15 What is visible to people on Earth once every 76 years?

ANSWERS

1. Laser light. 2. Elephants (connected with elephant rage). 3. 1930. 4. Killer whale. 5. At the base of the brain. 6. 70m² (84yds²). 7. Samuel Colt (in 1835). 8. Osmosis. 9. Prehistoric bird/reptile. 10. Loose fibre from old rope. 11. A pig. 12. A form of asbestos that causes asbestosis. 13. Soup from nests of cave-dwelling swifts in SE Asia. 14. Ears, noses and throats. 15. *Halley's Comet.*

ENTERTAINMENT

1   Which classical composer is also the name of a huge dog portrayed in a comedy film?

2   Fern Britton presents which TV cookery programme?

3   Which American singer had the nickname 'Little Miss Dynamite'?

4   Where was Charlie Chaplin born?

5   Who played 'Irene' in TV's *The Forsyte Saga*?

6   John Phillips, Michelle Phillips, Denny Doherty and Cass Elliot formed which group?

7   Who wrote the plays *Rosencrantz and Guildenstern are Dead* and *Jumpers*?

8   Who played the title role in the TV series *Rumpole of the Bailey*?

9   In which Beatles' film did the song 'Ticket to Ride' feature?

10 Who played Agent Dale Cooper in the TV series *Twin Peaks*?

11 Who played 'Captain Ahab' in the 1956 film *Moby Dick*?

12 Which of the duo 'Peter and Gordon' is the brother of Jane Asher, the actress?

13 What was the name of the cook in the TV series *Upstairs, Downstairs*?

14 Who asked 'I'm a loser baby, so why don't you kill me?'?

15 In 1995 an album was created with the intention of raising money and drawing attention to the plight of the children caught up in the war in former Yugoslavia. Name this album.

HISTORY

1 Jane Shore, Nell Gwyn and Lillie Langtry were all famous as what?

2 Which town did King Charles II of England sell to King Louis XIV of France in 1662?

3 Anne Hyde was the wife of which future king?

4 In which year did the Battle of the Boyne take place?

5 Who defeated whom at the Battle of the Boyne?

6 Who was tsar of Russia from 1682 to 1725?

7 In which year did King Louis XIV of France die?

8 The son and heir of which king of Britain was known as 'poor Fred'?

9 In which year did the Battle of Culloden take place?

10 Who commanded the loyalist British army at the Battle of Culloden?

11 In which year was the Authorized (King James) Version of the Bible published?

12 The first volume of which monumental historical work was published in 1776?

13 Who was prime minister of Great Britain throughout the American War of Independence?

14 Who was appointed governor of New South Wales in 1805?

15 In which year did Napoleon retreat from Moscow?

ANSWERS

1. Royal mistresses (the mistresses of Kings Edward IV, Charles II and Edward VII respectively). 2. Dunkirk. 3. James II of England (James VII of Scotland). 4. 1690. 5. King William III of England defeated King James II. 6. Peter the Great. 7. 1715. 8. King George II (nickname of Frederick Louis, Prince of Wales). 9. 1746. 10. The Duke of Cumberland ('Butcher' Cumberland). 11. 1611. 12. Gibbon's *Decline and Fall of the Roman Empire*. 13. Lord North. 14. William Bligh (formerly Captain Bligh of the *Bounty*). 15. 1812.

FAMOUS PEOPLE

1 Name the actress who had a Croydon theatre named after her.

2 Meryl Streep played a nuclear worker who was killed in a car accident. Name her.

3 Whose celebrated diary was originally written in cipher and ran from 1 January 1660 to 31 May 1669?

4 Name the English agriculturist who invented a seed drill and whose name was used by a rock band.

5 Who was shot by J. Wilkes Booth in Ford's Theatre?

6 Who wrote *Leaves of Grass*?

7 Who was the last Viceroy of India?

8 Who professed to be Richard, Duke of York, younger of the two brothers murdered in the Tower of London?

9 'Action Painting' was made popular by which pop artist?

10 At what age did William Pitt become prime minister: (a) 22, (b) 23 or (c) 24?

11 In 1605, who was caught red-handed in the cellar of the Palace of Westminster?

12 What is Johannes Gutenberg regarded as the inventor of?

13 Which war is often known as 'The War of Jenkins' Ear'?

14 Who was the commander-in-chief of the American army in the War of Independence?

15 Which British inventor developed the jet engine?

SPORT & LEISURE

1 In which year was the Ryder Cup established?

2 Which German has won the football World Cup as both a player and a manager?

3 'The Refrigerator' is famous for playing which sport?

4 What is the main trophy in American baseball?

5 Who partnered Martina Navratilova to four successive women's doubles championships at Wimbledon?

6 Who scored the last goal for France in the 1998 football World Cup Final?

7 Daley Thompson is famous for competing in which athletics event?

8 In which country would you watch Indy Car Racing?

9 Who became the youngest Formula One Racing Champion in 1972?

10 Complete the boxer's name 'Marvellous Marvin...'?

11 What are the officials called in a game of cricket?

12 What is the name of the Chicago basketball team?

13 If you were watching an 'Old Firm' derby, in which city would you be?

14 For what type of dancing do you dress up like cowboys and do moves like the 'camel walk' and 'the stomp'?

15 What is the nickname of Northampton Town FC?

166

1. 1927. 2. Franz Beckenbauer. 3. American Football. 4. The World Series. 5. Pam Shriver. 6. Emmanuel Petit. 7. The Decathlon. 8. USA. 9. Emerson Fittipaldi. 10. Hagler. 11. Umpires. 12. Chicago Bulls. 13. Glasgow. 14. Line dancing. 15. The Cobblers'.

GENERAL KNOWLEDGE

1   What is the French term used for a clear soup?

2   Who in the Bible said: 'What is truth?'?

3   What kind of fruit is a pearmain?

4   What does an epicure enjoy?

5   What is the American name for the game 'noughts and crosses'?

6   Which tree is associated with Lebanon?

7   What is the common name for the trachea?

8   Who, in Jane Austen's *Pride and Prejudice* said, 'I have been a selfish being all my life, in practice, though not in principle'?

9   What is a canapé?

10 In which musical are there two gangs called the 'Sharks' and the 'Jets'?

11 'Ladybird, ladybird, fly away home, Your house is on fire, and...' Finish the line of this nursery rhyme.

12 What is the metric unit of magnetic flux density named after a Croatian-born American electrician?

13 From which country does the drink Ouzo come?

14 On which French river are the ports of Le Havre and Rouen?

15 According to the proverb, of what will you repent at leisure?

167

1. Consommé. 2. Pilate. 3. Apple. 4. Good food and drink (good living). 5. Tick-tack-toe. 6. Cedar. 7. Windpipe. 8. Mr Darcy. 9. A small piece of toast with a savoury topping. 10. *West Side Story*. 11. '...your children all gone'. 12. Tesla. 13. Greece. 14. Seine. 15. Marrying in haste.

SCIENCE & NATURE

1   What are the colours of the rainbow?

2   What does AIDS stand for?

3   In degrees, what do the angles of a triangle add up to?

4   What is cassiterite?

5   What does the blue whale eat?

6   Why is there no noise on the Moon?

7   What name is used for the class of chemical compounds used in fridges that are harmful to the ozone layer?

8   How many chromosomes are there in a normal human cell?

9   What is the common name for *Atropa Belladonna*?

10 From which country did the astronomer Tycho Brahe come?

11 What is the common name for the sharp-tasting plant of the mustard family used in salads and garnishes?

12 Which was the fiercest of the dinosaurs?

13 What is the name of the effect that describes the deflection of winds and currents as a result of the Earth's rotation?

14 What colour are the flowers of the dill herb?

15 *Allium schoenoprasum* is the scientific name for which herb?

ENTERTAINMENT

1 Who starred in the 1961 film *Blue Hawaii*?

2 What was wrong with 'Clarence' the lion in the 1960s TV series *Daktari?*

3 Ray and Dave Davies were members of which group?

4 Who directed the film *J.F.K.*?

5 In which city was Stanley Baxter born?

6 Which nationality was the composer Edward Grieg?

7 Who plays the title role in the film *The Elephant Man*?

8 Who starred as 'Nellie Boswell' in the TV series *Bread*?

9 Which singer, whose father was a famous actor, had a hit with 'Windmills Of Your Mind' in 1969?

10 Who plays 'Miss Daisy' in the film *Driving Miss Daisy*?

11 The phrase 'Let's be careful out there' is associated with which American TV police series?

12 The bandleader and arranger, James Last, was born in which country?

13 In which year was the film *The Young Ones*, starring Cliff Richard, released?

14 Who performed the theme song for the Bond film, 'Tomorrow Never Dies'?

15 Which group did Louise Nurdin leave to start her solo career?

ANSWERS

1. Elvis Presley. 2. It was cross-eyed. 3. The Kinks. 4. Oliver Stone. 5. Glasgow. 6. Norwegian. 7. John Hurt. 8. Jean Boht. 9. Noel Harrison. 10. Jessica Tandy. 11. *Hill Street Blues*. 12. Germany. 13. 1962. 14. Sheryl Crow. 15. Eternal.

HISTORY

1 Ada Augusta Lovelace (1815–52) is famous for her work in which sphere?

2 Whose daughter was Ada Lovelace?

3 Where was Florence Nightingale born in 1820?

4 The Empress Eugénie (1826–1920) was the wife of which European ruler?

5 Elizabeth Fry, who died in 1845, is famous for her work in reforming what type of institution?

6 Whose *Book of Household Management*, previously serialized, was published in 1861?

7 Which British leader of the movement for women's suffrage was born in 1857?

8 Which woman scientist was awarded the Nobel prize twice, in 1903 and 1911?

9 Emily Hobhouse called attention to the atrocious conditions in concentration camps in which country?

10 Whose book *Married Love* caused a furore when it was first published in 1916?

11 Which German woman socialist revolutionary was a co-founder of the Spartacus league at the outbreak of World War I?

12 Helen Wills (Moody) was a famous inter-war champion in which sport?

13 Mrs Sirimavo Bandaranaike became prime minister of which country in 1960?

14 Which future prime minister of Israel was Israeli ambassador to the Soviet Union from 1948–49?

15 Who, in 1982, said 'The battle for women's rights has been largely won'?

ANSWERS

1. Mathematics and computing. 2. Lord Byron's. 3. In Florence (Italy). 4. The Emperor Napoleon III (Louis Napoleon) of France. 5. Prisons. 6. Mrs (Isabella Mary) Beeton's. 7. Mrs (Emmeline) Pankhurst (née Goulden). 8. Marie Curie. 9. South Africa (as set up by the British in the later stages of the (Anglo-)Boer War). 10. Marie Stopes. 11. Rosa Luxemburg. 12. Tennis. 13. Sri Lanka. 14. Golda Meir. 15. Margaret Thatcher (British prime minister 1979–90).

FAMOUS PEOPLE

1 Who composed music in which the score consisted only of short verbal texts, leaving the performers to invent the music themselves?

2 When Marilyn Monroe lived in Los Angeles in 1926, what was her full name?

3 In South America, who was known as 'The Liberator' from Spanish rule?

4 Who developed the Italian Fascist movement as a weapon against Bolshevism?

5 Who returned to Addis Ababa, capital of Abyssinia, on 5 May 1941, after five years of exile?

6 Which Danish king ruled over England between 1016 and 1035?

7 Claiming they had acted upon words spoken by the king, who did King Henry's knights murder in Canterbury Cathedral in 1170?

8 Who was the first Englishman to circumnavigate the world?

9 Allen Lane offered a five pound prize to his staff for the invention of a suitable logo. For which publishers was he Managing Director?

10 In what year did Queen Victoria die: (a) 1901, (b) 1905 or (c) 1910?

11 Who sponsored the building of the wall from the mouth of the Tyne to Solway Firth?

12 Who was crowned emperor of the Holy Roman Empire, in St. Peter's Church, Christmas Day AD800?

13 Who developed the technique of conversational 'free association' in place of hypnosis?

14 Which Nobel prize winning Indian writer resigned his knighthood as a gesture of protest against British repression?

15 Which English pop legend returned his MBE in protest against the Vietnam War?

ANSWERS

1. Karlheinz Stockhausen. 2. Norma Jean Baker. 3. Simon Bolivar. 4. Benito Mussolini. 5. Haile Selassie. 6. Canute. 7. Thomas à Becket. 8. Sir Francis Drake. 9. Penguin Books. 10. (a) 1901. 11. Hadrian. 12. Charlemagne (Charles The Great). 13. Sigmund Freud. 14. Rabindranath Tagore. 15. John Lennon.

SPORT & LEISURE

1 Who knocked England out of the 1986 Football World Cup Finals?

2 What animal do you associate with the Chicago American Football team?

3 When did Steffi Graf win her first Wimbledon singles title?

4 In what sport did Ingrid Kristiansen hold three world records during 1989?

5 What country does golfer Vijay Singh come from?

6 When was FIFA, the governing body of football, formed?

7 Who was Ayrton Senna's team mate for McLaren in 1990?

8 What is the official height of cricket stumps?

9 Where in America are the famous Dodgers baseball team from?

10 With which sport do you associate former World Champion Neil Adams?

11 What was the full name of the late sprinter 'Flo Jo'?

12 At what football ground in England might you find the home fans singing 'I'm forever blowing bubbles'?

13 In snooker, if you were to foul on the black ball, how many points would your opponent receive?

14 How many times was John Francome the Champion National Hunt jockey?

15 What is the nickname of Barnsley FC?

ANSWERS

1. Argentina. 2. Bears. 3. 1988. 4. Athletics (5,000m, 10,000m and the marathon). 5. Fiji. 6. 1904. 7. Gerhard Berger. 8. 26 inches (71.1 cm). 9. Los Angeles. 10. Judo. 11. Florence Griffith-Joyner. 12. West Ham United. 13. Seven. 14. Seven times. 15. 'The Tykes' (or The Reds and Colliers).

GENERAL KNOWLEDGE

1   For what purpose, in the nursery rhyme, did 'Jack and Jill' go up the hill?

2   What is the name given to the soft felt hat with an indented crown?

3   If you were playing a jew's harp, how would you be holding it?

4   From which Jane Austen novel is the quotation, 'Happiness in marriage is entirely a matter of chance' taken?

5   What kind of drink is porter?

6   What is the name for the mass of spongy tissue between the back of the nose and throat?

7   What state of being do Buddhists hope to achieve through regular meditation?

8   Having a holiday in Valletta, in which country would you be?

9   What is the American word for the English spring onion?

10   Which Spanish musical instrument is made of two wooden shells?

11   Of which country is Nairobi the capital?

12   What is the name for the process of building up and breaking down foodstuffs by the body cells?

13   According to the proverb, what proves the rule?

14   Which capital city stands on the River Tiber?

15   What is the name of the six-pointed star frequently used as the Jewish symbol?

SCIENCE & NATURE

1 What name is given to the process by which the world's atmosphere is becoming continually warmer?

2 What is the name of the island shared by the countries of Haiti and the Dominican republic?

3 Who discovered the neutron?

4 Which birds live the longest?

5 What name do geologists give to the epoch that includes the present?

6 What was the first spacecraft to be launched into orbit for the second time?

7 Who discovered the tuberculosis bacterium?

8 What is aformosa?

9 What is bladderwrack?

10 What is a Fibonacci series?

11 What is galvanized metal coated with?

12 What are the parts of a typical comet?

13 Rose mallow is the American term for which plant?

14 Which artery supplies blood to the heart and neck?

15 The first man-made object ever to reach the Moon was Russian. What was it called?

ENTERTAINMENT

1 'Somewhere' is a song from which musical?

2 Who played the title role in the TV series *The District Nurse*?

3 In which year was the film *E.T.* released?

4 Which singer had a hit with 'Speedy Gonzales'?

5 What was the name of the hospital in the series *Doctor in the House*?

6 Who directed the 1985 film *A Chorus Line*?

7 The song 'I Know Him So Well' was a hit for which two singers?

8 What is the name of the Rubbles' baby in the cartoon *The Flintstones*?

9 The 1995 film *Circle of Friends* is based on a novel by Maeve Binchy and set in which country?

10 Which actor/singer had a hit with 'Don't Give Up On Us'?

11 The TV series *Roots* was based on a novel by whom?

12 Which animal features in the Clint Eastwood film *Every Which Way But Loose*?

13 The song 'Clare' was a hit for whom?

14 What was the name of the children's television drama that features 'Sean Maguire' as a schoolboy?

15 'Ullo John Got A New Motor?' asked which comedian in 1984?

HISTORY

1   Knut Sveinsson was the Danish name of which king of England?

2   The Holy Roman Emperor Frederick I (*c.* 1123–90) is better known by what nickname?

3   Who fled from England to France in 1164?

4   Who was killed while besieging the castle of Chalus in France in 1199?

5   What did the Salic law prohibit?

6   Which English king married a French king's daughter at Troyes in 1420?

7   Which family of German bankers and merchants, based in Augsburg, came to prominence in the late 15th and early 16th centuries?

8   Who became tsar of Russia in 1533?

9   In which year did the Battle of Edgehill take place?

10 In which year did the Dutch sail up the Thames estuary into the Medway and burn the English fleet?

11 Which British monarch was known as 'the Sailor King'?

12 How many years after the Declaration of American Independence did the Battle of Gettysburg take place?

13 The Battle of Sedan took place during which war?

14 In which year did Oklahoma become the forty-sixth state of the US? (a) 1887, (b) 1897 or (c) 1907?

15 Who was president of the United States in 1920?

FAMOUS PEOPLE

1   Who created the book of engravings *Anatomy of the Horse*, first published in 1766?

2   Which universally known British mathematician developed theories about natural forces, including motion and light?

3   Born in Bristol, England, Archibald Leach went on to become which famous film star?

4   Who was badly criticized for his handling of the Suez crisis, which lead to his resignation?

5   Who commanded the 'Calypso' from 1951?

6   The month of July is named after which Roman general?

7   Name the American inventor who perfected the process of freezing small quantities of food in plastic bags.

8   Who said 'One can never be too thin or too rich'?

9   Who claimed to bend cutlery with his mind?

10   Name the millionaire who built Skibo Castle in Sutherland.

11   With what did the CIA reputedly try to assassinate Fidel Castro?

12   In which country was the French impressionist Camille Pissarro born?

13   In the Bible, who is described as 'a man after God's own heart'?

14   In which city was Mother Teresa known for her work among lepers and the dying?

15   What is the Englishman Charles Haddon Spurgeon best known for?

SPORT & LEISURE

1   Who was John McEnroe's partner in an extremely successful tennis doubles team?

2   At what football ground do Blackpool play?

3   What country does athlete Colin Jackson come from?

4   Who are the Lakers in American basketball?

5   Trevino, Player and Nicklaus are legends in what sport?

6   Which country won the 1988 European Football Championships?

7   How many players from one team are allowed on the field of play, at any one time, in a game of American football?

8   For which team did Damon Hill race in 1998?

9   What is the name for the piece of wood that rests on top of a set of cricket stumps?

10 Who won the Tour de France in 1987?

11 What is the nickname of Bournemouth FC?

12 In what sport would you use the term 'good to soft'?

13 How many points would you get for the word 'prized' in Scrabble?

14 From what team did Chelsea sign Dan Petrescu?

15 What is the full name of the St Louis baseball team?

1. Peter Fleming. 2. Bloomfield Park. 3. Wales. 4. Los Angeles Lakers. 5. Golf. 6. Holland. 7. 11 (12 in Canada). 8. Jordan. 9. The bails. 10. Stephen Roche. 11. 'The Cherries'. 12. Horse racing. 13. 18 points. 14. Sheffield Wednesday. 15. St Louis Cardinals.

GENERAL KNOWLEDGE

1 What is the American word for English 'sweets'?

2 In the nursery rhyme 'Ding dong bell', who put Pussy in the well?

3 In criminal terms, if someone is 'incarcerated', where are they?

4 What musical instrument would a timpanist play?

5 What type of competitor races in the 'St Leger'?

6 Which American president said: 'Think of your forefathers! Think of your posterity'?

7 From which language do the following come: 'fjord', 'ski', 'slalom'?

8 In music, which note follows 'soh'?

9 Who said, 'Give me a firm place to stand, and I will move the earth'?

10 According to the proverb, what part of clouds are silver?

11 Who was the founder of Methodism?

12 Complete the book title, *Men are from Mars, Women are...*?

13 Which seasoning is made from the cayenne plant?

14 Named after an American hat-maker, what is a wide-brimmed, high-crowned felt hat called?

15 In which century was the Hanseatic League first founded?

ANSWERS

1. Candy. 2. 'Little Johnny Green'. 3. In prison. 4. Drums (percussion instruments). 5. Horses. 6. John Quincy Adams. 7. Norwegian. 8. Lah. 9. Archimedes. 10. Linings. 11. John Wesley. 12. *From Venus*. 13. Pepper. 14. Stetson. 15. 13th century.

SCIENCE & NATURE

1 There are two varieties of artichoke: one of them is the Jerusalem artichoke; name the other.

2 What is the name of the small island south of the Isle of Man?

3 What has the chemical symbol 'Fe'?

4 What does stapedectomy involve?

5 Which spice is obtained from the stigmas of the crocus?

6 Which two letters of the alphabet are not used in the periodic table?

7 What is the Haber process?

8 Which part of the brain is responsible for balance and muscular co-ordination?

9 Which element has the atomic number 1?

10 From which plant does the drug atropine come?

11 What is the chemical name for 'oil of vitriol'?

12 What, in computer circles, is PROM?

13 What kind of astral body is Eros?

14 What is oriental topaz?

15 From which flower does the insecticide pyrethrum come?

ENTERTAINMENT

1 What did 'J. R.' stand for in the character played by Larry Hagman in *Dallas*?

2 Which group had a hit with 'Hippy Hippy Shake'?

3 Rowan Atkinson, Griff Rhys-Jones, Mel Smith and Pamela Stephenson performed in which TV comedy show?

4 Who plays 'Gregory' in the film *Gregory's Girl*?

5 'Any Dream Will Do' is a song from which musical?

6 Michael Brandon and Glynis Barber played the title roles in which TV series?

7 'Puff The Magic Dragon' was a hit for which folk group?

8 Who plays the title role in the Oscar winning film *Forrest Gump*?

9 Whose only top ten hit was 'Pump Up The Volume'?

10 In which fictitious town is *Dad's Army* set?

11 Who plays the character 'Dr Emmett Brown' in the *Back to the Future* films?

12 'Skin' fronted which 90s rock/pop band?

13 With whom did Elton John sing 'Don't Go Breaking My Heart'?

14 Who created *Not Only... But Also...*?

15 'Tannochbrae' was the setting for which TV series?

ANSWERS

1. John Ross. 2. Swinging Blue Jeans. 3. *Not The Nine O'Clock News*. 4. John Gordon Sinclair. 5. *Joseph and His Amazing Technicolour Dreamcoat*. 6. *Dempsey and Makepeace*. 7. 'Peter, Paul and Mary'. 8. Tom Hanks. 9. M/A/R/R/S. 10. 'Walmington-on-Sea'. 11. Christopher Lloyd. 12. Skunk Anansie. 13. Kiki Dee. 14. Peter Cook and Dudley Moore. 15. *Dr Finlay's Casebook*.

HISTORY

1   The poet Robert Browning and Alfred Krupp the founder of the famous German steel and armaments firm were both born in the year of a famous military disaster. What year was it?

2   The '1820 Settlers' from Britain went to which country?

3   Why did Queen Caroline not attend the coronation of her husband King George IV in 1821?

4   Who died at Missolonghi in Greece in 1824?

5   Which former American president died in 1826?

6   Who, also in 1826, founded the Royal Zoological Society and London Zoo?

7   In which European capital did a successful revolution take place in 1830?

8   Which European country became an independent kingdom for the first time in 1831?

9   On which ship did Charles Darwin set sail in 1831 as naturalist for a surveying expedition?

10   In which year was the first Reform Act, extending the franchise essentially to upper-middle-class voters, passed by the British Parliament?

11   What was the Zollverein, usually seen as a step on the road to German unification, which began to operate in the mid-1830s?

12   In which year were the Tolpuddle Martyrs sentenced to transportation in Britain for trade union activities?

13   The death of King William IV in 1837 brought to an end the 'personal union' whereby the King of Great Britain was also the ruler of which German state?

14   Who, in 1837, exhibited his electric telegraph to Congress and in New York?

15   In 1839 the first Opium War broke out between Britain and which country?

1. 1812. 2. South Africa. 3. Because the King had her barred from entering Westminster Abbey. 4. Lord Byron. 5. Thomas Jefferson. 6. Sir Stamford Raffles. 7. Paris. 8. Belgium. 9. HMS *Beagle*. 10. 1832. 11. A customs union. 12. 1834. 13. Hanover. 14. Samuel Morse. 15. China.

FAMOUS PEOPLE

1 Which conceptual artist wrapped islands in pink plastic sheets to make the largest work of art?

2 Who received applause for a record 1 hour 20 minutes after an operatic performance in 1991?

3 Who was the youngest prime minister of Britain?

4 Who was the son of a rich Argentinian family who changed career from being a doctor to being a revolutionary, which led to his death in 1967?

5 Which woman became president of the Philippines in 1986?

6 Who designed the cathedral of Sagrada Familia in Barcelona?

7 How did Emily Davison die in 1913?

8 Which violin virtuoso was said to be in league with the devil because his playing was so good?

9 In which year was Amy Johnson the first woman to fly from Britain to Australia? Was it: (a) 1930, (b) 1933 or (c) 1936?

10 Who wrote *Das Kapital*?

11 Which German composer moved to England in 1712 and composed many famous choral works including *Judas Maccabeus*?

12 Which Italian actress served 17 days in prison for tax fraud in 1982?

13 Who was the first premier of modern Israel?

14 Who developed the idea of 'lateral thinking'?

15 Who received the Nobel Peace Prize in December 1984 for his campaign for an end to apartheid in South Africa?

ANSWERS

1. Christo. 2. Plácido Domingo. 3. William Pitt ('the Younger'). 4. Ernesto 'Che' Guevara. 5. Corazon Aquino. 6. Antonio Gaudí. 7. She threw herself under the king's horse at a race meeting. 8. Niccolo Paganini. 9. (a) 1930. 10. Karl Marx. 11. George Frederick Handel. 12. Sophia Loren. 13. David Ben Gurion. 14. Edward de Bono. 15. Bishop Desmond Tutu.

SPORT & LEISURE

1   Who is the voice of BBC Golf?

2   Which country reached the 1974 and 1978 football World Cup Finals, but ended up runners up in both?

3   Denise Lewis competes for Great Britain in which athletic event?

4   On 28 January 1996, what sporting event was watched by over eight hundred million people world wide?

5   At which cricket ground would you find the Nursery End?

6   Who was the youngest woman to win the Wimbledon singles title beating Lottie Dod's record by a matter of days?

7   What sports company named a range of trainer after basketball legend Michael Jordan?

8   Black Jack and Stud Poker are what type of game?

9   Who was the manager of the England football team in the 1990 World Cup?

10 What shape are your skis in if you are 'snowploughing'?

11 In what sport do you play for the Pilkington Cup?

12 With which sport do you associate Roberto Duran?

13 What football club does well known BBC Sports presenter Des Lynam support?

14 From what country does racing driver Jacques Villeneuve come?

15 How many dice do you use in the popular game Yahtzee?

ANSWERS

1. Peter Alliss. 2. Holland. 3. The Heptathlon. 4. The Super Bowl. 5. Lords. 6. Martina Hingis. 7. Nike (Nike Air Jordan). 8. Card games. 9. Bobby Robson. 10. A 'V' shape. 11. Rugby Union. 12. Boxing. 13. Brighton and Hove Albion. 14. Canada. 15. Five dice.

GENERAL KNOWLEDGE

1   In the nursery rhyme, 'I had a little nut tree', it would only bear two things, what were they?

2   Which scale is commonly used to measure the magnitude of earthquakes?

3   What is the English word for American 'pants'?

4   Of what is a 'tintinnabulation' the sound?

5   Which county is particularly associated with the song 'On Ilkley Moor baht 'at'?

6   'Mother's Ruin' is a nickname for which drink?

7   From which main ingredient is sauerkraut made?

8   Who originally said, 'The woman that deliberates is lost'?

9   Which musical instrument is a national emblem of Eire?

10   In criminal terms, what does it mean to 'purloin' something?

11   What is the American word for English 'treacle'?

12   What did Baron Paul Julius von Reuter found?

13   According to the proverb, whose house is his castle?

14   What is the name of a Jewish boy's coming of age?

15   According to a song, to where in Ireland is it a long way?

185

1. A silver nutmeg and a golden pear. 2. Richter scale. 3. Trousers. 4. Ringing bells.
5. Yorkshire. 6. Gin. 7. Cabbage. 8. Joseph Addison. 9. Harp. 10. Steal something.
11. Molasses. 12. The first news agency. 13. An Englishman's. 14. Bar Mitzvah.
15. Tipperary.

SCIENCE & NATURE

1 What do astronomers call an exploding star?

2 Which country has land borders with Costa Rica and Colombia?

3 What is Kwok's disease?

4 What are Fraunhofer lines?

5 What is nephology?

6 Name two of the six noble gases.

7 To which animal is the cacomistle related?

8 What is vitreous humour?

9 What is the term for the behaviour guidelines evolved by users of the Internet?

10 What was the first subatomic particle to be discovered?

11 Who is the computer programming language 'Ada' named after?

12 What is the technical term for the outer layer of a mushroom cap?

13 What are the two brightest stars in the sky?

14 What is the test used to find out if an organic substance is a reducing agent?

15 What is the full name for the drug LSD?

1. A supernova. 2. Panama. 3. Allergy to monosodium glutamate. 4. Dark lines in the solar spectrum. 5. The study of clouds (a branch of meteorology). 6. Helium, neon, argon, krypton, xenon, radon. 7. Racoon. 8. A jelly-like substance in the eyeball. 9. Netiquette (Internet etiquette). 10. The electron (in 1895). 11. Mathematician Ada (Augusta) Byron, Countess of Lovelace and daughter of Lord Byron. 12. Pellicle. 13. Sirius and Canopus. 14. Fehlings test. 15. Lysergic acid diethylamide.

ENTERTAINMENT

1 Who were Bill Medley and Bobby Hatfield better known as?

2 Which comedian hosted the TV programme *Bullseye*?

3 What kind of animal stars in the film *Babe*?

4 Which group from Edinburgh had a hit with 'Bye Bye Baby'?

5 Who played 'Jim Rockford' in TV's *The Rockford Files*?

6 Which two actors play the lead roles in the film *Sleepless in Seattle*?

7 Whose 'design for life' got them to number two?

8 Who sang the theme to the film *What's New Pussycat?*?

9 Calista Flockhart stars in which American TV comedy series?

10 What was Robert Palmer addicted to in May 1986?

11 Who was the director of the comedy film *Blazing Saddles*?

12 Which nationality was the composer Franz Joseph Haydn?

13 Which TV comedy programme features rebellious residents in a home for the elderly?

14 Who plays the title role in the film *The Godfather*?

15 Which group had a hit with 'He Ain't Heavy He's My Brother'?

1. The Righteous Brothers. 2. Jim Bowen. 3. A pig. 4. The Bay City Rollers. 5. James Garner. 6. Tom Hanks and Meg Ryan. 7. 'Manic Street Preachers'. 8. Tom Jones. 9. *Ally McBeal*. 10. Love. 11. Mel Brooks. 12. Austrian. 13. *Waiting For God*. 14. Marlon Brando. 15. The Hollies.

HISTORY

1   The Battles of Lansdown, Roundway Down, Newbury and Langport were all fought during which war?

2   Who, according to a popular story, hid in an oak tree to escape from his pursuers?

3   Prince George of Denmark was the husband of which British queen?

4   Grigori Potemkin was the lover and minister of which Russian ruler?

5   Whom did Napoleon defeat at the Battle of Jena in 1806?

6   The 'Kaffir Wars' were fought in which country?

7   John Nash was the favourite architect of which British king?

8   Claude Monet, the French impressionist painter, and Auguste Rodin, the sculptor, were both born in the same year. Which year was it?

9   In which year was President Abraham Lincoln assassinated?

10 Who assassinated him?

11 In which year did Russian sailors mutiny aboard the battleship *Potemkin*?

12 Joseph Pilsudski was a prime minister of which country during the 1920s?

13 Which German battleship was involved in the Battle of the River Plate early in World War II?

14 What was the name of Adolf Hitler's mistress, whom he married shortly before committing suicide in 1945?

15 Patrice Lumumba became prime minister of which newly independent African country in 1960?

ANSWERS

1. The English Civil War. 2. King Charles II. 3. Queen Anne. 4. The Empress Catherine the Great (Catherine II). 5. The Prussians. 6. South Africa (between white settlers and native peoples). 7. George IV. 8. 1840. 9. 1865. 10. John Wilkes Booth. 11. 1905. 12. Poland. 13. *The Graf Spee*. 14. Eva Braun. 15. The Congo.

FAMOUS PEOPLE

1   Who invented the pneumatic tyre in 1887?

2   Who was the world's first freely elected Marxist president?

3   Who has contested the most elections or by-elections to the British House of Commons?

4   Whose last words were, 'All my possessions for a moment of time'?

5   Which royal widow died in March 1953 aged 85?

6   What position did Dag Hammarskjöld hold from 1953 until his death in a plane crash in 1961?

7   Who was the second man on the Moon?

8   Which 20th century architect, born in Germany, head of the Bauhaus, built a successful career designing skyscrapers in America?

9   Who was the first actor to become a Lord in 1970?

10 Who was the director of the US Federal Bureau of Investigation from 1924 to 1972?

11 Who designed the first successful helicopter in 1939?

12 Whose right ear was cut off by kidnappers in 1973?

13 Which US ecologist drew public attention to the dangers of pesticides in her book *Silent Spring*?

14 Which German physician discovered the bacteria that cause tuberculosis and cholera?

15 Who described the poet Byron as 'Mad, bad and dangerous to know'?

ANSWERS

1. John Dunlop. 2. Salvator Allende Gossens of Chile. 3. Screaming Lord Sutch of the Official Monster Raving Loony Party. 4. Queen Elizabeth I. 5. Queen Mary, widow of George V. 6. Secretary General of the United Nations. 7. Edwin 'Buzz' Aldrin. 8. Mies van der Rohe. 9. Laurence Olivier became Lord Olivier of Brighton. 10. John Edgar Hoover. 11. Igor Sikorsky. 12. John Paul Getty III. 13. Rachel Carson. 14. Robert Koch. 15. Lady Caroline Lamb.

SPORT & LEISURE

1   What sport does Laura Davies play?

2   'Gully', 'silly point' and 'third man' are all positions in which sport?

3   What is the name of Bristol City Football Club's home ground?

4   Who was the first unseeded player to win the men's singles title at Wimbledon?

5   If you were being trained by Emanuel Steward, what sport would you be competing in?

6   How many players are there on each side in a game of Olympic beach volleyball?

7   Where does the hooker stand for a scrum in Rugby Union?

8   Sensini, Roa and Veron played for what team in the 1998 Football World Cup?

9   How many times does an athlete have to run round an Olympic track in an 800 metre race?

10 In which year was table tennis made an Olympic sport?

11 How many times did the San Francisco 49ers win the Super Bowl in the 1980s?

12 Which race course is the home of the 'St Leger'?

13 In what country is the NHL the national Ice Hockey League?

14 What game is Nigel Short famous for?

15 From where did Newcastle United buy England International Robert Lee?

GENERAL KNOWLEDGE

1   What are you doing if you 'pull the wool over someone's eyes'?

2   If a picture is painted 'monochromatically', how is it painted?

3   What word do we get from Ambrose Everett Burnside, referring to our hair?

4   In his fable *The Jay and the Peacock,* who wrote, 'It is not only fine feathers that make fine birds'?

5   What does 'long in the tooth mean'?

6   Which type of meat is correctly used to make Wiener Schnitzel?

7   What is sold by a 'costermonger'?

8   From which language do the words 'caviar', 'kaftan' and 'kiosk' originate?

9   What is the name of the Muslim's annual month of fasting?

10   'Hey diddle diddle, the cat and the fiddle, the...' Finish the line of this nursery rhyme.

11   What kind of soup is bouillabaisse?

12   How many vowels are there in the Greek alphabet?

13   What do you do when you 'twist someone's arm'?

14   What kind of region does 'tundra' describe?

15   According to the proverb, what should not be washed in public?

1. Deceiving or tricking someone. 2. In black and white, in one colour or different shades of one colour. 3. Sideburns. 4. Aesop. 5. Getting old. 6. Veal. 7. Fruit and/or vegetables. 8. Turkish. 9. Ramadan. 10. '...cow jumped over the moon'. 11. Fish. 12. 7. 13. Persuade someone to do something. 14. Rolling, treeless plain of arctic region (particularly Russia). 15. Dirty linen.

SCIENCE & NATURE

1 Which Swedish chemist invented dynamite?

2 What are the tiny air sacs in the lungs called?

3 What is the unit of electrical conductance?

4 What does RNA stand for?

5 Which small metallic fastener was invented by the US inventor Walter Hunt?

6 How often does Neptune orbit the Sun (approximately)?

7 What does *aqua regia* (which can dissolve gold) contain?

8 What does the Internet domain '.edu' in an e-mail address specify?

9 Who invented the aqualung?

10 Of which animal is the chicken a domesticated form?

11 What is a henry?

12 What is the lightest metal?

13 What is a perfect number?

14 What is a plasmid?

15 What is a bubble chamber?

ENTERTAINMENT

1   Which role does Anthony Hopkins play in the film
    The Silence of the Lambs?

2   What nationality was the composer Bizet?

3   Who wrote the books on which the TV series *Inspector Morse*
    are based ?

4   Which father and daughter appeared in the film *On Golden Pond*?

5   Who starred in the film *Yankee Doodle Dandy*?

6   With whom is the catchphrase 'Hullo, good evening and
    welcome' associated?

7   In 1981, 'My Mum Is One In A Million' got into the top 30.
    Who performed it?

8   Who played the title role in the film *Lawrence of Arabia*?

9   'Ebony and Ivory' was a hit for which two singers?

10 In which year did the programme *Mastermind* first appear
    on television?

11 Mark Morrison got to number one in March 1996 with
    which song?

12 Who was the leader of the gang in the Ealing comedy
    The Lavender Hill Mob?

13 Which famous TV doctor did Tom Baker and Jon Pertwee play?

14 Who starred in the TV series *Lovejoy*?

15 In the film *The Good, The Bad and The Ugly*, Lee Van Cleef was
    'Bad', Eli Wallach was 'Ugly', who was 'Good'?

ANSWERS

1. 'Dr Hannibal Lecter'. 2. French. 3. Colin Dexter. 4. Henry and Jane Fonda.
5. James Cagney. 6. David Frost. 7. The Children of Tansley School. 8. Peter O'Toole.
9. Paul McCartney and Stevie Wonder. 10. 1972. 11. 'Return of the Mack'.
12. Alec Guinness. 13. Dr Who. 14. Ian McShane. 15. Clint Eastwood.

HISTORY

1 Who was murdered in 1916 by being shot and then thrown into the River Neva?

2 Who was prime minister of Russia from July 1917 until the Bolshevik Revolution?

3 In which year did Bonar Law succeed Lloyd George as prime minister of Great Britain?

4 In which year did Emperor Hirohito of Japan come to the throne?

5 What happened to Leon Trotsky in 1927?

6 Who was president of the United States in 1930?

7 Which country did Japan invade in 1931?

8 Which British battleship was sunk in Scapa Flow in 1939?

9 In which year was the island of Malta awarded the George Cross?

10 Where did F. D. Roosevelt, Stalin and Winston Churchill meet for a conference in 1943?

11 Who became British Chancellor of the Exchequer in 1947?

12 In which year did Sir Anthony Eden become prime minister of Great Britain?

13 In which year did the 'Cuban missile crisis' take place?

14 Who succeeded Anwar Sadat as president of Egypt in 1981?

15 Daniel Ortega became president of which Central American country in 1985?

FAMOUS PEOPLE

1   Who patented his internal combustion engine in 1892?

2   Who was assassinated with an ice-pick on Stalin's orders in 1940?

3   Who was the oldest British prime minister?

4   Who claimed that 'History is bunk'?

5   Who is said to have continued to play bowls when the Spanish Armada was sighted in 1588?

6   Who considered in 1943 that, 'There is no finer investment for any community than putting milk into babies'?

7   Who was the American vice president from 1969 until 1973, when he resigned because of charges of income tax evasion?

8   Who was emperor of Ethiopia for 58 years until he was deposed in 1974?

9   In which year did Margaret Thatcher become leader of the Conservative Party?

10   What name did cinema fans choose when MGM ran a contest to rename their new star, Lucille le Sueur?

11   Why did Louise Brown become famous in 1978?

12   Which 20th century pope had the shortest reign?

13   Which French feminist, associated with Jean-Paul Sartre, wrote *The Second Sex* in 1953?

14   What nationality was King Edward VII's wife, Queen Alexandra?

15   Which architect's designs include the Albert Memorial and St Pancras station?

ANSWERS

1. Rudolph Diesel. 2. Leon Trotsky. 3. William Gladstone, who was 84 when he left office. 4. Henry Ford. 5. Sir Francis Drake. 6. Winston Churchill. 7. Spiro T. Agnew. 8. Haile Selassie. 9. 1975. 10. Joan Crawford. 11. She was the first 'test-tube' baby. 12. John Paul I reigned for just one month in 1978. 13. Simone de Beauvoir. 14. Danish. 15. Sir George Gilbert Scott.

SPORT & LEISURE

1   If you were at the Augusta National Club, what sport would you be watching?

2   Who did cricketer Graham Gooch score 333 runs against in 1990?

3   Has Ivan Lendl ever won Wimbledon?

4   Who was the captain of England's football team that won the World Cup in 1966?

5   With what racing team did James Hunt win the Formula 1 World Championship?

6   How many points do you need in chess to become a 'Grand Master'?

7   What does the word Karate mean?

8   Who did Everton beat in the 1984 FA Cup Final?

9   In 1990, the San Francisco 49ers achieved the highest score ever in a Super Bowl. Who was it against?

10   Who won three Olympic long jump gold medals in a row?

11   Michael Chang is the youngest tennis player to win which Grand Slam event?

12   In gymnastics men use the horizontal bar. What is the female equivalent?

13   With which sport do you associate Greg LeMand?

14   Where was the 1970 Football World Cup held?

15   What sport and leisure activity is the film *Kingpin* about?

ANSWERS

1. Golf. 2. India. 3. No. 4. Bobby Moore. 5. McLaren. 6. 2,500 points. 7. Empty hand. 8. Watford. 9. Denver Broncos. 10. Carl Lewis. 11. French Open. 12. The asymmetric bars. 13. Cycling. 14. Mexico. 15. Ten Pin Bowling.

GENERAL KNOWLEDGE

1   What flavour is Crème de Menthe?

2   'Goosey goosey gander, Whither shall I wander, Upstairs and downstairs, And in...' Finish the line of this nursery rhyme.

3   What do we commonly call the thyroid cartilage in the neck when it is particularly prominent in men?

4   What is a 'laptop'?

5   During World War II, which vegetable did the Ministry of Food encourage people to eat to help them see in the dark?

6   What kind of food is gazpacho?

7   Who wrote the fable from which the term 'cry wolf' comes?

8   What does a 'cartographer' draw?

9   From what main ingredients is bubble and squeak usually made?

10 What is the familiar name of the medallion awarded annually for distinguished achievement in American theatre, named after the actress Antoinette Perry?

11 According to the proverb, what is as good as a feast?

12 What is Adam's Ale?

13 Which of Shakespeare's plays involves a pound of flesh?

14 Of what is 'Meaux' a type?

15 What is the capital of Algeria?

ANSWERS

1. Peppermint. 2. 'My lady's chamber'. 3. Adam's apple. 4. Portable computer. 5. Carrots. 6. Soup (cold). 7. Aesop. 8. Maps. 9. Boiled cabbage, potatoes and sometimes meat. 10. 'Tony'. 11. Enough. 12. Water. 13. *The Merchant of Venice*. 14. Mustard. 15. Algiers.

SCIENCE & NATURE

1   Where is the natural home of the world's lemurs?

2   Which famous scientist formulated the theory of relativity?

3   What is a bobolink?

4   How is 32 expressed as a binary number?

5   What dietary deficiency causes simple goitre?

6   What are the chemical symbols for the elements gold and silver?

7   Which vitamin is required in blood clotting?

8   If you came across the abbreviation BTW in an e-mail message what would it mean?

9   What is a buttonball?

10   What is the name of the orange food colour with E number 102?

11   Where in the human body would you find the thalamus gland?

12   Which two scientists shared the Nobel Prize with Alexander Fleming for their work on penicillin?

13   In what way is the axolotl (a type of salamander) unusual?

14   What do histologists study?

15   What type of bird is a sawbill?

1. Madagascar and surrounding islands. 2. Albert Einstein. 3. A type of songbird from America. 4. 00100000. 5. Iodine. 6. Au and Ag. 7. Vitamin K. 8. By the way. 9. An American plane tree. 10. Tartrazine. 11. Front of the brain. 12. Howard Florey and Ernst Chain. 13. Under normal conditions, it stays in its larval form throughout its life. 14. Animal and plant tissue. 15. A humming bird.

ENTERTAINMENT

1   Who played the title role in the TV series *The Equalizer*?

2   Who plays the mermaid in the film *Splash*?

3   Who composed 'Rhapsody in Blue'?

4   'Mrs Mangel' was a character in which TV soap?

5   Who plays the title role in the film *Alfie*?

6   Annie Lennox had a hit with 'No More I Love You's'. Who reached number 58 with this same song in August 1986?

7   The 'E Street Band' appeared with which singer?

8   'Officer Dibble' was a character in which cartoon series?

9   Who was frontman for 'The Bad Seeds'?

10 In which sixties sci-fi movie did 'Duran Duran' find their name?

11 Who sang the theme to the film *9 to 5*?

12 What was the original title of *Gardeners' Question Time*?

13 Which comedians appeared in the films *The Intelligence Men*, *That Riviera Touch* and *The Magnificent Two*?

14 What does the musical term 'pizzicato' mean?

15 *Coronation Street* is based on an idea by whom ?

1. Edward Woodward. 2. Daryl Hannah. 3. George Gershwin. 4. *Neighbours*.
5. Michael Caine. 6. 'The Lover Speaks'. 7. Bruce Springsteen. 8. *Top Cat*. 9. Nick
Cave. 10. *Barbarella*. 11. Dolly Parton. 12. *How Does Your Garden Grow?*
13. Morecambe and Wise. 14. Plucked. 15. Tony Warren.

HISTORY

1　Where did King Charles I raise his standard at the beginning of the English Civil War?

2　On which side did the third Earl of Essex fight in the English Civil War?

3　As what did Prince Rupert of the Rhine become famous during the English Civil War?

4　What relation was Prince Rupert of the Rhine to King Charles I?

5　How many battles were fought at Newbury during the English Civil War?

6　Where was King Charles I's headquarters during most of the Civil War?

7　What was the name of the cavalry regiment raised and trained by Oliver Cromwell?

8　To whom did King Charles I surrender at Newark in 1646?

9　Where on the Isle of Wight was King Charles I imprisoned before his trial?

10　In which year was King Charles I beheaded?

11　'Stone walls do not a prison make/Nor iron bars a cage' are lines written by which Cavalier poet imprisoned during the Civil War?

12　Where was Charles II crowned king on 1 January 1651?

13　Where did Oliver Cromwell decisively defeat Charles II's forces later in 1651?

14　Who was Latin secretary to the council of state of England from 1649 to 1660?

15　Which parliamentary general played a large part in negotiating the restoration of King Charles II in 1660?

1. Nottingham. 2. The side of parliament (he was commander of the parliamentary army at the beginning of the war). 3. A cavalry commander. 4. His nephew. 5. Two. 6. At Oxford. 7. The Ironsides. 8. The Scots. 9. Carisbrooke Castle. 10. 1649. 11. Richard Lovelace. 12. At Scone in Scotland. 13. At the Battle of Worcester. 14. John Milton. 15. George Monck.

FAMOUS PEOPLE

1 Who was British prime minister when Queen Victoria came to the throne?

2 In the Bible, who betrayed Jesus Christ?

3 What did Thomas Chippendale become famous for?

4 Who assassinated President Abraham Lincoln?

5 By what name is Isabella Mayson better known?

6 Who composed the oratorio *The Creation*?

7 Who wrote *Ivanhoe*?

8 Which Canadian-born newspaper magnate became proprietor of the *Daily Express* in 1919?

9 Which English artist produced a series of engravings depicting *A Rake's Progress*?

10 Who was the first Hanoverian king of Great Britain and Ireland?

11 Who remained in the command module when Armstrong and Aldrin landed on the Moon in 1969?

12 Who was known as 'The Empress of the Blues'?

13 Which Portuguese navigator discovered the southernmost point of Africa at the Cape of Good Hope?

14 Who wrote the poems published as *Cautionary Tales*?

15 Who modelled the bronze lions at the base of Nelson's Column?

1. Viscount Melbourne (William Lamb). 2. Judas Iscariot. 3. Furniture design (especially chairs). 4. John Wilkes Booth. 5. Mrs Beeton. 6. Haydn. 7. Sir Walter Scott. 8. Lord Beaverbrook (Max Aitken). 9. William Hogarth. 10. George I. 11. Michael Collins. 12. Bessie Smith. 13. (Bartholomeu) Dias (or Diaz). 14. Hilaire Belloc. 15. Edwin Landseer.

SPORT & LEISURE

1   If you were watching the 'Addicks', what football team would you be watching?

2   When did Alain Prost retire from competing in Formula 1 racing?

3   Can a catch in cricket be taken after hitting only the glove of the batsman?

4   Fanny Sunsesson was the well known caddie for what golfer?

5   How many times have Italy won the football World Cup?

6   In what year did Linford Christie win the 100 metres Olympic gold medal?

7   Who recorded the fastest tennis serve by hitting the ball at 149 mph in March 1998?

8   How many games did American football's Tampa Bay Buccaneers lose in a row during the season 1976–77?

9   What team did Robbie Earle play for in the 1998 Football World Cup Final?

10 Who won the Formula 1 World Title in 1982?

11 How many minutes is a game of rugby?

12 In what sport do you compete for the Lonsdale Belt?

13 From what football club did Tottenham Hotspur sign Darren Anderton?

14 With which sport is John McCririck involved?

15 'Traversing' is a term from what sport and leisure activity?

GENERAL KNOWLEDGE

1   What does 'heterogeneous' mean?

2   In which country would you take a holiday in Paphos?

3   Whose name is remembered for the closure of many British railway lines in the 1960s?

4   In which book of the Bible are the Ten Commandments first listed?

5   What does 'donkey's years' mean?

6   At least once in their lives, Muslims must try to make a pilgrimage to which holy city?

7   In the 1997 film *Titanic* who starred with Leonardo DiCaprio?

8   Of what is 'choux' a type?

9   Who was the sole prisoner in a German jail for 21 years?

10 Proverbially, who should we not teach to suck eggs?

11 In 1869 which major engineering feat linking two seas was opened?

12 Which novelist wrote *Tinker, Tailor, Soldier, Spy*?

13 What were accidentally discovered in some jars in Jordan in 1947?

14 In the nursery rhyme 'Georgie Porgie, pudding and pie', when did Georgie Porgie run away?

15 In which year did Kellog's launch their cereal product 'Rice Krispies'?

ANSWERS

1. Varied, consisting of unlike people or things. 2. Cyprus. 3. Richard Beeching. 4. Exodus. 5. A long time. 6. Mecca. 7. Kate Winslet. 8. Pastry. 9. Rudolf Hess. 10. Grandmother. 11. The Suez Canal. 12. John le Carré. 13. The Dead Sea Scrolls. 14. When the boys came out to play. 15. 1929.

SCIENCE & NATURE

1 What is the name given to the wide expanse of coral located off the coast of Australia?

2 What do carnivores eat?

3 Where was the Royal Greenwich Observatory moved to after World War II?

4 Which was the first rare earth element to be discovered?

5 What is a coniscope used to measure?

6 To which family do the apple and plum belong?

7 In computer terms what does the abbreviation DVD represent?

8 What is the largest classification order in the animal kingdom?

9 What is the technical term for the tear glands?

10 During which period did dinosaurs flourish?

11 For what is Albert Bruce Sabin famous?

12 By what name is the largest of the dark plains on the Moon known?

13 Which scientist wrote *The Sceptical Chymist*, produced in 1661?

14 What is phyllite?

15 What was the name of the communications satellite launched in 1965?

1. The Great Barrier Reef. 2. Meat. 3. Herstmonceux, Sussex. 4. Lanthanum. 5. Dust. 6. Rosaceae family including roses. 7. Digital video/versatile disc. 8. Beetles. 9. Lachrymal glands. 10. Jurassic. 11. The Sabin vaccine against polio(myelitis). 12. 'Ocean of Storms'. 13. Robert Boyle. 14. Rock that is rich in mica. 15. *Early Bird*.

ENTERTAINMENT

1   'If I Ruled The World' is a song from which musical?

2   Who played 'Rambling Syd Rumpo' in the radio programme *Round The Horne*?

3   Which singer starred with Kevin Costner in the film *The Bodyguard?*

4   Noddy Holder was a vocalist with which group?

5   Sharon Gless and Tyne Daly starred in which TV series?

6   Who was having a 'Garden Party' in June 1983?

7   Which couple starred in the 1965 film *Born Free*?

8   Who is the male vocalist in Hot Chocolate?

9   What is the name of the brewery that supplies the 'Rovers Return' in *Coronation Street*?

10 Who played George III in the film *The Madness of King George*?

11 Who featured in the movie *Breaking Glass* and went to number eight with the single 'Will You?' from the film's soundtrack ?

12 Brian, Dennis and Carl Wilson, Mike Love and Al Jardine formed which group?

13 The phrase 'Gi's a Job' comes from which TV programme?

14 Who plays 'Oskar Schindler' in the film *Schindler's List*?

15 Which instrument did Dizzy Gillespie play?

1. *Pickwick*. 2. Kenneth Williams. 3. Whitney Houston. 4. Slade. 5. *Cagney and Lacey*. 6. Marillion. 7. Virginia McKenna and Bill Travers. 8. Errol Brown. 9. 'Newton and Ridley'. 10. Nigel Hawthorne. 11. Hazel O'Connor. 12. The Beach Boys. 13. *The Boys From The Blackstuff*. 14. Liam Neeson. 15. Trumpet.

HISTORY

1 For her activities in what field is Selina, Countess of Huntingdon (1707–91) famous?

2 Which of the following aristocrats was twice briefly prime minister of Great Britain during the second half of the 18th century? The Earl of Bute, Lord North, the Marquis of Rockingham, the Duke of Portland?

3 What did John Montagu, 4th Earl of Sandwich invent?

4 Which 18th century ambassador's wife was noted as a travel writer and society hostess, besides quarrelling with poet Alexander Pope?

5 Which king of Britain was Duke of Clarence until his brother's death brought him to the throne?

6 Lord Raglan was commander-in-chief of British forces in which war?

7 Who unsuccessfully sued the 8th Marquess of Queensberry for libel in 1895?

8 Who was the 8th Marquess of Queensberry's poet son?

9 Lord Gort, Lord Howe, and Lord Roberts all at various times held what position?

10 Who was prime minister of Great Britain at the outbreak of the Crimean War?

11 Who became leader of the British Conservative party after the death of Disraeli (and subsequently prime minister)?

12 What was the title of the future King George VI before he became king through his brother's abdication?

13 How was William Joyce better known to British radio listeners during World War II?

14 The former Lord Stansgate has been known through most of his political career by what name?

15 In which year did Lord Lucan disappear after allegedly murdering his children's nanny in mistake for his wife?

FAMOUS PEOPLE

1   Who had a 'very fine cat' called Hodge?

2   What was Lancelot Brown's nickname?

3   Whose influential book *The Wealth of Nations* was published in 1776?

4   Who wrote the *'Unfinished' Symphony*?

5   Which king founded Eton College?

6   Which legendary cat owner became mayor of London in 1397?

7   Who led the Mormons to Utah and founded Salt Lake City?

8   Which king did William Rufus succeed?

9   Whose plays include *The Crucible* and *A View from the Bridge*?

10 What kind of objects did Thomas Tompion design?

11 Which monk exercised great influence over the Russian empress Alexandra?

12 Which 18th century English novelist was also a founder of the Bow Street Runners?

13 Who wrote *The Beggar's Opera*?

14 Who invented the spinning jenny?

15 Who was the notorious partner of Bonnie Parker?

ANSWERS

1. Dr Samuel Johnson. 2. Capability. 3. Adam Smith. 4. Schubert. 5. Henry VI. 6. Richard (Dick) Whittington. 7. Brigham Young. 8. William I (the Conqueror). 9. Arthur Miller. 10. Clocks (and watches). 11. Rasputin. 12. Henry Fielding. 13. John Gay. 14. James Hargreaves. 15. Clyde Barrow.

SPORT & LEISURE

1   Who is the chairman of Leyton Orient Football Club?

2   If a cricket umpire holds both arms straight up in the air, what is he indicating?

3   How many times in the 1980s did Severiano Ballesteros win the US Masters Golf?

4   If you were at Goodwood, what sport would you be watching?

5   When was the first Rugby Union World Cup held?

6   Who won the 1900 FA Cup Final?

7   How many times did Chuck Noll win the Super Bowl as the manager of the Pittsburgh Steelers?

8   If you were receiving a coaching lesson from David Leadbetter, what sport would you be attempting to play?

9   As well as Chris Waddle, who was the other player to miss a penalty in the 1990 football World Cup semi final?

10 What is the name of Damon Hill's famous father?

11 Who won the 1980 Snooker World title?

12 How many times have France won the football World Cup?

13 If a fielder stops a cricket ball with a cap, helmet or jumper, how many runs does he concede?

14 What is the shape of an Australian Rules football pitch?

15 Which Scottish football club did Danish International Brian Laudrup play for?

1. Barry Hearn. 2. Six runs scored. 3. Twice (1980 and 1983). 4. Horse racing. 5. 1987. 6. Bury. 7. Four times. 8. Golf. 9. Stuart Pearce. 10. Graham Hill. 11. Cliff Thorburn. 12. Once (1998). 13. Five runs. 14. An oval. 15. Glasgow Rangers.

GENERAL KNOWLEDGE

1   In the nursery rhyme, who tried to put 'Humpty Dumpty' together again?

2   Which herb also gives its name to a wise teacher, deeply respected for his experience and judgment?

3   Who was the first chancellor of the German Empire?

4   What is the English word for an American hobo?

5   Where are you living if you are living in 'cloud cuckoo land'?

6   To which French art movement did the artist Monet belong?

7   What is the name of the most massive tree in the world?

8   In the Bible, in the book of Genesis what did God create on the fifth day?

9   In which children's comic does 'Dennis the Menace' feature?

10   How many vowels altogether are there in the Russian alphabet?

11   In which year did the 'Great Train Robbery' take place?

12   Whose last words were, 'Get my swan costume ready'?

13   For which traditional dish is 'pilau' an accompaniment?

14   How many 'tarsal' bones do we have in each foot?

15   What are the surnames of 'Romeo' and 'Juliet' in Shakespeare's play *Romeo and Juliet*?

1. All the king's horses and all the king's men'. 2. Sage. 3. Otto von Bismarck. 4. Tramp. 5. An imaginary fantasy world. 6. Impressionism. 7. Giant Sequoia. 8. Animal life in the sea and air. 9. *The Beano*. 10. Ten. 11. 1963. 12. Anna Pavlova, the Russian ballerina. 13. Curry (pilau rice). 14. 7. 15. 'Montague' and 'Capulet'.

SCIENCE & NATURE

1 What is a rockhopper?

2 What is the common name for the astronomical phenomenon known as the *aurora borealis*?

3 Two units of measurement have the abbreviation 'nm', what is one of them?

4 Where is the deltoid muscle?

5 What is the difference between an isobar and an isotherm?

6 What is a nidifugous bird?

7 In computing, what is FORTRAN a contraction of?

8 Which colourless poisonous gas with a smell like geraniums was used in chemical warfare during World War II?

9 In what year did man first land on the Moon?

10 When was the dental drill invented?

11 What is the chemical formula for caustic soda?

12 Isaac Newton published several scientific works; which is considered his greatest?

13 What is a fumarole?

14 What do edentulous mammals lack?

15 What is a Reynolds number used to measure?

ENTERTAINMENT

1 Who played 'Edward' in TV's *Edward and Mrs Simpson*?

2 Who won an Oscar for her role in the 1990 film *Ghost*?

3 Which group had a hit with 'Lily The Pink'?

4 What was the name of the programme that was a spin-off of *Upstairs, Downstairs*?

5 In the 1991 film *Father of the Bride*, who played the title role?

6 'Shakin' All Over' was a hit for which group?

7 Jimmy Edwards played the headmaster in which children's TV comedy series?

8 Ian McNabb, whose career was revived in the 90s, was the frontman for which 80s pop group?

9 Who plays 'Cruella De Vil' in the 1996 version of the film *101 Dalmatians*?

10 Don McLean had a hit with 'American Pie', based on the death of which singer?

11 Which TV puppet celebrated its 50th birthday in 1998?

12 Laurie Anderson had approximately 8 minutes and 21 seconds of a top ten hit in October 1981. Name that track.

13 Who plays the title role in the film *Private Benjamin*?

14 Which group produced the albums 'Aftermath', 'Beggars Banquet' and 'Exile on Main Street'?

15 What was the occupation of Mr Dale in the radio programme *Mrs Dale's Diary*?

ANSWERS

1. Edward Fox. 2. Whoopi Goldberg. 3. Scaffold. 4. *Thomas and Sarah*. 5. Steve Martin. 6. 'Johnny Kidd and The Pirates'. 7. *Whacko*. 8. 'The Icicle Works'. 9. Glenn Close. 10. Buddy Holly. 11. 'Sooty'. 12. 'O Superman'. 13. Goldie Hawn. 14. The Rolling Stones. 15. Doctor.

HISTORY

1 In which century was the National Debt established in England?
2 Which English financial institution was founded in 1694?
3 Which famous mathematician was appointed warden of the Royal Mint in 1696 and became master of the mint in 1699?
4 What burst on the London stock exchange in the year 1720?
5 Which Scottish financier lived part of his life in France, produced a project for a French national bank that was approved in 1718, then almost bankrupted his adopted country with a scheme to reclaim and settle lands by the Mississippi?
6 Who formulated the 'law' of finance that is usually given as 'bad money drives out good money'?
7 Which major work of economic theory was published in 1776 by Adam Smith?
8 What was introduced in the United States in 1787 and minted for the first time in 1792?
9 The British branch of which European banking house was founded in London in 1805?
10 Was income tax first imposed in Great Britain in 1699, 1799 or 1899?
11 Which famous British economist resigned from the Treasury in 1919 because of his opposition to the economic terms of the Treaty of Versailles?
12 Where was the United Nations Monetary and Financial Conference held in 1944?
13 Which two international institutions were set up following the United Nations Monetary and Financial Conference?
14 Which American advocate of free market forces and monetarism was awarded the Nobel prize for economics in 1976?
15 In which year was Britain forced to leave the European Exchange Rate Mechanism (ERM) following massive speculation against the pound?

ANSWERS

1. The 17th century. 2. The Bank of England. 3. Sir Isaac Newton. 4. The South Sea Bubble (a period of frenzied speculation in stocks and shares, centred on the South Sea Company, that ended in a financial crash). 5. John Law. 6. Sir Thomas Gresham (1519–79), the founder of the Royal Exchange. 7. The Wealth of Nations'. 8. A coinage based on the dollar. 9. Rothschild's. 10. 1799. 11. J. M. Keynes. 12. Bretton Woods, New Hampshire. 13. The International Monetary Fund and the World Bank (International Bank for Reconstruction and Development). 14. Milton Friedman. 15. 1992.

FAMOUS PEOPLE

1   What was the profession of Auguste Escoffier?

2   What religious sect was founded by 'Mother' Ann Lee?

3   With what decorative form of art was Grinling Gibbons principally associated?

4   Which king allegedly sat on the shore in front of a rising tide, to demonstrate to his followers that he could control the waves?

5   What was William Bonney's nickname?

6   Who gave the name of 'Etruria' to his pottery works?

7   Which clergyman wrote the famous hymn 'Rock of Ages'?

8   Who composed the marches *Stars and Stripes* and *Liberty Belle*?

9   Whose novels include *Sense and Sensibility*, *Mansfield Park*, and *Persuasion*?

10 Who invented the locomotive called the *Rocket*?

11 Who was the first Englishman to sail round the world?

12 Who was the original illustrator of *Alice's Adventures in Wonderland* and *Through the Looking Glass*?

13 In what area of social reform was John Howard involved?

14 Who, in 1799, settled in Dove Cottage, Grasmere with her poet brother?

15 What was the name of the Confederate general who surrendered to General Grant in April 1865?

ANSWERS

1. Chef. 2. The Shakers. 3. Wood carving. 4. Canute. 5. 'Billy the Kid'. 6. Josiah Wedgwood. 7. Reverend Augustus Toplady. 8. John Philip Sousa. 9. Jane Austen. 10. George Stephenson. 11. Francis Drake. 12. (Sir John) Tenniel. 13. Prison conditions. 14. Dorothy Wordsworth. 15. Robert E. Lee.

SPORT & LEISURE

1   What sport do Roger Clements and Pedro Martinez play?

2   What is the height of a badminton net?

3   Who won the 1976–77 Le Mans race in France?

4   What international team did footballer Vinny Jones captain?

5   What sport is played at Wentworth, Sunningdale and Turnberry?

6   With which Formula 1 team do you associate Ron Dennis?

7   How many Wimbledon titles did Billie Jean King win between 1961 and 1979?

8   Between both teams, how many times have the San Francisco 49ers and the Dallas Cowboys won the Super Bowl (until 1998)?

9   Who won the FA Cup in 1968?

10 What implement do competitors pass on in a relay race?

11 What country does chess player Gary Kasparov come from?

12 Dr James Naismith is responsible for creating the modern version of what sport?

13 Who did Australia beat in the final of the 1991 Rugby Union World Cup?

14 Which football team has the nickname 'The Villains'?

15 In which sport did Lloyd Honeyghan formerly compete?

1. Baseball. 2. One and a half metres (five feet). 3. Porsche. 4. Wales. 5. Golf. 6. McLaren. 7. Twenty. 8. Ten. 9. West Bromwich Albion. 10. A baton. 11. Russia. 12. Basketball. 13. England. 14. Aston Villa. 15. Boxing.

GENERAL KNOWLEDGE

1 What kind of seafood are 'Moules à la Marinière'?

2 'Hickory dickory dock, The mouse ran up the clock, The clock struck...' What did the clock strike?

3 In which year did the Battle of Agincourt take place?

4 What two types of 'palate' are there in the mouth?

5 According to the proverb, at what will a drowning man clutch?

6 What is the American word for a fringe (of hair)?

7 Who was the leader of the 'Free French' forces during World War II?

8 What colour is angelica?

9 What six parts of the body must a Muslim wash before they pray?

10 According to Benjamin Franklin, what makes a man healthy, wealthy and wise?

11 What is the special name for the caller who calls people to prayer from the top of a mosque in Muslim countries?

12 The famous 'To be or not to be' speech is in which Shakespeare play?

13 What is the English word for an American 'sedan'?

14 Who invented the pneumatic bicycle tyre in 1888?

15 What does to 'get someone's goat' mean?

1. Mussels. 2. One. 3. 1415. 4. Soft and hard palates. 5. A straw. 6. Bangs. 7. Charles de Gaulle. 8. Green. 9. Wash their hands, face, head, arms, legs and feet. 10. Early to bed and early to rise. 11. Muezzin. 12. *Hamlet*. 13. Saloon (car). 14. John Dunlop. 15. To annoy or irritate someone.

SCIENCE & NATURE

1   Snowy, tawny and barn are examples of which creatures?

2   What name is given to a male swan?

3   What was John Napier's famous invention?

4   Where would you find a synapse?

5   What is the origin of the word tulip?

6   The letters 'http' usually precede the address of a web site; what are these letters an abbreviation for?

7   What was the name of the first Space Shuttle and when was it launched?

8   Why is Wallace Carothers famous?

9   What is pinchbeck?

10 Which mother and daughter won Nobel prizes for science?

11 What is the Mercalli scale used for?

12 How does carbon monoxide affect the body?

13 What is dendochronology?

14 How hot does it get on the Moon?

15 What is the largest active volcano?

ENTERTAINMENT

1   The Hollies were formed in 1962 in which city?

2   Which cartoon character has the catchphrase 'What's up, Doc?'?

3   Who were carrying out their own 'Private Investigations' in September 1982?

4   Who plays the title role in the film *Shirley Valentine*?

5   Which 14 year old girl had a hit in the early 1960s with 'Don't Treat Me Like A Child'?

6   The phrase 'The truth is out there' is associated with which TV programme?

7   Who plays 'Wanda' in the film *A Fish Called Wanda*?

8   Which father and daughter had a hit with 'Somethin' Stupid'?

9   Which Raymond Briggs' cartoon character is traditionally shown on television at Christmas?

10 Who starred in the film *Dead Poets Society*?

11 Lisa Loeb and Nine Stories had a top ten hit with which song in 1994?

12 Which nationality were the Swingle Singers?

13 Which poet won TV's *Opportunity Knocks* in 1975?

14 In which year did the actor Richard Burton die?

15 The talented young people from the show *Fame* live in which American city?

ANSWERS

1. Manchester. 2. 'Bugs Bunny'. 3. 'Dire Straits'. 4. Pauline Collins.
5. Helen Shapiro. 6. *X-Files*. 7. Jamie Lee Curtis. 8. Frank and Nancy Sinatra.
9. 'The Snowman'. 10. Robin Williams. 11. 'Stay (I missed you)'. 12. French.
13. Pam Ayres. 14. 1984. 15. New York.

HISTORY

1   Who was king of England in the year 1500?

2   Lima, the capital of Peru was founded in 1535. By whom?

3   Catherine Howard, Henry VIII's fifth wife, was the grand-daughter of which duke?

4   What was the connection between Catherine Howard and Henry Mannock and Thomas Culpepper?

5   Of what was Lord Howard of Effingham the commander?

6   Which famous Flemish painter was sent as an envoy to England in 1629 and made sketches for decorating a Whitehall ceiling during his visit?

7   In which year was the Guinness brewery founded in Dublin?

8   The Russians occupied and burned which city in 1760?

9   Who signed the American Declaration of Independence first?

10 In which year was the Peace of Amiens concluded between Britain and France?

11 Who wrote that 'War is the continuation of politics by other means'?

12 Which famous French author was exiled to Guernsey in 1851?

13 Which chiefs led the Native American forces that annihilated General Custer and his troops at the Battle of the Little Bighorn?

14 In which year did 'Custer's Last Stand' take place?

15 Who was British Foreign Secretary at the outbreak of World War I?

1. King Henry VII. 2. Francisco Pizarro. 3. The Duke of Norfolk. 4. A sexual one (they were accused of being her lovers) or a fatal one (all three were executed for the crime). 5. The English fleet that defeated the Spanish Armada. 6. Peter Paul Rubens. 7. 1759. 8. Berlin. 9. John Hancock (president of the Continental Congress). 10. 1802. 11. Karl von Clausewitz (1780–1831), a Prussian general and author of a book 'On War'. 12. Victor Hugo. 13. Sitting Bull and Crazy Horse. 14. 1876. 15. Sir Edward Grey (Lord Grey of Fallodon).

FAMOUS PEOPLE

1   Who created the fictional detective 'Miss Marple'?

2   Which Welsh chieftain led a revolt against Henry IV's rule in Wales ?

3   Whose name has been given to a type of portrait in which the outline profile is completely blacked-in?

4   Who wrote the hymn 'Holy, holy, holy'?

5   How is Harold Philby better known?

6   Who was the first British woman cabinet minister?

7   Which king of England was proclaimed king of France before he was one year old?

8   What did Christopher Latham Sholes invent in 1868, selling the patent to the Remington company in 1873?

9   Who wrote *The Tenant of Wildfell Hall*?

10 Who composed the *Symphony No.9 From the New World*?

11 Which artist painted the *Sistine Madonna*?

12 Which member of Captain Scott's Antarctic expedition walked out into a blizzard in the hope that his companions would be better able to reach safety without him?

13 Who instigated the first translation into English of the Bible?

14 Who was Queen Victoria's personal attendant at Balmoral for 34 years?

15 Which Quaker family founded a chocolate factory in York?

ANSWERS

1. Agatha Christie. 2. Owen Glendower. 3. Étienne de Silhouette. 4. Reginald Heber. 5. Kim Philby (Soviet spy). 6. Margaret Bondfield (1929–31). 7. Henry VI. 8. The typewriter. 9. Anne Brontë. 10. Anton Dvorak. 11. Raphael. 12. Captain Oates. 13. John Wycliffe. 14. John Brown. 15. Rowntree.

SPORT & LEISURE

1   For which country does footballer George Weah play?

2   In what sport do you use woods and irons?

3   Gerald McCellan beat Jay Bell in a world title fight during 1993. How many seconds did it last?

4   What country does sprinter Frankie Fredricks come from?

5   In Rugby it is called a try. What is the equivalent in American football?

6   Who is the third highest test wicket taker in history?

7   When did indoor volleyball become an Olympic sport?

8   Who won the FA Cup in 1961 and 1962?

9   When did Martina Navratilova win her final women's singles title at Wimbledon?

10 At what football club did Gary Lineker begin his football career?

11 In what year did Nick Faldo win both the US Masters and the Open Championship?

12 Which county cricket side has three swords on their team badge?

13 Who was the famous owner of the horse 'Indian Skimmer'?

14 Which two nations competed in the final of the 1995 Rugby Union World Cup Final?

15 What colour is the eight ball in a game of pool?

1. Liberia. 2. Golf. 3. Twenty seconds. 4. Namibia. 5. A touchdown. 6. Courtney Walsh. 7. 1964. 8. Tottenham Hotspur. 9. 1990. 10. Leicester City. 11. 1990. 12. Essex. 13. Sheikh Mohammed. 14. South Africa and New Zealand. 15. Black.

GENERAL KNOWLEDGE

1 Which two continents does the Bosphorus link?

2 What was the name of the toy spaceman in *Toy Story*?

3 Which US political party has the nickname 'Grand Old Party'?

4 Who was the author of 'The Thirty-Nine Steps'?

5 At which battle was General Custer defeated in 1876?

6 What are the three primary colours?

7 From which quiz programme does the phrase
'Your starter for 10' come?

8 Whose *Modern English Usage* was first published in 1926?

9 What is the US term for a 'big wheel'?

10 What do the initials ISA stand for?

11 In which year did President de Gaulle veto UK membership of the
European Economic Community?

12 The 'Mappa Mundi' is displayed at which English cathedral?

13 The actress Norma Jean Baker is better known as who?

14 Who is famous for his weekly *Letter from America*?

15 Where does the phrase 'a fly in the ointment' come from?

ANSWERS

1. Europe and Asia. 2. 'Buzz Lightyear'. 3. Republican Party. 4. John Buchan. 5. Little Bighorn. 6. Red, yellow and blue. 7. *University Challenge*. 8. Henry Watson Fowler. 9. A Ferris wheel. 10. Individual Savings Account. 11. 1963. 12. Hereford. 13. Marilyn Monroe. 14. Alistair Cooke. 15. The Bible, Ecclesiastes.

SCIENCE & NATURE

1 Which condition usually affecting children is characterized by a harsh cough and difficulty in breathing?

2 What is the more common name given to the Chilean pine tree?

3 In which part of the body is the brachial artery?

4 What was the first entirely computer-animated full-length feature film?

5 Who was the first British person in space?

6 Which scientific unit is the Greek letter omega a symbol for?

7 What was the philosopher's stone?

8 What chemical substance has a form known as 'plaster of Paris'?

9 What is the principal use of the element germanium?

10 Who discovered the uncertainty principle?

11 What is 'plate tectonics'?

12 What sort of creature is a natterjack?

13 What is ALGOL?

14 How cold does it get on the Moon?

15 Why do birds swallow grit?

1. Croup. 2. Monkey puzzle tree. 3. Arm. 4. *Toy Story* (1996). 5. Helen Sharman, from USA in 1991. 6. Ohm (used as a measure of resistance). 7. A hypothetical substance believed to turn base metals into gold. 8. Calcium sulphate. 9. As an electronic semi-conductor. 10. Werner Heisenberg. 11. Theory of the formation of the Earth's surface based on interaction of rigid plates moving over the underlying mantle. 12. A toad. 13. A computer programming language (*algorithmic* language). 14. Below -160 degrees C. 15. To help them grind food in their gizzard.

ENTERTAINMENT

1 What was the name of the pianist who had hits with 'Side Saddle' and 'Roulette'?

2 Which song has been a hit for The Four Tops, Gloria Gaynor and Michael Bolton?

3 What was the 'Rolling Stones' first number one hit record?

4 In which TV series did the organization 'THRUSH' appear?

5 Which was the first 'talking' film?

6 When it came to party time, where would you always find Jona Lewie?

7 Who is the host of TV's *Changing Rooms*?

8 Who played the headmaster in the film *Clockwise*?

9 Which TV police series features the character 'Greengrass'?

10 Who did Bananarama team up with on Comic Relief's 'Help' single of 1989?

11 Which Monkee had played 'Corky' in the children's TV series *Circus Boy*?

12 Who had the catchphrase 'Hullo, My Darlings'?

13 The TV series *Emmerdale* is set in which place?

14 What is the name of presenter Gloria Hunniford's daughter?

15 Who was the male lead in the film *The Graduate*?

1. Russ Conway. 2. 'Reach Out And I'll Be There'. 3. 'It's All Over Now'. 4. *The Man From U.N.C.L.E.* 5. *The Jazz Singer*. 6. 'In the kitchen'. 7. Carol Smillie. 8. John Cleese. 9. *Heartbeat*. 10. 'Lananeeneenoonoo'. 11. Mickey Dolenz. 12. Charlie Drake. 13. 'Beckindale, Yorkshire'. 14. Caron Keating. 15. Dustin Hoffman.

HISTORY

1   Malcolm Canmore, Donald Bane, William the Lion and John de Baliol were all at various times kings of which country?

2   Who defeated the army of King Henry III of England and captured his son, Prince Edward, at the Battle of Lewes in 1264?

3   What title did Edward I confer on his eldest son in 1301?

4   Who was the leader of the Peasants' Revolt in 1381?

5   What was the profession of John Ball, one of the main rebels in the Peasants Revolt?

6   According to John Ball's famous dictum, 'When Adam delved and Eve span, who was then...' what?

7   Who were 'The Princes in the Tower'?

8   Who is usually held responsible for the disappearance of the 'Princes in the Tower'?

9   Who was Catherine of Aragon's first husband?

10   The 'Pilgrimage of Grace', which took place in 1536, was a protest against what?

11   In which port did Sir Francis Drake 'singe the king of Spain's beard' by burning a large part of his fleet?

12   Sir Richard Grenville was the commander of which ship, sunk in 1591 battling alone against a huge Spanish fleet and celebrated in a poem by Alfred Lord Tennyson?

13   Where was there a disastrous attempt to found a Scottish colony in 1688?

14   In which year did Queen Anne come to the British throne?

15   Aphra Behn and Susannah Centlivre achieved fame in Britain in the late 17th and early 18th centuries respectively as what?

ANSWERS

1. Scotland. 2. Simon de Montfort. 3. Prince of Wales. 4. Wat Tyler. 5. He was a priest (albeit an excommunicated one). 6. '...the gentleman'. 7. The sons of King Edward IV (Edward V and his brother the Duke of York). 8. Their uncle King Richard III. 9. Prince Arthur, eldest son of King Henry VII and elder brother of King Henry VIII. 10. The dissolution of the monasteries. 11. Cadiz. 12. *The Revenge*. 13. In Darien in Central America (at the lower end of the Isthmus of Panama mainly in the present-day state of Panama). 14. 1702. 15. Dramatists.

FAMOUS PEOPLE

1 Which Englishwoman made two journeys of exploration in West Africa and died while serving as a nurse during the Boer War?

2 Who joined with his rival James Bailey to form a circus in 1818?

3 Which English explorer reached Baffin Island in 1576, when attempting to find the north-west passage to China?

4 Who wrote *The Fortunes and Misfortunes of Moll Flanders*?

5 What was the name of Mary Queen of Scots' private secretary, who was murdered at Holyrood palace by her husband Darnley?

6 Which writer founded the weekly periodical *Household Words*, in which his later novels were serialized?

7 Who became the first president of the republic of Chile in 1817?

8 Who invented the jet engine for aircraft?

9 Against which disease did Jonas Salk develop a vaccine?

10 Who said 'I have nothing to declare except my genius'?

11 Who composed *Finlandia*?

12 Which woman performed as a sharp-shooter in 'Buffalo Bill's Wild West Show'?

13 Which cinema pioneer made the film entitled *The Birth of a Nation*?

14 Who was the last Roman Catholic archbishop of Canterbury?

15 Who patented the electric light bulb, in 1879?

1. Mary Kingsley. 2. Phineas Barnum. 3. Martin Frobisher. 4. Daniel Defoe. 5. (David) Rizzio. 6. Charles Dickens. 7. Bernado O'Higgins. 8. Sir Frank Whittle. 9. Poliomyelitis. 10. Oscar Wilde. 11. Sibelius. 12. Annie Oakley. 13. D. W. Griffith. 14. Reginald Pole. 15. Thomas Edison.

SPORT & LEISURE

1 Who was the most expensive footballer in the Brazilian squad for the 1998 Football World Cup?

2 In 1991, who was the non playing captain of the European Ryder Cup team?

3 WBA and WBC are governing bodies in what sport?

4 Which country holds the most Davis Cup tennis titles?

5 Cricketer Salim Malik scored 215 runs in an innings for Essex in 1991. Who was it against?

6 Who was the top scorer in the 1966 football World Cup Final?

7 Where were the 1988 Olympic Games held?

8 In what year did Michael Schumacher win his first Formula One World Championship?

9 What sport do Neath and Llanelli play?

10 How tall are the hurdles in a 110m hurdles race?

11 Celebrity cook Delia Smith is on the board of what football club?

12 What player receives the Cy Young award in American Baseball every year?

13 In which sport is Wayne Gretzky a superstar?

14 How many goals did Gary Lineker score in the 1986 football World Cup Final?

15 For what hobby would you need maggots, worms and crab?

GENERAL KNOWLEDGE

1 Who was the first woman prime minister of Britain?

2 Who wrote the book *Pilgrim's Progress*?

3 On what play was the musical *My Fair Lady* based?

4 The word 'metamorphose' means (a) to change into a different form; (b) to become dead; or (c) to fly into the sky?

5 Mills and Boon is famous for publishing what kind of books?

6 In the Bible what was the name of the woman who was a prophet and judge of Israel?

7 Who wrote *A Brief History of Time*?

8 What was the profession of Frank Lloyd Wright?

9 Who invented the idea of lateral thinking?

10 In which Scottish lake is a monster said to live?

11 What is another name for the Decalogue?

12 What is the name of the mountain face in the USA into which the faces of four US presidents have been carved?

13 For what did Bertrand Russell receive the Nobel Prize in 1950?

14 What is the capital of Spain?

15 In *Star Trek* 'Mr Spock' comes from which planet?

1. Margaret Thatcher. 2. John Bunyan. 3. *Pygmalion*. 4. (a) to change into a different form. 5. Stories about love and romance. 6. Deborah. 7. Stephen Hawking. 8. Architect. 9. Edward de Bono. 10. Loch Ness. 11. The Ten Commandments. 12. Mount Rushmore. 13. Literature. 14. Madrid. 15. Vulcan.

SCIENCE & NATURE

1 Where is bile stored in the human body?

2 What is the SI unit of illumination?

3 Who was the first man to reach the North Pole?

4 Which animal secretes the pigment sepia?

5 What does the acronym ASCII (used in computing) represent?

6 Who was the first person to orbit the Earth?

7 What is turpentine made from?

8 What are isotopes?

9 For which invention is James Dewar noted?

10 How does the secretary bird get its name?

11 What was the first virus to be isolated?

12 Which nocturnal African mammal is known as the ant bear?

13 What is the common name for *Convallaria majalis*?

14 What is a gar?

15 Which is the largest planet in the Solar System?

1. The gall bladder. 2. The lux. 3. Robert Peary, in 1909. 4. Cuttlefish. 5. American Standard Code for Information Interchange. 6. Yuri Gagarin, from USSR in 1961. 7. The sap of the pine (or other coniferous tree). 8. Atoms of an element with the same atomic number but different properties. 9. Vacuum flask (about 1872). 10. From its crest, which looks like a bunch of quills behind a clerk's ear. 11. Tobacco mosaic virus (affecting plants). 12. Aardvark. 13. 'Lily of the Valley'. 14. A freshwater fish. 15. Jupiter.

ENTERTAINMENT

1   How many friends are there in the TV programme of the same title?

2   What was the name of Humphrey Bogart's bar in *Casablanca*?

3   Who had a number one hit in 1979 with 'When You're in Love With a Beautiful Woman'?

4   Cyril Mead and Eddie McGinnis were the real names of which comedians?

5   Which Italian instrumentalist had a hit with 'Children' in 1996?

6   Who played the title role in the TV comedy series *Father, Dear Father*?

7   Who had hits in the 1960s with 'Happy Birthday Sweet Sixteen' and 'Breaking Up Is Hard to Do'?

8   Name the marine spaceship in the film *Aliens*.

9   Which character did Frankie Howerd play in the TV comedy series *Up Pompeii*?

10 Who had a number one hit in 1974 with 'You're The First, The Last, My Everything'?

11 Oasis got to number two with 'Wonderwall' in November 1995. Who got to number two with the same song in December 1995?

12 Who has presented the TV programmes *Points of View* and *Watchdog*?

13 'The Rebels' performed with which guitarist in the 1950s and 1960s?

14 'Schnorbitz' was a St Bernard dog who appeared with which comedian in the late 1970s and early 1980s?

15 Dawn featuring Tony Orlando, had a number one hit in 1973 with which song?

HISTORY

1　In which year was Robert the Bruce crowned king of Scotland?

2　Before becoming king, Robert the Bruce had joined in a revolt led by which early champion of Scottish independence?

3　Was the Stone of Scone removed to England before or after Robert the Bruce was crowned?

4　At which battle of 1314 did Robert the Bruce inflict a massive defeat on an English army led by King Edward II?

5　Who was the first Scottish king of the Stewart (Stuart) dynasty?

6　In which century did Edinburgh become the capital of Scotland?

7　Which city was the previous capital?

8　What event led to the change of capital?

9　What was the profession of 'Blind Harry' who was at the court of King James IV of Scotland in the later years of the 15th century?

10　James IV was the last king of Scotland to speak which language?

11　At which battle of 1513 was King James IV defeated by the English and slain?

12　Which Scottish religious reformer spent the year and a half that he was held prisoner by the French as a galley slave?

13　This same religious reformer in 1558 published 'The First Blast of the Trumpet Against...' what?

14　Who was the last king to be crowned king of Scotland at Scone?

15　Is the Stone of Scone still in Westminster Abbey?

1. 1306. 2. Sir William Wallace. 3. Before – in 1296. 4. The Battle of Bannockburn. 5. Robert II (1316–90, reigned 1371–90). 6. The 15th century (1437). 7. Perth. 8. The murder of King James I in Perth. 9. He was a poet and chronicler, his major work being a life of Sir William Wallace. 10. Gaelic. 11. The Battle of Flodden. 12. John Knox. 13. 'The Monstrous Regiment of Women'. 14. King Charles II of Scotland (and England) in 1651. 15. No – it was recovered after being stolen by Scottish nationalists in 1950 but finally returned in 1996.

FAMOUS PEOPLE

1 Which jazz singer was known as 'Lady Day'?

2 Who was the inventor of dynamite?

3 Who created the fictional naval hero 'Horatio Hornblower'?

4 Which English nurse was executed by the Germans in World War I?

5 Which continent did Matthew Flinders explore?

6 Who composed the *Brandenburg Concertos*?

7 Who made the first non-stop transatlantic flight?

8 Who painted *Mona Lisa*?

9 Who was the leader of the mutineers on the *Bounty*?

10 Which famous violin maker lived in Cremona, Italy?

11 Who was crowned as Edward VI at Dublin in 1487?

12 Whose writing was first published under the name Currer Bell?

13 What kind of books are principally associated with the illustrator Kate Greenaway?

14 Who led the government troops who defeated Bonnie Prince Charlie at the Battle of Culloden in 1745?

15 Who, with her husband, founded the Hogarth Press in 1917?

ANSWERS

1. Billie Holiday. 2. Alfred Nobel. 3. C. S. Forester. 4. Edith Cavell. 5. Australia. 6. J. S. Bach. 7. Charles Lindbergh. 8. Leonardo da Vinci. 9. Fletcher Christian. 10. Antonio Stradivari (or Stradivarius). 11. Lambert Simnel. 12. Charlotte Brontë. 13. Children's books, especially nursery rhymes. 14. Duke of Northumberland. 15. Virginia Woolf.

SPORT & LEISURE

1   Who won the first Johnnie Walker Golf World Championship in 1991?

2   Peter Schmeichel won the football European Championships with which country?

3   What sport does Lee Janzen play?

4   Who launched the new McLaren car for season 1997?

5   What colour rose do your associate with Lancashire Cricket Club?

6   From what football club did Arsenal buy Ian Wright?

7   What English tennis player was disqualified from a doubles match at Wimbledon for hitting a ball girl with a ball?

8   In which year did Steve Ovett win an Olympic gold medal in the 800 metres?

9   There are two major leagues in American baseball, one is the American League. What is the other?

10   How many players are there per team in an Australian Rules football match?

11   What sport did Jocky Wilson play?

12   What is the maximum break in Snooker?

13   For which club did Paul Ince play in Italy?

14   What is the name of Jacques Villeneuve's famous father?

15   What is the maximum length of a Rugby Union field of play?

1. Fred Couples. 2. Denmark. 3. Golf. 4. The Spice Girls. 5. Red. 6. Crystal Palace. 7. Tim Henman. 8. 1980. 9. National League. 10. 18 a side. 11. Darts. 12. 147. 13. Inter Milan. 14. Gilles Villeneuve. 15. 100 metres.

GENERAL KNOWLEDGE

1 From what main ingredient is hummus made?

2 For which fruit is Seville famous?

3 In which year did the Automobile Association launch its 'Relay' service?

4 Charles II of England, Scotland and Ireland, died in which year?

5 Who coined the phrase: A country 'fit for heroes to live in'?

6 What is the name of the Israeli parliament?

7 What do the initials CBI stand for?

8 What was the name of the groups of women who, in the early 20th century, tried to gain for women the right to vote?

9 Who became known as 'Saint Mugg'?

10 What cheese is traditionally eaten with Christmas cake?

11 In which year was the Battle of Bosworth Field?

12 Monday is named after the Moon. True or false?

13 What is the name of the long, narrow lengths of paper sometimes thrown in the US to greet famous people?

14 What do the initials SALT stand for?

15 Who was the main introducer of the TV programme *That's Life*?

1. Chick peas. 2. Oranges. 3. 1973. 4. 1685. 5. Lloyd George. 6. The Knesset. 7. Confederation of British Industry. 8. The Suffragettes. 9. Malcolm Muggeridge. 10. Stilton cheese. 11. 1485. 12. True. 13. Tickertape. 14. Strategic Arms Limitation Talks. 15. Esther Rantzen.

SCIENCE & NATURE

1 What name is given to the fruit of the forest trees (like beech) which are used as fodder for pigs?

2 'Sn' is the chemical symbol for which element?

3 What is a nictitating membrane?

4 How many vertebrae are there in the human neck?

5 What is the name given to the IBM chess-playing computer that defeated Garry Kasparov in 1996?

6 What is a toxin?

7 What is a newton?

8 *Drosophila melanogaster* is the Latin name for which insect?

9 What is the difference between cocci and bacilli?

10 Which element is a constituent of all proteins but not carbohydrates?

11 Which living mammal is closely related to the giraffe?

12 What name is given to the unit of distance equal to a thousandth of a metre?

13 What is the heaviest organ in the human body?

14 Through which arteries does blood leave the human heart?

15 Caprine means relating to which animal?

ENTERTAINMENT

1 Who played the president in the film *Air Force one*?

2 Which school choir had a number one hit in 1980 with 'There's No One Quite Like Grandma'?

3 Who played the prison officer 'Mr MacKay' in the TV comedy series *Porridge*?

4 Who went 'All Around The World' looking for her baby?

5 Who won an Oscar for Best Actress in the 1988 film *The Accused*?

6 Which group had a number one hit in 1977 with 'Angelo'?

7 What is the surname of the four brothers who starred in the TV drama *The Hanging Gale*?

8 Which singer starred in the 1976 film *The Man Who Fell To Earth*?

9 Which character worked in the windmill in the children's programme *Camberwick Green*?

10 Brian and Michael had a number one hit in 1978 inspired by the paintings of L. S. Lowry. What was it called?

11 Who was the original presenter of the TV programme *The Crystal Maze*?

12 Mark Owen got to number three with his song 'Child' in November 1996. Which group launched his career?

13 Which actor starred in the film *National Lampoon's Vacation*?

14 Which singer had hits in the 1960s with 'Can't Take My Eyes Off You' and 'Can't Help Falling in Love'?

15 Which character did Robert Hardy play in TV's *All Creatures Great and Small*?

ANSWERS

1. Harrison Ford. 2. St Winifred's. 3. Fulton Mackay. 4. Lisa Stansfield. 5. Jodie Foster. 6. Brotherhood of Man. 7. McGann. 8. David Bowie. 9. 'Windy Miller'. 10. 'Matchstalk Men and Matchstalk Cats and Dogs'. 11. Richard O'Brien. 12. Take That. 13. Chevy Chase. 14. Andy Williams. 15. 'Siegfried'.

HISTORY

1   Who was the mother of Mary Queen of Scots? Anne of Austria, Margaret of Scotland, or Mary of Guise?

2   How many husbands had Mary Queen of Scots?

3   Who was her first husband?

4   What position did David Rizzio hold in the household of Mary Queen of Scots?

5   Where was Rizzio murdered in 1566?

6   Which of Mary's husbands was involved in the plot to kill Rizzio?

7   How did Mary's second husband meet his death?

8   The so-called 'casket letters' are said to have been written by Mary Queen of Scots to whom?

9   James VI (of Scotland) and I (of England) was Mary's child by whom?

10 What finally and decisively turned the nobles and people of Scotland against Mary?

11 What was the basis of Mary Queen of Scots claim to the English throne?

12 In which year did Mary flee to England?

13 What was the name of Mary's page who plotted in 1586 to assassinate Elizabeth I and place Mary on the English throne?

14 Where was Mary held prisoner and executed?

15 In which year was Mary Queen of Scots executed?

ANSWERS

1. Mary of Guise. 2. Three. 3. The Dauphin of France (who was briefly king of France as Francis II). 4. He was her private secretary. 5. In the queen's antechamber in Holyrood Palace. 6. Her second husband, Lord Darnley. 7. The house in which Darnley was staying was blown up (his body was found outside the house and he may have been strangled). 8. Mary's third husband, the Earl of Bothwell. 9. Lord Darnley. 10. Her marriage to Bothwell, widely suspected of being Darnley's murderer, three months after the latter's death. 11. She was a great-granddaughter of King Henry VII. 12. 1568. 13. Anthony Babington. 14. Fotheringay Castle. 15. 1587.

FAMOUS PEOPLE

1 Which prime minister conferred the title of Empress of India on Queen Victoria?

2 Who was Dr Johnson's companion and biographer?

3 What aid to criminal detection was devised by Sir Francis Galton?

4 Which British businessman made his fortune in sugar and founded the Art Gallery which is named after him?

5 What was Thomas Sheraton's profession?

6 Which French explorer travelled down the Mississippi to the sea in 1681?

7 Who was the lighthouse keeper's daughter famous for her rescue of some shipwrecked sailors in 1838?

8 What type of musical instrument was manufactured by the company founded by Karl Bechstein?

9 Who edited the poetry anthology *The Golden Treasury*, first published in 1861?

10 Who composed *Peter and the Wolf*?

11 Which land did the Dutch navigator Abel Tasman first sight in 1642?

12 Which English clergyman wrote the *Natural History and Antiquities of Selborne*?

13 Who was the first wife of Henry VIII?

14 Who in 1834 invented his 'Analytical Engine' which was the forerunner of the modern computer?

15 Whose poems include *Ode to a Nightingale* and *To Autumn*?

ANSWERS

1. Disraeli. 2. James Boswell. 3. Fingerprint identification. 4. Sir Henry Tate. 5. Cabinetmaker and furniture designer. 6. Robert de La Salle. 7. Grace Darling. 8. Pianos. 9. Francis Palgrave. 10. Prokofiev. 11. Tasmania (first named Van Diemen's Land by him). 12. Reverend Gilbert White. 13. Catherine of Aragon. 14. Charles Babbage. 15. John Keats.

SPORT & LEISURE

1   Which current Premier Football manager was nicknamed the 'Stroller' when he played football?

2   What country does golfer Bernhard Langer come from?

3   Who trained both Muhammad Ali and Sugar Ray Leonard?

4   Where do Barnsley Football Club play?

5   Who became Michael Schumacher's team mate at Ferrari in 1996?

6   What letter in the alphabet are the goal posts in rugby shaped like?

7   How many races did Desert Orchid win out of the 55 jump races that he started?

8   In what sport would you do a 'lay up shot'?

9   How many points do you get for a touch down in American football?

10 Where was tennis player Anna Kournikova born?

11 How many times does a 1500m runner run round the track to complete a race?

12 What footballer scored 126 goals in 1959?

13 In what game might you have a 'straight', 'two pair' and a 'full house'?

14 What colour jacket do you get to wear if you win the US Masters Golf?

15 How many teams played in the first ever World Cup Finals?

GENERAL KNOWLEDGE

1 Who wrote the *Just So Stories*?

2 Who wrote the novel *The Corridors of Power*?

3 What is the French name for chicken casserole with red wine?

4 Who is the chairman of Microsoft?

5 In which year did Vasco da Gama discover the sea route from Portugal to India, around the Cape of Good Hope?

6 Which US state lies between Illinois and Ohio?

7 In which year was the play *Look Back in Anger* first presented?

8 Which designer and businessman founded the Habitat stores?

9 Which character in *David Copperfield* by Charles Dickens was known for being 'ever so umble'?

10 From which language do the words 'algebra' and 'alcohol' originate?

11 In which year is Middle English said to have ended – the year in which printing was introduced in England by William Caxton?

12 From which folk song does the phrase 'Uncle Tom Cobbleigh and all' come?

13 According to tradition, what social act takes place beneath mistletoe at Christmas?

14 Which dynasty ruled China from 1368 to 1644?

15 What is thremmatology?

1. Rudyard Kipling. 2. C. P. Snow. 3. Coq-au-vin. 4. Bill Gates. 5. 1498. 6. Indiana. 7. 1956. 8. Terence Conran. 9. 'Uriah Heep'. 10. Arabic. 11. 1476. 12. Widdicombe Fair. 13. Kissing. 14. The Ming Dynasty. 15. The science of breeding domestic animals and plants.

SCIENCE & NATURE

1 Where in the human body is the pineal gland?

2 What is mitosis?

3 What is the name of the computer software organization founded in 1975 by Bill Gates and Paul Allen?

4 Who was the first person to walk on the Moon?

5 What is the largest of the bivalve molluscs?

6 Which chemical element has the symbol Sb?

7 What fish is also called the white whale?

8 'Tragus', 'concha' and 'helix' are all parts of what?

9 What term describes the study of earthquakes?

10 What kind of asp probably killed Cleopatra

11 What is the second hardest mineral after diamond?

12 Which planet was discovered in 1781?

13 Caries refers to decay in what?

14 Which was the first person to look at space through a telescope?

15 Which device for lifting water was invented by, and named after, an ancient Greek mathematician?

ANSWERS

1. In the forehead. 2. Cell division. 3. Microsoft. 4. Neil Armstrong, from USA 1969. 5. Giant clam. 6. Antimony. 7. Beluga. 8. The external ear. 9. Seismology. 10. An Egyptian cobra. 11. Corundum. 12. Uranus discovered by William Herschel. 13. Bones or teeth. 14. Galileo Galilei. 15. Archimedes screw.

ENTERTAINMENT

1   What was the name of the 1957 war film based on the life of Douglas Bader?

2   The actor Telly Savalas had a number one hit in 1975 with which record?

3   The TV drama *Brideshead Revisited* was based on a novel by which author?

4   Who played the title role in the 1975 film *Tommy*?

5   Which band had a number one hit in 1961 with 'You're Driving Me Crazy'?

6   What is the name of the character played by Robbie Coltrane in the TV series *Cracker*?

7   What were Mel and Kim rockin' around in December 1987?

8   Which two actors starred in the film *Sleepless in Seattle*?

9   Smokie had a hit in 1976 with 'Living Next Door to...' whom?

10 Who plays the comic character 'The Baldy Man'?

11 The Shamen got to number six in 1992 with their song 'LSI'. What did LSI stand for?

12 Which actress won an Oscar for the film *Howard's End*?

13 'Dance to the Music' was a hit in 1968 for Sly and which group?

14 Which actor provided the voices for the children's programme *Will O' The Wise*?

15 Which singer had a hit in 1975 with 'Happy To Be On An Island In The Sun'?

ANSWERS

1. *Reach For The Sky*. 2. 'If'. 3. Evelyn Waugh. 4. Roger Daltry. 5. Temperance Seven. 6. 'Fitz'. 7. The Christmas Tree. 8. Tom Hanks and Meg Ryan. 9. Alice. 10. Gregor Fisher. 11. Love, Sex, Intelligence. 12. Emma Thompson. 13. The Family Stone. 14. Kenneth Williams. 15. Demis Roussos.

HISTORY

1 What did the diplomat Jean Nicot (1530–1600) introduce into France?

2 In which English county was Sir Walter Raleigh born?

3 On which day in which year was the Gunpowder Plot to blow up the king of England and both Houses of Parliament intended to be carried out?

4 King James I was so fond of the Cecil family's mansion at Theobalds in Hertfordshire that he asked to exchange it for which former royal house, also in Hertfordshire, which is still the home of the Cecil family today?

5 The Earl of Strafford was chief adviser to which English king?

6 In which year did Samuel Pepys give up making entries in his diary?

7 Which French coastal town was the stronghold of the Huguenots (French Protestants) until besieged and captured by royal troops in 1628?

8 Who became king of Prussia in 1740?

9 Who became archduchess of Austria and queen of Hungary also in 1740?

10 Which Austrian province (now part of Poland) was the main bone of contention between this king and this archduchess?

11 In which year did the naval Battle of St Vincent take place in which Jervis and Nelson defeated a combined French, Spanish and Dutch force?

12 In which year did Hong Kong become a British colony?

13 For what length of time were the New Territories (the mainland part of Hong Kong) leased by China to Britain?

14 In what year was Hong Kong returned to China?

15 Who was the last British governor of Hong Kong?

1. Tobacco (the words 'nicotine' and 'nicotiana' derive from his name). 2. Devon. 3. 5 November 1605. 4. Hatfield House. 5. Charles I. 6. 1669. 7. La Rochelle. 8. Frederick the Great (Frederick II). 9. Maria Theresa. 10. Silesia. 11. 1797. 12. 1842 (Hong Kong Island was leased by China in that year, the mainland New Territories were leased later). 13. 99 Years. 14. 1997. 15. Chris Patten.

FAMOUS PEOPLE

1 Who wrote a series of books on architecture under the general title of *The Buildings of England*?

2 Whose paintings include *Sunflowers* and *Starry Night*?

3 Which woman became prime minister of India in 1966?

4 Which English historian wrote *The History of the Decline and Fall of the Roman Empire*?

5 Who commanded the British fleet at the Battle of Trafalgar?

6 Who invented, and gave his name to, the dirigible or airship?

7 Who composed the opera *Hansel and Gretel*?

8 Who allegedly was drowned in a butt of Malmsey wine in 1478?

9 Who led the baronial revolt against Henry III and was defeated at the Battle of Evesham?

10 Which instrument did the jazz musician Jelly Roll Moreton play?

11 Who set up a permanent exhibition of waxworks in London in 1835?

12 Who was the accomplice of the infamous 'bodysnatcher' William Hare?

13 Which American artist is particularly noted for his paintings of birds, collected and published in *Birds of America*?

14 Who was known as the 'Iron Duke'?

15 What were the names of the two explorers who led an overland expedition across America from St Louis to the Pacific?

ANSWERS

1. Sir Niklaus Pevsner. 2. Vincent van Gogh. 3. Indira Gandhi. 4. Edward Gibbon. 5. Lord (Horatio) Nelson. 6. (Count Fernand von) Zeppelin. 7. Engelbert Humperdinck. 8. George, Duke of Clarence. 9. Simon de Montfort. 10. Piano. 11. Madame Tussaud. 12. William Burke. 13. James Audubon. 14. The Duke of Wellington. 15. (Meriwether) Lewis and (William) Clark.

SPORT & LEISURE

1 Which country did Dino Zoff famously play football for?

2 What sport is Jonah Lomu famous for?

3 Old Trafford is the headquarters for which cricket team?

4 Who became the youngest ever scorer in the football World Cup in 1998?

5 Which man won 12 Grand Slam tennis titles between 1961 and 1967?

6 Whose record of four gold medals in Olympic track and field did Carl Lewis equal in 1984?

7 Joe DiMaggio played 56 consecutive baseball games for which team?

8 When was the Australian Football Council formed?

9 How many pole positions did the late Ayrton Senna win?

10 What sport do you associate the Harlem Globetrotters with?

11 Which football club was revived after many years by owner Jack Walker?

12 What is the name of Michael Schumacher's motor racing brother?

13 What piece of clothing is golfer Payne Stewart famous for wearing?

14 What does WD stand for in Netball?

15 What are the traditional home colours of Southampton FC?

1. Italy. 2. Rugby Union. 3. Lancashire. 4. Michael Owen. 5. Roy Emerson. 6. Jesse Owens. 7. New York Yankees. 8. 1906. 9. 65. 10. Basketball. 11. Blackburn Rovers. 12. Ralph. 13. Plus Fours (Knicker in US). 14. Wing defence. 15 Red and white stripes.

GENERAL KNOWLEDGE

1 In which year did Adenauer become Chancellor of West Germany?

2 Proverbially, who should we be careful not to empty out along with the bath water?

3 The phrase 'Not a lot of people know that' was made famous by whom?

4 What does the Russian word 'perestroika' mean?

5 Who wrote *War and Peace*?

6 From which language do the words 'geisha', 'rickshaw' and 'kamikaze' originate?

7 Which TV interviewer, who interviewed politicians, was famous for wearing a bow tie with spots on it?

8 What do the initials CAD stand for?

9 What is the Burrell collection in Glasgow?

10 Who did Margaret Thatcher follow as leader of the Conservative party?

11 What is the pseudonym of Herman Cyril McNeile, creator of Hugh 'Bulldog' Drummond?

12 What is the American English name for the boot of a car?

13 Who wrote *Robinson Crusoe*?

14 What was the name of the Jewish girl who became known for her diary written in hiding during World War II?

15 Which novel, by the American writer Ira Levin, was made into a film in 1968?

ANSWERS

1. 1949. 2. The baby. 3. Michael Caine. 4. Restructuring. 5. Leo Tolstoy. 6. Japanese. 7. Sir Robin Day. 8. Computer aided design. 9. An art collection. 10. Ted Heath. 11. Sapper. 12. Trunk. 13. Daniel Defoe. 14. Anne Frank. 15. *Rosemary's Baby*.

SCIENCE & NATURE

1 What stage in the life cycle of the butterfly follows the larva?

2 Which edible bulb of the onion family is composed of small segments called cloves?

3 What is the computer scientist Kevin Mitnick famous for?

4 In which year did an astronaut make the first untethered 'walk' in space?

5 In scientific measurement what does the term 'nano' indicate?

6 If you suffer from Bright's disease, which part of the body is affected?

7 What is geotropism?

8 What is a 'black hole'?

9 Which metal is added to steel to make it stainless?

10 What is the literal meaning of the word 'atom'?

11 What is a grayling?

12 What is the full name for the US government agency NASA?

13 What common vegetable has the Latin name *Solanum tuberosum*?

14 Of which well-known mineral are pyrope and andradite varieties?

15 What is dry ice?

1. Pupa/chrysalis. 2. Garlic. 3. World's most wanted computer hacker (caught in 1994). 4. 1984 by Bruce McCandless using a manned manoeuvring unit. 5. One thousand millionth of (10^{-9}). 6. Kidney. 7. The growth of a plant or part of a plant towards the pull of the Earth's gravity. 8. A region of space with a gravitational field that is so strong that nothing can escape. 9. Chromium. 10. It comes from the Greek meaning 'indivisible'. 11. A type of fish. 12. National Aeronautics and Space Administration. 13. Potato. 14. Garnet. 15. Solid carbon dioxide.

ENTERTAINMENT

1   Which group sang with Ian Dury?

2   What is the name of the 1987 film based on the life of South African Steven Biko?

3   The TV soap *Coronation Street* was first shown in which year?

4   In their number one hit in 1979 which day did the Boomtown Rats not like?

5   The play *Pygmalion* is the basis for which 1964 film?

6   In which year was Tony Hancock born?

7   Who played 'Porkpie' in the TV comedies *Desmond's* and *Porkpie*?

8   'Way Down' was the last number one hit for which singer?

9   'Blofeld' in *You Only Live Twice* was one of many villains played by which actor?

10 Who replaced Sue Cook as a presenter on TV's *Crimewatch UK*?

11 Which singer starred in the 1967 musical *Half a Sixpence*?

12 The Spice Girls' first three singles all went to number one. Name them.

13 Who directed and starred in the film *The Bridges of Madison County*?

14 Which disc jockey presented the programme *TV Heroes*?

15 Which group had a number one hit in 1968 with 'Blackberry Way'?

1. The Blockheads. 2. *Cry Freedom*. 3. 1960. 4. Mondays. 5. *My Fair Lady*. 6. 1924. 7. Ram John Holder. 8. Elvis Presley. 9. Donald Pleasance. 10. Jill Dando. 11. Tommy Steele. 12. 'Wannabe', 'Say You'll Be There' and '2 Become 1'. 13. Clint Eastwood. 14. Danny Baker. 15. The Move.

HISTORY

1 Which archbishop of Canterbury held out his hand to the fire in which he was about to be burned as a punishment for signing a recantation of his Protestant principles?

2 Who became chief minister and effective ruler of France in 1629?

3 Who was the high church archbishop of Canterbury who was executed in 1645?

4 What, according to popular legend, did Jenny Geddes do to a bishop preaching in St Giles' Cathedral Edinburgh?

5 Who was chief minister of France during the minority of King Louis XIV?

6 Which bishop of Cloyne in southern Ireland is famous as a philosopher who argued that external reality is a creation of the mind?

7 Which famous letter-writer's advice regarding a troublesome preacher was: 'Make him a bishop and you will silence him at once'?

8 Bishop Samuel Wilberforce debated which contentious issue of the day with the scientist Thomas Huxley in Oxford in 1860?

9 In which year was the doctrine of papal infallibility defined by the First Vatican Council?

10 The Anglican bishop, John Colenso, excommunicated for heresy in 1864 and deposed in 1869, was a bishop in which country?

11 Which of the following was not an archbishop of Canterbury? William Temple, Michael Ramsey, Francis Bourne, Donald Coggan?

12 Which pope was in office during World War II?

13 Which archbishop of Canterbury presided at the coronation of Queen Elizabeth II in 1953?

14 Which bishop published the controversial book *Honest to God* in 1963?

15 A fire damaged York Minster in 1984 after the enthronement of which bishop with controversial views on the Virgin Birth and the Resurrection?

1. Archbishop Thomas Cranmer. 2. Cardinal Richelieu. 3. Archbishop William Laud.
4. She threw her stool at him. 5. Cardinal Mazarin. 6. Bishop George Berkeley.
7. Lord Chesterfield's. 8. Evolution. 9. 1870. 10. South Africa (he was the first
Bishop of Natal). 11. Francis Bourne (he was a cardinal and Archbishop of
Westminster). 12. Pope Pius XII. 13. Geoffrey Fisher. 14. John Robinson, Bishop of
Woolwich. 15. David Jenkins, Bishop of Durham.

FAMOUS PEOPLE

1. Who compiled *A History of the Kings of Britain*, which is completely fictitious?

2. Whose musical compositions include the *Water Music* and *The Messiah*?

3. Who was the first Westerner to sail round the Cape of Good Hope to Asia?

4. By what popular title was Edward the eldest son of King Edward III known?

5. What type of aircraft was pioneered by Igor Sikorsky?

6. Which judge presided over the so-called 'Bloody Assize'?

7. Which Canadian author said, 'The medium is the message'?

8. What was the profession of Inigo Jones?

9. What instrument did the jazz musician Django Reinhardt play?

10. To which royal house did Henry VIII belong?

11. In which year was Paul McCartney born?

12. Who wrote the play *Pygmalion*, on which the musical *My Fair Lady* is based?

13. What was the name of the brothers who collaborated to produce the first breakfast cereal?

14. Who was the captain of the *Bounty* against whom the crew mutinied?

15. Who composed the operas *Peter Grimes* and *Billy Budd*?

ANSWERS

1. Geffrey of Monmouth. 2. Handel. 3. Vasco da Gama. 4. 'The Black Prince'. 5. The helicopter. 6. Judge George Jeffreys. 7. Marshall McLuhan. 8. Architect. 9. Guitar. 10. Tudor. 11. 1942. 12. George Bernard Shaw. 13. Kellogg (John Harvey and Will Keith). 14. Captain Bligh. 15. Benjamin Britten.

SPORT & LEISURE

1 In what sport do you score by dunking a ball?

2 Which ex-Liverpool player was Kevin Keegan's right hand man at Newcastle United?

3 Moses Kiptanui was the first man to run the 3,000 metres under how many minutes?

4 How many Grand Slam tournaments did Margaret Court achieve in her career?

5 Who is Alexander Lyle better known as?

6 What animal do you associate with Leicester City?

7 Grace Road is the home of what cricket club?

8 How many Grand Prix did Jonny Herbert win in 1995?

9 Who won the 1986 Snooker World Championships?

10 Who is the oldest player to ever play in the football World Cup Finals?

11 What is the name of the kick in Rugby Union which follows a try?

12 Which boxer married actress Robbin Givens?

13 'Party Politics' won the Grand National in what year?

14 Who is the only footballer ever to play in three World Cup winning teams?

15 How many triple word score squares are there on a Scrabble board?

ANSWERS

1. Basketball. 2. Terry McDermott. 3. Eight minutes. 4. 24 times. 5. Sandy Lyle. 6. Foxes. 7. Leicestershire. 8. Two. 9. Joe Johnson. 10. Roger Milla. 11. Conversion. 12. Mike Tyson. 13. 1992. 14. Pele. 15. Eight.

GENERAL KNOWLEDGE

1 In which year did women sit on a coroner's jury for the first time?

2 OO, HO and N are all types of what?

3 Which US state is south of Kentucky?

4 Proverbially, if we do not spread the risk, what have we put in one basket?

5 Of which country is Buenos Aires the capital?

6 In which European country is the port of Bergen?

7 What is meant by a 'ballpark figure'?

8 On what night is Hallowe'en?

9 What do the initials CAP stand for?

10 In December 1936 King Edward VIII abdicated in order to marry who?

11 Who do the initials SAS stand for?

12 What are crocodile tears?

13 From which language do the words 'bamboo', 'sago' and 'batik' originate?

14 What do the initials R & R stand for?

15 For what was the slogan 'All human life is there' used to advertise?

1. 1933. 2. Model railway gauges. 3. Tennessee. 4. All our eggs. 5. Argentina. 6. Norway. 7. A rough estimate. 8. 31 October. 9. Common Agricultural Policy. 10. Mrs Wallis Simpson. 11. Special Air Service. 12. False tears. 13. Malay. 14. Rest (or relaxation) and recreation. 15. *News of the World.*

SCIENCE & NATURE

1 What is the common name of the star called Sirius?

2 In which part of the body would you find the tympanic membrane?

3 What are the chemical constituents of Bakelite?

4 What is the name given to the fin at the end of a fish's tail?

5 What is the lithosphere?

6 What is the colouring of the adult Colorado beetle?

7 What is the common name for polytetrafluoroethylene?

8 What are the Van Allen belts?

9 What is the name given to the art of decorating iron and steel by inlaying with gold or silver?

10 In which year was the Hubble Space Telescope launched?

11 The computer language BASIC is an acronym used in computing, what is its full form?

12 What is unusual about the reproduction cycle of a seahorse?

13 What is the function of a swim bladder in a fish?

14 'Fellow traveller' is the translation of the name for the first satellite to orbit the Earth, launched by the USSR in 1957. What was the name of the satellite?

15 Where is ambergris (formerly used in perfumery) formed?

1. The Dog Star. 2. The middle ear. 3. Formaldehyde and phenol. 4. Caudal fin. 5. The rigid outer part of the Earth's surface (Earth's crust). 6. Yellowish-orange-red with black stripes on its wing cases. 7. PTFE or Teflon. 8. Zones of electrically charged particles circling the Earth. 9. Damascening. 10. 1990. 11. Beginner's all-purpose symbolic instruction code. 12. The male carries and hatches the eggs. 13. Balance/buoyancy. 14. *Sputnik*. 15. In the intestines of the sperm whale.

ENTERTAINMENT

1　The TV series *Poldark* was set in which county?

2　Which actress starred in the film *Truly, Madly, Deeply*?

3　Who had a hit in 1961 with 'Take Good Care Of My Baby'?

4　What was the name of the series starring Richard Griffiths as a detective and restaurant owner?

5　Who had baggy trousers?

6　Which actor starred in the 1985 film *Teen Wolf*?

7　Which singers are known as 'The Three Tenors'?

8　Ian Smith plays which character in the TV soap *Neighbours*?

9　Who played 'Phileas Fogg' in the 1956 film *Around the World in Eighty Days*?

10　Which singer had hits in the 1960s with 'Runaway', 'Hats Off To Larry' and 'Little Town Flirt'?

11　Who played the lead roles in the comedy shows *Murder Most Horrid*?

12　Who got to number four in the charts with 'Cornflake Girl'?

13　Who had a number one hit in 1974 with 'Down, Down'?

14　What is the name of the wife of 'Victor Meldrew' in the TV comedy series *One Foot in the Grave*?

15　Who starred in the film *The Man in the Iron Mask*?

ANSWERS

1. Cornwall. 2. Juliet Stevenson. 3. Bobby Vee. 4. *Pie in the Sky*. 5. Madness. 6. Michael J. Fox. 7. Jose Carreras, Placido Domingo and Luciano Pavarotti. 8. 'Harold Bishop'. 9. David Niven. 10. Del Shannon. 11. Dawn French. 12. Tori Amos. 13. Status Quo. 14. 'Margaret'. 15. Leonardo DiCaprio.

HISTORY

1   Anne of Austria was the mother of which French king?

2   Which family provided the electors of Brandenburg, kings of Prussia and emperors of Germany from 1415 to 1918?

3   Who was the first king of Prussia?

4   Which British admiral was executed by firing squad in 1757 after failing in an attempt to relieve Minorca?

5   Who suggested that this admiral was shot 'in order to encourage the others'?

6   In which year did Captain Cook discover Botany Bay in Australia?

7   Who was the captain of *HMS Beagle* on the voyage around the world in which Charles Darwin took part?

8   Dwight D. Eisenhower, President of the United States, and Charles de Gaulle, president of France, were both born in the same year. Which year was it?

9   In which year did King Edward VII of Great Britain come to the throne?

10 Who said 'The lamps are going out all over Europe; we shall not see them lit again in our lifetime'?

11 What did these words refer to?

12 Imre Nagy was a prime minister of which country during the 1950s?

13 In which year were Penguin, the British publishers, tried for obscenity after publishing an unexpurgated version of D. H. Lawrence's *Lady Chatterley's Lover*?

14 Who became general secretary of the Soviet Communist Party in 1964?

15 In which year did Gro Harlem Brundtland become Norway's first female prime minister?

1. King Louis XIV. 2. The Hohenzollerns. 3. Frederick I (reigned 1701–13). 4. John Byng. 5. Voltaire. 6. 1770. 7. Robert Fitzroy. 8. 1890. 9. 1901. 10. Sir Edward Grey, British foreign secretary. 11. The outbreak of World War I. 12. Hungary. 13. 1961. 14. Leonid Brezhnev. 15. 1981.

FAMOUS PEOPLE

1 Which king of England was canonized in 1611?

2 Which 19th-century British clergyman is remembered for the diary of his life in the Welsh border country?

3 Who was known as 'The Swedish Nightingale'?

4 Which British explorer led the first surface crossing of the frozen Arctic Ocean, in 1968–69?

5 What form of lighting was pioneered by William Murdock?

6 In the Bible, who was proverbially famous for his patience?

7 With which artistic movement is Picasso associated?

8 Who wrote *Lord of the Flies*?

9 Who wrote *The Adventures of Huckleberry Finn*?

10 Who first broadcast a 'Letter from America' in 1946?

11 Who succeeded Richelieu as chief minister to Louis XIII?

12 Who was the Austrian monk whose botanical studies formed the basis for the science of genetics?

13 Who was the first Protestant Archbishop of Canterbury?

14 Who composed *The Planets* suite?

15 At which battle did Admiral Horatio Nelson die?

ANSWERS

1. Edward 'the Confessor'. 2. Reverend Francis Kilvert. 3. Jenny Lind. 4. Wally Herbert. 5. Gas lighting. 6. Job. 7. Cubism. 8. William Golding. 9. Mark Twain. 10. Alistair Cooke. 11. (Jules) Mazarin. 12. (Gregor) Mendel. 13. Thomas Cranmer. 14. Gustav Holst. 15. Trafalgar (1805).

SPORT & LEISURE

1 Which footballer became the most expensive defender in the world in May 1998?

2 Who set the 100 metres World Record in Atlanta during 1996?

3 On what surface is the French Open Tennis Championship held?

4 Name the Glasgow born golfer who turned professional in 1987?

5 Trent Bridge is home to which cricket club?

6 How many times did Alain Prost win the Formula One World Championships?

7 Who was the English footballer that scored a goal against France in 27 seconds?

8 How many points do you get for potting a pink in snooker?

9 For which sport are Freddie Spencer and Barry Sheene famous?

10 Which song did Glenn Hoddle and Chris Waddle release into the UK Top 40?

11 Was legendary tennis player Jimmy Connors left or right handed?

12 In what sport would you do an 'Arab Spring'?

13 Complete the name of the boxer, Herol Bomber...?

14 Apart from Jamaica and South Africa which other two nations competed in the football World Cup for the first time in 1998?

15 What does AP stand for in the game Pictionary?

GENERAL KNOWLEDGE

1. Who wrote *Home Thoughts from Abroad*?

2. In which European country is the city of Strasbourg?

3. From which language do the words 'harem' and 'carafe' originate?

4. From what family of vegetables does the haricot come?

5. In which town was the comedian Eric Sykes born?

6. Who is said to have said 'Doctor Livingstone, I presume?'

7. What do the letters HMV stand for?

8. Who wrote the book *The Compleat Angler*?

9. In which year did Amy Johnson fly solo from England to Australia?

10. A samizdat is (a) a Russian tea urn, (b) secret printing and publishing in the Soviet Union, or (c) a Turkish long range weapon?

11. In which country is the Isle of Capri?

12. Who wrote *The Book of Household Management*?

13. What phrase, which originated in *Punch* magazine, is used to refer to something that is good in parts?

14. What is the name given to the beam placed above a window or door?

15. In which year was John Lennon shot?

SCIENCE & NATURE

1 Which Scottish physicist is credited with the invention of radar?

2 Which basic feature distinguishes true flies from most other insects?

3 What is the lowest region of the Earth's atmosphere?

4 In which part of the human body is the thymus?

5 In computing, what is the motherboard?

6 The Sun protection factor (spf) in sunscreen lotions protects against which form of light?

7 Which month has no full or new Moon?

8 Who said: 'Science without religion is lame. Religion without science is blind'?

9 What is the largest poisonous snake in Africa?

10 What is El Niño?

11 In the storage and reproduction of sounds, what does CD-I stand for?

12 What is unusual about the ginkgo tree?

13 What is graphite composed of?

14 What is the name of the unit equivalent to 1 cubic decimetre and/or 1,000 cubic centimetres?

15 Which variety of hard green-skinned apple is named after an Australian woman who died in 1870?

1. Robert Watson-Watt, in 1935. 2. True flies only have one pair of wings, most other insects have two. 3. Troposphere. 4. The base of the neck. 5. Printed circuit board that contains the main components of a computer. 6. Ultraviolet light in sunlight (uvb not uva). 7. February (29 days between new Moons, therefore February too short). 8. Albert Einstein. 9. Black mamba. 10. Warm ocean surge of the Peru current off S. America causing other currents and winds. 11. Compact disc interactive. 12. It exists now as a species and earliest fossils indicate its existence over 250 million years ago. 13. Carbon. 14. One litre. 15. Granny (Maria Ann) Smith.

ENTERTAINMENT

1 Which comic actor presented the TV programmes *Orchestra*?

2 In which year was the film *Jurassic Park* released?

3 'Moon River' was a number one hit in 1961 for which singer?

4 Ronnie Corbett played 'Timothy Lumsden' in which 1980s TV comedy series?

5 Jefferson Starship got to number 21 in 1980 with which girl's name?

6 Which actress co-starred with Mel Gibson in the 1997 film *Conspiracy Theory*?

7 Which two singers had a hit in 1966 with 'River Deep, Mountain High'?

8 Richard Briers and Prunella Scales starred in which TV comedy series in the early 1960s about a young married couple?

9 Who starred in the film *The Nutty Professor*?

10 Which group had a number one hit in 1979 with 'Message In A Bottle' and 'Walking On The Moon'?

11 Patrick Campbell and Frank Muir were the original team captains in which TV show?

12 Whose version of 'She's Leaving Home' got to number one in May 1988?

13 In the 1967 film *In The Heat Of The Night*, who played the character 'Virgil Tibbs'?

14 Who had a hit in 1964 with the song 'My Guy'?

15 Jack Shepherd plays the title role in which TV series?

259

HISTORY

1   In which battle of World War I were angels reported to have fought beside the British troops?

2   In which year of World War I did the Christmas truce take place in which British and German troops exchanged gifts, sang carols and played football between the lines?

3   Whom did the Germans defeat at the Battle of Tannenberg in 1914?

4   Who were the successful German generals who won the Battle of Tannenberg?

5   With whom was Italy allied during World War I?

6   Which Belgian town was at the centre of a salient in the western front, held by British forces during World War I, and almost totally destroyed in the conflict?

7   In which year did the ill-fated landings by British, Australian and French troops take place at Gallipoli?

8   In which year did the Battle of Verdun take place?

9   Which Irish former member of the British colonial service was hanged for high treason in 1916 after being landed in Ireland from a German submarine?

10   Which German airman was known as the 'Red Baron'?

11   Who defeated whom at the Battle of Caporetto in 1917?

12   Who commanded the US forces on the western front during World War I?

13   Albert Ball, Billy Bishop and Eddie Rickenbacker all became famous as what during World War I?

14   Who become supreme commander of all Allied forces on the western front in March 1918?

15   Where was the armistice that ended the fighting on the western front signed in November 1918?

FAMOUS PEOPLE

1 What organization was founded by Chad Varah in 1953?

2 Who narrated the 1954 radio production of Dylan Thomas' *Under Milk Wood*?

3 What was the occupation of Jack Yeats, brother of the poet W. B. Yeats?

4 In which city was Bobby Kennedy assassinated?

5 King Zog was head of state of which country from 1928 to 1939?

6 Who wrote *Of Mice and Men* and *The Grapes of Wrath*?

7 Who wrote the book *Small is Beautiful: Economics as if People Mattered*?

8 Whose face appeared on recruiting posters during World War I urging 'Your country needs you'?

9 What anniversary did Queen Victoria celebrate in 1897?

10 One of Marilyn Monroe's husbands was a famous US baseball player. Who was he?

11 Whose autobiography was titled *The Naked Civil Servant*?

12 According to the Bible how old was Methuselah when he died?

13 Which US president had a sign on his desk saying 'The buck stops here'?

14 What is the name of the former shipyard worker and trade union leader who was elected president of Poland in 1990?

15 Who did Winston Churchill describe as 'a sheep in sheep's clothing'?

ANSWERS

1. The Samaritans. 2. Richard Burton. 3. Painter. 4. Los Angeles, in 1968. 5. Albania. 6. John Steinbeck. 7. Ernest Friedrich Schumacher. 8. Lord Kitchener. 9. The diamond jubilee of her succession to the throne. 10. Joe DiMaggio. 11. Quentin Crisp. 12. 969 years old. 13. Harry S. Truman. 14. Lech Walesa. 15. Clement Attlee.

SPORT & LEISURE

1 If you were in the Maracana Municipal Stadium what sport would you be watching?

2 What country does sprinter Merlene Ottey come from?

3 Who won the 1993 Golf Open Championship?

4 In what sport does David Coulthard compete?

5 If you are a man between 70kg (154lbs) and 74kg (163lbs), what weight category would you be in for karate?

6 Which was the richest football club in the world in 1998?

7 What country is legendary cricketer Sir Donald Bradman from?

8 If you take a shot in basketball from 22 feet away from the basket, how many points do you get?

9 When did Pat Rafter win the US Open Tennis Championships?

10 Anatoly Karpov and Jan Timman play what game?

11 How many goals did Stephan Stanis score for Lens against Aubry-Asturies in 1942?

12 Which two famous Rugby Union clubs have letters instead of numbers on the back of their shirts?

13 Where is the 'Princess Elizabeth Stakes' held?

14 Ingemar Stenmark is famous for which winter sport?

15 How many caps did Pelé win for Brazil?

ANSWERS

1. Football. 2. Jamaica. 3. Greg Norman. 4. Formula 1 Racing. 5. Middleweight. 6. Manchester United. 7. Australia. 8. Three. 9. 1997. 10. Chess. 11. 16. 12. Leicester and Bristol. 13. Epsom. 14. Slalom skiing. 15. 111 caps.

GENERAL KNOWLEDGE

1   Which US state lies between California and Utah?

2   In which year was the St Lawrence Seaway completed?

3   According to a famous speech by Shakespeare, how many ages of man are there?

4   What is the more common French name for zucchini?

5   Who partners Richard Madeley on daytime television?

6   In which year did Buddy Holly die?

7   Who coined the phrase 'A little learning is a dangerous thing'?

8   Which Chinese philosopher is sometimes referred to when giving wise advice?

9   Who was the first woman member of a British cabinet?

10 What kind of creature is a skink?

11 From which country does Emmenthal cheese come?

12 Proverbially, out of what should we not make a mountain?

13 In the Bible, which donkey was given the power of speech?

14 What is the eighth letter of the Greek alphabet?

15 From which animal does chèvre come?

ANSWERS

1. Nevada. 2. 1959. 3 Seven. 4. Courgette. 5. Judy Finnigan. 6. 1959.
7. Alexander Pope. 8. Confucius. 9. Margaret Bondfield (1929). 10. A lizard.
11. Switzerland. 12. A molehill. 13. Balaam's donkey. 14. Theta. 15. Goat.

SCIENCE & NATURE

1 What was the invention of the British scientist Joseph Swan?

2 Which is the more common name given to the constellation Ursa Major?

3 What is another name for the wild horse of North America?

4 What is the main constituent of china clay?

5 What is the SI unit of radioactivity?

6 What is a geophyte?

7 Which animal has the longest gestation period?

8 William Shockley, John Bardeen and Walter Brattain are credited as inventors of which device?

9 What is the jejunum?

10 What is shareware?

11 From which goat is mohair obtained?

12 Which metal forms part of the chlorophyl molecule?

13 What is the closest relative to the duck-billed platypus?

14 Where in the body would you find the hyoid bone?

15 What are all honey bee larvae fed on?

1. The electric lamp. 2. The Great Bear. 3. Mustang. 4. Kaolin. 5. Becquerel (Bq). 6. A plant, such as a bulb, that survives winter as an underground structure. 7. The Asian elephant (645 days). 8. The transistor. 9. Part of the small intestine. 10. Computer software distributed freely. 11. Angora. 12. Magnesium. 13. The spiny anteater. 14. The throat. 15. Royal jelly.

ENTERTAINMENT

1 Sergeant 'Pepper Anderson' was a character in which TV series?

2 What was the name of the 1973 film about a plot to assassinate de Gaulle, based on Frederick Forsyth's thriller?

3 The Pipes and Drums and Military Band of The Royal Scots Dragoon Guards had a number one hit in 1972 with which record?

4 'Popeye Popplewell', 'Claude Snudge' and 'Excused Boots Bisley' were characters in which TV comedy series, popular in the late 1950s and early 1960s?

5 Who had a number one hit in 1975 with 'Hold Me Close'?

6 Which actress played the title role in the 1965 film *Cat Ballou*?

7 What colour was The Artist Formerly Known as Prince's rain?

8 Who first presented the children's TV programme *Newsround*?

9 What was the surname of Freddy of Freddy and the Dreamers?

10 What was the name of the first film featuring 'Inspector Clouseau', played by Peter Sellers?

11 'Onslow' is a character in which TV series?

12 What letters of the alphabet had a hit with 'The Look of Love'?

13 Who had hits in 1968 with 'Jennifer Juniper' and 'Hurdy Gurdy Man'?

14 Which former *Blue Peter* presenter has also presented TV programmes about Crufts?

15 Which group sang with Desmond Dekker?

HISTORY

1   Who was king of England in the year 1600?

2   In which year did the Pilgrim Fathers set sail for New England aboard the *Mayflower*?

3   In which New England town was there a series of notorious witch trials in 1692?

4   Under the terms of which treaty did Britain obtain the territory of Gibraltar?

5   'The War of (Captain) Jenkins' Ear' involved which two European countries?

6   When was 'The War of Jenkins' Ear'?

7   Which Frenchman commanded a division of troops under George Washington in the American War of Independence and was a leading figure in the early stages of the French Revolution?

8   What was the name of the moderate party in the National Assembly during the French Revolution?

9   Robespierre was the leading figure in which somewhat inappropriately named committee during the 'Terror' period of the French Revolution?

10 The Battle of Inkerman took place during which war?

11 In which year did a World Exhibition take place in Paris in the latter part of the 19th century? (a) 1879, (b) 1889 or (c) 1899?

12 Which structure in Paris was built to mark the World Exhibition of that year?

13 Who told the parliament in Cape Town in 1960 that 'a wind of change' was blowing through the continent of Africa?

14 Antonio Salazar was the dictator of which country from 1932–68?

15 In which year were the first women priests ordained in the Church of England?

ANSWERS

1. There was no king of England in 1600. England was then ruled by Queen Elizabeth I. 2. 1620. 3. Salem, Massachusetts. 4. The Treaty of Utrecht, 1713. 5. Britain and Spain. 6. 1739. 7. The Marquis de Lafayette. 8. The Girondins or Girondists. 9. The Committee of Public Safety. 10. The Crimean War. 11. (b) 1889. 12. The Eiffel Tower. 13. British prime minister Harold Macmillan. 14. Portugal. 15. 1994.

FAMOUS PEOPLE

1 Which German statesman was nicknamed 'the Iron Chancellor'?

2 Who wrote: 'All I need to make a comedy is a park, a policeman and a pretty girl'?

3 Which British architect's buildings include Stansted Airport, the HQ of Hong Kong and Shanghai Bank, Hong Kong?

4 Which Irish writer had the middle names of Fingal O'Flahertie Wills?

5 Who was shot dead by Jack Ruby in November 1963?

6 Which female English biochemist won the Nobel Prize for Chemistry in 1964?

7 What name is shared by a 19th-century explorer, anthropologist and translator and a 20th-century stage and film actor?

8 Which influential English theologian converted from the Church of England to the Roman Catholic Church in 1845, becoming a cardinal in 1879?

9 Which US president said in his inaugural address: 'The only thing we have to fear is fear itself'?

10 Who in the Bible was swallowed by a large fish?

11 Who succeeded Nasser as president of Egypt in 1970?

12 Who met on the shore of Lake Tanganyika in 1871?

13 What was the surname of Nicholas II, the last tsar of Russia?

14 Which emperor of Ethiopia was known as 'the Lion of Judah'?

15 Whose book *Household Management* was published in 1861?

SPORT & LEISURE

1   Abel Resino holds the record for the longest period without conceding a goal. What Spanish football team was he playing for when he achieved it?

2   Björn Borg won Wimbledon five times. How many times did he win the French Open?

3   If you were at Waimea Bay, Hawaii, what sport would you be watching?

4   What is the distance between the two uprights on a Rugby goal?

5   Who scored the winning goal in the 1991 FA Cup Final?

6   Which man won 122 consecutive 400-metre hurdles races over a period of ten years?

7   Who was Michael Spinks' boxing brother who also won the Heavyweight World Championship?

8   In what county is the race course Kempton Park?

9   At which golf course did Nick Faldo win the 1987 and 1992 Open Championships?

10 In which South American country did William Weiler send 20 players off in a match?

11 How many players from a team do you have on the court at any one time in indoor volleyball?

12 Marcelo Rios became the world tennis number one in 1998. What country does he come from?

13 Is the Wing Attack allowed in the goal circle in the game of netball?

14 A triathlon consists of swimming, running and which other sport?

15 What sport did former TV breakfast presenter Sharron Davies compete in?

1. Athletico Madrid. 2. Six times. 3. Surfing. 4. 5.6 metres. 5. Des Walker. 6. Edwin Moses. 7. Leon Spinks. 8. Middlesex. 9. Muirfield. 10. Paraguay. 11. Six. 12. Chile. 13. No. 14. Cycling. 15. Swimming.

GENERAL KNOWLEDGE

1   What acronym describes the type of sleep associated with dreaming?

2   With which country do we associate haggis?

3   Of which country is Accra the capital?

4   Whose catchphrase was 'Who loves ya, baby'?

5   From which language do the words 'rabbi', 'amen' and 'kosher' originate?

6   What is the name of the famous French policeman played by Peter Sellers in the *Pink Panther* films?

7   In which year did the first Brook Advisory Clinic open to give birth control advice?

8   What is the name of the society that re-enacts historical scenes from the English Civil War?

9   Who first proposed the theory of relativity?

10 What is the nineteenth hole of a golf course?

11 What was Uri Geller famous for?

12 What is Thomas Bewick famous for?

13 Who coined the phrase 'God is dead'?

14 Who wrote the words of the hymn 'Amazing Grace'?

15 How long did rationing last during and after World War II?

1. REM (Rapid Eye Movement) sleep. 2. Scotland. 3. Ghana. 4. 'Kojak'. 5. Hebrew. 6. 'Inspector Jacques Clousseau'. 7. 1964. 8. The Sealed Knot Society. 9. Albert Einstein. 10. The bar of the clubhouse. 11. Bending spoons. 12. Engravings in wood and metal. 13. Nietzsche. 14. John Newton. 15. Fourteen and a half years.

SCIENCE & NATURE

1 Which is the world's fastest moving land mammal?

2 Which manmade construction connects the Pacific and Atlantic Oceans?

3 Where would you find the 'Great Red Spot'?

4 Which animals have an 'electric organ'?

5 What is another name for a tumblebug?

6 What is special about the temperatures of 16°C and 28°C?

7 From which plant is Java cotton, used for stuffing cushions, soft toys, etc, obtained?

8 Where in the human body would you find rods and cones?

9 Which species of dolphin is more usually befriended by humans?

10 How many bytes are there in a kilobyte of computer memory?

11 Which chemical element has the symbol Xe?

12 Salyicylic acid is the important ingredient of which drug?

13 SAD describes a form of depression which occurs in winter and is relieved by the coming of spring. What does the acronym stand for?

14 What is the full name for TNT?

15 To which phylum do humans belong?

15. Phylum Chordata.
11. Xenon. 12. Aspirin. 13. Seasonally Affective Disorder. 14. Trinitrotoluene.
8. In retina of the eye. 9. Bottlenose dolphin. 10. 1,000 but more accurately 1,024.
where the numbers are transposed: 61°F and 82°F. 7. Kapok.
5. Scarab beetle. 6. The equivalent temperature in Fahrenheit is equal to the figure
1. The cheetah. 2. Panama Canal. 3. On Jupiter. 4. Fish (used for stunning prey).

ENTERTAINMENT

1　Who starred in the TV series *Knight Rider*?

2　Who had a hit in 1961 with 'Hole in the Bucket'?

3　In 1987 Steven Spielberg directed a war-time film based on a novel by J. G. Ballard. What was it called?

4　What was the name of Bob's wife in the TV comedy series *The Likely Lads*?

5　Who played 'Fletcher Christian' in the 1984 film *The Bounty*?

6　In which year did The Beach Boys have a number one hit with 'Good Vibrations'?

7　Who was 'Labelled with Love' in 1981?

8　Which jazz musician had a hit in 1968 with 'What a Wonderful World'?

9　Who played the title role in the 1969 film *Hello Dolly*?

10　'Rhinestone Cowboy' was a hit in 1975 for which singer?

11　Who played the Irish policeman in the 1987 film *The Untouchables*?

12　Ugly Kid Joe got to number three with which song in May 1992?

13　'Garth' is a character in which TV comedy series?

14　Who played the title role in the 1964 film *Zorba the Greek*?

15　Who had hits in 1958 with 'Catch a Falling Star' and 'Magic Moments'?

HISTORY

1 In which year was Queen Elizabeth the Queen Mother born?

2 The Treaty of Vereeniging ended which war?

3 The first flight in a powered aircraft was made by the Wright brothers in which year?

4 In which year was the Entente Cordiale signed between Britain and France?

5 Which Scandinavian country became an independent kingdom in 1905?

6 Which Russian fleet was involved in the battle of Tsushima between Korea and Japan in 1905?

7 Which Japanese admiral led the victorious Japanese fleet in the Battle of Tsushima?

8 The first of what type of warship was launched in Britain in 1906?

9 In 1906 the USA sent a force of troops to restore order in which Caribbean island?

10 In which year did Robert Baden-Powell found the Boy Scout movement?

11 Which city hosted the Olympic Games of 1908?

12 Who were the joint winners of the Nobel prize for Physics in the year 1909?

13 In which year did the Union of South Africa come into being as a dominion within the British Empire?

14 Who, in 1910, founded Tolstoy Farm near Johannesburg as a co-operative for Indian workers?

15 Which famous Russian novelist died in November 1910?

ANSWERS

1. 1900. 2. The (Anglo-)Boer War. 3. 1903. 4. 1904. 5. Norway. 6. The Baltic fleet (it sailed halfway round the world to be crushingly defeated). 7. Admiral Togo. 8. The first dreadnought (HMS *Dreadnought*). 9. Cuba. 10. 1908. 11. London. 12. Guglielmo Marconi and Karl Ferdinand Braun. 13. 1910. 14. Gandhi. 15. Leo Tolstoy.

FAMOUS PEOPLE

1   Which South African writer won the Nobel Prize for Literature in 1991?

2   Who wrote the book *The Female Eunuch*?

3   What feat did John Alcock and Arthur Brown accomplish on 14–15 June 1919?

4   What nationality was the writer Jorge Luis Borges?

5   Who said 'How can you govern a country which has 246 varieties of cheese?'?

6   Which pope convened the Second Vatican Council?

7   Who painted *The Raft of the Medusa* (1816)?

8   Who is the only British prime minister to have been assassinated?

9   Who founded the Standard Oil Company in 1870?

10   Dion Fossey, the US zoologist, was best known for studying which animals?

11   Under what name did Vladimir Ilich Ulyanov become better known?

12   Who wrote the song 'White Christmas'?

13   What was the name of the English art critic who wrote *The Stones of Venice*?

14   Of which actress did Dorothy Parker say 'She ran the whole gamut of the emotions from A to B'?

15   What was the nickname of the German field marshal Erwin Rommel?

1. Nadine Gordimer. 2. Germaine Greer. 3. The first non-stop transatlantic flight. 4. Argentinian. 5. Charles de Gaulle. 6. John XXIII. 7. Theodore Géricault. 8. Spencer Perceval. 9. John D. Rockefeller. 10. Mountain gorillas. 11. Lenin. 12. Irving Berlin. 13. John Ruskin. 14. Katherine Hepburn. 15. The 'Desert Fox'.

SPORT & LEISURE

1 How many points do you get for a conversion in Rugby Union?

2 What sport evolved from the Polynesian practice of standing on canoes?

3 Where did Arsenal sign England International David Seaman from?

4 When were the women's singles added to the All England Tennis Championship?

5 Kingdom and Jackson were great rivals in what sporting event?

6 Who was the manager of Coventry City before Gordon Strachan?

7 Where is the Grand National held every year?

8 In what sport would you find a governing body called the PGA?

9 What cricket club do you associate with Geoffrey Boycott?

10 What does a yellow and red striped flag mean in Formula 1 racing?

11 What did Tottenham Hotspur win under the management of Bill Nicholson?

12 What position did the great Joe Montana play in American football?

13 How many fouls can a player commit in basketball until he/she has to leave the court?

14 Who was Eric Cantona playing against when he infamously kicked a supporter after being sent off?

15 In what hobby might you use a bell weight or/and a watch weight?

GENERAL KNOWLEDGE

1   With which country do we associate pizzas?

2   What is the raising agent in a cheese soufflé?

3   What is the name of the Danes, Norwegians and Swedes who raided Europe from the 8th to the 11th centuries?

4   Who wrote *Four Quartets* and *The Waste Land*?

5   In which year did J. Sainsbury open the first self-service store in Britain?

6   Who wrote the poems *The Rime of the Ancient Mariner* and *Kubla Khan*?

7   Who do the initials KFC stand for?

8   Who was the first Director-General of the BBC?

9   What is the name of the RAF jet aircraft aerobatics display team?

10   In which year was *Lady Chatterley's Lover* published?

11   Which philosophy was founded by L. Ron Hubbard?

12   What was Oliver Hardy's catchphrase?

13   'Gazza' is the nickname for who?

14   In computer language, what is 'spam'?

15   What country is called Blighty?

ANSWERS

1. Italy. 2. Eggs. 3. Vikings. 4. T. S. Eliot. 5. 1950. 6. Samuel Taylor Coleridge. 7. Kentucky Fried Chicken. 8. John Reith, 1st Baron. 9. The Red Arrows. 10. 1960. 11. Scientology. 12. 'Here's another fine mess you've gotten me into'. 13. Paul Gascoigne. 14. Unwanted e-mail messages. 15. England.

SCIENCE & NATURE

1   At what temperature do the Celsius and Fahrenheit scales converge?

2   Which planet in the Solar System takes over 247 years to orbit the Sun?

3   What is the astronomical name of the North Star?

4   What is another name for the rorqual whale?

5   What is the technical name for visual purple, the light sensitive pigment in the retina of the eye?

6   What are teratogenic substances?

7   What is spirogyra?

8   What is Kipps apparatus used for?

9   Who won the 1923 Nobel Prize for discovering insulin?

10 What is the name of the computer language developed at Sun Microsystems for network computing, especially on the Internet?

11 What is a baobab?

12 Where is myxomatosis indigenous?

13 What is the name of the process by which soft fats and oils are hardened to produce margarine?

14 What is a langur?

15 Besides heat, what is always formed when you mix an alkali and an acid?

ENTERTAINMENT

1   What is the name of the Australian wind instrument made from bamboo, made famous by Rolf Harris?

2   Who drove all night?

3   What was the setting for the TV comedy series *The Brittas Empire*?

4   The film *The Godfather* won the Best Picture Oscar in 1972. In which year did *The Godfather Part II* win an Oscar?

5   Who played Elizabeth I on television in 1971?

6   The song 'Come Follow the Band' comes from which musical?

7   'The Management' appear on which TV comedy show?

8   Which orchestra normally performs at the *Last Night of the Proms*?

9   What was the name of the character played by David Jason in the TV comedy series *Open All Hours*?

10 Who had a hit in 1960 with 'It's Now or Never'?

11 Who sang the TV theme for the 1990 World Cup?

12 Which American TV series featured Twiki, the helpful robot?

13 Who was the featured vocalist on Adamski's 'Killer'?

14 What was the follow-up series to *Porridge* starring Ronnie Barker?

15 In which cartoon film did a crab sing the song 'Under the Sea'?

HISTORY

1   What was the name of Christopher Columbus's flagship on his expedition of 1492?

2   In which group of islands did Columbus make his first landfall after crossing the Atlantic in 1492?

3   Which part of South America was discovered by Vincente Pinzón around 1500?

4   Who was asked to establish a line of demarcation to divide off Spanish from Portuguese territory in the new World?

5   Which Spanish conquistador burnt his fleet on the coast of Mexico in order to prevent his men from deserting?

6   Who was the Aztec emperor who initially welcomed the Spanish in a friendly fashion, but was imprisoned by them and forced to do homage to Spain?

7   Why was the Aztec emperor somewhat in awe of the Spaniards and disposed to be friendly to them?

8   Which modern city stands on the site of the old Aztec capital?

9   Who conquered the Inca empire and executed the Inca emperor Atahualpa?

10   The Spanish explorer Juan Rodriguez Cabrillo was the first European to sail the coast of which state of the USA?

11   Who was the author of the book *The History of the Conquest of New Spain*, which is an invaluable source of information about the activities of the conquistadors?

12   In which century did most of South America achieve their independence from Spain?

13   Which leader of Irish descent proclaimed the independence of Chile in 1817?

14   From 1821 to 1903 Panama formed part of which country?

15   Who was the first Englishman to see the Pacific Ocean?

1. *The Santa Maria*. 2. The Bahamas. 3. The Pope (Alexander VI). 4. Brazil. 5. Hernando Cortés. 6. Montezuma. 7. He thought they were gods arriving to fulfil an ancient prophecy. 8. Mexico City. 9. Francisco Pizarro. 10. California. 11. Bernal Díaz. 12. The 19th century. 13. Bernardo O'Higgins. 14. Colombia. 15. Sir Francis Drake.

FAMOUS PEOPLE

1 Which novelist, when working for the General Post Office, introduced the pillar-box to Britain?

2 Which US inventor said: 'Genius is one per cent inspiration, ninety-nine per cent perspiration'?

3 Who was the first woman to win a Nobel Prize?

4 Which British architect designed the Pompidou Centre in Paris and the Lloyd's building in London?

5 What nationality was the composer Franz Joseph Haydn?

6 Which Hollywood film producer said: 'A verbal contract isn't worth the paper it is written on'?

7 Who painted *A Bar at the Folies-Bergère* and *Déjeuner sur l'herbe*?

8 How was Wilhelm II popularly known during World War I?

9 How many times was Franklin D. Roosevelt elected president?

10 What was George Eliot's real name?

11 In what city did Sigmund Freud have his private practice from 1186 to 1938?

12 Who wrote *Waiting for Godot*?

13 To whom is the phrase 'There's a sucker born every minute' attributed?

14 Who was the founder of Pakistan?

15 How did Margaretha Geertruida Zelle become better known?

1. Anthony Trollope. 2. Thomas Edison. 3. Marie Curie. 4. Richard Rogers. 5. Austrian. 6. Sam Goldwyn. 7. Édouard Manet. 8. Kaiser Bill. 9. Four. 10. Mary Ann Evans. 11. Vienna. 12. Samuel Beckett. 13. Phineas T. Barnum. 14. Mohammad Ali Jinnah. 15. Mata Hari.

SPORT & LEISURE

1 How many years are there between Jimmy Connors' first win at Wimbledon and his last?

2 What country is famous golfer Gary Player from?

3 How many test matches did John Agnew play for England at cricket?

4 On what Formula 1 track do you find Copse Corner?

5 Who won the 1988 FA Cup Final?

6 In what athletic event did Emma George break the indoor and outdoor world record within the space of a week?

7 In what sport would you find Tony Allcock competing?

8 How many points do you get for a field goal in American football?

9 Who was the first foreign footballer (outside the UK) to captain a winning FA Cup side?

10 When did boxing become legal in Great Britain?

11 Which race course is the home of the Jockey Club?

12 What is the name of the type of skiing in which competitors have to go through gates?

13 If you have an ace, king, queen, jack and ten, of the same suit, what is this called in poker?

14 How many caps did Bobby Moore win for the England football team?

15 There are two types of competition in snow boarding. One is Alpine, what is the other called?

GENERAL KNOWLEDGE

1. What was the name of the yacht in which Sir Francis Chichester sailed around the world in 1966–67?

2. What is the stage name of Harry Roger Webb?

3. In radio, what do the initials CB stand for?

4. From which language do the words 'taffeta', 'bazaar' and 'caravan' originate?

5. Who wrote the novel *Frankenstein*?

6. Who was the 39th president of the USA?

7. What do the initials PVC stand for?

8. With which country do we associate sweet and sour dishes?

9. What do the initials RSI stand for?

10. Which canal links the Atlantic and Pacific Oceans?

11. What is a brioche?

12. What do the initials SEATO stand for?

13. Who was known as the Lady of the Lamp?

14. Who directed the films *Mr Smith Goes to Washington* and *It's a Wonderful Life*?

15. The word 'recondite' means (a) difficult to understand, (b) talkative, or (c) valuable?

1. *Gipsy Moth IV*. 2. Cliff Richard. 3. Citizens' Band. 4. Persian. 5. Mary Shelley. 6. Jimmy Carter. 7. Polyvinyl chloride. 8. China. 9. Repetitive strain injury. 10. The Panama Canal. 11. A kind of soft roll or loaf. 12. South East Asia Treaty Organization. 13. Florence Nightingale. 14. Frank Capra. 15. (a) difficult to understand.

SCIENCE & NATURE

1. What name is given to the female swan?

2. What name is commonly given to the line of longitude lying at 0 degrees?

3. What is another name for a snapdragon?

4. What is 'blue vitriol'?

5. If you suffer from agoraphobia, what are you afraid of?

6. What is the build-up of lactic acid in the body associated with?

7. What is a piddock?

8. How many centimetres are there in a metre?

9. What do saprophytes feed on?

10. In which year did the US spacecraft *Mars Pathfinder* land on Mars?

11. MDMA is another name for which illegal drug?

12. Approximately how many genes are there on one human DNA molecule?

13. Pb is the chemical symbol for which element?

14. Equilateral and scalene are types of what?

15. Maglev is a form of high speed surface transport. What does the name 'maglev' mean?

1. Pen. 2. The Greenwich Meridian. 3. Antirrhinum. 4. Copper sulphate. 5. Open spaces. 6. Excessive exercise. 7. A bivalve mollusc that bores into rocks and shells. 8. 100. 9. Non-photosynthesising plants feed on dead organic matter. 10. 1997. 11. Ecstasy (modified amphetamine). 12. About 80,000 genes. 13. Lead. 14. Triangle. 15. Magnetic levitation.

ENTERTAINMENT

1 Who had hits in the 1960s with 'England Swings' and 'Little Green Apples'?

2 Who played the title role in the TV series *Spender*?

3 The 1955 film *Blackboard Jungle* featured a song which became very important in the history of rock 'n' roll. What was it?

4 Which TV character refers to his wife as 'She who must be obeyed'?

5 The Pips were the backing group for which singer?

6 Which actor starred in the 1977 film *Smokey and the Bandit*?

7 In which year did Tony Hancock take his own life?

8 Which part did Angela Lansbury play in TV's *Murder She Wrote*?

9 Who had a number one hit in 1976 with 'Under the Moon of Love'?

10 Which real-life brothers played the Kray twins in the film *The Krays*?

11 Which TV current affairs presenter was known for wearing a bow-tie?

12 Who played Jesus Christ in the 1972 musical *Godspell*?

13 What kind of moon did Echo and the Bunnymen sing of?

14 Who played 'Wicksie' in the TV soap *EastEnders*?

15 Which animal featured in the film *Ring of Bright Water*?

1. Roger Miller. 2. Jimmy Nail. 3. 'Rock Around the Clock' by Bill Haley and the Comets. 4. 'Rumpole'. 5. Gladys Knight. 6. Burt Reynolds. 7. 1968. 8. 'Jessica Fletcher'. 9. Showaddywaddy. 10. Gary and Martin Kemp. 11. Robin Day. 12. David Essex. 13. 'The Killing Moon'. 14. Nick Berry. 15. An otter.

HISTORY

1 Which king of England set out on a crusade to Palestine in 1190?

2 Which sultan of Egypt and Syria and fierce opponent of the crusaders died in 1193?

3 Prince Arthur, a grandson of King Henry II of England, was murdered on the orders of his uncle. Who was his uncle?

4 Who was defeated and killed at the Battle of Evesham in 1265?

5 Edward, the Black Prince, was the son of which king of England?

6 At which battle is the Black Prince said to have won his nickname on account of the black armour that he wore?

7 Which son of the Black Prince became king of England?

8 What nationality was the religious reformer John or Johan Huss?

9 Lucrezia Borgia was the illegitimate daughter of which pope?

10 How many of the sons of Catherine de Medici (1519–89) became kings of France?

11 1618 marked the beginning of which major and long-running war on the continent of Europe?

12 Gustavus Adolphus was a king of which country?

13 John Hampden was prosecuted in 1637 for refusing to pay which tax imposed by King Charles I?

14 John Hampden was also one of how many members of the House of Commons that Charles I endeavoured to arrest in 1642?

15 The Long Parliament began to sit in 1640. In which year was it dissolved?

FAMOUS PEOPLE

1   Which US general was known as 'Blood and Guts'?

2   According to the Bible, who did God give the Ten Commandments to?

3   Who succeeded Leonid Brezhnev as General Secretary of the Communist Party of the USSR?

4   Which writer said: 'There are three kinds of lies; lies, damned lies, and statistics'?

5   Who wrote the 'Ode to Joy', which was later to be sung in Beethoven's Choral Symphony?

6   Which conductor founded the Royal Philharmonic Orchestra in 1947?

7   In 1918 who aimed 'to make Britain a fit country for heroes to live in'?

8   Whose works include The Seagull and The Cherry Orchard?

9   What was the real name of the 'Elephant Man'?

10 Which unit of speed is named after a 19th-century Austrian physicist?

11 What was the name of the British anthropologist and classical scholar who wrote The Golden Bough?

12 Of what country was Hastings Banda appointed prime minister in 1964?

13 The Nobel Prize for Literature was won by which Australian novelist in 1973?

14 Which actress is Warren Beatty's older sister?

15 Which English murderer lived at 10 Rillington Place?

285

SPORT & LEISURE

1 Who scored the winning goal in the 1987 FA Cup Final?

2 What athlete broke six world records in the space of 45 minutes?

3 What country does footballer Zinedine Zidane come from?

4 Who is tennis player Andre Agassi married to?

5 What is the name of the Cup in which female American professional golfers play against those from Europe?

6 Who won the 1995 Cricket World Cup?

7 On what circuit is the German Grand Prix held?

8 How many times did Liverpool win the FA Cup in the 1980s?

9 In what game do you have guards, centres and forwards?

10 What is the name of the Buffalo American football team?

11 Who did Naseem Hamed beat at Cardiff Arms Park in September 1995?

12 How many people are there in the front row in a Rugby Union team?

13 If you were at Sandown Park, what sport would you be watching?

14 When was the first Oxford and Cambridge University Boat Race?

15 Where did Newcastle buy striker Andy Cole from?

1. Gary Mabbutt. 2. Jesse Owens. 3. France. 4. Actress Brooke Shields. 5. Solheim Cup. 6. Sri Lanka. 7. Hockenheim. 8. Twice. 9. Basketball. 10. Buffalo Bill. 11. Steve Robinson. 12. Three players. 13. Horse racing. 14. 1829. 15. Bristol City FC.

GENERAL KNOWLEDGE

1 With which country do we associate moussaka?

2 'Nation shall speak peace unto nation' is the motto of which British institution?

3 What was the name of the kind of art that was popular in the late 1960s and was marked by swirling patterns of vivid colours?

4 Who hosted the TV talent spotting show *Opportunity Knocks*?

5 Which philosopher wrote *The Republic*?

6 Where is the Monaco Grand Prix held?

7 What was the name of the US Air Force base near Newbury at which anti-nuclear protesters set up camp?

8 What was the name of the three BBC TV science fiction series broadcast in the 1950s?

9 According to the proverb, who cannot be choosers?

10 What do the initials FBI stand for?

11 'Rapacity' means (a) greed, (b) haste or (c) severity?

12 Who shot Lee Harvey Oswald?

13 Which lesbian actor came out and saw her TV ratings fall dramatically?

14 Which BBC news correspondent became an MP at the general election in 1997?

15 What is an ostrich reputed to do when being pursued?

ANSWERS

1. Greece. 2. The BBC. 3. Psychedelic. 4. Hughie Green. 5. Plato. 6. In the streets of Monte Carlo. 7. Greenham Common. 8. *Quatermass*. 9. Beggars. 10. Federal Bureau of Investigation. 11. (a) greed. 12. Jack Ruby. 13. Ellen DeGeneres. 14. Martin Bell. 15. Bury its head in the sand.

SCIENCE & NATURE

1 Dietary deficiency of vitamin C gives rise to which disease?

2 A liquid with a pH of 6 is: (a) alkaline, (b) acid or (c) neutral?

3 The change in frequency of sound waves emitted by an object moving towards, then away from an observer is known as...?

4 Where is Britain's largest radiotelescope dish?

5 How many grams are there in one pound weight (avoirdupois)?

6 What 'E' number is tartrazine?

7 Conduction and radiation are two modes of heat transmission. What is the third?

8 What is the common name given to that part of the gut in which food is digested then absorbed?

9 What instrument would be used to examine the interior of the human eye?

10 Which is the only even prime number?

11 What name is given to the length of time between conception and birth, 40 weeks in humans?

12 Referring to temperature, what does the symbol 'K' stand for?

13 What does a hydrographer study?

14 Name three fat-soluble vitamins.

15 Give the number 'pi' to three decimal places.

ENTERTAINMENT

1   Which actress has starred in the TV series *The Darling Buds of May* and *Where The Heart Is*?

2   Who had a hit in 1967 with 'Silence is Golden'?

3   Which actor, born in 1895, played romantic heroes and whose best known film was *The Sheik*?

4   Robson and Jerome had a number one hit in 1996 with which song that had been a number one for Frankie Laine in 1953?

5   Sally Field, Dolly Parton, Julia Roberts and Daryl Hannah starred in which film about a beauty parlour?

6   Who played 'Audrey Fforbes-Hamilton' in *To The Manor Born*?

7   What did Musical Youth pass from the left hand side in September 1982?

8   Who had a hit in 1965 with 'Leader of the Pack'?

9   Who directed the 1984 film *Dune* and the TV series *Twin Peaks*?

10 What character does Roger Lloyd Pack play in the TV comedy series *Only Fools and Horses*?

11 Who played 'Major Gowen' in *Fawlty Towers*?

12 Which group had a hit in 1966 with 'Dedicated Follower of Fashion'?

13 Which role do Roger Moore and Val Kilmer have in common?

14 Who replaced Lesley Crowther as the presenter of TV's *Stars in Their Eyes*?

15 Who won an Oscar for Best Actor in 1997 for the film *As Good As It Gets*?

HISTORY

1 What makes Pope Adrian IV unique?

2 'Fair Rosamond' or Rosamunda was the mistress of which English king?

3 Hugh de Merville, William de Tracy, Reginald Fitzurse and Richard le Breton are notorious for which crime?

4 Santiago de Compostela became a centre of medieval pilgrimage through housing the relics of which saint?

5 The Court of the Star Chamber was established during the reign of which king of England?

6 Susanna Hall (her married name) was the daughter of which famous figure in English literary history?

7 William the Silent was one of the liberators from Spain of which country?

8 Which piece of territory in India, now the site of a major city, was given to England as part of the dowry of Catherine of Braganza, Charles II's queen?

9 What relation was the rebellious Duke of Monmouth to King Charles II?

10 The Duke of Wellington and the Emperor Napoleon were both born in the same year. Which year was it?

11 John Keble, Henry Newman and Edward Pusey were all leaders of which movement in the Church of England of the 1830s and 40s?

12 Which secret and feared organization in the USA was first founded in Pulaski Tennessee in 1865?

13 Where was the first steel-framed building erected in 1890?

14 Who was the prime minister of France who presided over the Peace Conference at Versailles in 1919?

15 Who was the first chancellor of West Germany after World War II?

ANSWERS

1. He is the only English pope (to date!). 2. Henry II. 3. The murder of Thomas à Becket. 4. Saint James (the Great). 5. King Henry VII. 6. William Shakespeare. 7. The Netherlands. 8. Bombay. 9. His illegitimate son (by Lucy Walter). 10. 1769. 11. The Oxford Movement. 12. The Ku Klux Klan. 13. In Chicago. 14. Georges Clemenceau. 15. Konrad Adenauer.

FAMOUS PEOPLE

1   Which German politician said that 'Politics is the art of the possible'?

2   Who wrote the short story *The Secret Life of Walter Mitty*?

3   Which US president used the atom bomb against Japan?

4   According to the Bible who met with Jesus Christ on the road to Damascus?

5   When was 'American Pie' released?

6   Who was known as the English 'Railway King'?

7   Who was the first American in space?

8   What was the pseudonym used by Hablot Knight Browne, illustrator of Dickens' novels?

9   Who wrote *Around the World in Eighty Days*?

10 What nationality was the mountaineer Edmund Hillary?

11 Who wrote the fable *The Tortoise and the Hare*?

12 London's National Theatre was designed by which architect?

13 Who was the supreme commander of the Allied forces during the Gulf War?

14 Which French writer and philosopher said: 'Hell is other people'?

15 In the 1940s whose legs were insured with Lloyds for $1 million?

ANSWERS

1. Otto von Bismarck. 2. James Thurber. 3. Harry S. Truman. 4. Saul (Paul).
5. 1972. 6. George Hudson. 7. Alan Shepard. 8. Phiz. 9. Jules Verne.
10. New Zealander. 11. Aesop. 12. Denys Lasdun. 13. General Norman Schwarzkopf.
14. Jean-Paul Sartre. 15. Betty Grable.

SPORT & LEISURE

1 Who won the 1980 FA Cup Final?

2 What does 'scratch' mean in golfing terms?

3 Clive Lloyd was the cricket captain of which country?

4 Who won the 1997 Formula 1 Constructors' Championship?

5 What club did Glenn Hoddle manage before he became the coach of the England national team?

6 If you are a Sixth Dan in Judo, what colour belt would you have?

7 Which Williams test driver became a Formula 1 World Champion?

8 Which football club did Chelsea sign Gian Luca Vialli from?

9 With which sport do you associate Vitus Gerulaitus?

10 What is the name given to the 'up and under' which is named after a famous Irish club?

11 Name the ex-Liverpool footballer that created the 'Predator' football boots?

12 On which racecourse would you find the Beecher's Brook jump?

13 What event is Bob Beamon famous for competing in?

14 How many players in a lacrosse team?

15 Does a netball goal post have a backboard?

ANSWERS

1. West Ham United. 2. No handicap (zero). 3. West Indies. 4. Williams Renault. 5. Chelsea. 6. Red and white belt. 7. Damon Hill. 8. Juventus. 9. Tennis. 10. Garryowen. 11. Craig Johnston. 12. Aintree. 13. Long jump. 14. Ten a side. 15. No.

GENERAL KNOWLEDGE

1   According to legend, who was fiddling while Rome burned?

2   What do the initials PRO stand for?

3   The predictions of which 16th century French prophet were used by the Nazis in World War II?

4   With which country do we associate paella?

5   Nepotism is (a) criticism, (b) favouritism, or (c) authoritarianism?

6   Which Australian singer who moved to Britain in the 1950s is well known for playing the didgeridoo?

7   Which satirical magazine was first published in October 1961?

8   In which year was the Barbie doll first produced?

9   Who played Dr Kildare in the TV series of that name?

10 What was Windscale later known as?

11 What was the name of the fat and greedy schoolboy created by Frank Richards?

12 What do the initials NIMBY stand for?

13 What does the Russian word 'glasnost' mean?

14 What do the initials EFTPOS stand for?

15 The Oder-Neisse line marked the frontier between which two countries after World War II?

1. Nero. 2. Public Relations Officer. 3. Nostradamus. 4. Spain. 5. (b) favouritism. 6. Rolf Harris. 7. *Private Eye*. 8. 1959. 9. Richard Chamberlain. 10. Sellafield. 11. 'Billy Bunter'. 12. Not in my back yard. 13. Openness. 14. Electronic funds transfer at point of sale. 15. Germany and Poland.

SCIENCE & NATURE

1   What is the name by which the food component non-starch polysaccharides are more commonly known?

2   At what temperature (Celsius) does water reach its minimum density?

3   What name is given to the heat required to turn boiling water into steam?

4   What name is given to an organism that lives on, and off its host?

5   Name the process that coats ferrous metals with a layer of zinc to prevent rusting.

6   What ingredient is used, with sugar, to make meringue?

7   Which light has the shortest wavelength – ultra-violet or infra-red?

8   The disease atopic dermatitis is more commonly known by what name?

9   What is the pigment that gives most plants their green colour?

10 What did Joseph Bramah invent in 1778?

11 The smallest blood-vessels in the human body are known as...?

12 What element comprises 70 percent of our sun's mass?

13 What animals would you find in an apiary?

14 What disease is caused by an intolerance to the cereal protein gluten?

15 How many degrees are there in a quadrant?

ENTERTAINMENT

1   Which actor starred in the TV comedy series *Roseanne* and the film *The Borrowers*?

2   'Tiger Feet' was a number one hit in 1974 for which group?

3   In the Disney film *Robin Hood*, which animal played the title role?

4   Gillian Taylforth played which character in TV's *EastEnders*?

5   Which song has been a number one for Jimmy Young in 1955, the Righteous Brothers in 1990 and Robson and Jerome in 1995?

6   What was the name of the lion in the 1966 film *Born Free*?

7   Name the two number ones Wham had in 1984.

8   Which comedian portrays the character 'Theophilus P. Wildebeaste' in sketches?

9   Who played the title roles in the film *Twins*?

10   What are the names of the 'Teletubbies'?

11   Which group had a hit in 1965 with 'Mr Tambourine Man'?

12   Which singer starred in the film *Moonstruck*?

13   Who got blinded with science?

14   Nick Hancock presents which TV sports quiz programme?

15   Which two people had a 1960 hit with 'Goodness Gracious Me'?

1. John Goodman. 2. Mud. 3. A fox. 4. Kathy Mitchell. 5. Unchained Melody'.
6. 'Elsa'. 7. 'Wake Me up Before You Go Go' and 'Freedom'. 8. Lenny Henry.
9. Arnold Schwarzenegger and Danny De Vito. 10. 'Tinky Winky', 'Dipsy', 'Laa-Laa'
and 'Po'. 11. The Byrds. 12. Cher. 13. Thomas Dolby. 14. *They Think It's All Over*.
15. Peter Sellers and Sophia Loren.

HISTORY

1   Which English cathedral was damaged by an earthquake during the Middle Ages?

2   Which European capital city was devastated by an earthquake in 1755?

3   Which American city was largely destroyed by a fire in 1871 that supposedly began when a cow kicked over a lantern?

4   The first fire insurance in the USA was organized in 1752. By whom?

5   In which year did the volcano erupt on Krakatoa?

6   In which year was San Francisco devastated by an earthquake?

7   An estimated 20 million deaths were caused worldwide in 1918 and 1919 by an epidemic of which disease?

8   Which seaside town in England was devastated by a flash flood in August 1952?

9   The Aberfan disaster in Wales, in which 144 people were killed by a collapsing slag heap, occurred in which year?

10 In which year of the 20th century did Mount St Helens in the northwestern United States erupt after lying dormant for over 100 years?

11 On which river was one of the world's largest flood barriers opened in 1983?

12 Who in 1984 established the 'Bandaid Trust' principally to raise money for famine relief in Africa?

13 A cyclone and tidal wave killed 10,000 people in which country in 1985?

14 The world's largest oil spillage took place in Alaska in 1989 as a result of damage to which ship?

15 Which Japanese city suffered a devastating earthquake in 1995?

ANSWERS

1. Canterbury Cathedral. 2. Lisbon. 3. Chicago. 4. Benjamin Franklin. 5. 1883. 6. 1906. 7. Influenza. 8. Lynmouth in Devon. 9. 1966. 10. 1980. 11. The River Thames (at Woolwich). 12. Bob Geldof. 13. Bangladesh. 14. *The Exxon Valdez*. 15. Kobe.

FAMOUS PEOPLE

1 What invention did James Hargreaves patent in 1770?

2 In 1991 an actress posed naked and heavily pregnant on the front cover of *Vanity Fair*. Who was she?

3 Who commanded the US forces at the Normandy invasion in 1944?

4 The same name is shared by an Irish nationalist leader and a US astronaut. What is it?

5 Who was Britain's prime minister when Queen Victoria died?

6 The new cathedral at Coventry was designed by which architect?

7 Who painted *The Fighting Téméraire* (1838)?

8 In what country was the writer Albert Camus born?

9 Who said on 10 March 1876, 'Mr Watson, come here; I want you'?

10 What was named after Theodore Roosevelt?

11 Who successfully renounced the title Viscount Stansgate in 1963 so that he could sit as an MP in the House of Commons?

12 Which one of Jesus' disciples was originally a tax collector?

13 Who said in 1940: 'I'm glad we've been bombed. It makes me feel I can look the East End in the face'?

14 At what address did Sherlock Holmes live?

15 Whose compositions include the choral work *War Requiem*, based on the poems of Wilfred Owen?

ANSWERS

1. The spinning-jenny. 2. Demi Moore. 3. Omar Bradley. 4. Michael Collins. 5. Robert Cecil, Lord Salisbury. 6. Basil Spence. 7. J. M. W. Turner. 8. Algeria. 9. Alexander Graham Bell. 10. The teddy bear. 11. Tony Benn. 12. Matthew (Levi). 13. Queen Elizabeth, the Queen Mother. 14. 221B Baker Street. 15. Benjamin Britten.

SPORT & LEISURE

1 Who did Aston Villa beat in the Coca Cola Cup Final in season 1996/97?

2 In Britain, what is the term used for a score of three under par on a hole in golf?

3 In what year was the first women's cricket World Cup?

4 The A1 Ring is the home of what Formula 1 Grand Prix?

5 Jonathan Edwards and Willie Banks are famous for what sporting event?

6 Who are the Celtics in American football?

7 Who is Sheffield's Boxing Prince?

8 How many spiked points are there on a Backgammon board?

9 Who replaced Gary Lineker as a substitute in what turned out to be Lineker's final match for England?

10 What animal do you associate with the touring British Isles Rugby Union touring team?

11 On which racecourse is the Whitbread Gold Cup held?

12 What is darts player Eric Bristow's nickname?

13 What kind of games are Round the Clock, Seven Up and Lovely Lucy?

14 Which ex-player became the president of Bolton Wanderers?

15 Where did Manchester United buy Eric Cantona from?

298

GENERAL KNOWLEDGE

1   In which year did the government launch its campaign 'Careless Talk Costs Lives'?

2   The slogan ' It's the real thing' was used to advertise what product?

3   In which chapter of the book of Exodus in the Bible are the Ten Commandments quoted?

4   What is the connection between an explanation of the origin of the universe and the major modernization, in 1986, of the London Stock Exchange?

5   How are you travelling if you do so as the crow flies?

6   What is the common name for the larynx?

7   Who created the character 'Biggles'?

8   What is the name of the practice of raising the price of a house after agreeing a price verbally with an intended buyer?

9   In which county is the River Medway?

10 Which famous military march was written by Major F. J. Ricketts?

11 In which book come the words 'It is a far, far better thing that I do, than I have ever done; it is a far, far better rest that I go to, than I have ever known'?

12 Who was the first woman to read the main evening news on BBC TV?

13 What was the nickname of Louis Armstrong?

14 From which language do the words 'bungalow', 'chintz' and 'bangle' originate?

15 Who starred in the film *Rebel Without A Cause*?

ANSWERS

1. 1940. 2. Coca-Cola. 3. Chapter 20. 4. They are both called the Big Bang. 5. In a straight line. 6. Voice box. 7. Captain W. E. Johns. 8. Gazumping. 9. Kent. 10. 'Coloney Bogey'. 11. *A Tale of Two Cities*. 12. Angela Rippon. 13. Satchmo. 14. Hindi. 15. James Dean.

SCIENCE & NATURE

1 How many calories (kcal) are gained from eating 1g (0.03oz) of fat?

2 How many sides has an octagon?

3 What travels at 330m (360.8yds) per second?

4 Does a refracting telescope use a lens or a mirror to collect light from a distant object?

5 What unit is used to measure sound?

6 What is the atomic number for the chemical element carbon?

7 What is measured with an aneroid barometer?

8 What name is given to the type of enzyme that catalyses the breakdown of fats?

9 What is the name of the major vein by which blood returns from the head to the heart?

10 What would you measure with a hygrometer?

11 Icterus is an alternative name for what?

12 What is the name of the compound that comprises 25 to 30 percent of the wood in trees?

13 Your computer has a BIOS. What do the letters of this acronym stand for?

14 A dietary deficiency of which trace element, gives rise to a loss of the senses of taste and smell?

15 Two circles with the same centre point are said to be...?

ANSWERS

ENTERTAINMENT

1   Which actor appeared in TV's *EastEnders* and *Paradise Club*?

2   Gary Puckett sang with which group?

3   Who played the title role in the 1974 film *The Great Gatsby*?

4   What is the nickname of the DIY expert on TV's *Changing Rooms*?

5   Who had number one hits in the early 1970s with 'In the Summer Time' and 'Baby Jump'?

6   Which actress starred with Bing Crosby and Frank Sinatra in the film *High Society*?

7   In 1988, 'The King of Rock 'n' Roll' was a top ten hit for which band?

8   Spike Milligan had a series of comedy shows whose title was which letter of the alphabet?

9   Harry Belafonte in 1957 and Boney M in 1978 had number one hits with which song?

10 Tommy Lee Jones and Will Smith starred in which 1997 film?

11 Which folk group had a hit in the 1960s with 'Leavin' on a Jet Plane'?

12 Which classical actor won an Oscar for his role in the 1981 film *Arthur*?

13 What was the favourite fruit of The Presidents of the United States of America?

14 Colin Firth played which character in the 1990s TV serialization of *Pride and Prejudice*?

15 Who had a hit in 1964 with 'I Love You Because'?

301

1. Leslie Grantham. 2. Union Gap. 3. Robert Redford. 4. 'Handy Andy'. 5. Mungo Jerry. 6. Grace Kelly. 7. Prefab Sprout. 8. 'Q'. 9. 'Mary's Boy Child'. 10. *Men in Black*. 11. Peter, Paul and Mary. 12. John Gielgud. 13. Peaches. 14. 'Mr Darcy'. 15. Jim Reeves.

HISTORY

1   The architect Louis Le Vau began the extension and remodelling of which French palace in 1661?

2   Richard 'Beau' Nash was a notable Master of Ceremonies and improver of manners in which English city?

3   Joseph Addison and Richard Steele founded which famous British periodical in 1711?

4   Lancelot Brown, William Kent and Humphrey Repton all achieved success in 18th-century Britain as what?

5   Which friend of the writers Pope and Swift made a fortune by improving the postal service between Bath and London and providing stone for the rebuilding and expansion of the city of Bath?

6   To which remote part of the British Isles did Dr Samuel Johnson and his biographer James Boswell make a journey in 1773?

7   'Who's your fat friend?' was a slighting reference to the future King George IV made by which former friend of his?

8   Who was responsible for the introduction of the penny post in Britain in 1840?

9   Frederick Law Olmsted and Calvert Vaux designed which major feature of the city of New York in 1857?

10   Which town-planner remodelled and improved Paris for the Emperor Napoleon III?

11   The model industrial town of Port Sunlight on the Mersey was founded in the late 19th century by which industrial magnate?

12   Sir Ebenezer Howard is associated with what type of urban environment?

13   In which year was the centre of the English city of Coventry devastated by an air raid?

14   In which year was the new Coventry cathedral consecrated?

15   Which new capital city was begun in 1957, dedicated in 1960 and contains many buildings by the architect Oscar Niemeyer?

FAMOUS PEOPLE

1 Who did Idi Amin overthrow in 1971 to seize power in Uganda?

2 What is Tony Blackburn famous for doing first?

3 Who wrote the poem *The Owl and the Pussy-Cat*?

4 Which US politician said: 'Power is the great aphrodisiac'?

5 What was Jenny Lind also known as?

6 Which 1st-century BC Egyptian queen was renowned for her beauty, charm and luxurious living?

7 Which Irish writer wrote the autobiographical novel *Borstal Boy*?

8 The first use of radio for police purposes resulted in the arrest of which murderer?

9 What nationality was the composer Béla Bartók?

10 To whom is the phrase 'Publish and be damned' attributed?

11 Who wrote *The Condition of the Working Classes in England (1845)*?

12 Who was the 40th president of the US?

13 Who sailed solo around the world in 1966–67 in *Gipsy Moth IV*?

14 From whose painting *Impression: Sunrise* is the term Impressionism derived?

15 Where was Martin Luther King assassinated?

ANSWERS

1. President Milton Obote. 2. He was the first DJ on Radio 1. 3. Edward Lear. 4. The 'Swedish nightingale'. 5. Jenny Lind. 6. Cleopatra. 7. Brendan Behan. 8. Hawley Harvey Crippen. 9. Hungarian. 10. The Duke of Wellington. 11. Friedrich Engels. 12. Ronald Reagan. 13. Francis Chichester. 14. Claude Monet. 15. Memphis, Tennessee.

SPORT & LEISURE

1 What is the name of Derby County's former ground?

2 If you have the 'Yips' in golf, what do you have?

3 In what year did Michael Atherton become the England cricket captain?

4 What colour flag is held out to warn of dangerous conditions on a Formula 1 racing track?

5 Willie Wood and Peter Belliss are famous for what game?

6 When a Quarter Back is tackled or put down in American football, what is this called?

7 'Posh' is the nickname of which football club?

8 In which year did Virginia Wade win the women's Wimbledon singles title?

9 Which Premiership football club did Nigel Winterburn, Dennis Wise and Dave Beasant all play for at one time?

10 In football they are called assistant referees, what are they called in Rugby?

11 If you are at the *Prix de L'Arc de Triomphe*, what sport would you be watching?

12 In what game might you 'spike the ball'?

13 What did boxer Walker Smith change his name to?

14 What game is about the rise and fall of empires and the conquest of the world?

15 Who was the manager of Leeds United when they won the Premier League in the 1990s?

1. The Baseball Ground. 2. A nervous twitch which inhibits putting. 3. 1993. 4. Yellow Flag. 5. Bowls. 6. Sacked. 7. Peterborough. 8. 1977. 9. Wimbledon. 10. Touch Judges. 11. Horse racing. 12. Volleyball. 13. Sugar Ray Robinson. 14. Risk. 15. Howard Wilkinson.

GENERAL KNOWLEDGE

1 Who said that his goal was thanks to 'the hand of God'?

2 Where is Traitors' Gate?

3 Which German village is famous for its Passion Play performed every ten years in thanksgiving for the end of the Black Death?

4 Which town is the capital of the Isle of Man?

5 What died on 29 August 1882?

6 Who wrote the play *Cavalcade*?

7 Which Scottish novelist and dramatist in his play *Housemaster* wrote: 'Funny peculiar, or funny ha-ha'?

8 St Francis de Sales is the patron saint of whom?

9 Which novelist created the characters 'Bertie Wooster' and 'Jeeves'?

10 If your surname is 'Murphy', what might your nickname be?

11 From which language do the words 'robot', 'pistol' and 'howitzer' originate?

12 Which anniversary does a crystal wedding celebrate?

13 Which novel set in Yorkshire features 'Catherine Earnshaw' and 'Heathcliff'?

14 What does 'circa' or '*c.*' in connection with dates mean?

15 A kohlrabi is a cross between which two vegetables?

1. Maradona. 2. The Tower of London. 3. Oberammergau. 4. Douglas. 5. English cricket, after the England cricket team's defeat by the Australians; the 'ashes' were taken to Australia. 6. Noël Coward. 7. Ian Hay (John Hay Beith). 8. Authors and journalists. 9. P. G. Wodehouse. 10. 'Spud'. 11. Czech. 12. The fifteenth. 13. *Wuthering Heights*. 14. About or around. 15. A cabbage and a turnip.

SCIENCE & NATURE

1   Pellagra is the disease caused by a dietary deficiency of which vitamin?

2   How many sides has a dodecagon?

3   Which element is the best conductor of heat: copper or helium?

4   What is the chemical symbol for mercury?

5   What name is given to a device that stores energy in a rotating mechanism?

6   What is the major stimulant compound to be found in tea?

7   What instrument will refract white light into its component colours?

8   If you were suffering from an epistaxis, what would be happening to you?

9   What is the Latin name given to the class of vertebrates commonly called fish?

10 Which direction does a horizontal magnetic needle naturally turn to?

11 What is the name given to the great artery carrying oxygenated blood away from the heart?

12 What name is given to cells which combine to make up nervous tissue?

13 Which traditional Christmas evergreen plant is named after an American diplomat?

14 Goitre (enlarged thyroid gland) is caused by a dietary deficiency of which trace element?

15 For a right angled triangle, with sides a, b, and c, state the algebraic description of Pythagoras' theorem.

ANSWERS

1. Nicotinic acid (Niacin). 2. Twelve. 3. Copper. 4. Hg. 5. A flywheel. 6. Caffeine. 7. A prism. 8. Your nose would be bleeding. 9. *Pisces*. 10. North. 11. The aorta. 12. Neurones. 13. Poinsettia, from Joel Roberts Poinsett. 14. Iodine. 15. $a^2 + b^2 = c^2$.

ENTERTAINMENT

1   Which actor, famous for appearing in westerns starred with Bob Hope in *Son of Paleface*?

2   Who composed *The Rite of Spring*?

3   Tony Britton and Nigel Havers played father and son doctors in which TV comedy series?

4   What is the name of the 1968 film, starring Jack Lemmon and Walter Matthau, based on a play by Neil Simon?

5   Who had a number one hit in 1968 with 'Ob-La-Di, Ob-La-Da'?

6   Which comedian has appeared on TV commercials for John Smith's beer?

7   Who encouraged you to 'Pull Up to the Bumper'?

8   The *Naked Gun* films were developed from which TV comedy series?

9   What is the name of the famous male Russian ballet dancer, who died in 1950?

10 Who plays 'Deirdre Rachid' in *Coronation Street?*

11 Which ex-member of Roxy Music went on to pursue a solo career of electronic composition and has produced many bands including U2?

12 What was the name of the early successful monster film, based on a story by Edgar Wallace?

13 Who played the title role in the TV series *Maigret*?

14 What names were the three Marx brothers known by in their films?

15 In Harry Enfield's TV comedy shows, who plays 'Waynetta Slob'?

1. Roy Rogers. 2. Igor Stravinsky. 3. *Don't Wait Up*. 4. *The Odd Couple*. 5. Marmalade. 6. Jack Dee. 7. Grace Jones. 8. *Police Squad*. 9. Nijinsky. 10. Anne Kirkbride. 11. Brian Eno. 12. *King Kong*. 13. Rupert Davis. 14. 'Chico', 'Harpo' and 'Groucho'. 15. Kathy Burke.

HISTORY

1 Who was king of England in the year 1700?
2 What relation was Charles Edward Stewart (Bonnie Prince Charlie) to King James II of England (VII of Scotland)?
3 Who helped Bonnie Prince Charlie to escape from the Scottish mainland after his defeat at Culloden in 1746?
4 The French general Louis Montcalm was killed in the defence of which city in 1759?
5 In which year did British forces win the Battle of Minden in Germany?
6 Edmund Burke and Richard Brinsley Sheridan were among the Members of Parliament who played an active part in the impeachment of which former English adminstrator in India?
7 Who, reflecting on the French Revolution, lamented that 'the age of chivalry has gone. That of sophisters, economists and calculators has succeeded; and the glory of Europe is extinguished for ever'?
8 Which of the following leading French revolutionaries did not end his life on the guillotine: Danton, Camille Desmoulins, Mirabeau, Robespierre, Saint-Just?
9 The British author of the book *The Rights of Man* escaped to revolutionary France to escape being indicted for treason in Britain – who was he?
10 Two future British foreign secretaries fought a duel over the failure of the Walcheren expedition against Napoleon in 1809. Who were they?
11 Which British prime minister was assassinated in 1812?
12 Who defeated whom at the Battle of Blood River in 1838?
13 The Australian city of Adelaide was named after the wife of which British monarch?
14 Count Radetzky (1766–1858) was a noted commander in which army?
15 Who was the first king of Italy?

FAMOUS PEOPLE

1 Who was the first American woman in space?

2 How is Allen Stewart Konigsberg better known?

3 Who, in 1935, became the first man to break 300 mph on land at Bonneville Salt Flats, Utah?

4 What was Bessie Smith also known as?

5 Whose novels include *Lord Jim* and *Nostromo*?

6 Which US president said: 'Read my lips: no new taxes'?

7 Who succeeded Charles de Gaulle as president of France in 1969?

8 What nationality was the psychologist Carl Jung?

9 Who was the founder of the Church of Scientology?

10 Who delivered the Gettysburg Address?

11 'He hasn't an enemy in the world, and none of his friends like him.' Who was Oscar Wilde talking about?

12 When was the first successful human heart transplant performed?

13 Who composed the opera *Fidelio*?

14 How is William Frederick Cody better known?

15 Who was the 'Acid bath murderer'?

ANSWERS

1. Sally Ride. 2. Woody Allen. 3. Malcolm Campbell. 4. 'Empress of the Blues'. 5. Joseph Conrad. 6. George Bush. 7. Georges Pompidou. 8. Swiss. 9. L. Ron Hubbard. 10. Abraham Lincoln. 11. George Bernard Shaw. 12. 1967. 13. Ludwig von Beethoven. 14. Buffalo Bill. 15. John George Haigh.

SPORT & LEISURE

1 In what sport does Heinz Harald Frentzen compete?

2 Who missed a penalty in the 1988 FA Cup Final?

3 Who was the captain of the winning team in the 1987 Cricket World Cup Final?

4 What is a 'one wood' better known as in golf?

5 Who was the manager of Charlton Athletic in season 1998/99?

6 Robin Cousins is famous for which sport?

7 Where do the Ireland Rugby Union team play their home games?

8 Did John Francome ever win the Grand National?

9 Which Premiership football team were formerly called the 'Thames Ironworks FC'?

10 Can a Goal Attack score in a game of netball?

11 What stroke is swimmer Nick Gillingham known for?

12 Which is older, the London or the New York marathon?

13 How many metres are there between hurdles in a 400m hurdle race?

14 Who is the chairman of Chelsea Football Club?

15 What colour is Piccadilly Circus in the game of *Monopoly*?

ANSWERS

1. Formula 1. 2. John Aldridge. 3. Allan Border. 4. A Driver. 5. Alan Curbishley. 6. Figure Skating. 7. Lansdowne Road. 8. No. 9. West Ham United. 10. Yes. 11. Breaststroke. 12. New York. 13. 35m (38.3 yds). 14. Ken Bates. 15. Yellow.

GENERAL KNOWLEDGE

1 Which English painter is known for his paintings of bleak industrial scenes with dark, matchsticklike figures?

2 Who, or what, is 'Ernie'?

3 What is the meaning of the expression 'lily livered': (a) cowardly, (b) brave or (c) white?

4 Osiris was a god of ancient Egypt. What was his domain?

5 What did 'Tonto' always call the 'Lone Ranger'?

6 Who was Sir Frank Brangwyn?

7 Who won the Five Nations Rugby Union Championship in 1997?

8 What does it signify when eight bells are sounded at sea?

9 The Jolly Roger is the traditional flag of what?

10 Westminster Abbey is over 166 metres long. True or false?

11 With which country do we associate poppadoms and chapattis?

12 St Peter is the patron saint of whom?

13 A Bramley is what kind of fruit?

14 What is fascism?

15 Which is Scotland's largest lake?

ANSWERS

1. L. S. Lowry. 2. The Electronic Random Number Indicator Equipment for drawing Premium Bonds. 3. (a) cowardly. 4. The underworld. 5. 'Kemo Sabe'. 6. Artist, illustrator and designer. 7. France. 8. The end of a watch of four hours. 9. Pirates. 10. True. 11. India. 12. Fishermen. 13. Apple. 14. A system of government which has only one political party headed by a dictator. 15. Loch Lomond.

SCIENCE & NATURE

1   Which vitamin is also produced in human skin on exposure to sunlight?

2   The Universal Gravitational Constant is represented by which letter?

3   What popular organic compound is represented by the formula $C_2H_{50}H$?

4   In which year did men last walk on the Moon; (a) 1973, (b) 1971 or (c) 1972?

5   What is the chemical name for Heavy Water?

6   What is the Murray-Darling?

7   What is measured using a photometer?

8   Veins carry blood towards, or away from the heart?

9   What name is given to the phase of the heart beat when cardiac muscle contracts?

10   What collective name is given to the group of elements comprising; Fluorine, Chlorine, Bromine, and Iodine?

11   What is the name given to the light-sensitive layer at the back of the eye?

12   What was the name of the priest, credited with having founded the science of genetics?

13   What do the letters VGA denote?

14   What is the name of the principal disaccharide found in all milks?

15   How many centimetres are there in one inch (to two decimal places)?

ANSWERS

1. Vitamin D. 2. G. 3. Ethyl alcohol. 4. (a) 1973. 5. Deuterium Oxide. 6. The longest river in Australia. 7. Light intensity. 8. Away from the heart. 9. Systole. 10. The Halogens. 11. The retina. 12. Abbé Gregor Mendel. 13. Video Graphics Array. 14. Lactose. 15. 2.54.

ENTERTAINMENT

1 David McCallum and Joanna Lumley starred in which TV series?

2 Who provided the cartoon character 'Mickey Mouse' with his voice in the first few years?

3 The Beatles' song 'Norwegian Wood' features which Indian instrument?

4 What was the nickname of the TV cook Graham Kerr?

5 Which composer wrote the cycle of operas called *The Ring*?

6 What is the maiden name of 'Marge Simpson' of the TV cartoon series *The Simpsons*?

7 Who played the title role in the film *Hans Christian Anderson*?

8 Name the star who interrupted Michael Jackson's Brit Awards performance, and the band from which this person came.

9 Who had a number one hit in 1968 with 'Mighty Quinn'?

10 In which year was the first *Monty Python's Flying Circus* shown on TV?

11 Which film actor had a leading role in the TV series *Rawhide*?

12 'Mezzanine' was the 1998 album for which creators of electronic music?

13 Which female entertainer, born in 1870, was a great star of London's music halls and was famous for the song 'Don't Dilly Dally on the Way'?

14 Who played the title roles in the 1990s TV series *Jeeves and Wooster*?

15 The song 'Can You Feel the Love Tonight' won an Oscar for Best Original Song from which film?

ANSWERS

1. *Sapphire and Steel*. 2. Walt Disney. 3. Sitar. 4. 'The Galloping Gourmet'. 5. Richard Wagner. 6. 'Bouvier'. 7. Danny Kaye. 8. Jarvis Cocker from Pulp. 9. Manfred Mann. 10. 1969. 11. Clint Eastwood. 12. Massive Attack. 13. Marie Lloyd. 14. Stephen Fry ('Jeeves') and Hugh Laurie ('Wooster'). 15. *The Lion King*.

HISTORY

1   What did the USA purchase from France for 15 million dollars in 1803?

2   Which future American president was involved in negotiating this purchase?

3   Which American state was an independent republic for ten years before joining the Union in 1845?

4   Which territory did General Stephen Kearny claim for the United States in 1846?

5   Brigham Young was the leader of which American religious group?

6   The followers of Brigham Young settled and founded which US state?

7   John Charles Frémont is famous for exploring what?

8   Who acted as Frémont's scout on several of his expeditions?

9   In which year did the California gold rush take place?

10 Which means of communication in the American West was inaugurated in 1860?

11 Which legendary American lawman and gunfighter settled at Tombstone, Arizona in 1879?

12 What was Billy the Kid's real name?

13 From whom did the USA purchase Alaska in 1867?

14 Which future American president was born in the cattle town of Abilene, Kansas in 1890?

15 Which territory, now a state of the Union, was formally annexed by the USA in 1898?

FAMOUS PEOPLE

1   Who did Clementine Ogilvy Hozier marry in 1908?

2   Whose stories were translated into English in 1846?

3   Who became US president after Abraham Lincoln was shot?

4   Who wrote *To the Lighthouse*?

5   Which jazz musician was known as 'Bird'?

6   What did Prince Charles describe in 1984 as 'a monstrous carbuncle on the face of a much-loved and elegant friend'?

7   Of whose life is the film *Yankee Doodle Dandy* (1942) the story?

8   What nationality was the soprano Dame Nellie Melba?

9   Which film actress was 'the It Girl'?

10 What was the name of the leader of Czechoslovakia removed from office after the Soviet-led invasion in 1968?

11 In 1948 who, as Minister of Health, introduced the National Health Service?

12 Which French painter spent much of his life in Tahiti?

13 Who founded the Habitat company in 1971?

14 Who described religion as 'the opium of the people'?

15 Which architectural historian wrote *The Buildings of England* (1951–74)?

1. Winston Churchill. 2. Hans Christian Andersen. 3. Andrew Johnson. 4. Virginia Woolf. 5. Charlie Parker. 6. The proposed extension to the National Gallery, London. 7. George Cohan. 8. Australian. 9. Clara Bow. 10. Alexander Dubcek. 11. Aneurin Bevan. 12. Paul Gauguin. 13. Terence Conran. 14. Karl Marx. 15. Nikolaus Pevsner.

SPORT & LEISURE

1. Who became the oldest player to play in the NBA in April 1997?

2. Newton Heath became which world famous club?

3. Is the Walker Cup golf competition for amateurs or professionals?

4. When was the first Cricket World Cup?

5. Renaldo Nehemiah was famous for which athletic event?

6. Who scored the winning goal in the 1979 FA Cup Final?

7. What was the nickname of legendary West Indian fast bowler Joel Garner?

8. How many players in an ice hockey team?

9. What sport is Alberto Tomba known for?

10. Who won the Snooker World Championships between 1992 and 1995?

11. Who saved a penalty in the 1991 FA Cup Final?

12. In what year was Tim Henman born?

13. How many times did Muhammad Ali draw a boxing contest?

14. Which goalkeeper scored in the 1967 Charity Shield?

15. What is the first property that you come to in the game of Monopoly?

GENERAL KNOWLEDGE

1 According to the fairy story, who was the long-haired beauty who is locked in a tower by a witch?

2 What is euchre?

3 From which Shakespeare play does the phrase 'at one fell swoop' come?

4 St Agatha is the patron saint of whom?

5 Which song was popular during the Civil Rights Movement in the US and is sung by groups protesting against unfair treatment?

6 Which close relative of the onion has a similar, but more delicate flavour?

7 According to the nursery rhyme, where did 'Doctor Foster' go to?

8 To what did Buncombe, North Carolina, give its name?

9 From which language do the words 'dachshund', 'lager' and 'frankfurter' originate?

10 A penny farthing is a type of what?

11 Which character in the Bible asked 'What is truth?'

12 According to the New Testament, which Roman governor condemned Jesus to death?

13 Who wrote the *Pollyanna* novels?

14 With which sport is Henry Cooper associated?

15 Who succeeded Richard Nixon as US president in 1974?

ANSWERS

1. 'Rapunzel'. 2. A card game. 3. *Macbeth*. 4. Nurses. 5. 'We Shall Overcome'. 6. The leek. 7. Gloucester. 8. Bunkum or nonsense. 9. German. 10. Bicycle. 11. Pontius Pilate. 12. Gustav Holst. 13. Eleanor H. Porter. 14. Boxing. 15. Gerald Ford.

SCIENCE & NATURE

1   What is the name of the longest river in Europe?

2   Of which planet in our Solar System is Titan a satellite?

3   What name is given to the study of carbon compounds?

4   How many sides does a heptagon have?

5   What is the basic unit of power measurement named after a Scottish engineer?

6   Whey is one major component of milk protein. What is the other?

7   What is measured using a photometer?

8   What is the pigment within red blood cells that carries oxygen around the human body?

9   What is the value of the acceleration due to gravity (g) in feet/second^2?

10 What does a cartographer do?

11 Where in the human body do you find cervical vertebrae?

12 What colour is chlorophyll?

13 In computing, what is Pascal?

14 How many grams of protein are there in a pint (568 ml) of whole cows milk?

15 How many metres are there in a kilometre?

ENTERTAINMENT

1   Who played the title role in the TV series *Hadleigh*?

2   What was the first film starring 'Wallace' and 'Gromit'?

3   Which male entertainer, born in 1870, was a great star of music halls and was famous for the song 'Keep Right On to the End of the Road'?

4   What was the name of the 1990s TV comedy sketch programme, starring Steve Punt, Hugh Dennis, Rob Newman and David Baddiel?

5   Which actor starred in the films *The Big Boss* and *The Way of the Dragon*?

6   Who had a hit in the 1970s with the song 'Rhinestone Cowboy'?

7   Bernard Butler left which band to pursue a solo career?

8   Which actress, born in 1905, starred in the films *Camille*, *Grand Hotel* and *Queen Christina*?

9   Who sang the title song of the film *To Sir With Love*?

10 Which 1990s TV comedy series takes place in the offices of a news TV station?

11 Which German band had a number one hit with 'Computer Love/The Model'?

12 Which author created the character 'Tarzan'?

13 Who composed *Peer Gynt*?

14 Who starred in the TV series *The Bionic Man*?

15 What is the name of the character of the cultural attaché, portrayed by Barry Humphries?

1. Gerald Harper. 2. *A Grand Day Out*. 3. Harry Lauder. 4. *The Mary Whitehouse Experience*. 5. Bruce Lee. 6. Glen Campbell. 7. Suede. 8. Greta Garbo. 9. Lulu. 10. *Drop the Dead Donkey*. 11. Kraftwerk. 12. Edgar Rice Burroughs. 13. Edvard Grieg. 14. Lee Majors. 15. 'Sir Les Patterson'.

HISTORY

1 King Edward VII opened which major museum at South Kensington on 26 June 1909?

2 In 1853, the *Wellingtonia gigantea* was discovered in California. What was it?

3 London and Paris were linked in 1891 by which new device?

4 From 1965, London comprised the City of London and how many boroughs?

5 In what year did Columbus make his first major voyage?

6 What, politically speaking, was 'the Axis' before World War II?

7 Which is the oldest royal residence in Britain?

8 Following an earthquake in London in 1580, how many people died? (a) None, (b) 2 or (c) 43.

9 What were the Nuremberg Laws?

10 What century-long event ended after the English were defeated at Castillon in 1453?

11 May Day became a Bank Holiday in which year?

12 In Delhi, India, on 1 January 1877, Queen Victoria was proclaimed what?

13 Which American city became the 'Motor Capital' of the world from 1903 onwards?

14 What street conveyance appeared in London for the first time in 1861?

15 What disaster caused the Tay Bridge, Scotland, to collapse in December 1879?

ANSWERS

1. The Victoria and Albert. 2. The largest tree in the world. 3. The public telephone. 4. 32. 5. 1492. 6. The alliance between Germany, Italy and (later) Japan in World War II. 7. Windsor Castle. 8. (b) 2. 9. German laws enacted in 1935, outlawing the Jews. 10. The Hundred Years' War. 11. 1978. 12. Empress of India. 13. Detroit. 14. Trams. 15. A tornado struck the area, and 75 people were killed.

FAMOUS PEOPLE

1 Who wrote *One Day in the Life of Ivan Denisovich*?

2 Who did Erskine Childers succeed as president of Ireland in 1973?

3 Which film actor was known as 'the Man of a Thousand Faces'?

4 Who designed the large altar tapestry for the new Coventry cathedral?

5 Which two men shared the Nobel Peace Prize in 1993?

6 How is Charles Lutwidge Dodgson better known?

7 'In defeat unbeatable: in victory unbearable.' Who was Winston Churchill describing?

8 Who wrote *The Scarlet Pimpernel*?

9 Who did James Earl Ray assassinate?

10 Who was British prime minister at the time of the Abdication in 1936?

11 Which singer is known as the 'Queen of Soul'?

12 With what art form is Ninette de Valois associated?

13 What nationality is the German baritone Dietrich Fischer-Dieskau?

14 Who created the character 'Rip Van Winkle'?

15 What was the name of the Sioux chief who defeated Custer at Little Bighorn?

SPORT & LEISURE

1 Where do Wolverhampton Wanderers play football?

2 Who won a gold medal in the 1980 Moscow Olympics for the 1,500m?

3 What sport is Karen Brigg famous for?

4 What is the perfect score in Gymnastics?

5 Why couldn't David Bryant compete in the 1982 Commonwealth Games bowling competition?

6 What Liverpool footballer scored in the final of Euro '96?

7 When did Pete Sampras win his first US Open tennis title?

8 What is boxer James Smith's nickname?

9 Who won the 'Golden Boot' in the 1990 Football World Cup?

10 When the ball in Rugby goes over the touch line, how is the game restarted?

11 When was the first Grand National held at Aintree?

12 Mike Brearley captained England at cricket 31 times. How many of those matches did they lose?

13 What country were the runners up in the 1988 European Football Championship?

14 In what outdoor activity might you do a forward sweep or a draw stroke?

15 If you were in the *Giro d'Italia*, what sport would you be participating in?

GENERAL KNOWLEDGE

1 Who wrote *Old Possum's Book of Practical Cats*?

2 If your surname is Miller, what might your nickname be?

3 Who coined the expression 'one-upmanship'?

4 What does an epidemic become when it spreads across many countries?

5 What is the capital of Australia?

6 Which word, beginning with 'post', means 'published after the death of the composer or author?'

7 What is the connection between walking under a ladder and breaking a mirror?

8 What kind of food item comes from Bakewell?

9 Who coined the slogan, 'All animals are created equal but some are more equal than others'?

10 Which country is denoted by the prefix 'Luso-'?

11 Which 'everyday story of country folk' celebrated 40 years of broadcasting in 1990?

12 Who was Jesus?

13 Who designed the 'bouncing bombs' used to break up dams during World War II?

14 What was the occupation of Sir Jacob Epstein?

15 Whose *Symphony No.9* is 'from the New World'?

SCIENCE & NATURE

1 At what age is it current best practice to introduce solid foods to infants?

2 What takes 8 minutes 18 seconds to reach the Earth?

3 What is the name of the first synthetic fibre produced by polymerization in 1935?

4 What was the name of the rocket that launched all the manned spaceflights to our Moon?

5 Who was the British inventor of television, first demonstrated in 1936?

6 What is the name given to the type of human milk produced by a mother for the first few days after the birth of her baby?

7 What is the name given to the unit of electrical resistance?

8 The gall-bladder acts as reservoir for which secretion from the liver?

9 What is the name of the second cranial nerve joining the retina of the eye to the brain?

10 What strength of wind, as measured on the Beaufort scale, is a gale?

11 What are the finger-like processes that line the jejunum, and through which nutrients are absorbed?

12 How many sides does a decagon have?

13 What is the name of the process by which plants convert light energy into glucose?

14 What does the sum of two even numbers always equal?

15 What is the disease state that occurs when the pancreas stops producing insulin?

1. Four months. 2. Light from the Sun. 3. Nylon. 4. *Saturn V*. 5. John Logie Baird. 6. Colostrum. 7. The Ohm. 8. Bile. 9. The optic nerve. 10. Force 9. 11. Villi. 12. Ten. 13. Photosynthesis. 14. Another even number. 15. Diabetes mellitus.

ENTERTAINMENT

1 Who had a hit in 1965 with 'Go Now'?

2 Which actor played 'The Fonz' in the TV comedy series *Happy Days*?

3 The world's first film studio was built in the USA in 1893 by whom?

4 What was the name of the famous ragtime composer who wrote 'The Entertainer' and 'Elite Syncopations'?

5 In the 1980s which actress presented shows as a tribute to Joyce Grenfell, performing her 'famous monologues'?

6 Who starred in the film *Ace Ventura: Pet Detective*?

7 1998 saw which spice leave the Spice Girls?

8 'Motown' music originated in which American city?

9 'Noh' and 'Kabuki' are forms of theatre from which country?

10 Who had a hit in 1969 with the song 'Where do you go to my lovely?'?

11 Which actor from *Last of the Summer Wine* appeared as his character's father in *First of the Summer Wine*?

12 Name the Human League's 1981 hit album.

13 The 1930 film *The Blue Angel* starred which actress?

14 Which singer starred in the film *From Here To Eternity*?

15 Which two actors starred in the TV comedy series *A Fine Romance*?

HISTORY

1 When did Eva Péron of Argentina die?

2 Which European country overthrew its monarchy and became a republic on 5 October 1910?

3 Which group of people was set legally free in the British Empire in August 1834?

4 Who succeeded Neville Chamberlain as prime minister in 1940?

5 What took the place of the *Daily Herald*, which ceased publication on 14 September 1964?

6 What disaster struck Lynmouth, Devon, in 1952?

7 The first meeting of which international peace body was held in Paris in 1920?

8 When did decimal coinage replace the old pounds, shillings and pence?

9 When did Queen Victoria die?

10 What was the *Lusitania*?

11 10,000 people died of what 1854 epidemic in London?

12 Who landed on Pitcairn Island in 1790?

13 In what year were identity cards abolished in Britain?

14 In March 1837 which new Australian city was named after the then prime minister?

15 When was the royal fortress of Bastille stormed by French workers?

FAMOUS PEOPLE

1. Whose 'law' states that work expands to fill the time available for its completion?

2. Which Mongol emperor directed the building of the Taj Mahal?

3. Which American astronaut flew in the space shuttle 36 years after he flew in orbit around the Earth?

4. Who composed *The Sorcerer's Apprentice*?

5. Who was the last king of Egypt?

6. Who was the English music-hall comedian known as the 'Prime Minister of Mirth'?

7. Who discovered the xerography process, paving the way for the development of xerox copiers?

8. Which child star of cinema in the 1930s became US Ambassador to Ghana in 1974?

9. What were the first names of the Wright Brothers, aviation pioneers?

10. Who led the Catholic uprising known as the Pilgrimage of Grace, in protest against Henry VIII's dissolution of the monasteries?

11. Who was the last Viceroy of India?

12. Who wrote the autobiographical novel *I Know Why the Caged Bird Sings*?

13. Whose Report in 1942 formed the basis for social-security provision in Britain?

14. Who shared the 1903 Nobel prize for physics with her husband and Henri Becquerel?

15. Which Scottish artist and architect designed the Glasgow School of Art?

ANSWERS

1. Cyril Northcote Parkinson. 2. Shah-Jahan. 3. John Glenn. 4. Paul Dukas. 5. King Farouk I (abdicated 1952). 6. George Robey. 7. Chester F. Carlson. 8. Shirley Temple Black. 9. Wilbur and Orville. 10. Robert Aske. 11. Earl Mountbatten (Lord Louis). 12. Maya Angelou. 13. William Beveridge. 14. Marie Curie. 15. Charles Rennie Mackintosh.

SPORT & LEISURE

1 In what country was Martina Hingis born?

2 Who won the Super Bowl in 1997 for the first time in 29 years?

3 What two players make up the half backs in Rugby Union?

4 Why did Middlesbrough have three points deducted in season 1996–97?

5 In what sport do you play in the 'Silk Cut Challenge Cup'?

6 Whose Arsenal goal scoring record did Ian Wright beat?

7 What sport do you associate Don King with?

8 What sport does Ken Doherty play?

9 In what outdoor pursuit would you do a 'J lean', 'body lean' and 'bell lean'?

10 Dennis Rodman is famous for what sport?

11 What football team do rock stars Oasis support?

12 How many first class centuries did cricketer Don Bradman score?

13 What jockey fell within yards of the finish line in the Grand National on the Queen Mother's horse 'Devon Lock'?

14 How many seconds did it take Roberto Di Matteo to score in his first FA Cup Final?

15 When did snowboarding become an Olympic sport?

1. Switzerland. 2. Green Bay Packers. 3. Scrum half and Fly half. 4. They didn't put out a team to play against Blackburn Rovers. 5. Rugby League. 6. Cliff Bastin. 7. Boxing. 8. Snooker. 9. Kayaking. 10. Basketball. 11. Manchester City. 12. 117. 13. Dick Francis. 14. 43 seconds. 15. 1998.

GENERAL KNOWLEDGE

1   What is a chateaubriand?

2   If you suffered from theophobia, what would you fear?

3   Who wrote the poem *I Wandered Lonely as a Cloud*?

4   Who was the first 'Supermac'?

5   In which city is the Champs Élysées?

6   In which county is Stansted Airport?

7   According to the nursery rhyme, what was the queen eating in the parlour?

8   In a pack of cards, which way does the king of spades look, to his left or to his right?

9   What was the name of Agatha Christie's first detective novel?

10   What does 'kosher' mean?

11   Which German historian, in 1973, designed a modified map projection, aiming to show countries more accurately according to their true size?

12   What word, beginning with 'ante-', means 'going before, in time'?

13   Which country joined the European Union in 1981?

14   What is an ampersand?

15   In which year did Bobby and Jack Charlton retire from football?

1. A thick, large fillet steak. 2. God. 3. William Wordsworth. 4. Harold Macmillan. 5. Paris. 6. Essex. 7. Bread and honey. 8. To his left. 9. *The Mysterious Affair at Styles*. 10. Fit to be eaten according to Jewish law. 11. Arno Peters. 12. Antecedent. 13. Greece. 14. The symbol & meaning 'and'. 15. 1973.

SCIENCE & NATURE

1   What is the world's third largest desert?

2   What is the name of the fifth planet from our Sun?

3   What is the full name of the organic material with the initial letters PVC?

4   Who was the first Soviet cosmonaut to be launched into space?

5   Who invented the miners safety lamp in 1815?

6   Glucose and fructose are examples of what type of sugar?

7   What name is given to sound that has a frequency greater than that which can be heard by the human ear?

8   Which compound is used in the human body as an immediately available source of energy?

9   Give the name of a three-horned, frilled dinosaur that weighed up to 8 tons.

10   What colour is the mineral Malachite?

11   Give the name used to describe a mammalian egg that has just been fertilized.

12   What is the name given to a young goose?

13   What is the name given to the process by which plants are grown in a nutrient solution?

14   What name is given to an organism that lives both on and off its host?

15   How many kcal (calories) are there in a pint 100ml (3.5fl.oz) of whole cows' milk?

ANSWERS

1. The Gobi desert. 2. Jupiter. 3. Poly vinyl chloride. 4. Yuri Gagarin. 5. Sir Humphrey Davy. 6. Monosaccharide. 7. Supersonic. 8. Glucose. 9. Triceratops. 10. Bright green. 11. A zygote. 12. A gosling. 13. Hydroponics. 14. A parasite. 15. 66 kcals (calories) (± 2).

ENTERTAINMENT

1   In which year did the film *Four Weddings and a Funeral* win a 'BAFTA' Best Film award?

2   'Reggae' music originated in which country?

3   What was the name of the first dog to appear on the children's TV programme *Blue Peter*?

4   What was Cary Grant's real name?

5   Who had a hit in 1967 with the song 'Mellow Yellow'?

6   When was *Whicker's World* first broadcast?

7   Who played the title role in the film *Georgy Girl*?

8   Ginger Baker, Eric Clapton and Jack Bruce were the members of which group?

9   Who was running up that hill in 1985?

10   Which children's TV presenter had the mascot 'Gordon the Gopher'?

11   Who starred in the TV series *M*A*S*H* and the film *The Four Seasons*?

12   Who had a hit with the song 'Great Balls of Fire'?

13   Which band carried on even though their drummer lost an arm?

14   What were the characters 'Harold' and 'Hilda' known for in the TV comedy series *Ever Decreasing Circles*?

15   Larry Adler is famous for playing which instrument?

331

ANSWERS

1. 1995. 2. Jamaica. 3. 'Petra'. 4. Archibald Leach. 5. Donovan. 6. 1959. 7. Lynn Redgrave. 8. Cream. 9. Kate Bush. 10. Phillip Schofield. 11. Alan Alda. 12. Jerry Lee Lewis. 13. Def Leppard. 14. Wearing identical clothes. 15. Harmonica.

HISTORY

1 What did Russia sell to the US in 1867?

2 Which national leaders took part in the Yalta Conference in 1945?

3 What happened in Krakatoa island in August 1883?

4 By winning the Battle of Plassey in India, 1757, what did the British commander, Robert Clive achieve?

5 What was Sir Francis Drake doing when the Spanish Armada was sighted?

6 Which group of men first arrived in Botany Bay, Australia in 1788?

7 Which princess died in a car crash in September 1982?

8 The Italian Fascist party was founded by whom in 1919?

9 Europe's first bank notes were issued in 1661 in which country?

10 What took place aboard the Russian battleship *Potemkin* in 1905?

11 Which great liner was launched at Birkenhead in 1938?

12 Hong Kong was taken by the British in which year?

13 Which religious group was founded in 1534 by Ignatius de Loyola?

14 Who was found dead in Whitechapel, London, in 1888?

15 What was the Ottoman Empire?

FAMOUS PEOPLE

1 Who patented the first sewing machine?

2 Who was the famous pupil of Anne Sullivan Macy?

3 Who in 1671 headed a plot to steal the crown jewels from the Tower of London?

4 Whose compositions include the *Enigma Variations* and the *Dream of Gerontius*?

5 Who became the first governor-general of Pakistan in 1947?

6 In the Bible, who was the son of Abraham and Hagar?

7 What 'first' did Alexei Leonov achieve in 1965?

8 By what name was Agnes Bejaxhu known?

9 Who rode through Massachusetts on the night of 18 April 1775 to warn the American colonists that the British were coming?

10 Which astronomer discovered that the planets orbit around the Sun in an elliptical pattern, not circular?

11 Who was president of France from 1958–69?

12 Who wrote *Moby Dick*?

13 Which German field marshal of World War II was nicknamed 'the Desert Fox'?

14 What was the name of George IV's wife, who was barred from entering Westminster Abbey on the occasion of his coronation?

15 Which 17th-century English public executioner was notorious for his barbarism?

1. Elias Howe. 2. Helen Keller. 3. (Colonel) Thomas Blood. 4. Sir Edward Elgar. 5. Mohammed Ali Jinnah. 6. Ishmael. 7. He was the first man to walk in space. 8. Mother Theresa. 9. Paul Revere. 10. Johann Kepler. 11. Charles de Gaulle. 12. Herman Melville. 13. Rommel. 14. Caroline (of Brunswick). 15. Jack Ketch.

SPORT & LEISURE

1. In a Rugby maul is the ball being carried or is it on the floor?

2. Whose rules were adopted in boxing in the 1860s?

3. When was the International Boxing Federation formed?

4. Who was Alex Ferguson's right-hand man at Manchester up until November 1998?

5. Complete the name of the Russian tennis player Yevgeny...?

6. Who is Matthew Pinsent's very successful partner?

7. Who set a World Record for the 200 metres at 19.32 seconds?

8. American Kerri Strug became known for competing in what Olympic sport?

9. Which country failed to turn up to a match against Scotland in 1996?

10. What colour band goes across the jerseys of jockeys racing for Khalid Abdullah?

11. What club did BBC football expert Alan Hansen play for?

12. What sport does Chris Boardman compete in?

13. What golfer was Europe's leading money earner in 1997?

14. Who took over from his brother to become captain of the Australian cricket team in the 1970s?

15. Where did Peter Shilton begin his professional career?

GENERAL KNOWLEDGE

1 Who wrote *Watership Down*?

2 Which musician was known as 'Flash Harry'?

3 Off which country's north-east coast is the Great Barrier Reef?

4 Who was Sir Malcolm Campbell?

5 What word is used to refer to both a woman's loose long-sleeved blouse and a kind of biscuit containing a layer of currants?

6 What is a group of geese called?

7 Of what two main ingredients does a Bloody Mary consist?

8 Who founded the National Viewers and Listeners Association?

9 'Boys and girls come out to play, the moon doth...' Finish the line from the nursery rhyme.

10 Who made the phrase, 'Clunk, Click – Every Trip' famous?

11 What is the name of the US TV programme for young children that teaches numbers and letters, and whose characters include 'Big Bird' and the 'Cookie Monster'?

12 What does 'schmaltz' mean?

13 In politics who was nicknamed 'The Iron Lady'?

14 How much was a pennyweight?

15 Who has been leader of the PLO since 1969?

ANSWERS

1. Richard Adams. 2. Sir Malcolm Sargent. 3. Australia. 4. Land-speed and water-speed record holder. 5. Garibaldi. 6. A gaggle. 7. Vodka and tomato juice. 8. Mary Whitehouse. 9. '...shine as bright as day'. 10. Jimmy Savile. 11. *Sesame Street*. 12. Sickly sweet, sentimental. 13. Margaret Thatcher. 14. Twenty-four grains. 15. Yasser Arafat.

SCIENCE & NATURE

1 Which group of foods is acknowledged as being the best source of dietary calcium?

2 Phobos is the name given to one of the Moons of which planet in our Solar System?

3 What is the name given to the class of Arthropods including spiders, scorpions and ticks?

4 Which gas makes up the greater part of Earth's atmosphere?

5 What percentage of the Earth's surface is covered by oceans?

6 What name is given to the organic compounds which are the building blocks of proteins?

7 What physical law describes the inverse relationship between the volume and pressure of a gas?

8 What name is given to the type of animal cell that forms new bone?

9 What name is given to the fossil believed to represent the first feathered birds?

10 What is the name of the inorganic compound once known by the name Blue Vitriol?

11 What name is given to the use of computer graphics to simulate a three-dimensional environment so that users explore it as if it were real?

12 What is the name given to the curved surface of a liquid in a capillary tube?

13 What is the name given to the phenomenon in which water passes across a semi-permeable membrane from a weak to a strong solution?

14 Pliohippus was a prehistoric ancestor of which well-known modern domestic animal?

15 What gas, produced by yeast fermentation of starch, makes bread dough rise while 'proving'?

ENTERTAINMENT

1   Who was the youngest of The Beatles?

2   What was the name of the first hospital drama series to appear on British TV?

3   'The Sound of Silence' is a song from which film?

4   Who played the title role in TV's *I, Claudius*?

5   Who had hits in the 1970s with 'Co-Co', 'Poppa Joe' and 'Blockbuster'?

6   In which year was the TV comedy series *Dad's Army* first shown?

7   Who starred in the film *Funny Girl*?

8   Who had a 'New Gold Dream'?

9   What is the name of Mike Oldfield's famous album, released in 1973?

10 The musical *Gentleman Prefer Blondes* features which song about jewellery?

11 Basil Rathbone was famous for playing which character in films in the 1940s?

12 In which year was Ted Ray born?

13 Who was 'Too Shy' in 1983?

14 *Forrest Gump* won an Oscar for 'Best Picture' in which year?

15 Who starred in *At the Drop of A Hat*?

HISTORY

1 Who met at the Munich Agreement of 1938?

2 In what year did food rationing end?

3 The slavery abolitionist John Brown made a raid at Harper's Ferry in the US in 1859. What was the result?

4 What was the Field of the Cloth of Gold?

5 In which year did the Gunpowder Plot take place?

6 What did the Boers in South Africa begin in December 1835?

7 What happened to Cardinal Karol Wojtyla on 16 October 1978?

8 Parliament passed the Stamp Act in 1765 to tax which group of people?

9 In which city in 1921 did a mutiny take place on a Russian battleship?

10 The Dorset labourers in Tolpuddle, Dorset, were punished for what action?

11 When were Premium Bonds first introduced: (a) 1956, (b) 1960 or (c) 1970?

12 What happened in August 1914, so starting World War I?

13 Of which country was King Farouk the sovereign from 1936?

14 The foundation stone of which great bank was laid in August 1732?

15 What happened at Chernobyl, USSR, in April 1986?

FAMOUS PEOPLE

1 Who was the soap manufacturer who founded the model industrial town of Port Sunlight?

2 Which instrument did the virtuoso musician Paganini play?

3 Who edited an anthology of poetry called *Wheels*?

4 Who wrote *Paradise Lost*?

5 Who became king of Spain in 1975, following the death of Franco?

6 Who was the American producer of a series of extravagant theatrical revues which he called his *Follies*?

7 Who composed the operatta *The Merry Widow*?

8 Which British engineer had a factory at Soho in Birmingham and went into partnership with James Watt to manufacture steam engines?

9 Who wrote the Gothic novel *The Mysteries of Udolpho*?

10 Which French actress was regarded as one of the greatest tragic actresses, and continued to act even after her leg was amputated?

11 Which French painter, noted for his dreamlike pictures in a naive style, was nicknamed 'Le Douanier'?

12 Under whose Plan was the railway network of the United Kingdom drastically reduced?

13 Who created the fictional police detective 'Maigret'?

14 Which American general and later president of the United States was known as Ike?

15 Which English painter is noted for his depiction of northern industrial scenes, peopled with 'matchstick men'?

ANSWERS

1. Lord Leverhulme (William Lever). 2. Violin. 3. Dame Edith Sitwell. 4. John Milton. 5. Juan Carlos I. 6. Florenz Ziegfeld. 7. Franz Lehar. 8. Matthew Boulton. 9. Mrs Ann Radcliffe. 10. Sarah Bernhardt. 11. Henri Rousseau. 12. Richard Beeching. 13. Georges Simenon. 14. Dwight D. Eisenhower. 15. L. S. Lowry.

SPORT & LEISURE

1 Who is the only heavyweight boxing champion to have won every professional fight in his career?

2 Who was the much loved vice chairman of Chelsea FC who unfortunately died in a helicopter accident?

3 In 1986 and 1987 which tennis player won both the US and French Opens?

4 Mark Williams won the British Open Snooker Championship, but in what year?

5 What sport does Jan Ullrich compete in?

6 For which Italian football club did Zola and Asprilla play?

7 What Rugby playing country are called the 'Springboks'?

8 Who is the owner of the Williams Formula One racing team?

9 Where is the Dubai Champion Stakes held?

10 How much money do you get for passing 'Go' in Monopoly?

11 What sport do the Brisbane Broncos play?

12 Which country do football team Trabzonspor play in?

13 What country does cricketer Martin Crowe come from?

14 29,000 people started this event on 13 April 1997. What was it?

15 What football club have Trevor Francis, David Pleat and Ron Atkinson managed?

340

GENERAL KNOWLEDGE

1   Which saint's feast day falls on 26 December?

2   What is a 'blockbuster'?

3   Whose last words were: 'Oh, I am so bored with it all'?

4   The fava, or Windsor bean, is better known as what?

5   Who wrote the *Doctor Dolittle* books?

6   Which European princess had children named Albert, Caroline and Stephanie?

7   From which language do the words 'brandy', 'coleslaw' and 'sloop' originate?

8   Who is the patron saint of sailors?

9   What team has Alex Ferguson been manager of since 1986?

10 Who was Honoré de Balzac?

11 According to the nursery rhyme, what did the cow jump over?

12 Which day is the Jewish sabbath?

13 In which county is Lizard Point, the southernmost point in the British Isles?

14 What is stroganoff?

15 In which country is Vesuvius?

1. St Stephen. 2. A great success, as of a book, film or stage show. 3. Sir Winston Churchill. 4. The broad bean. 5. Hugh Lofting. 6. Princess Grace of Monaco. 7. Dutch. 8. St Cuthbert. 9. Manchester United. 10. French novelist. 11. The Moon. 12. Saturday. 13. Cornwall. 14. Thinly-cut meat, onions and mushrooms in a sour cream sauce. 15. Italy.

SCIENCE & NATURE

1 An optical large telescope orbits the Earth at a height of 300 miles. After which astronomer is it named?

2 What does a palaeontologist study?

3 How long does our Sun take to rotate once around its axis? (a) 13 days, (b) 6 days or (c) 27 days?

4 What is the chemical formula for common salt?

5 What name is given to the organ in animals that produces eggs?

6 Wernher von Braun is known for his expertise in what?

7 Which colour light has the longest wavelength?

8 What is the name of the membrane that surrounds the human heart?

9 What name do we give to the period of geological history between 190 million and 136 million years ago?

10 Starches are a complex branch-chained polymer of which monosaccharide?

11 What name is given to the first cranial nerve connecting the organs of smell to the brain?

12 The transformation of a substance from the solid, direct to the gaseous phases is known as...?

13 What is the common name for calcium carbonate, formed from the shells of tiny prehistoric marine animals?

14 What is the meaning of the term dinosaur?

15 What is the old common name for the disease tuberculosis, or TB?

ENTERTAINMENT

1 Who played the role of the 'agony aunt' in the TV comedy series *Agony*?

2 'Margaret' and 'Victor' are the married couple in which TV sitcom?

3 Who had a number one hit in 1967 with 'San Francisco (Be Sure To Wear Some Flowers In Your Hair)'?

4 Who presented the children's TV programme *Vision On* for many years?

5 Who composed 'Walking In The Air', the theme tune to the cartoon film *The Snowman*?

6 Who was the original presenter of TV's *Treasure Hunt*?

7 Whose 'Earth Song' got to number one on 9 December 1995?

8 Who wrote the lyrics in the Gilbert and Sullivan musical partnership?

9 In the TV comedy series *Bread*, what was the name of the Boswell's daughter?

10 'Reach Out (I'll Be There)' was a number one hit in 1966 for which group?

11 What was The Jam's town called?

12 Which actress starred in the TV comedy series *Second Thoughts*?

13 Who played the female lead in the 1954 film *A Star is Born*?

14 David Yip starred in which TV crime series?

15 Which group performed with Bryan Ferry?

343

HISTORY

1 What did the Jameson Raid into the Transvaal on 29 December 1895 lead to?

2 In what year did the first motor-bus appear in London: (a) 1880, (b) 1899 or (c) 1901?

3 In France, on 7 April 1795, what measuring unit was made official?

4 What happened to the Shah of Iran in 1979?

5 What was the *General Belgrano,* and what happened to it in May 1982?

6 What historical event took place in England from 1642 to 1646?

7 Which historic document was published by Marx and Engels in February 1848?

8 In 1945, 15 August was celebrated as VJ Day. What was that?

9 Which driver-less, computer-run railway began operating on 30 July 1987?

10 What did the 1763 Peace of Paris end?

11 What experiment took place in Monte Bello islands, off northwest Australia, in 1952?

12 What, in Nazi Germany, was the SS?

13 Which well known Irish political party was founded in Dublin in 1905?

14 Which area in Southern Africa became a British colony in 1813?

15 What was called 'Dad's Army'?

FAMOUS PEOPLE

1 Who wrote the novels *A Journey to the Centre of the Earth* and *Twenty Thousand Leagues Under the Sea*?

2 Which English king led his troops to victory over France at the Battle of Agincourt?

3 Who was elected mayor of West Berlin in 1957?

4 Whose compositions include *The Four Seasons*?

5 In the Bible who, as a young boy, heard God speak to him in the temple?

6 Who invented the electric battery?

7 Who was the producer of silent comedy films who formed the Keystone Company?

8 Which Indian religious leader founded Sikhism?

9 Which astronomer discovered the planet Uranus?

10 Whose discovery of insulin in 1921 was a breakthrough in the treatment of diabetes?

11 Which French revolutionary was assassinated in his bath by Charlotte Cordey in July 1793?

12 By what name is Karol Jozef Wojtyla better known?

13 Who became first secretary of the Soviet Communist Party in 1953, following Stalin's death?

14 Which 19th-century Frenchman developed immunization against anthrax and rabies?

15 Who wrote a collection of four biographical essays entitled *Eminent Victorians* (1918)?

ANSWERS

1. Jules Verne. 2. Henry V. 3. Willy Brandt. 4. Vivaldi. 5. Samuel.
6. Alessandro Volta. 7. Mack Sennett. 8. Guru Nanak. 9. William Herschel.
10. Sir Frederick Banting and his assistant Charles Best. 11. Jean Paul Marat.
12. Pope John Paul II. 13. Nikita Khrushchev. 14. Louis Pasteur.
15. Lytton Strachey.

SPORT & LEISURE

1 What football team won the English Coca Cola Cup in 1997?

2 The Bradford Bulls compete in what sport?

3 What is the final property on a Monopoly board?

4 What sport is Robert Sangster involved in?

5 In which sport would you do an 'Eskimo Roll'?

6 If you were watching in the *San Siro*, what country would you be in?

7 The BCF are the governing body for which sport?

8 Who was the heavyweight boxing champion for 11 years and 252 days?

9 Who was the manager of the losing team in the 1982 FA Cup Final?

10 In Rugby Union if one of the home countries defeats the other three nations in a season's international matches, what do they achieve?

11 Dario Gradi is the manager of what football team?

12 Which two Australians won the Wimbledon Double Tennis Championships from 1993 to 1997?

13 Boca Juniors are a football team in which country?

14 At what county did David Gower finish his cricket career?

15 How many segments do you need to complete a game of Trivial Pursuits?

1. Leicester. 2. Rugby League. 3. Mayfair. 4. Horse racing. 5. Canoeing. 6. Italy. 7. Cycling (British Cycling Federation). 8. Joe Louis. 9. Terry Venables. 10. The Triple Crown. 11. Crewe Alexandra. 12. Woodbridge and Woodforde. 13. Argentina. 14. Hampshire. 15. Six.

GENERAL KNOWLEDGE

1   What is named after the Australian gardener Maria Ann Smith?

2   What is an agnostic?

3   In the nursery rhyme beginning 'cock a doodle doo', what had 'my dame' lost in the next line?

4   According to the 'language of flowers', what does the veronica signify?

5   Who was the captain of the England women's cricket team between 1966 and 1977?

6   Which anniversary does an iron or sugar-candy wedding celebrate?

7   In 1991, Anthony Hopkins won the Academy Award for Best Actor in which film?

8   Which is the holy city of Hindus?

9   Clark Kent is a reporter for which newspaper?

10 What is a dolma?

11 Who is the one-legged sailor with a parrot on his shoulder that is the main character in *Treasure Island*?

12 St Sebastian is the patron saint of whom?

13 Who wrote *The Wind in the Willows*?

14 The fish represent which sign of the Zodiac?

15 In which country is the Simpson Desert?

ANSWERS

1. Granny Smith apples. 2. Someone who believes that we cannot know whether God exists or not. 3. Her shoe. 4. Fidelity. 5. Rachel Heyhoe-Flint. 6. The sixth. 7. *The Silence of the Lambs*. 8. Varanasi (Benares). 9. *Daily Planet*. 10. A vine or cabbage leaf with savoury stuffing. 11. Long John Silver. 12. Athletes. 13. Kenneth Grahame. 14. Pisces. 15. Australia.

SCIENCE & NATURE

1   Which is the only group of mammals capable of sustained flight?

2   If a doctor carried out a cholecystectomy, what part of a patient's anatomy would he have removed?

3   Which electronic device was developed in 1947 at Bell Telephone Laboratories, New Jersey?

4   What is magnesium sulphate heptahydrate more commonly known as?

5   Where were the first atomic and hydrogen bombs developed?

6   What is the term for a parallelogram with four equal sides?

7   What are arches, whorls, loops and composites?

8   What is the commonest element in the Universe?

9   What is the name given to the science of the production, transmission and effect of sound waves?

10   Where is the hottest and lowest place in America?

11   Who developed the first photographic negative?

12   What does an ergometer measure?

13   Which common viral infection is caused by Epstein-Barr virus?

14   In which geological period did the dinosaurs flourish?

15   What is the position of the Sun on 21 March and 23 September at the Equator?

ANSWERS

1. Bats. 2. The gall bladder. 3. The transistor. 4. Epsom Salts. 5. Los Alamos, New Mexico, in 1943. 6. A rhombus. 7. They are types of fingerprint. 8. Hydrogen. 9. Acoustics. 10. Death Valley. 11. William Henry Fox Talbot, in 1839. 12. It measures the work performed by a person exercising. 13. Glandular fever. 14. The Jurassic Period. 15. It is directly overhead.

ENTERTAINMENT

1 What was the name of the film released in 1953 featuring two couples taking part in the London to Brighton Vintage Car Race?

2 Noddy Holder was a member of which pop group?

3 Who wrote the TV thriller series *Widows*?

4 What is the name of the 1988 comedy film starring Tom Hanks, about a boy who gets his wish to become a man?

5 Which group performed with Bob Marley?

6 From which musical did the song that gave Jason Donovan his number one hit come from?

7 What was the follow-up series to the TV comedy *Fresh Fields*?

8 Who had a hit in 1966 with 'Wild Thing'?

9 What was the last film made by the actor James Dean before he was killed in a car accident in 1955?

10 What kind of energy did Blondie sing about?

11 What is the name of the fictional village in *Noel's House Party*?

12 In which year did Gloria Gaynor have a number one hit with 'I Will Survive'?

13 Of what is BAFTA an acronym?

14 Who played 'Diana' in the TV comedy series *Waiting For God*?

15 Who had hits in the 1970s with 'Ride A White Swan' and 'Hot Love'?

HISTORY

1   What flag was first adopted in Britain in 1606?

2   Who succeeded Anthony Eden as prime minister in 1957?

3   Which wars took place in England starting in 1455 and ending in 1471?

4   In what year was the introduction of the Penny Post in Britain?

5   Who set sail aboard *HMS Beagle* to South America in December 1831?

6   Which war between Britain and the US ended on 24 December 1814?

7   By what new country name was Persia known after 1935?

8   The US Navy was formed in 1794. True or false?

9   The first underground trains in Paris started in (a) 1900, (b) 1905 or (c) 1910?

10 In 1812, Napolean's armies began the invasion of which country?

11 What set sail from Spain to England in 1588?

12 What status did Hawaii assume in 1959?

13 What social practice was abolished in Turkey in 1924?

14 Which large South African city was founded in 1886?

15 What momentous event occurred off the Falkland Islands in 1914?

FAMOUS PEOPLE

1 Whose claim that Spanish coastguards had cut off his ear provoked a war between Britain and Spain in 1739?

2 In which of the arts is Henry Moore famous?

3 Who published the first translation of the Bible into English?

4 Who was Atahualpa?

5 Which Anglo-Saxon rebel had the nickname 'the Wake'?

6 Richard Nash became Master of Ceremonies at Bath in 1704, how is he better known?

7 Which Boer statesman became president of the Transvaal in 1883?

8 Who were Hugh de Merville, William de Tracy, Reginald Fitzurse and Richard le Breton?

9 Who introduced printing in Europe in the mid-15th century?

10 Who in 1923 became president of the new republic of Turkey?

11 Who invented the hovercraft?

12 Who founded the periodical *The Tatler* in 1709?

13 Which explorer perished in 1847 when his expedition to discover the north-west passage became beleaguered by pack ice?

14 Who wrote *Hard Times*?

15 Who composed the opera *Dido and Aneas*?

ANSWERS

1. Captain Robert Jenkins (hence War of Jenkins' Ear) 2. Sculpture. 3. Miles Coverdale. 4. Last Inca Emperor of Peru. 5. Hereward. 6. Beau Nash. 7. Paul Kruger. 8. The four knights who assassinated Thomas à Becket in Canterbury Cathedral. 9. Johann Gutenberg. 10. Mustafa Kemal Ataturk. 11. Sir Christopher Cockerell. 12. Sir Richard Steele. 13. Sir John Franklin. 14. Charles Dickens. 15. Purcell.

SPORT & LEISURE

1 Was Alan Ball in England's World Cup winning football team?

2 If you were playing in the AXA Life Insurance League, what sport would you be playing?

3 What sport are Olga Korbut and Nadia Comaneci famous for?

4 What sport does Herbie Hyde compete in?

5 With which club did Middlesbrough manager Bryan Robson start his playing career?

6 How old was Lester Piggott when he won the Derby on Never Say Die?

7 Who won the British Open Golf Championship in 1997?

8 Carl Foggarty is well known in what sport?

9 What English county side is cricketer Richard Hadlee famous for playing for?

10 Which Italian football team did Ruud Gullit play for?

11 What is the difference between rowing and sculling?

12 Marco Pantani is known for competing in which sport?

13 Who was the first footballer to be capped over one hundred times for England?

14 What individual events did Michael Johnson win in the Atlanta Olympic Games?

15 If a Rugby Union referee puts his arm straight up in the air and blows his whistle, what is he indicating?

GENERAL KNOWLEDGE

1 What does a couch potato do all the time?

2 What is a bruxelloise?

3 From which language do the words 'fascism', 'fiasco' and 'pizza' originate?

4 Who was the Beast of Bolsover?

5 What is the name of the Greek version of the Old Testament?

6 What is colcannon?

7 What is the name of the old English country dancing performed outdoors by men who wear special white clothes to which small bells are often fixed?

8 Who in the world would be called 'Digger'?

9 Who wrote *Titus Groan* and *Gormenghast*?

10 The goat represents which sign of the Zodiac?

11 On which island (to which he had been exiled) did John write the book of Revelation?

12 Who is Allah?

13 Who wrote the words, 'If I should die, think only this of me: That there's some corner of a foreign field that is forever England'?

14 Who wrote 'Auld Lang Syne' and 'Tam O'Shanter'?

15 Who, according to the nursery rhyme, killed 'Cock Robin'?

ANSWERS

1. Watch television. 2. A French sauce for asparagus. 3. Italian. 4. Dennis Skinner. 5. The Septuagint. 6. An Irish dish of mashed potatoes and cabbage. 7. Morris dancing. 8. An Australian. 9. Mervyn Peake. 10. Capricorn. 11. Patmos. 12. According to the Muslims, the Supreme Being, or God. 13. Rupert Brooke. 14. Robert Burns. 15. 'The Sparrow'.

SCIENCE & NATURE

1   What is the common name of *Quercus robur*?

2   Which Russian spacecraft sent the first pictures of the far side of the Moon in 1959?

3   What type of soil do rivers changing course deposit?

4   Where in the human body is the trapezium?

5   Which scientist was Master of the Royal Mint between 1699–1727?

6   What is a common use for sodium hypochlorite?

7   What is the time taken for the planet Mercury to turn once on its axis? Is it (a) 5.9 days, (b) 32.9 days or (c) 58.7 days?

8   What exist in orthorhombic, monoclinic, tetragonal, and hexagonal forms?

9   What is an abbreviation of 'light amplification by stimulated emission of radiation'?

10   Who developed the first controlled nuclear fission chain reaction in 1942?

11   How many compartments does a cow have in its stomach?

12   What is the name given by geologists to the 'supercontinent' which began to break up 200 million years ago?

13   What is the meteorological term for a 'mackerel' cloud formation?

14   In which hemisphere are penguins found?

15   If someone suffered from acromegaly what effect would this have on the body?

ANSWERS

1. English Oak. 2. *Luna 3*. 3. Alluvial soil. 4. It is a small wrist bone. 5. Sir Isaac Newton. 6. It is used as a fixative in photography. 7. (c) 58.7 days. 8. Crystals. 9. Laser. 10. Enrico Fermi. 11. Four. The obomasum, the omasum, the reticulum and the rumen. 12. Pangaea. 13. Cirrocumulus. 14. The Southern hemisphere. 15. The patient would grow extremely tall, as a result of the pituitary gland producing too much growth hormone.

ENTERTAINMENT

1 Which TV comedy series featured the 'Sunshine Cab Company'?

2 With what name did Alvin Stardust start his pop career?

3 Charlie Chaplin carried his cane in which hand?

4 Who played the title role in the TV series *McCloud?*

5 'Dark Side Of The Moon' was a successful album in 1973 for which group?

6 The James Bond films and the film *Chitty Chitty Bang Bang* were based on books by which author?

7 Everything But The Girl got to number three with their version of 'I Don't Want To Talk About It' in 1988. Who got to number one with this same song in April 1977?

8 Who had a number one hit in 1970 with 'Tears of a Clown'?

9 'Dr Cliff Huxtable' is a character in which TV comedy series?

10 In the 1956 film *Reach for the Sky* who played the role of Douglas Bader?

11 Dr Robert was the frontman for which band?

12 Who was the original presenter of TV's *A Question of Sport*?

13 Which group sang with Johnny Kidd?

14 In 1961, who became the first member of the Royal Family to be interviewed on TV?

15 Who starred in the film *Air Force One*?

355

1. *Taxi.* 2. Shane Fenton. 3. Left. 4. Dennis Weaver. 5. Pink Floyd. 6. Ian Fleming. 7. Rod Stewart. 8. Smokey Robinson And The Miracles. 9. *The Cosby Show.* 10. Kenneth More. 11. The Blow Monkeys. 12. David Vine. 13. The Pirates. 14. Prince Philip. 15. Harrison Ford.

HISTORY

1 Which London department store opened on 15 March 1909?

2 How many ships were there in the Spanish Armada (a) 329, (b) 1,029 or (c) 129?

3 What did Britain buy 176,602 shares of on 25 October 1875?

4 What body of men did Louis-Philippe of France found in North Africa in 1831?

5 What was the Berlin Wall?

6 On 14 January, in both 1205 and 1814, what were held on the River Thames?

7 Which famous ship, sunk in 1545, was lifted from the seabed in 1982?

8 What was CND, launched in 1958?

9 How did Sir Francis Drake die?

10 The Kingdom of Serbs, Croats and Slovenes was established in 1919. What was it eventually called?

11 What, in 1858, was the Miracle of Lourdes?

12 What started in California in 1848?

13 What international document was signed on 11 November 1918?

14 What status did New York assume in 1788?

15 Who were the 'Brylcreem Boys'?

ANSWERS

1. Selfridges. 2. (c) 129. 3. Shares in the Suez Canal. 4. The French Foreign Legion. 5. A wall erected to prevent East Germans from escaping to the West. 6. Frost fairs when the river froze over. 7. *The Mary Rose*. 8. The Campaign for Nuclear Disarmament. 9. He died of dysentery off the coast of Panama. 10. Yugoslavia. 11. When St Bernadette is believed to have had a vision of the Virgin. 12. The Gold Rush. 13. The Armistice between the Allies and Germany. 14. It became the 11th of the United States. 15. Young RAF officers in World War II.

FAMOUS PEOPLE

1 Whose assassination in Sarajevo precipitated World War I?

2 Which writer's works include *The Screwtape Letters* and *The Allegory of Love* in addition to a series of children's books featuring a lion called 'Aslan'?

3 With what branch of design is Clarice Cliff famous?

4 Which female playwright wrote the Restoration plays *The Forced Marriage* and *The Rover*?

5 The explorer La Salle claimed the territory surrounding the Mississippi for his patron; who was that patron?

6 Who invented the 'Polaroid' camera?

7 Which political leader led his followers on a 'Long March' in 1934–36?

8 Who was the scientist noted for his study of conditioned reflexes in dogs?

9 Which astronomer perfected the refracting telescope and was forced by the Inquisition to recant his support of Copernican theory ?

10 Who commanded the British army in the Peninsular War and was killed at the battle of Corunna in 1809?

11 Which English public school was founded by William of Wykeham in 1382?

12 What was the name of Shakespeare's first daughter?

13 Who joined with his friend Richard Steele in founding the periodical *The Spectator*?

14 Who created the fictional character of 'Billy Bunter'?

15 Which Scottish mathematician invented logarithms?

ANSWERS

1. Archduke Franz Ferdinand. 2. C. S. Lewis. 3. Ceramics (pottery). 4. Aphra Behn.
5. Louis XIV. 6. Edwin Land. 7. Mao Zedong (Mao Tse-Tung). 8. Ivan Pavlov.
9. Galileo. 10. Sir John Moore. 11. Winchester. 12. Susanna. 13. Joseph Addison.
14. Frank Richards. 15. John Napier.

SPORT & LEISURE

1. Iwan Thomas runs what athletic event for Great Britain?

2. How many players in a Rugby Union team?

3. What job did Christopher Dean do before becoming an ice skater?

4. Who is Gary Neville's footballing brother?

5. When was mountain biking first included in the Olympics?

6. What is the oldest Classic in horse racing?

7. How many players are there in a polo team?

8. Who scored the second goal for England against Scotland in Euro '96?

9. At what weight did Cassius Clay win an Olympic Boxing gold medal in Rome 1960?

10. What fits round your waist and round the rim of the cockpit of a canoe?

11. What would a racer in the Tour de France wearing a red polka dot jersey signify?

12. Who did Aston Villa buy Dion Dublin from?

13. What fielding position did former England cricketer Alan Knott play?

14. Who won the Scottish Football Premiership in 1997–98?

15. In Bridge the men play for the Bermuda Bowl but what trophy do the women play for?

GENERAL KNOWLEDGE

1   Who wrote *Winnie the Pooh*?

2   What is vermouth?

3   What is the name for a five line poem in which the first two and the last lines rhyme?

4   If you were a printer, how many points would make an inch?

5   In which country is the Taurus mountain range?

6   Until 1935, by what name was Iran known?

7   In the nursery rhyme, what could 'Jack Sprat's wife' not eat?

8   Who, or what, is the old Lady of Threadneedle Street?

9   What is the name of the fruit developed as a hybrid of the loganberry, blackberry and raspberry?

10 'Grapnel' and 'kedge' are types of what?

11 Who wrote *Westward Ho!*?

12 If your surname is 'Martin', what might your nickname be?

13 What do the initials MCP stand for?

14 A culverin is (a) a cannon, (b) a gutter or (c) a unit of coinage?

15 In which film did 'George Dixon' first appear?

ANSWERS

1. A. A. Milne. 2. A wine-based drink flavoured with herbs. 3. A LIMERICK.
4. Twelve. 5. Turkey. 6. Persia. 7. No lean. 8. The Bank of England. 9. Boysenberry.
10. Anchor. 11. Charles Kingsley. 12. Pincher. 13. Male chauvinist pig.
14. (a) a cannon. 15. *The Blue Lamp*.

SCIENCE & NATURE

1 What is measured in curies?

2 What is the largest flower on earth?

3 In which species of fish does the male incubate the young?

4 Who was the first person to split the atom in 1919?

5 How many bits make a byte?

6 What is also known as negative acceleration?

7 Which group of plants are the most successful on earth?

8 Which vitamin is essential for the blood clotting process?

9 What is the largest living bird?

10 How many bones are there in the cranium, (excluding bones in the face)?

11 What is the material an insect exoskeleton is made of?

12 What is the name for the zone of seashore, which is exposed between tides?

13 How many kilograms are in 1 metric tonne?

14 What kind of animal is a breed known as a Tamworth?

15 What is '90' in Roman numerals?

1. Radioactivity. 2. Rafflesia, which is 1m (1.09yds) in diameter. 3. The seahorse. 4. Ernest Rutherford. 5. 8. 6. Deceleration. 7. Grasses. 8. Vitamin K. 9. The ostrich. 10. 8. 11. Chitin. 12. The littoral zone. 13. 1,000. 14. It is a breed of pig. 15. XC.

ENTERTAINMENT

1 Who directed the 1955 film *To Catch A Thief* starring Grace Kelly and Cary Grant?

2 What TV programme does the comedian Roy Walker present?

3 What was the number one hit in 1973 for Peters and Lee?

4 What was the lion's name in the children's TV series *The Herb Garden*?

5 Stephen 'Tin Tin' Duffy was originally a member of Duran Duran. True or False?

6 Was the film musical *South Pacific* released in (a) 1958, (b) 1959 or (c) 1960?

7 Who played 'Steed' in the original TV series?

8 'Love Rears It's Ugly Head' was a top twenty hit for which American band?

9 Who starred in the comedy films *The Bulldog Breed* and *The Early Bird*?

10 How many guests are on the panel on TV's *Question Time*?

11 Which cartoon character has the vital statistics 19-19-19?

12 'Wonderful Land', 'Dance On' and 'Kon Tiki' were hits in the 1960s for which group?

13 Who played Jesus in the film *Jesus of Nazareth*, directed by Franco Zeffirelli?

14 In which year was 'Bohemiam Rhapsody' a number one hit for Queen?

15 What was the outer-space serial in the TV show *The Muppets*?

361

1. Alfred Hitchcock. 2. *Catchphrase*. 3. 'Welcome Home'. 4. 'Parsley'. 5. True. 6. (a) (1958). 7. Patrick Macnee. 8. Living Colour. 9. Norman Wisdom. 10. 4. 11. 'Olive Oyl'. 12. The Shadows. 13. Robert Powell. 14. 1975. 15. *Pigs in Space*.

HISTORY

1   Which Mediterranean island became an independent republic in 1960?

2   What object was erected on the Thames Embankment in 1878?

3   In 1940, the RAF made the first raid on which city?

4   The Crusaders were successful in capturing what in 1099?

5   Which famous Australian bridge opened on 19 March 1932?

6   Which patriotic song was sung for the first time on 28 September 1745?

7   Which Chinese dynasty ruled between 1368 and 1644?

8   The first 'Peelers' appeared on the streets of London in 1829. What were they?

9   Which famous British aircraft carrier was sunk off Gibraltar on 12 November 1941?

10   What event was televised in June 1953?

11   Henry V of England defeated the French in 1415. What was the battle?

12   What is the Bayeux Tapestry?

13   What did 75,000 Londoners die of during 1665?

14   The Treaty of Paris was signed in 1763. What was its purpose?

15   What was laid beneath the sea between Dover and Calais in 1850?

FAMOUS PEOPLE

1 Who created the fictional character 'Sherlock Holmes'?

2 Who invented the water closet in 1778?

3 What nationality was the composer Delius?

4 Who was president of North Vietnam from 1954–69?

5 What feat was achieved by John Ridgeway and Chay Blythe in 1966?

6 Which former mayor of Birmingham became prime minister in 1937?

7 Who was the first murderer in the Bible?

8 What did Lord Elgin bring from Greece to England in the early 19th century?

9 Which instrument did the jazz musician Bix Beiderbecke play?

10 Which Pre-Raphaelite artist painted *The Boyhood of Raleigh* and *Bubbles* ?

11 Whose plays include *A Doll's House* and *Hedda Gabler*?

12 Who was 'the Young Pretender'?

13 Which Lord Chancellor and author of *Utopia* was found guilty of treason and executed in 1535?

14 Which English artist is noted for his woodcuts, for example in his *History of British Birds*, and has a species of swan named after him?

15 What nationality was Leonardo da Vinci?

SPORT & LEISURE

1   What sport do you associate Mike Hailwood with?

2   Joe Frazier won 32 fights in his professional boxing career. How many did he win by knockout?

3   What football team does former prime minister John Major support?

4   What does *Hajime* mean in Judo?

5   Who scored 501 not out in one innings during 1994?

6   Which snooker player was famously nicknamed 'Hurricane'?

7   How many times did Bernard Hinault win the Tour de France?

8   How many forwards are there in a Rugby Union team?

9   Who did Roy Keane play for before moving to Manchester United?

10 In what sport would you do a 'draw shot', 'drive', 'resting shot' or 'jack trail'?

11 If you were at Edgbaston what sport would you be playing?

12 Who rode 'Shergar' to victory in the 1981 Derby?

13 What team won the European Champions League in 1997–98?

14 Mark Todd and Ian Stark are known for what sport?

15 What team have Kevin Keegan, Alan Shearer, Matthew Le Tissier and Tim Flowers all played for?

ANSWERS

1. Motor cycling. 2. 27 by KO. 3. Chelsea. 4. To begin or start the competition. 5. Brian Lara. 6. Alex Higgins. 7. Five times. 8. Eight. 9. Nottingham Forest. 10. Bowls. 11. Cricket. 12. Walter Swinburn. 13. Real Madrid. 14. Three day eventing. 15. Southampton.

GENERAL KNOWLEDGE

1   What were Laurel and Hardy's first names?

2   What is a 'shemozzle'?

3   Which Welsh designer of fabrics in a floral Victorian style opened a chain of shops under her own name in the 1960s?

4   Which country was the home of 'Dracula'?

5   From which language do the words 'marmalade' and 'molasses' originate?

6   In which sport does it matter if you get an 'LBW'?

7   In the story, who eats 'Little Red Ridinghood's Grandmother'?

8   What's the connection between baloney and polony?

9   According to the Bible, what were the names of the sons of Adam and Eve?

10 Scorpions are immune to their own poison. True or false?

11 To which American film producer is 'in two words: im-possible' attributed?

12 What is the name of the stretch of water between Denmark and Sweden?

13 In which country is the River Fraser?

14 What anniversary does a wooden wedding celebrate?

15 Who was 'the marmalade cat'?

SCIENCE & NATURE

1   What disease is caused by malabsorption of vitamin B12?

2   How many canine teeth does a squirrel have?

3   What is rubber made from?

4   What colour is lobster blood?

5   What gas forms the largest percentage of the air we breathe?

6   What is the name of the smallest British bat?

7   Where are epicanthic folds located?

8   What is the name of the luminous atmospheric phenomenon that occurs near the North Pole?

9   What is the basic SI unit of length?

10   What are isobaths?

11   What is a patellar reflex?

12   What chemical element is Zr the symbol of?

13   What is an ISP?

14   Which parasitic bird is seen to herald spring in this country?

15   Which asteroid passes closer to the Sun than the planet Mercury?

ENTERTAINMENT

1   Which disc jockey presented the TV programme *Pop Quiz*?

2   Which singer, popular in the late 1950s and early 1960s, had a hit with 'Little White Bull'?

3   'B. A. Baracus' was a character in which TV series?

4   Who played the title role in the 1990 film *Cyrano de Bergerac*?

5   'Alan Partridge' is a character played by which comedian?

6   Who had a number one hit in 1979 with 'Heart of Glass'?

7   Who were losing their religion?

8   Who starred in the 1954 film *The Wild One*?

9   What was the name of the ranch in TV's *Dallas*?

10 'Ronald Wycherley' was the real name of which 1960s pop singer?

11 Who played the title role in the TV serial *The Charmer*?

12 What was the name of the duo which launched Alison Moyet's pop career?

13 Who had a number one hit in 1964 with 'Juliet'?

14 Who played 'Hawkeye' in the 1991 film *The Last of the Mohicans*?

15 Who played 'Marriette' in TV's *The Darling Buds of May*?

1. Mike Read. 2. Tommy Steele. 3. *The A Team*. 4. Gérard Depardieu.
5. Steve Coogan. 6. Blondie. 7. REM. 8. Marlon Brando. 9. 'Southfork'.
10. Billy Fury. 11. Nigel Havers. 12. Yazoo. 13. Four Pennies.
14. Daniel Day-Lewis. 15. Catherine Zeta Jones.

HISTORY

1   In which German city were the Holy Roman Emperors elected and, from 1562, crowned?

2   The position of Holy Roman Emperor remained, with one brief exception, in the hands of a single family from 1438 until the Empire was abolished. Which family was it?

3   The Holy Roman Emperor Charles V (1500–58), besides ruling Austria, large areas of Germany and Italy and the Netherlands, was also king of which country with vast overseas possessions?

4   What did Charles V do after abdicating as Emperor in 1556?

5   Francis of Lorraine became Holy Roman Emperor in 1745 largely thanks to his marriage to which Austrian archduchess?

6   Which daughter of the Emperor Francis I became queen of France?

7   Who was Holy Roman Emperor for most of the lifetime of Wolfgang Amadeus Mozart?

8   In which year was the Holy Roman Empire abolished?

9   Who became Austrian Emperor in 1848, retaining the title until his death in 1916?

10 Lajos Kossuth attempted to obtain independence from Austria for which country in 1848 and on various occasions later in the century?

11 At the Battle of Sadowa in 1866 the Austrians were defeated by which other nation?

12 The Republic of Czechoslovakia came into existence following the break-up of the Austrian empire in which year?

13 Which Austrian Chancellor was murdered by Nazi sympathizers in 1934?

14 The Anschluss between Austria and Hitler's Third Reich took place in which year?

15 Which Austrian became Secretary General of the United Nations in 1972?

FAMOUS PEOPLE

1 Who in 1855 patented an economical process for converting iron into steel by means of a Convertor which is named after him?

2 Who was said to be 'fiddling while Rome burned'?

3 Who demonstrated, by means of the pendulum named after him, the Earth's rotation on its axis?

4 Who composed the operettas *The Student Prince* and *The Desert Song*?

5 Which car manufacturer founded his motor works at Longbridge in Birmingham?

6 What is the name of the architect who designed the Cenotaph in Whitehall, London?

7 Who succeeded her brother-in-law William III to become queen of England and Scotland in 1702?

8 Who led an expedition to cross the Australian continent from south to north in 1860–61?

9 Who was famous for his saying, 'I think, therefore I am'?

10 Who wrote the Barsetshire series of novels?

11 The boundary between the American states of Maryland and Pennsylvania is popularly known by the names of the two men whose survey established it – who were they?

12 Which pope inspired the First Crusade?

13 Who preceded Thomas More as Chancellor to Henry VIII?

14 Whose investigations into the plight of the London poor were published under the title of *London Labour and the London Poor* in 1851?

15 Which king originated the Christmas Day broadcasts to the nation in 1932?

ANSWERS

1. Sir Henry Bessemer. 2. Emperor Nero. 3. Michel Foucault. 4. Sigmund Romberg. 5. Herbert Austin. 6. Sir Edwin Lutyens. 7. Queen Anne. 8. Robert O'Hara Burke. 9. René Descartes. 10. Anthony Trollope. 11. (Charles) Mason and (Jeremiah) Dixon. 12. Pope Urban II. 13. Cardinal Thomas Wolsey. 14. Henry Mayhew. 15. George V.

SPORT & LEISURE

1 In 1997 why couldn't the Grand National be staged on the correct day?

2 What is the name of Sunderland FC's former ground?

3 Boxer Muhammad Ali chose Islam as a faith. What religion did George Foreman opt for?

4 What sport has a governing body with the initials ARA?

5 Who took over from Michael Atherton as England cricket captain?

6 Who won the Five Nations Rugby Tournament in 1997?

7 What country does Leeds United's Lucas Radebe come from?

8 What job does Martin Pipe do in horse racing?

9 John Parrott is famous for what sport?

10 What is the name of the faith healer used by Glenn Hoddle?

11 In what sport do you find two 'props', two 'locks' and two 'flanks'?

12 What sport does Neil Hodgson compete in?

13 Who are the 'Blades' in football?

14 How many yards must a 'short jack' be away from the mat in bowls?

15 Why was the first Test between the West Indies and England abandoned after 10.1 overs in 1998?

1. Because of an IRA bomb scare. 2. Roker Park. 3. Christianity. 4. Rowing.
5. Alec Stewart. 6. France. 7. South Africa. 8. A trainer. 9. Snooker.
10. Eileen Drewry. 11. Rugby. 12. Super Bikes. 13. Sheffield United.
14. 25 yards. 15. The pitch was deemed too dangerous.

GENERAL KNOWLEDGE

1 When was the Samaritans founded?

2 Water is also known as whose 'ale'?

3 Who was 'Lady Penelope's' chauffeur?

4 Of what group does one find a posse?

5 According to Greek myth what was Nemesis the goddess of?

6 Who is the patron saint of workers?

7 Who wrote *The Lord of the Rings*?

8 In 'A Christmas Carol' what is Scrooge's first name?

9 What common sight in urban town centres derives its name from the Minister of Transport for 1934 to 1937?

10 What are gnocchi?

11 Who said 'I am just going outside, and may be some time'?

12 Who in the world would be called 'Taffy'?

13 What was the popular name of the *Thoughts of Chairman Mao*?

14 Which word, beginning with 'post-', means 'those coming after'?

15 Who wrote *The Lion, the Witch and the Wardrobe*?

1. 1953. 2. Adam. 3. 'Parker'. 4. Cowboys, constables, police. 5. Retribution and vengeance. 6. St Joseph. 7. J. R. R. Tolkein. 8. Ebenezer. 9. Belisha beacon, named after 1st Baron Leslie Hore-Belisha. 10. Italian savoury dumplings. 11. Captain Lawrence Oates, English Antarctic explorer. 12. A Welshman. 13. *The Little Red Book*. 14. Posterity. 15. C. S. Lewis.

SCIENCE & NATURE

1 What is an ungulate?

2 What is the term for a substance which fixes dyes in fabric?

3 What is the skeleton of a shark made of?

4 Who developed the first mercury thermometer in 1714?

5 What is the meteorological term for a thundercloud?

6 What is the basic SI unit of mass?

7 C.F. is the commonest inherited fatal disease caused by a single gene defect. What is its full name?

8 What is the depth of the deepest sea trench? Is it (a) 10.9 km (6.8 miles), (b) 15.9 km (9.9 miles) or (c) 20.9 km (13 miles)?

9 What is the name of a desert located in China?

10 Which Nobel Prize winner wrote a book called *The Double Helix*?

11 Where would you find an address bus and a control bus?

12 What is the unit of measurement of the brightness of a star?

13 What fatty substance is a component of gallstones?

14 What is dendrology?

15 How many tastes can the human tongue detect?

ANSWERS

1. A hoofed mammal. 2. A mordant. 3. Cartilage. 4. Gabriel Fahrenheit. 5. Cumulonimbus. 6. The kilogram. 7. Cystic fibrosis. 8. (a) 10.9 km (6.8 miles). It is called the Mariana Trench and it is situated east of the Philippines. 9. The Gobi Desert. 10. James D. Watson, on the discovery of the structure of DNA. 11. Inside a PC. 12. Magnitude. 13. Cholesterol. 14. A branch of botany dealing with trees and shrubs. 15. Four. The tongue can detect sweet, sour, salt and bitter tastes.

ENTERTAINMENT

1 Who presented the comedy series *Through the Cakehole*?

2 'Mr Tambourine Man' was a number one hit in 1965 for which group?

3 In the 1987 film *Three Men And A Baby*, Ted Danson and Steve Guttenberg were two of the men. Who was the third?

4 'Ria and Ben Parkinson' were characters in which TV comedy series?

5 Which jazz band had hits in 1962 with 'March of the Siamese Children' and 'The Green Leaves of Summer'?

6 Who played the title role in the film *Buster* in 1988?

7 The phrase 'So who would live in a house like this?' comes from which TV programme?

8 Vic Reeves had a top ten hit with which movie theme?

9 Who had a number one hit in 1975 with 'Sailing'?

10 In which year was the first *Comic Relief* show shown on TV?

11 'When Will I See You Again' was a number one hit in 1974 for which group?

12 In which year was the film *633 Squadron* released?

13 The character 'Huggy Bear' appeared in which TV crime series?

14 Which group sang with Joe Brown in the 1960s?

15 In 1967, Franco Zeffirelli directed a film of which Shakespeare play?

1. Jo Brand. 2. Byrds. 3. Tom Selleck. 4. *Butterflies*. 5. Kenny Ball and His Jazz Men. 6. Phil Collins. 7. *Through the Keyhole*. 8. 'Born Free'. 9. Rod Stewart. 10. 1986. 11. Three Degrees. 12. 1964. 13. *Starsky and Hutch*. 14. The Bruvvers. 15. *Romeo and Juliet*.

HISTORY

1 Which famous London theatre burned down during a performance in 1613?

2 What was the name of the company of actors to which William Shakespeare belonged?

3 Who is generally reckoned to have been the first poet laureate?

4 Where did the playwright and theatre manager Thomas Killigrew build a Theatre Royal in 1663?

5 Thomas Killigrew is also credited with obtaining permission for which innovation in English theatrical life in the 1660s?

6 Who became organist of Westminster Abbey in 1679?

7 Which theatre company was founded in Paris in 1680?

8 In which year was Handel's *Messiah* first performed?

9 Who succeeded Harold Wilson as prime minister in 1970?

10 Which of the following was not a famous actor: Edward Alleyn, Thomas Betterton, Edmund Kean, John Kemble, Thomas Linley?

11 Which of the following was not a famous actress: Mrs Cibber, Mrs Jordan, Mrs Radcliffe, Mrs Robinson, Mrs Siddons?

12 Whose first opera *Oberto* was produced at La Scala, Milan in 1839?

13 In which year was the Savoy theatre in London built where many of Gilbert and Sullivan's light operas were performed: (a) 1861, (b) 1871 or (c) 1881?

14 Who built the Savoy theatre?

15 Hollywood stars Marlon Brando, Dustin Hoffmann and Sidney Poitier were all trained in which style of acting?

FAMOUS PEOPLE

1 Who wrote *Whisky Galore* (1947)?

2 Who invented vulcanized rubber?

3 Which architect drew up plans for the city of Brasilia?

4 Whose compositions include *Fanfare for the Common Man* and the ballet music for *Rodeo*?

5 Who was the sixth wife of Henry VIII?

6 Who was prime minister of the British Coalition Government 1916–22?

7 Which poet, designer, and craftsman founded the Kelmscott Press in 1890?

8 Which American explorer reached the North Pole in 1909?

9 Which cartoonist created the *Beano's* 'Bash Street Kids' and 'Minnie the Minx'?

10 Who, in 1948, published a report on his study of human sexual behaviour?

11 Which American champion of women's rights gave her name to the baggy trousers she introduced as women's wear in the mid-19th century?

12 For which sport is Gary Sobers famous?

13 Which car manufacturer founded the motor works at Cowley in Oxford?

14 Who founded a settlement at Singapore as a station for the East India Company?

15 Which king of Scotland was defeated by the English led by Thomas Howard at Flodden Field in 1513?

ANSWERS

1. Sir Compton Mackenzie. 2. Charles Goodyear. 3. Lucio Costa. 4. Aaron Copland. 5. Catherine Parr. 6. David Lloyd-George. 7. William Morris. 8. Robert Peary. 9. Leo Baxendale. 10. Alfred Charles Kinsey. 11. Mrs Amelia Bloomer. 12. Cricket. 13. William Morris (Lord Nuffield). 14. Sir Stamford Raffles. 15. James IV.

SPORT & LEISURE

1 How many times did Willie Carson become Champion Jockey?

2 If you got a 'turkey' and a 'spare' what leisure activity would you be playing?

3 What colour jersey do the South African Rugby Union team wear?

4 What colour shirts do West Ham United play in?

5 Wigan and St Helen's are top clubs in what sport?

6 How many sixes did Wasim Akram hit in his 257 runs against Zimbabwe in 1996?

7 In what sport are the Thomas Cup and Uber Cup played for?

8 What is the start of a game of Ice Hockey called?

9 What country does footballer David Ginola come from?

10 What country does jockey Steve Cauthen originally come from?

11 Cassius Clay was floored on his debut at Madison Square Gardens. Which boxer did he get up to defeat in the fourth round?

12 Who won the 1988 Olympic Basketball title?

13 In what year did Damon Hill equal his father's record of 14 Grand Prix wins?

14 Jim Smith is the manager of what Premiership football team?

15 When was the long jump first included in the Olympic Games?

GENERAL KNOWLEDGE

1 From which language do the words 'tsar', 'steppe' and 'vodka' originate?

2 What is an éclair?

3 What does the prefix 'neo' mean?

4 Who is the reigning monarch of Japan?

5 What is Modulator and Demodulator more commonly called?

6 The twins represent which sign of the Zodiac?

7 In which ocean is the island of Mauritius?

8 Whose statue stands in front of Wesley's Chapel in City Road, London?

9 In the Bible, what virtue was Job famous for?

10 Who said, 'Father, I cannot tell a lie'?

11 Who is 'Old Nick'?

12 What year was the Battle of Britain?

13 Köchel numbers refer to the works of which composer?

14 Which artist was renowned for his paintings of horses?

15 What do the initials DC stand for after 'Washington'?

SCIENCE & NATURE

1　What is the appearance of a gibbous moon?

2　If a child suffers from fluorosis, what effect does it have on the teeth?

3　What is the chemical symbol for tungsten?

4　On what day of the year is the summer solstice?

5　What disease is treated with the drug L-dopa?

6　What does a histopathologist study?

7　If someone suffers from nyctophobia, what do they fear?

8　What is an orrery?

9　What is the term for the curved surface of a liquid in a vessel?

10　What is the green deposit formed upon copper called?

11　Which hormone stimulates the ejection of milk in mammals?

12　What is an otoscope?

13　Helicobacter pylori infection is thought to cause what condition?

14　What common household substance is produced by boiling sodium hydroxide with fats?

15　*Musca domestica* is a well-known pest, which spreads diseases. What is it?

ENTERTAINMENT

1   What is the name of the archaeology-based TV programme hosted by Tony Robinson?

2   In which year did Tom Jones have a number one hit with 'Green Green Grass of Home'?

3   Who stars with Jasper Carrot in TV's *The Detectives*?

4   Who had a hit in 1963 with 'I Who Have Nothing'?

5   Which radio disc jockey presented his own TV chat show in the late 1960s?

6   Who played 'Sam Malone' in the TV comedy series *Cheers*?

7   Who sang 'Ballad of Bonnie and Clyde' in 1968?

8   Who were dancing in the street for Live Aid?

9   What is the name of Rodney's wife in TV's *Only Fools and Horses*?

10 Who starred in the 1965 film *The Ipcress File*?

11 Who had a hit in 1961 with 'Johnny Remember Me'?

12 Who played 'Bradley Hardacre' in the TV comedy series *Brass*?

13 Who wanted to go wild in the country?

14 Was the film *The Greatest Story Ever Told* released in (a) 1963, (b) 1964 or (c) 1965?

15 In *The Greatest Story Ever Told*, who played the part of 'Jesus'?

1. *Time Team*. 2. 1966. 3. Robert Powell. 4. Shirley Bassey. 5. Simon Dee. 6. Ted Danson. 7. Georgie Fame. 8. Mick Jagger and Davie Bowie. 9. 'Cassandra'. 10. Michael Caine. 11. John Leyton. 12. Timothy West. 13. Bow Wow Wow. 14. (c) 1965. 15. Max Von Sydow.

HISTORY

1   In 1007 King Ethelred II (the Unready) paid £30,000 to the Danes to guarantee freedom from attack for two years. This was one of several payments known as what?

2   Which of the following was a king of Denmark: Harold Bluetooth, Harold Fairhair, Harold Harefoot, Harold Hadrader (or Hardraade)?

3   The German towns of Hamburg and Lübeck, later joined by Bremen and Danzig, were the leading members of what, from the 14th century on?

4   The Union of Kalmar (1397) united which three kingdoms?

5   What, during the 1520s, became the state religion of Sweden?

6   Which champion of the Protestant cause in Europe became king of Sweden in 1611?

7   Which French philosopher went to the court of Queen Christina of Sweden in 1649 and died there the following year?

8   Of which Swedish king did Dr Samuel Johnson write: 'He left the name at which the world grew pale/To point a moral or adorn a tale'?

9   By the peace of Kiel in 1814, Denmark ceded which island to Great Britain?

10 What did the USA purchase from Denmark in 1917?

11 Which Scandinavian country signed a non-aggression pact with Nazi Germany in 1939?

12 Which leader of the National Union party became head of the Norwegian government in 1940?

13 In which year did Iceland proclaim itself a Republic fully independent of Denmark?

14 Which prime minister of Sweden was murdered in Stockholm in 1986?

15 Which of the three Scandinavian countries is not a member of the European Union?

FAMOUS PEOPLE

1   Under what name was Martha Jane Burke better known?

2   Which president of the United States instituted the New Deal?

3   Which West Indian poet and playwright won the Nobel Prize for literature in 1992?

4   Which sculptor designed the monumental *Angel of the North*?

5   How did the Englishman Nicholas Breakspear achieve fame in 1154?

6   Who composed the *Hebrides* overture, otherwise known as *Fingal's Cave*?

7   What was Enid Blyton's middle name?

8   What was the name of Henry I's son who drowned in 1120, and whose death ultimately resulted in the civil war between Stephen and Matilda?

9   In the Bible, who had a vision of a valley of dry bones?

10   Under which British prime minister was the secret ballot for elections introduced?

11   Alfred Brendel is famous for playing which musical instrument?

12   What 'first' in aviation history was achieved by Floyd Bennett and Richard Evelyn Byrd?

13   Which playwright wrote the play *Rhinoceros*, and was a leading exponent of the theatre of the absurd?

14   Who composed the opera *Rigoletto*?

15   What did John Boyd Dunlop invent?

ANSWERS

1. Calamity Jane. 2. F. D. Roosevelt. 3. Derek Walcott. 4. Anthony Gormley. 5. He became Pope Adrian IV (only Englishman to become Pope). 6. Mendelssohn. 7. Mary. 8. William. 9. Ezekiel. 10. William Ewart Gladstone. 11. The piano. 12. First aeroplane flight over the North Pole. 13. Eugene Ionesco. 14. Verdi. 15. The pneumatic tyre.

SPORT & LEISURE

1   What horse did Bob Champion ride to victory in the 1981 Grand National?

2   How often are the Basketball World Championships held?

3   Did Frank Bruno become the Heavyweight Champion of the World?

4   If you were at a *Serie A* football match, what country would you be in?

5   Where do the Scottish Rugby Union team play their home internationals?

6   What pop star entertained rain soaked spectators at Wimbledon in 1996?

7   How many points is a 'double top' in darts?

8   Monica Seles won the Australian Open tennis title in 1996. How many times had she already won it?

9   What was the name of the computer that chess player Gary Kasparov played against?

10 In what country was footballer Michael Owen brought up?

11 Tracy Edwards is known for what sport?

12 Who did Charlton beat in the 1997–98 play off final?

13 Which former cricket player is team captain on the quiz show *They Think It's All Over*?

14 What is the perfect score in ten pin bowling?

15 Did Liverpool win the FA Cup under Bob Paisley?

GENERAL KNOWLEDGE

1 Who played 'The Prisoner' in the TV series of that name?

2 The 'jolly swagman' went 'Waltzing Matilda'. What was a matilda?

3 Which Czech-born newspaper owner and businessman died suddenly, falling into the water from his boat?

4 How did teddy bears receive their name?

5 What is the name of the founding prophet of the Islamic faith?

6 In wartime, what was a WAAF?

7 What does the prefix 'cardio-' mean?

8 Which architect designed Waterloo Bridge and the Anglican Cathedral in Liverpool?

9 Who, in 1976, opened her first Body Shop?

10 What kind of food is baklava?

11 Which mountain is Europe's highest?

12 Who in the world would be called a 'Jock'?

13 Who wrote the 'William' books?

14 A stitch in time will save how many?

15 In which year was John F. Kennedy assassinated?

1. Patrick McGoohan. 2. The swagman's roll containing his blanket. 3. Robert Maxwell. 4. They were named after the American president, Theodore 'Teddy' Roosevelt. 5. Mohammed. 6. A member of the Women's Auxiliary Air Force. 7. To do with the heart. 8. Sir Giles Gilbert Scott. 9. Anita Roddick. 10. Pastry filled with nuts and honey. 11. Elbrus. 12. A Scotsman. 13. Richmal Crompton. 14. Nine. 15. 1963.

SCIENCE & NATURE

1 Aboard which ship did Charles Darwin travel from 1831–36?

2 Which common vegetable belongs to the same family as the tomato?

3 When was the world's first human heart transplant performed?

4 What element has the symbol Hg?

5 Which cow disease was first identified in Britain in 1986 and by 1996 had claimed 158,000 cattle?

6 What is St Vitus dance?

7 The 16th-century Danish astronomer Tycho Brahe made accurate observations of the planets but what other, more personal feature, is he known for?

8 What is the name of the scale used to compare sound intensities?

9 If you were given a sapphire on your wedding anniversary, how many years would you have been married?

10 Which product, used extensively in the clothing industry, did the Du Pont chemical company launch in 1959?

11 What is the more common name of nitrous oxide?

12 In computing, what is an 'expert system'?

13 On which day is the winter solstice?

14 Which word describes the flat area of alluvial deposits on the mouth of some rivers?

15 What was the name of the first US satellite in orbit?

ENTERTAINMENT

1   Which group had a hit in 1963 with 'Sweets for My Sweet'?

2   'The Nag's Head' is the name of the pub in which comedy series?

3   Who wrote and directed the 1989 film *Erik The Viking*?

4   Which actress plays 'Edie' in the TV comedy series *Last of the Summer Wine*?

5   Who hosted TV's *Sale of the Century*?

6   Who composed the song 'Step Inside Love', sung by Cilla Black?

7   In which 1984 TV drama series did Tim Piggot-Smith play the role of 'Merrick'?

8   DNA's version of 'Tom's Diner' reached number two. Who recorded the original version?

9   Who had a hit in 1963 with 'Dominique'?

10 The characters 'Alice' and 'Hugo Horton' feature in which 1990s TV comedy series?

11 The song 'We May Never Love Like This Again' is from which disaster film in 1974?

12 The theme for *The Saint* movie in 1997 was performed by which electronic dance act: (a) Propellerheads, (b) Orbital or (c) The Chemical Brothers?

13 *Tucker's Luck* was a spin-off of which children's TV series?

14 In which year was the film *Star Wars* nominated for a Best Picture Oscar?

15 The entertainer, Victor Borge, was born in which country?

1. The Searchers. 2. *Only Fools and Horses*. 3. Terry Jones. 4. Thora Hird. 5. Nicholas Parsons. 6. Paul McCartney. 7. *The Jewel In The Crown*. 8. Suzanne Vega. 9. The Singing Nun. 10. *The Vicar of Dibley*. 11. *The Towering Inferno*. 12. (b) Orbital. 13. *Grange Hill*. 14. 1977. 15. Denmark.

HISTORY

1 The 'Plantation of Ulster', involving the confiscation of land from the native Irish and the introduction of settlers from the mainland of Britain took place under which king of England?

2 The Peace of Westphalia in 1648 ended which European war?

3 Which Scottish nobleman led the Royalist forces successfully in several campaigns in Scotland during the Civil War until he was finally defeated and executed in 1650?

4 Which title was offered to Oliver Cromwell by Parliament in 1657 and rejected?

5 Who defeated whom at the battle of Poltava in 1709?

6 General George Wade is mainly famous for building what in Scotland between 1726 and 1737?

7 'Man is born free, but everywhere he is in chains'. Of which major work of political theory, published in 1762, is this the opening sentence?

8 In which year was the Bastille stormed, signifying the start of the French revolution?

9 In 1808, the Duke of Wellington was sent to help the forces of which country in their fight against the French?

10 Who was prime minister of Great Britain from 1812 to 1827?

11 In 1829 the Royal Zoological Society took over a menagerie which subsequently formed the basis of the collection at London Zoo. Where had the menagerie been kept?

12 In 1890 Britain ceded the North Sea island of Heligoland to Germany and received which African possession in return?

13 The Baron de Coubertin was the main founder and organizer of which sporting event?

14 The Trans-Siberian railway was completed in which year: (a) 1881, (b) 1891 or (c) 1901?

15 Which Soviet leader was born Lev Davidovich Bronstein?

FAMOUS PEOPLE

1. In which year did Benjamin Disraeli die?

2. Who wrote the music for *The Lion King*?

3. Which American civil rights leader was assassinated in 1968?

4. Who reached America in 1492?

5. 'Elementary, my dear Watson'. Who supposedly said that?

6. For how long was Lady Jane Grey queen of England in 1553?

7. Who is the current Duke of Cornwall?

8. Who was assassinated in Delhi, India, on 20 January 1948?

9. Who was Mr Five-Per-Cent?

10. What 'British' character was invented by John Arbuthnot in 1712?

11. Who was Madame de Pompadour?

12. The first issue of the *Daily News* newspaper appeared on 21 January 1846. Who was the editor?

13. What is the surname of the Queen?

14. Who was the 34th president of the USA?

15. Which monarch this century was almost sixty when he was crowned?

ANSWERS

1. 1881. 2. Elton John. 3. Martin Luther King. 4. Christopher Columbus. 5. 'Sherlock Holmes'. 6. For only nine days. 7. Prince Charles. 8. Mahatma Gandhi. 9. Calouste Gulbenkian, oil millionaire. 10. 'John Bull'. 11. The mistress of King Louis XV of France. 12. Charles Dickens. 13. The Queen has no surname, but is a member of the House of Windsor. 14. Dwight David Eisenhower. 15. King Edward VII.

SPORT & LEISURE

1 What was the English football team's song for Euro '96?

2 Why couldn't Diane Modahl compete for England in athletics for 19 months?

3 Tennis player Richard Krajicek is from which country?

4 What sport does Pat Eddery compete in?

5 What are the discs used in tiddlywinks called?

6 Jane Sixsmith is famous for playing what sport?

7 What film did Bobby Moore and Pele star in alongside Michael Caine?

8 At what club did Ian Botham finish his cricket career?

9 Who are the 'Super Sonics' in Basketball?

10 What is the name of Serena Williams's tennis playing sister?

11 How many points do you receive for a penalty try in Rugby Union?

12 Which famous Australian bowler was born in 1969 and made his international debut against New Zealand in 1993?

13 Why was Linford Christie disqualified from the 100-metres at the Atlanta Olympics?

14 At which club did John Barnes start his professional football career?

15 Which Australian cricketer also made 95 appearances for the Victoria football club?

GENERAL KNOWLEDGE

1 Who wrote *Hancock's Half Hour*?

2 What does 'bespoke' mean (a) to do with a bicycle, (b) made-to-measure or (c) committed?

3 What is the correct name of the Christian denomination commonly referred to as the 'Quakers'?

4 What is a quiche?

5 What sort of creature is a drongo?

6 In Cockney rhyming slang, what is meant by 'plates of meat'?

7 What does the prefix 'kilo' mean?

8 Mercury is another name for the messenger of the gods, Hermes. True or false?

9 Who played 'Meg Richardson' in the TV soap *Crossroads*?

10 Which anniversary does a golden wedding celebrate?

11 Who launched his Virgin Atlantic airline in 1984?

12 The American cartoonist Chester Gould conceived which character?

13 Who left *The Big Breakfast Show* to concentrate on *Don't Forget Your Toothbrush*?

14 What does AWOL stand for?

15 Who wrote the *Barchester* novels?

ANSWERS

1. Ray Galton and Alan Simpson. 2. (b) made-to-measure. 3. The Religious Society of Friends. 4. A shell of unsweetened pastry which can hold a savoury filling. 5. A bird. 6. Feet. 7. Thousand. 8. True. 9. Noele Gordon. 10. The fiftieth. 11. Richard Branson. 12. Dick Tracy. 13. Chris Evans. 14. Absent Without Leave. 15. Anthony Trollope.

SCIENCE & NATURE

1 What type of fruit is a morello?

2 What is the common name of *Gryllus campestris*?

3 Which bird is known as the 'man-of-war' bird?

4 What is a garganey?

5 In 1948 the United Nations created a special environment agency. What is it called?

6 In which year was insulin first used to treat diabetes?

7 Each month of the year is associated with a certain flower, which month is linked with morning glory?

8 What does eight indicate on the Beaufort scale?

9 How did the term 'quasar' originate?

10 What does the internationally recognized symbol of a skull and cross bones in a triangle indicate when associated with a chemical substance?

11 Lack of which chemical compound in the body is linked with Parkinson's disease?

12 What is a tsunami?

13 Ratites is a collective name for birds with which characteristic?

14 Which of the following is the hardest mineral: (a) topaz, (b) apatite or (c) quartz?

15 Which form of radiation in the electromagnetic spectrum has the longest wavelength?

ENTERTAINMENT

1 The songs 'Getting To Know You' and 'Hello, Young Lovers' are from which musical?

2 Which short-lived TV soap was based in Spain?

3 What was the name of the pink hippopotamus on the children's TV programme *Rainbow*?

4 Who had a hit in 1963 with 'I Only Want To Be With You'?

5 What is the name of the computer in the TV comedy series *Red Dwarf*?

6 What did World party want to put in the box?

7 Which 1984 film won Oscars for Best Picture, Best Director, Best Actress and Best Supporting Actor?

8 Who played the curate in the TV comedy series *All Gas and Gaiters*?

9 Joy, Babs and Teddie are the first names of which group?

10 'Take My Breath Away' is a song featured in which film?

11 Who had a top ten hit with 'Stairway To Heaven' in 1993?

12 What is the name of the TV comedy series in which Nicholas Lyndhurst travels back in time to war-time?

13 Which singer performed regularly on the satirical programme *That Was The Week That Was*?

14 Karl Malden and Michael Douglas starred in which TV crime series?

15 Which actor starred in the TV comedy series *Mork and Mindy*?

HISTORY

1 In 1747 Johann Sebastian Bach presented his 'Musical Offering' to which king?

2 In the course of his travels around Europe as an infant prodigy, Wolfgang Amadeus Mozart is said to have offered to kiss which Austrian princess, daughter of the Empress Maria Theresa?

3 Who was Mozart's first employer?

4 Which famous European composer was made a Doctor of Music at Oxford University in 1791?

5 Beethoven's *Eroica Symphony* was initially dedicated to which historical figure?

6 Besides Beethoven, which other major composer was present in Vienna in 1809 when it was besieged and eventually taken by the French?

7 Beethoven's *Battle Symphony* commemorates which of the Duke of Wellington's victories of 1813?

8 The opera composers Guiseppe Verdi and Richard Wagner were both born in the same year. Which year was it?

9 Which composer's best-known oratorio was first performed in Birmingham in 1846?

10 Which famous composer was forced to flee from Dresden in 1848 because of his involvement in revolutionary activities?

11 Which composer wrote a special overture to commemorate receiving an honorary doctorate in music from the University of Breslau?

12 Which European composer was appointed director of the National Conservatory of Music in New York in 1892?

13 The opera *The Golden Cockerel* was banned from the Russian stage in 1906 because it was a satire on autocracy. Who was its composer?

14 Which composer's *Seventh Symphony* was written in Leningrad while the city was being besieged by the Germans in World War II?

15 Which British composer was commissioned to write a work for the dedication of the new Coventry cathedral in 1962?

1. Frederick the Great (Frederick II of Prussia). 2. Marie Antoinette. 3. The Prince Archbishop of Salzburg (Colloredo). 4. Joseph Haydn. 5. Napoleon Bonaparte. 6. Joseph Haydn. 7. The Battle of Vitoria. 8. 1813. 9. Felix Mendelssohn (*Elijah*). 10. Richard Wagner. 11. Johannes Brahms. 12. Antonin Dvorak. 13. Nikolai Rimsky-Korsakov. 14. Dimitri Shostakovich. 15. Benjamin Britten (the *War Requiem*).

FAMOUS PEOPLE

1 Which queen bathed every three months, 'whether she needed to or not'?

2 Which British prime minister was awarded the Nobel Prize for Literature?

3 A German banker, whose first names were Meyer Amschel, founded a famous company in Frankfurt. What was his surname?

4 Who was called 'the wisest fool in Christendom'?

5 Mother Theresa received the Order of Merit from whose hands in 1983?

6 Who was the only English pope?

7 Who was John Cabot?

8 Which French ruler was reported to be afraid of cats?

9 Who, in World War II, was Bomber Harris?

10 Who was the last of the Plantagenet kings?

11 Who was 'the Lady with the Lamp'?

12 Who was Aristotle?

13 To which president was Eleanor Roosevelt married?

14 Who was proclaimed Empress of India on 1 January 1877?

15 Who opened his first shelter for abandoned children in Stepney, London, in 1867?

1. Queen Elizabeth I. 2. Sir Winston Churchill. 3. Rothschild. 4. King James VI of Scotland/James I of England. 5. The Queen. 6. Nicholas Breakspear (Pope Adrian IV). 7. An explorer from Genoa who discovered Newfoundland. 8. Napoleon. 9. Sir Arthur Harris, Marshall of the RAF. 10. King Richard II (1377–99). 11. Florence Nightingale. 12. A Greek philosopher of enormous knowledge. 13. Franklin D. Roosevelt. 14. Queen Victoria. 15. Dr Thomas Barnardo.

SPORT & LEISURE

1   What team does Shaquille O'Neal play for in the NBA?

2   What football team won 'the double' in 1986?

3   John Lowe is famous for what sport?

4   'Googlies', 'flippers' and 'wrong 'uns' can be found in which sport?

5   For what country did Gavin and Scott Hastings both play Rugby Union?

6   Who are England's joint leading goal scorers of all time?

7   In fencing there are three types of sword. What are they?

8   The game 'Fives' originates from which public school?

9   Who came second in the Grand National on Garrison Savannah in 1991?

10 In the game of nim, what small items are most commonly removed?

11 In what sport would you find the governing body ABC?

12 The late Tim Gullikson coached which top tennis player?

13 Who was the captain of the India cricket team who was controversially sacked in 1997, but reinstated in 1998?

14 Three Day Eventing encompasses what three activities?

15 Who won the 1934 and 1938 Football World Cup Finals?

1. LA Lakers. 2. Liverpool. 3. Darts. 4. Cricket. 5. Scotland. 6. Bobby Charlton and Gary Lineker. 7. Foil, épée and sabre. 8. Eton. 9. Mark Pitman. 10. Matchsticks. 11. Ten pin bowling. 12. Pete Sampras. 13. Mohammed Azharuddin. 14. Dressage, cross country and jumping. 15. Italy.

GENERAL KNOWLEDGE

1   In which modern-day country did the ancient city of Troy lie?

2   What is a 'Walter Mitty'?

3   From which language do the words 'fjord', 'floe' and 'slalom' originate?

4   In which city, apart from London, would you find Soho?

5   What is Neil Armstrong famous for?

6   What is cribbage?

7   Alpha, epsilon and lambda are all what?

8   Which musical play featured the song 'Climb Ev'ry Mountain'?

9   In which year was the Berlin Wall destroyed?

10 Campanology is the art of what?

11 Who launched London Weekend Television's *The South Bank Show* in 1978?

12 In ancient times, what was King Midas's big problem?

13 Which character was also a civilian bank manager in *Dad's Army*?

14 Where is the Golden Gate?

15 What was the name of the American statesman who was the first to sign the Declaration of Independence and whose name has come to mean 'a signature'?

ANSWERS

1. Turkey. 2. A day-dreaming fantasist. 3. Norwegian. 4. Birmingham. 5. Being the first man to walk on the Moon. 6. A card game. 7. Letters in the Greek alphabet. 8. *The Sound of Music*. 9. 1989. 10. Ringing bells. 11. Melvyn Bragg. 12. Everything he touched turned to gold. 13. 'Captain Mainwaring'. 14. The entrance to the bay of San Francisco. 15. John Hancock.

SCIENCE & NATURE

1   Which constellation is depicted as the Hunter?

2   Who, born in 1642, devised the three laws of motion and is credited with the discovery of gravity?

3   What is a Rhode Island Red?

4   What was the name of the Greenpeace boat that was sunk by French intelligence agents in New Zealand (in 1985) during a protest against French nuclear testing?

5   The 'clusec' is a unit of measurement for what?

6   In which year was the first test-tube baby born in the UK?

7   What is the name of the Austrian monk who experimented with peas and is considered the founder of genetics?

8   In printing, one pica or one pica em equals how many points?

9   Which oily blister-inducing liquid has been used as a poison during warfare?

10 What is the unusual feature of the mudskipper fish?

11 The Sun consists mainly of two gases, one is hydrogen, what is the other?

12 How was the SI base unit of length, the metre, originally defined?

13 What are the chemical elements that are present in fertilizer?

14 Where would you find the letters A S D F G H next to one another?

15 What is the common name for the herbaceous plant *Helleborus niger*?

ANSWERS

1. Orion. 2. Isaac Newton. 3. A type of chicken. 4. *Rainbow Warrior*. 5. Unit for measuring power of a vacuum pump. 6. 1978, Louise Brown. 7. Gregor Mendel (1822-84). 8. Twelve. 9. Mustard gas. 10. These fish spend three-quarters of their time out of water (climbing tangled roots and stems of mangrove vegetation in the swamps that they inhabit). 11. Helium. 12. As one ten-millionth of the distance from the North Pole to the Equator on a line through Paris. 13. Nitrogen, phosphorous and potassium. 14. On a computer keyboard. 15. Christmas rose.

ENTERTAINMENT

1 Which important event was shown on TV on 20 July 1969?

2 The song 'Nobody Does It Better' comes from which James Bond film?

3 In which TV series was the character 'Richard DeVere'?

4 Who had a hit with 'Let's Twist Again'?

5 Which character did John Forsythe play in the TV soap *Dynasty*?

6 Which actress starred in the 1972 film *Cabaret*?

7 Who performed the theme for the *Ghostbusters* films?

8 Which famous conductor appeared on a *Morecambe and Wise* show?

9 'Mrs Overall' in the comedy sketches *Acorn Antiques* is played by which actress?

10 Which science fiction film won an Oscar for Visual Effects in 1979?

11 Who had a top ten hit with 'Love and Pride' and now presents music television?

12 What was the name of the Saturday morning children's television show hosted by Noel Edmonds?

13 Who wrote the theme tune for *Coronation Street*?

14 Who played the title role in the TV comedy *Blott on The Landscape*?

15 What was Cliff Richard's first number one hit record?

397

1. The first manned Moon landing. 2. *The Spy Who Loved Me*. 3. *To The Manor Born*. 4. Chubby Checker. 5. 'Blake Carrington'. 6. Liza Minelli. 7. Ray Parker Jr. 8. André Previn. 9. Julie Walters. 10. *Aliens*. 11. Paul King. 12. *Multi-Coloured Swap Shop*. 13. Eric Spear. 14. David Suchet. 15. 'Livin' Doll'.

HISTORY

1 The union of which two countries was formalized by an Act of Union in 1536?

2 Where was Edward I's son, who became the first Prince of Wales, born?

3 Who led a rebellion in Wales against the English crown in 1402?

4 Which English royal dynasty could boast Welsh origins?

5 Where in Wales did a small French force land during the Napoleonic Wars in the 'last invasion of Britain'?

6 In which century was the first modern eisteddfod held?

7 Where was David Lloyd George born in 1863?

8 What post did Lloyd George hold at the outbreak of World War I?

9 Lloyd George became prime minister in 1916. In which year did he resign the office after being defeated in a general election?

10 In which year was the Church of England dis-established in Wales?

11 Which political party was founded in Wales in 1925?

12 Aneurin Bevan sat for which Welsh constituency from 1929 to 1960?

13 Which post did Aneurin Bevan hold in Attlee's post-war government?

14 In which year did Neil Kinnock become leader of the Labour Party?

15 Which Secretary of State for Wales resigned in 1998 after admitting a 'serious error of judgment'?

FAMOUS PEOPLE

1 Who came to power in Japan in 1926?

2 After seven months of resistance, the South African town of Mafeking was relieved by troops under the command of which military figure?

3 Whose last words were 'Et tu, Brute'?

4 In the Bible, who is known as 'the weeping prophet'?

5 Who was Ernesto 'Che' Guevara?

6 Who was George Blake, who escaped from Wormwood Scrubs in 1966?

7 Which world-famous discoverer died in poverty in 1506?

8 Which well-known priest was ex-communicated by the Roman Catholic Church in 1521?

9 Who was knighted aboard his ship, *The Golden Hind*, in 1581?

10 Whom did Philip of Spain marry in 1554?

11 What did Matthew Webb, the swimmer, achieve in 1875?

12 Henry Cecil Booth patented which household appliance in 1901?

13 Constantine II (1964–67) was the last monarch of which country?

14 Who was Eamon De Valera?

15 President McKinley of the US died on 14 September 1901, following what?

ANSWERS

1. Emperor Hirohito. 2. Col. Robert Baden-Powell. 3. Julius Caesar's. 4. Jeremiah. 5. A Latin American revolutionary. 6. A traitor and spy. 7. Christopher Columbus. 8. Martin Luther. 9. Francis Drake. 10. Queen Mary I of England. 11. He became the first man to swim the Channel. 12. The vacuum cleaner. 13. Greece. 14. President of the Irish Republic (1959–73). 15. Being shot and wounded eight days earlier.

SPORT & LEISURE

1 In what sport would you do a *Harai goshi*?

2 Boxer Michael Spinks only lost once in his reign as heavyweight champion. Who beat him?

3 What pop star is footballer Jamie Redknapp married to?

4 What country does former tennis player Ilie Nastase come from?

5 What is the horse piece in chess called?

6 What is the player called who puts the ball into the scrum in Rugby Union?

7 What is the highest score you can check out on in darts?

8 What job did England player Rory Underwood do outside of Rugby?

9 How many Classics are there in the flat season of horse racing?

10 Who were the 1988 men's Olympic Hockey Champions?

11 From what team did Chelsea buy Gustavo Poyet?

12 How often are the Lacrosse World Championships held?

13 Kevin Pressman became the goalkeeper for what football club in 1993–94?

14 Edgbaston is the home of what cricket team?

15 What is the nickname of Luton Town FC?

400

1. Judo. 2. Mike Tyson. 3. Louise. 4. Romania. 5. Knight. 6. Scrum half. 7. 170. 8. RAF pilot officer. 9. Five. 10. Great Britain. 11. Real Zaragoza. 12. Every four years. 13. Sheffield Wednesday. 14. Warwickshire. 15. 'The Hatters'.

GENERAL KNOWLEDGE

1 What canal links the North and Baltic Seas?

2 In a pack of cards, which way does the Jack of hearts look, to his left or to his right?

3 According to the proverb, what should you not put into one basket?

4 What are 'devils on horseback'?

5 Who is known as the Bard of Avon?

6 Which French drink has a strong anise taste?

7 What aspect of grammar is illustrated in the phrase 'to boldly go'?

8 Who painted landscapes of the Suffolk countryside?

9 What is the name of the Muslim's holy book?

10 St Cecilia is the patron saint of whom?

11 Who wrote a famous biography of Dr Johnson?

12 Which anniversary does a bronze or electrical appliance wedding celebrate?

13 Who wrote the 'Tintin' picture stories?

14 Which word, beginning with 'post-', means 'after dinner'?

15 Who played 'Sir Charles' in *The Pink Panther*?

1. Kiel Canal. 2. To his left. 3. All your eggs. 4. Prunes stuffed with chutney and grilled, or fried rolled up in bacon. 5. William Shakespeare. 6. Absinthe. 7. Split infinitive. 8. John Constable. 9. Koran (Qur'an). 10. Singers and musicians. 11. James Boswell. 12. The eighth. 13. G. R. Hergé. 14. Postprandial. 15. David Niven.

SCIENCE & NATURE

1 Which cereal disease can cause food poisoning and gangrene of the fingers if consumed?

2 Who, born in 1781, built the *Rocket* steam locomotive?

3 What is a lumpsucker?

4 What silvery reactive metal was discovered by Humphrey Davy in 1808?

5 In computing, how did the term 'bit' originate?

6 Which precious metal is almost always found in galena ore?

7 What is a jabiru?

8 The world's largest flower with a diameter up to 1 metre is born by the parasitic plant *Rafflesia*. What is the other distinctive property of the plant?

9 What is the equivalent Arabic numeral for the Roman 'CM'?

10 What well-known drug comes from the yellow cinchona plant?

11 If you suffer from ailuophobia, what is your greatest fear?

12 RSI is a technology-related condition, what is it?

13 In April 1970 the flight of which spacecraft to the Moon resulted in a near escape for its three astronauts after an explosion on board?

14 Which chemical compound in the body is linked to atherosclerosis (hardening of the arteries)?

15 In which year was there an explosive leak from a nuclear reactor at Chernobyl in the Ukraine?

ENTERTAINMENT

1   'Sicknote' is a character in which TV series?

2   Who has the catchphrase 'Izzy Wizzy, Let's Get Busy'?

3   In 1939, which film was the first in colour to win a
    Best Picture Oscar?

4   Who played Henry VII in TV's *The Six Wives of Henry VIII* in 1970?

5   Actress Wendy Richards had a hit in 1962 with 'Come Outside'
    with which singer?

6   Name the bluesman whose explosive song reached number
    sixteen in the charts in 1992.

7   'Jed and Elly May Clampett' were characters in which popular
    1960s TV comedy series?

8   What was the name of the first film made by The Beatles?

9   Which television cook chose cranberries as her ingredient of the
    year in 1995 and caused a major shortage of them in shops?

10 In which year did the England World Cup Squad have a number
    one hit with 'Back Home'?

11 Who played 'The Prince Regent' in *Blackadder The Third*?

12 Who married one of his coconuts?

13 In the 1963 film *Cleopatra* who played the role of 'Caesar'?

14 In which year did the TV comedy series *Friends* begin?

15 Who had a hit in 1978 with 'Baker Street'?

ANSWERS

1. London's Burning. 2. 'Sooty'. 3. Gone With The Wind. 4. Keith Michell. 5. Mike Sarne. 6. John Lee Hooker. 7. The Beverly Hillbillies. 8. A Hard Day's Night. 9. Delia Smith. 10. 1970. 11. Hugh Laurie. 12. Kid Creole. 13. Rex Harrison. 14. 1994. 15. Gerry Rafferty.

HISTORY

1 Who was king of Great Britain in the year 1800?

2 Who began printing parliamentary reports in 1774, becoming printer to the House of Commons in 1798?

3 In which year did the 'Peterloo Massacre' take place, in which a radical meeting was broken up by a cavalry charge?

4 In which English city did the 'Peterloo Massacre' take place?

5 An insurrection in Monmouthshire in 1839 led to the imprisonment of several leaders of which movement?

6 What were repealed in 1846, largely as a result of agitation by Richard Cobden, 'the Apostle of Free Trade'?

7 William Howard Russell became famous as what during the Crimean War?

8 What office was held by Lord John Russell from 1846 to 1852?

9 The plight of the wounded after the Battle of Solferino in 1859 inspired the Swiss Jean Henri Dunant to found what?

10 Who fought whom at the Battle of Solferino?

11 Who was the first Labour Party MP?

12 Who ceased to be leader of the Opposition in the British House of Commons in 1931?

13 François Duvalier was president of which Caribbean island from 1957 to 1971?

14 What was François Duvalier's nickname?

15 In which year was the Shah of Persia, Mohammed Reza Pahlavi, deposed?

FAMOUS PEOPLE

1 Who was Dag Hammarskjöld?

2 Margaret Thatcher visited which Eastern European country in March 1987?

3 Who was Alexander the Great?

4 How did Cardinal Wolsey die in 1530?

5 Who was leader of the Labour Party immediately before Tony Blair?

6 Who was Alfred the Great?

7 Of whom or what was St Pancras the patron saint?

8 Who wrote *The Decline and Fall of the Roman Empire*?

9 Which queen was discovered to be bald at the time of her execution?

10 Who was the first king of the Israelites?

11 Who was the Supreme Commander of the Allies at the end of World War I?

12 Which king acceded to the throne of England on Boxing Day, 1135?

13 What is significant about the death of Ruth Ellis in 1955?

14 Which American senator was fatally wounded in Los Angeles on 5 June 1968?

15 Who was the fattest of all British monarchs?

SPORT & LEISURE

1 What sport do Rodber and Ubogu play?

2 What country does Dwight Yorke come from?

3 In what sport might you play on the ATP Tour?

4 What sport is basically a combination of cross country running and map reading?

5 Neil Ardley plays for what Premiership football team?

6 How many players are there in a Rugby League team?

7 What sport is Matt Biondi known for?

8 What are the two main forms of competition weight lifting?

9 Cricketer Viv Richards, during his career, moved from Somerset to which county side?

10 How many points do you get for a 'bullseye' in darts?

11 If you potted the yellow, green and brown in snooker, how many points would you score?

12 When was women's hockey introduced to the Olympic Games?

13 What is the exact length of a cricket pitch?

14 'Googlies' and 'flippers' can be found in which sport?

15 What is the nickname of Grimsby Town FC?

1. Rugby Union. 2. Tobago, West Indies. 3. Tennis. 4. Orienteering. 5. Wimbledon FC. 6. 13. 7. Swimming. 8. Snatch and Clean, and Jerk. 9. Glamorgan. 10. 50 points. 11. Nine. 12. 1980. 13. 22 yards. 14. Cricket. 15. 'The Mariners'.

GENERAL KNOWLEDGE

1   In secretarial terms, what do the initials w.p.m. stand for?

2   What is ratatouille?

3   Who succeeded David Steel as leader of the Liberal Democrats?

4   St Barbara is the patron saint of whom?

5   Who starred in the TV programmes *Around the World in Eighty Days* and *Pole to Pole*?

6   According to the 'language of flowers', what does the nasturtium signify?

7   Which US city is the home of jazz?

8   'Rule by a privileged class' is called what?

9   Apollo, Eros and Iris are all what?

10 'Peregrination' means (a) a bird, (b) travelling or (c) reading a newspaper?

11 What is the collective noun for a group of lions?

12 What city lies at the northernpost point of the River Danube?

13 What part did Kenneth More play in the film *Genevieve*?

14 Who was George Cadbury?

15 Who wrote the *Waverley* novels?

1. Words per minute. 2. A vegetable stew containing tomatoes, aubergines, peppers, etc. 3. Paddy Ashdown. 4. Miners. 5. Michael Palin. 6. Patriotism. 7. New Orleans. 8. Aristocracy. 9. Greek gods. 10. (b) travelling. 11. A pride. 12. Regensburg. 13. 'Ambrose Claverhouse'. 14. A businessman and philanthropist from the famous chocolate firm. 15. Sir Walter Scott.

SCIENCE & NATURE

1   What is the common name of the flower *Kniphofia*?

2   What does the Earth's core mainly consist of?

3   Rayon is a textile made from what?

4   Which cloud form has the abbreviation Cb?

5   Which well-known drug comes from the dog button plant?

6   What is a bathyscaphe?

7   In 1990 the CJD Surveillance Unit was set up in Edinburgh to monitor occurrence of the disease. Name the disease.

8   Name one of the two moons, or satellites, orbiting Mars?

9   Where is Silicon Valley?

10 What does the medical abbreviation LD stand for?

11 What was Linus Yale's invention of 1851?

12 Which animal has a reputation for being more slothful than the sloth?

13 Which living fish was found 60 million years after its supposed extinction?

14 Name the organs that are involved in a triple transplant?

15 What is the Latin name for the brown rat?

ENTERTAINMENT

1 Who played 'Ilya Kuryakin' in *The Man from U.N.C.L.E.*?

2 Who had a hit in 1970 with 'Raindrops Keep Falling On My Head'?

3 The TV programme *The Biederbecke Affair* starred Barbara Flynn and which actor?

4 Which comedian had a number one hit in 1965 with 'Tears'?

5 Which famous milkman got back into the top forty in 1992?

6 In which year was the first *Rocky* film released?

7 Which group had a hit in 1960 with 'Shaking All Over'?

8 What was the name of the popular 1960s TV puppet series, written by Eric Thompson?

9 In which year did The Beatles first have number one hits?

10 What was the name of the 1976 film based on the Watergate scandal in America?

11 According to Haysi Fantayzee, what is John Wayne?

12 Who wrote and performed in the TV comedy shows *It's A Square World*?

13 In which year did Dana win the Eurovision Song Contest with 'All Kinds of Everything'?

14 Which children's TV programme included sketches and the game 'Double or Drop?

15 'Up Where We Belong' is a song featured in which film?

409

HISTORY

1 In which decade of the 19th century was gold discovered on the Witwatersrand in the Transvaal, South Africa?

2 Who defeated whom at the battle of Majuba Hill in 1881?

3 By what name were foreigners known who were working in the Transvaal, especially in the gold mines, towards the end of the 19th century?

4 Who led a raid on the Transvaal in December 1895 in an attempt to provoke an uprising and take over the country?

5 Who sent a telegram to President Kruger of the Transvaal in 1896 congratulating him on his defeat of the raiders?

6 In which year did the (Anglo-)Boer War begin?

7 Who was sent to command the British forces in Natal at the outbreak of the Boer War?

8 Which battle in the Natal campaign was fought mainly on the flat top of a hill?

9 Which war correspondent was taken prisoner by the Boers when the armoured train in which he was travelling was ambushed?

10 In which town besieged by the Boers was Cecil Rhodes one of the defenders?

11 Who commanded the British garrison during the siege of Mafeking?

12 In which year was Ladysmith relieved?

13 Who was in overall command of the British advance that resulted in the capture of the Boer capitals of Bloemfontein and Pretoria?

14 Which future leader of the movement for Indian independence organized an ambulance corps and commanded a Red Cross unit for the British army during the Boer War?

15 Three future prime ministers of the Union of South Africa were Boer commanders during the Boer War. Who were they?

FAMOUS PEOPLE

1. Who was British prime minister for a total of over 20 years?

2. What was the name of the wife of King Louis XVI of France?

3. In Whitechapel, East London, in 1888, many prostitutes were murdered. Who was held responsible?

4. Who was Edward Longshanks?

5. The pedal cycle was perfected in 1839 by whom?

6. Which Chinese leader died on 9 September 1976?

7. George Pullman died on 9 October 1897. For what was he famous?

8. Which pope died in 1978 after reigning for only 33 days?

9. What did Frank Hornby patent in 1901?

10. Which Russian socialist died in 1883, and was buried in Highgate Cemetery, London?

11. What happened to James Garfield, US President, in 1881?

12. What Atlantic communication was completed in 1858 by Cyrus Field?

13. Which Roman landed in Britain in 55 BC?

14. Which European queen abdicated in 1940 in favour of her daughter?

15. Which famous British statesman died on 24 January 1965?

1. Sir Robert Walpole. 2. Marie Antoinette. 3. Jack the Ripper. 4. King Edward I. 5. Kirkpatrick Macmillan. 6. Mao Tse-tung. 7. He designed the first Pullman railway coaches. 8. Pope John Paul I. 9. The Meccano set. 10. Karl Marx. 11. He was shot and, later, died from his wounds. 12. The Atlantic cable. 13. Julius Caesar. 14. Queen Wilhelmina of the Netherlands. 15. Sir Winston Churchill.

SPORT & LEISURE

1   Who won the 1988 Rugby League World Cup?

2   When sailing what is the right hand side of a boat called when one is looking forward?

3   What races make up the US Triple Crown in horse racing?

4   When was the Biathlon introduced as an Olympic sport?

5   What football team play at the Sixfields Stadium?

6   Where do the English Rugby Union team play their home internationals?

7   Except for in America, how many players are there in a softball team?

8   What is the name of the American goalkeeper who plays for Leicester City?

9   What Open Championship did Arantxa Sanchez Vicario win in 1989 and 1994?

10 How tall is Antiguan fast bowler Curtly Ambrose?

11 Where was footballer David Beckham born?

12 What sport was pioneered by Ralph Samuelson, from USA, on Lake Pepin in 1922?

13 What sport is Michael Gross famous for?

14 Who are the Premiership's 'Sky Blues'?

15 Where is the 'tin' on a squash court?

GENERAL KNOWLEDGE

1   In which century was the English Civil War?

2   Who were expelled from the Garden of Eden?

3   From which language do the words 'armadillo', 'siesta' and 'guerilla' originate?

4   What items are called by Plantin, Baskerville and Garamond?

5   Who plays 'Inspector Morse' in the TV series of that name?

6   From which fruit is cider made?

7   Off which island in the UK are The Needles?

8   What was, or is, an Annie Oakley?

9   In which year was *The Sky at Night* first shown on TV?

10   Who was Albrecht Dürer?

11   What is the collective noun for a group of rhinoceros?

12   If something is held 'in camera', what does it mean?

13   Who directed the 1992 film *Hook*?

14   Sir William Alexander Smith founded what boys' organization?

15   Which sign of the Zodiac is represented by a pair of scales?

ANSWERS

1. 17th century. 2. Adam and Eve. 3. Spanish. 4. Printers' typefaces. 5. John Thaw. 6. Apples. 7. The Isle of Wight. 8. A free ticket for a circus or theatre. 9. 1957. 10. A German painter and engraver. 11. A crash. 12. In secret, with the public as a whole excluded. 13. Steven Spielberg. 14. The Boys' Brigade. 15. Libra.

SCIENCE & NATURE

1 What is the old name for the chemical element now called sulphur?

2 What is another common name for the fish hawk?

3 Which is the most abundant element occurring in the human body?

4 What is the generic name for the commonly occurring mushrooms 'fly agaric' and 'liberty cap'?

5 What is the greatest depth of the ice that covers the Antarctica?

6 What is the generic name for fuels such as natural gas, coal and oil?

7 Alfred Nobel is known as the inventor of dynamite and founder of prizes that bear his name, but what did his father Emmanuel invent?

8 What is the main chemical pollutant that causes acid rain?

9 What is the base SI unit of time?

10 Which was the tallest tree ever measured?

11 How did the white rhino (which is a grey colour) get its name?

12 Which animals have to keep swimming to survive?

13 What is the name of the complex carbohydrate that forms the cell wall of most plants?

14 What is the largest freshwater animal?

15 What are viroids?

ENTERTAINMENT

SESSION 68 QUIZ 6

1 Which actor won an Oscar for his role in the 1971 film *The French Connection*?

2 Which school did 'Billy Bunter' attend?

3 Which TV quiz programme does the comedian Les Dennis present?

4 Which group performed with Martha Reeves?

5 Who had hits with 'Everyone's Gone To The Moon' and 'Una Paloma Blanca'?

6 What car does 'Mr Bean' drive?

7 What appears in brackets after the Eurythmics hit 'There Must Be An Angel'?

8 Who played Queen Victoria in the film *Mrs Brown*?

9 Which comedian was known for his 'odd odes'?

10 Which TV crime series was presented by Shaw Taylor?

11 Which partnership was responsible for the comedy series *Hancock's Half Hour* and *Steptoe and Son*?

12 Name Culture Club's first number one.

13 Which comedian has a friend 'Chalky' and the catch-phrase 'nick-nick'?

14 Where was the film director Alfred Hitchcock born?

15 Which comedian starred in the 1960s TV series *The Worker*?

415

ANSWERS

1. Gene Hackman. 2. 'Greyfriars'. 3. *Family Fortunes*. 4. The Vandellas. 5. Jonathan King. 6. A Mini. 7. (playing with my heart). 8. Judi Dench. 9. Cyril Fletcher. 10. *Police 5*. 11. Ray Galton and Alan Simpson. 12. 'Do You Really Want To Hurt Me?' 13. Jim Davidson. 14. London. 15. Charlie Drake.

HISTORY

1 'What hath God wrought' was the first message transmitted from Washington DC to Baltimore in 1844 using which then-new method of communication?

2 This message was transmitted in which then new form?

3 What device was patented by Alexander Graham Bell in 1876?

4 The 'telegraphone' produced by the Danish inventor Poulsen in 1896 was a forerunner of which modern device?

5 Which inventor moved from Italy to Great Britain in 1896?

6 The German inventor Paul Nipkow was the earliest pioneer in what field of communication?

7 Where did the Westinghouse Electric Corporation establish the first radio station in the USA in 1920?

8 In which year was the BBC founded?

9 Who broadcast a televised image to an audience at the Royal Academy of Science in 1926?

10 In which year did the BBC begin experimental television transmission in the London area?

11 Who in 1936 published a paper 'On Computable Numbers' which introduced the concept of a machine regarded as a forerunner of the modern digital computer?

12 In which year did commercial television broadcasting begin in Britain?

13 What was the name of the communications satellite launched from Cape Canaveral in 1962?

14 The United States Department of Defense Advanced Research Projects Agency sponsored the development of what in the early 1970s?

15 Which 19th-century English mathematician is generally regarded as the pioneer of modern computers?

FAMOUS PEOPLE

1 Following the death of King Edward VII on 6 May 1910 who became king?

2 Which newspaper proprietor was found dead in the sea off Tenerife in 1991?

3 Which American general was known as 'Old Blood and Guts'?

4 Who was the last Danish king of England?

5 Which former general became president of the French Fifth Republic in 1959?

6 Who was the first English king able to sign his name?

7 Who became commander-in-chief of the American forces in 1775?

8 Under what name is the former Elizabeth Bowes-Lyon now known?

9 Who was the last monarch of Russia?

10 Who was taken hostage in Beirut in January 1987?

11 Who wrote, 'A little sincerity is a dangerous thing, and a great deal of it is absolutely fatal'?

12 Who was the last king of Scotland?

13 Which notorious Australian bush-ranger was hanged at Melbourne in 1880?

14 Which king of England is believed to have had 23 children?

15 Which Soviet president visited the Queen at Windsor in 1989?

SPORT & LEISURE

1   What is the women's equivalent to the Davis Cup in tennis?

2   Where do Ipswich Town play football?

3   Before Newcastle what Rugby team did Rob Andrew play for?

4   What country did racing driver Juan Manuel Fangio come from?

5   Who did Slaven Bilic play for before Everton?

6   In 1985 how many horse racing Classics did Steve Cauthen win?

7   In what sport would you play for the Stanley Cup?

8   What is footballer Sol Campbell's full Christian name?

9   At what public school was the game of squash developed?

10 What sport did Trevor Berbick and Tim Witherspoon compete in?

11 Mark Spitz has won nine Olympic gold medals for swimming, but how many of those medals were swum in a World Record time?

12 Can you water-ski barefooted?

13 Who are the 'Rams' in football?

14 What sport did Eddie 'The Eagle' Edwards compete in?

15 Where in the batting order is Graham Gooch famous for playing?

GENERAL KNOWLEDGE

1 Albion, Crown Derby and Meissen are all kinds of what?

2 By what name is Robert Louis Stevenson's novel *The Sea Cook* better known?

3 Ascension Day always falls on which day of the week?

4 Who is said to have brought up Romulus and Remus?

5 Which Italian city is famous for its leaning tower?

6 Who, on stage in 1937, did the Lambeth Walk?

7 From which European language do the words 'coracle' and 'corgi' originate?

8 What anniversary does a tin wedding celebrate?

9 Who played 'Mallory' in the film *The Guns of Navarone*?

10 What is the Naval equivalent of a Field Marshal?

11 What is the collective noun for a group of crows?

12 Friday is named after 'Frigga', the German goddess of married love. True or false?

13 Who played 'Mrs Potts' in Disney's *Beauty and the Beast*?

14 What kind of food comes from Kendal?

15 When was decimal currency introduced in Britain?

1. Ceramic ware. 2. *Treasure Island*. 3. Thursday. 4. A wolf. 5. Pisa. 6. Lupino Lane. 7. Welsh. 8. The tenth. 9. Gregory Peck. 10. Admiral of the Fleet. 11. A murder. 12. True. 13. Angela Lansbury. 14. A mint cake. 15. 1971.

SCIENCE & NATURE

1 Which creature gives its name to a protein found in human blood?

2 Which animal has the Latin name *Indicator indicator*?

3 Which fruit does neroli oil, used in perfumery, come from?

4 What causes gout?

5 What is a nephron?

6 What edible creature has the Latin name *Helix pomatia*?

7 What is an auxin?

8 *Drosera linearis* is the Latin name for a carnivorous plant. What is its common name?

9 The obstetricians Patrick Steptoe and Robert Edwards pioneered which technique?

10 Which is the world's largest spider?

11 Which king of England devised the yard, foot and inch?

12 What are ectotherms?

13 What is the derivation of the word 'fossil'?

14 Which is the world's rarest snake?

15 To which group of birds do the grouse, partridge, pheasant and turkey belong?

1. The rhesus monkey. 2. The greater honey guide, a bird that finds bees' nests. 3. Seville orange. 4. Excess of uric acid in the blood. 5. A filtering unit in the kidney. 6. The Roman snail, escargot. 7. A plant hormone. 8. Sundew. 9. IVF, in vitro fertilization. 10. Goliath bird eating spider (weighs 122grams/4.3 ounces). 11. Henry 1 (he decreed that a yard was the length of his extended arm from nose to fingertip). 12. Cold-blooded animals. 13. Latin *fossilis* 'dug up'. 14. The Antiguan racer. 15. Galliformes.

ENTERTAINMENT

1 Robert Carlyle starred in which TV series about a Scottish policeman?

2 Which jazz musician was known as 'Satchmo'?

3 What is the nickname of the TV presenter Keith Chegwin?

4 What did Terry Wogan have a hit with in 1978?

5 What was the name of the ranch in *Bonanza*?

6 Which TV programme featured the characters 'Luke and Bo Duke'?

7 Which comedy actress had a hit in 1963 with 'All I Want For Christmas Is A Beatle'?

8 'Chicago' had a number one hit in 1976 with which song?

9 The song 'Walking In The Air', from the film *The Snowman*, was a hit for which choir boy?

10 Who were on the 'Nightshift' in 1985?

11 Who had a number one hit in 1960 with 'My Old Man's A Dustman'?

12 Reg Varney played the character 'Stan Butler' in which comedy series?

13 Who hosted the TV programme *That's Showbusiness*?

14 Which actor has starred in TV's *The Professionals* and *The Chief*?

15 What are the first names of the six friends in the TV programme of that name?

HISTORY

1 Which king of England was the illegitimate son of a tanner's daughter?

2 Which Holy Roman Emperor was forced to do penance at Canossa in Italy in 1076 in order to have the excommunication placed on him by the Pope lifted?

3 From 1309 to 1377, the popes did not reside in Rome. Where were they based?

4 Six burghers of which city famously offered themselves as hostages to King Edward III of England in 1347?

5 Who was the father of the English king Henry IV?

6 Whose daughter did King Henry VII of England marry in 1486, symbolically bringing the Wars of the Roses to an end?

7 Which English king was awarded the title 'Defender of the Faith' by Pope Leo X?

8 In which year was the first Book of Common Prayer published?

9 Which English poet, according to John Aubrey's 'Brief Lives', 'was so fair that they called him the lady of Christ's College'?

10 Frederick William 'The Great Elector' (1620–88) was elector for which German state?

11 The Great Elector's son became king of which state?

12 The German electors elected the holders of which title?

13 Who was King Louis XIV of France's extremely able minister of finance?

14 Turgot and Neckar were both finance ministers who battled unsuccessfully with the problems of which French king?

15 The 'Battle of the Nations' in 1813 leading to the final withdrawal of Napoleon's forces from Germany took place near which city?

ANSWERS

1. William the Conqueror (his father was Robert Duke of Normandy). 2. Emperor Henry IV. 3. In Avignon in southern France. 4. Calais. 5. John of Gaunt. 6. The daughter (Isabela) of King Edward IV. 7. King Henry VIII. 8. 1549. 9. John Milton. 10. Brandenburg. 11. Prussia. 12. The Holy Roman Emperor. 13. Jean Baptiste Colbert. 14. Louis XVI. 15. Leipzig.

FAMOUS PEOPLE

1 Who was the first English monarch to be addressed as 'Your Majesty'?

2 Which Mongol conqueror succeeded his father at the age of 13?

3 Who entered Havana in triumph in January 1959?

4 Which Bohemian prince commanded the Royalist cavalry during the English Civil War?

5 Who attended schools in Cheam, Surrey; Gordonstoun, Scotland; and Timbertop, Australia?

6 The baby of which famous US airman was kidnapped in March 1932?

7 Who was stabbed to death in the Senate House in Rome in 44 BC?

8 What did Dr Samuel Johnson publish in 1755?

9 Who was Chiang Kai-shek?

10 Who became leader of the Conservative Party on 10 February 1975?

11 Who was assassinated in Dallas in 1963?

12 Who was the last English monarch to lead his troops in battle?

13 Which French prime minister was reputed to have slept fully clothed?

14 Who was Jomo Kenyatta?

15 Which famous consort of an English king sold oranges outside the Theatre Royal in London?

ANSWERS

1. King Henry VIII. 2. Genghis Khan. 3. Fidel Castro. 4. Prince Rupert. 5. Prince Charles. 6. Charles Lindbergh. 7. Julius Caesar. 8. His English dictionary. 9. The last non-communist leader of China. 10. Margaret Thatcher. 11. President John Kennedy. 12. King George II at Dettingen in 1743. 13. Georges Clemenceau. 14. President of Kenya. 15. Nell Gwynn.

SPORT & LEISURE

1   In what year did Stan Smith win the Wimbledon singles title?

2   What is the real name of Hawaiian born Sumo wrestler 'Akebono'?

3   What country does goalkeeper Mark Bosnich come from?

4   What is the name of England's best loved boxer turned pantomime star?

5   In which sport would you use a foil?

6   What football team play at Roots Hall?

7   Who became the first woman to complete the Grand National course in 1982?

8   How many people compete in the annual University Boat Race?

9   In snooker, how many consecutive pots must be made when scoring a maximum break?

10   What football team were the runners up in both the major English Cups in 1993?

11   What sport do you associate Greg Louganis with?

12   What position did Brian Moore play for England's Rugby Union team?

13   Phil Tuffnell is known for playing what sport?

14   What is the nickname of Port Vale FC?

15   What horse racing event is famous for its hats?

GENERAL KNOWLEDGE

1 Who first said, 'A week is a long time in politics'?

2 In which city is the Heriot-Watt university?

3 Little Moreton Hall is an example of what kind of house?

4 Where can the Venus de Milo be seen?

5 In which German city does the Oktoberfest take place?

6 What did Mrs Mary Baker Eddy found?

7 Mars was the Roman god of what?

8 What are profiteroles?

9 Which poet wrote *The Divine Comedy?*

10 St Isidore is the patron saint of whom?

11 Who are listed in the reference book *Crockford's*?

12 What was the occupation of 'Lovely Rita'?

13 What is the surname of the writer whose first names were William Makepeace?

14 Who, in a music-hall song, went to Crewe in mistake for Birmingham?

15 Which vegetable is traditionally hollowed out and used as a lantern at Hallowe'en?

1. Harold Wilson. 2. Edinburgh. 3. Timber frame. 4. The Louvre, Paris. 5. Munich. 6. Christian Science. 7. War. 8. Small puffs of choux pastry, filled with cream and covered in chocolate sauce. 9. Dante. 10. Farmers. 11. The clergy of the Church of England. 12. She was a traffic warden. 13. Thackeray. 14. Marie Lloyd. 15. A pumpkin.

SCIENCE & NATURE

1   Which equine creature is particularly associated with the Shetland Isles?

2   What are the longest cells in the human body?

3   If you were an ethologist, what would you be studying?

4   *Panthera tigis* is the Latin name for which threatened animal species?

5   Cast is a collective name for which group of animals?

6   What is the name of the densest gas known which is formed from the natural radioactive decay of radium?

7   What is the name given to the former large single mass that all continents are derived from?

8   What is special about a guppy fish?

9   In statistics, what is the mode of a set of values?

10 In which year was the bar code, widely used in retailing, patented?

11 In computing, what do the initials CPU stand for?

12 What does a pedologist study?

13 Where in the body would you find the *corpus callosum*?

14 If a carnivore eats meat, what does a detrivore eat?

15 What is the cube root of 27?

ENTERTAINMENT

1   What make of car does 'Inspector Morse' drive in the TV series of the same name?

2   Who played 'Mr Darcy' in the BBC TV production of *Pride and Prejudice*?

3   Which film was a sequel to *Saturday Night Fever*?

4   Who was the original host of the TV game show *The Generation Game*?

5   What was the name of the cow in *The Magic Roundabout*?

6   In 1994, whose song 'A Girl Like You' got to number 45 in the charts and then number four the following year?

7   What is the name of the 'talking' car in the TV series *Knight Rider*?

8   The group Scaffold were formed in 1962. In which city?

9   Who played 'Hutch' in the original TV series of *Starsky and Hutch*?

10 Who narrated the original *Paddington Bear* TV series?

11 What was the name of the 'Ewing Ranch' in the TV series *Dallas*?

12 Who played the part of 'Sapphire' in the TV series *Sapphire and Steel*?

13 'Tiberius' is which famous starship captain's middle name?

14 Who rocked the Casbah?

15 In which American city is the TV police series *Columbo* set?

427

HISTORY

1 Around the year 1000, Leif Ericson is thought to have journeyed to and explored what?

2 Who was the first European to sail around the Cape of Good Hope?

3 In which century did the first voyage around the Cape of Good Hope take place?

4 Vasco da Gama was the first European to reach what by sea?

5 On his voyage da Gama sighted part of the coast of present-day South Africa and named it Natal. Why did he give it this name?

6 On a subsequent voyage, da Gama founded a Portuguese colony in East Africa. This colony eventually became which country?

7 Who was the first European to sail around the world?

8 The first expedition around the world set sail in 1519. In which year did it return?

9 The French navigator Jacques Cartier is famous as the discoverer and explorer of which American river?

10 Which did Abel Tasman discover first, the mainland of Australia or the islands of New Zealand?

11 Which real-life Scottish sailor, marooned on an island off the coast of Chile in 1704, was the model for the fictional hero 'Robinson Crusoe'?

12 Which British naval officer sailed around the world between 1740 and 1744 and subsequently published an account of his voyages?

13 Captain James Cook's first voyage to the South Seas was to transport a party of British what to Tahiti?

14 In which year did Captain Cook discover and claim the coast of New South Wales for Britain?

15 Captain Cook was killed in 1779 in what were then called the Sandwich Islands. How are these islands known today?

ANSWERS

1. Part of the east coast of North America (possibly Nova Scotia). 2. Bartholomew Diaz. 3. The 15th century. 4. India. 5. Because the land was sighted on Christmas Day 1497 (the name derives from the Portuguese word for Christmas). 6. Mozambique. 7. Ferdinand Magellan. 8. 1522. 9. The St Lawrence. 10. New Zealand (which he discovered on his first voyage (1642) along with Tasmania, touching northern Australia on his second voyage (1644). 11. Alexander Selkirk. 12. George Anson. 13. Astronomers (going to observe the transit of Venus in 1769). 14. 1770. 15. The Hawaiian islands.

FAMOUS PEOPLE

1 Who was the first monarch of the House of Tudor?

2 Which ex-movie actor became the 40th US president?

3 On 4 November 1605 who was arrested in the vaults of the Houses of Parliament?

4 Who was the last viceroy of India?

5 Who did Kaiser Wilhelm II dismiss in 1890, an event that became known as 'dropping the pilot'?

6 Who was murdered by the Bolsheviks at Ekaterinburg in July 1918?

7 Who was Attila?

8 At the Battle of Ashdown, in AD 871, the Danes were defeated by forces under which famous king?

9 Who was Roald Amundsen?

10 Which English queen is said to have had six fingers on one hand?

11 Which rogue had a hook instead of a hand?

12 What kind of music did Louis Armstrong and Duke Ellington play?

13 Who wrote the operas *Don Giovanni* and the *Magic Flute*?

14 Who led the Israelites out of captivity in Egypt?

15 Which naval hero won the battles of Cape St Vincent, the Nile and Copenhagen?

429

ANSWERS

1. Henry VII. 2. Ronald Reagan. 3. Guy Fawkes. 4. Rear Admiral Lord Louis Mountbatten in 1947. 5. Bismarck. 6. The whole Russian royal family. 7. King of the Huns. 8. King Alfred. 9. Norwegian explorer who was first to reach the South Pole. 10. Anne Boleyn. 11. 'Captain Hook' in *Peter Pan*. 12. Jazz. 13. Mozart. 14. Moses. 15. Horatio Nelson.

SPORT & LEISURE

1. Who holed the first televised 'hole in one'?

2. What country does footballer Phillipe Albert come from?

3. In what year did Liz McColgan win the London Marathon?

4. Who rode 'Nijinsky' to a Derby win in 1970?

5. Frank Bruno lost when he defended his world title against Mike Tyson in March 1996. What belt did Tyson win?

6. Did Sterling Moss ever win the Formula 1 World Championship?

7. From 501 what is the least number of darts that can be used to check out?

8. What country does Rugby player Joel Stransky come from?

9. Leicester City brought centre back Matt Elliott from what lower league side?

10. What is the back of a boat called?

11. What is the nickname of Bradford City FC?

12. What are the first names of cricket's Waugh brothers?

13. Where do both Crystal Palace and Wimbledon play football?

14. Who would wear the Green Jersey in the Tour de France?

15. What sport is Fred Perry famous for?

GENERAL KNOWLEDGE

1   What kind of creature is an impala?

2   Who is the patron saint of travellers?

3   How, in art, is the god Janus depicted?

4   What is a madeleine?

5   From which language do the words 'cobalt', 'nickel' and 'quartz' originate?

6   What do the initials SAS stand for?

7   On which river does the border town of Berwick stand?

8   What famous landmark stands on the site of Tyburn Tree in London?

9   Where in Britain is 'Spaghetti Junction'?

10 Who chaired 'Juke Box Jury'?

11 According to the book of Genesis, what did God set in the sky as a promise that he would never again destroy the world through a flood?

12 What is the singular of 'dice'?

13 What shade of colour is vermilion?

14 Who sponsors the British Telecom speaking clock?

15 What is the slogan on the World War I poster that featured Lord Kitchener's face and pointing hand?

431

1. An antelope. 2. St Christopher. 3. With two heads each facing opposite ways.
4. A small, shell-shaped sponge cake. 5. German. 6. Special Air Service. 7. Tweed.
8. Marble Arch. 9. Gravelly Hill motorway interchange, Birmingham.
10. David Jacobs. 11. A rainbow. 12. Die. 13. Bright red. 14. Accurist.
15. 'Your Country Needs You.'

SCIENCE & NATURE

1 What was first built by Enrico Fermi, an Italian-American physicist, in 1942?

2 Lemurs are found only in one country. Where is it?

3 Which element has the lowest boiling point?

4 What is the cube of 9?

5 What is measured in coulombs?

6 What is the name of the study of substances containing carbon?

7 Which are the only birds that moult their beaks?

8 What is the term for the tendency of an object to keep moving in a straight line?

9 When do 'crepuscular' birds and animals hunt for food?

10 What is the largest bird of the crow family?

11 Which tropical disease does an insect of the Anophales genus transmit?

12 In statistics, what is the lower quartile?

13 From which duck did the down to stuff quilts come from?

14 How many nerve cells does the average brain contain?

15 Who, in the early 19th century, invented the stethoscope?

ENTERTAINMENT

1. Which famous actor starred in both *Some Like It Hot* and *The Odd Couple*?

2. Which 1970s pop icon had alter egos known as Ziggy Stardust and Aladdin Sane?

3. Who starred in the silent film *Sherlock, Jr.*?

4. What is the name of the character who is killed in every episode of the TV cartoon show *South Park*?

5. Who starred in the film *Tom Jones*?

6. Name the controversial lead singer with Pulp?

7. Which comic provided the voice of the genie in Disney's first *Aladdin*?

8. Which band features the grandson of Sir John Mills?

9. In which film did Sylvester Stallone play in goal while Pele and Michael Caine were on the pitch?

10. Who won the Best Male Artist Award in the 1998 BRITs?

11. Who starred in the film *Forty Ninth Parallel*?

12. Who believed in Father Christmas in 1975, 1982 and 1983?

13. Who shared the lead with Maggie Smith in the film *A Room with a View*?

14. In 1988, who sang 'Don't worry, be happy'?

15. How many episodes were there in the 1914 serial film *The Exploits of Elaine*?

HISTORY

1   Meriwether Lewis and William Clark between 1804 and 1806 led an expedition across what stretch of then unexplored territory?

2   David Livingstone first went to Africa in 1840 in what capacity?

3   Livingstone is particularly associated with the exploration of which African river?

4   Who found Livingstone at Ujiji in 1871, after nothing had been heard from him for a considerable period?

5   Which newspaper sponsored the expedition to find Livingstone?

6   John Hanning Speke discovered the source of which river in 1858?

7   Which other British explorer accompanied Speke on the first part of his expedition?

8   Robert Burke and William Wills were the first Europeans to cross which continent?

9   Of the four men who took part in Burke and Wills expedition, how many survived?

10 Which explorer on reaching his goal wrote in his journal 'Great God! This is an awful place'?

11 In which century did the first expedition reach the North Pole?

12 Who led the first expedition to reach the North Pole?

13 Who led the first expedition to reach the South Pole?

14 The first overland crossing of the Antarctic continent took place in which decade of the 20th century?

15 Who led this expedition?

ANSWERS

1. The American West between the Mississippi River and the Pacific Coast. 2. As a missionary. 3. The Zambezi. 4. Henry Morton Stanley. 5. *The New York Herald*. 6. The River Nile. 7. Sir Richard Francis Burton. 8. Australia. 9. One (the other three died of starvation). 10. Captain Robert Scott (Scott of the Antarctic). 11. The 20th century. 12. Robert Edwin Peary. 13. Roald Amundsen. 14. The 1950s. 15. Sir Vivian Fuchs and Sir Edmund Hillary.

FAMOUS PEOPLE

1 In which sport was Rocky Marciano unbeatable?

2 Who was Al Capone?

3 Who wrote, 'To choose time is to save time'?

4 To whom was Anne Hathaway married?

5 Who wrote *Pride and Prejudice*?

6 Who was the original Nosey Parker?

7 Which Nazi leader landed by parachute near Glasgow on 10 May 1941?

8 Who was Jean Batten?

9 Who discovered the Pacific Ocean?

10 Who was the last monarch of Italy?

11 Which English monarch was never crowned?

12 Who was the 36th president of the USA?

13 Which public figure made her first journey by rail on 13 June 1842?

14 Who arrived back in Spain from America in 1493?

15 Whose first novel was *Things Fall Apart*?

1. Boxing. 2. An American gangster. 3. Francis Bacon. 4. William Shakespeare. 5. Jane Austen. 6. Matthew Parker, Archbishop of Canterbury (1504-75). 7. Rudolf Hess, Hitler's deputy. 8. A New Zealander who flew solo from England to Australia. 9. Francisco Pizarro in 1513. 10. Humbert II (1946). 11. Edward VIII. 12. Lyndon Baines Johnson. 13. Queen Victoria. 14. Christopher Columbus. 15. Chinua Achebe.

SPORT & LEISURE

1 Which two male swimmers hold the record of seven medals in a single Olympic Games?

2 What manager signed Mark Wright for Liverpool in 1991?

3 What is Mike Tyson's boxing nickname?

4 Which sport is Joe Davis known for?

5 What colour jerseys do the New Zealand Rugby Union team wear?

6 What is Tino Asprilla's full Christian name?

7 What swimming race would competitors start in the water rather than diving in?

8 In what outdoor activity would you find classes called 'C1', 'C2', 'K1' and 'K2'?

9 What England cricket captain got in trouble for allegedly rubbing dirt and soil on a ball?

10 Where do Walsall play football?

11 What sport are Tom Watson and Tom Kite famous for?

12 In which year was Muhammad Ali born?

13 In 1988–89 who became Champion Jockey for the fifth time?

14 Who, in football, are known as 'The Gunners'?

15 In how many professional fights did boxer Larry Holmes beat 36 people by knock out?

436

GENERAL KNOWLEDGE

1   In financial terms, what do the initials IMF stand for?

2   Which anniversary does a silver wedding celebrate?

3   Where did troglodytes live?

4   Wednesday is named after 'Woden', the German god of war. True or false?

5   With which country do we associate flamenco dancing?

6   What Italian artist was also an architect, philosopher, poet, composer, sculptor and mathematician?

7   What shop traditionally had a pole painted in red and white stripes outside?

8   Where did the Flintstones live?

9   Who is the patron saint of television?

10   Who in the world would be called a Canuck?

11   How many farthings were there in half a crown?

12   Where in Britain would you find our oldest surviving clock?

13   In Roman mythology who was the messenger of the gods?

14   In which land did *Gulliver's Travels* take place?

15   What is a four-leaf clover supposed to be a sign of?

SCIENCE & NATURE

1   What is the medical term used to describe painkillers?

2   What is a commensal relationship?

3   What is the drug 'amitriptyline' usually used to treat?

4   In which year was the silicon chip introduced?

5   Could you take a mud-puppy for a walk?

6   Calcium carbonate is more familiarly known as what?

7   The leek is a plant relative of the lily. True or false?

8   Which gem was produced artificially in 1955?

9   What is a group of antelope called?

10 What is the medical condition called 'myopia'?

11 Which is the world's largest amphibian?

12 Which is the largest planet?

13 The barn owl's night vision is much better than ours.
    Is it (a) twice as good or (b) a hundred times as good?

14 Between which planets is the astroid belt situated?

15 Which nationality was Galileo?

ANSWERS

1. Analgesics. 2. A one-sided relationship in which one organism gains benefit but the other is not harmed. 3. Depression. 4. 1965, in the US. 5. No. It's a kind of salamander. 6. Chalk. 7. True. 8. Diamond. 9. A herd or a troop. 10. Short-sightedness. 11. The giant salamander, found in China and Japan, can be six feet long. 12. Jupiter. 13. (b) A hundred times as good. 14. Mars and Jupiter. 15. Italian.

ENTERTAINMENT

1 Who starred in the film *The Sound of Music*?

2 Who covered The Artist Formerly Known as Prince's hit 'Kiss' with The Art of Noise?

3 Who received an Oscar for his creation of 'Wallace and Gromit'?

4 Which English ballad singer was born Terry Parsons in 1932?

5 This ex-member of *Monty Python* directed such films as *Brazil* and *The Fisher King*. Who is he?

6 Which band did Phil Oakey front in the late 70s and 80s?

7 Who starred in the film *Blow Up*?

8 Which card helped Motorhead into the top twenty?

9 Which well known actress played herself in *Airport 75*?

10 Who were 'Walking on Sunshine' when they won the 1997 Eurovision Song Contest with 'Love Shine a Light'?

11 Who starred in the film *The Private Life of Henry VIII*?

12 What was the name of the group for which Morissey was the lead singer?

13 Terence Stamp, Anthony Newley and Laurence Harvey all turned down a part in the 1966 film which made Michael Caine a star. What was the film?

14 With which band was TV presenter Jools Holland the keyboard player?

15 From which film did the song 'A Couple of Swells' come?

439

1. Julie Andrews. 2. Tom Jones. 3. Nick Park. 4. Matt Monro. 5. Terry Gilliam. 6. Human League. 7. David Hemmings, Sarah Miles. 8. The Ace of Spades. 9. Gloria Swanson. 10. Katrina and the Waves. 11. Charles Laughton. 12. The Smiths. 13. *Alfie*. 14. Squeeze. 15. *Easter Parade*.

HISTORY

1. Which was the first European country to begin importing slaves from Africa?

2. In which century did the import of slaves to that country begin?

3. The Slave Coast, the centre of the slave trade in West Africa from the 17th to the 19th centuries, included areas of which present-day Commonwealth countries?

4. William Wilberforce, the campaigner against slavery, was born in and became MP for which city?

5. Which was the first European country to abolish the slave trade in 1792?

6. In which year was the slave trade abolished in Great Britain?

7. Which of the following heroes of the American Revolution did not own slaves: (a) George Washington, (b) Benjamin Franklin or (c) Thomas Jefferson?

8. Which country in West Africa was founded in the 1820s as a colony for former slaves from America?

9. What was the 'Underground Railroad' in the USA before the Civil War?

10. In which year was slavery itself abolished in the British Empire?

11. Which former president of the US spoke on behalf of the escaped slaves from the schooner *Amistad* at their trial in 1839?

12. In which decade of the 19th century was the novel *Uncle Tom's Cabin* published?

13. Which famous anti-slavery campaigner led a group that seized the US arsenal at Harpers Ferry, Virginia in 1859?

14. Which explorer campaigned vigorously against slavery in Portuguese African colonies?

15. What was abolished in Russia in 1861?

ANSWERS

1. Portugal. 2. The 15th century. 3. Ghana and Nigeria. 4. Hull. 5. Denmark. 6. 1807. 7. (b) Benjamin Franklin. 8. Liberia. 9. A network that assisted slaves from the southern states to flee to the north or Canada. 10. 1833. 11. John Quincy Adams. 12. The 1850s (1851 serialized, 1852 in book form). 13. John Brown. 14. David Livingstone. 15. Serfdom.

FAMOUS PEOPLE

1 Which British monarch spoke no English?

2 Who conquered Mexico for Spain?

3 Who in 1895 set sail from Boston on the first solo round-the-world voyage?

4 Who was Herbert Hoover?

5 Which British novelist and statesman was a friend of Queen Victoria?

6 Who was the first monarch to be crowned in Westminster Abbey?

7 Britain's first prime minister was appointed in 1721. Who was he?

8 Who assumed the throne of Denmark in 1972?

9 Which notorious American outlaw was shot by his own gang in 1882?

10 What did Charles Macintosh patent in 1823?

11 Burgess and Maclean were two diplomats. What did they do in 1951?

12 Which Zulu chief was received by Queen Victoria in 1882?

13 Who wrote, 'Familiarity breeds contempt – and children'?

14 Who created 'Jeremy Fisher' and 'Peter Rabbit'?

15 Who were Pavlova, Nijinsky and Fonteyn?

441

1. King George I. 2. Hernando Cortés. 3. Joshua Slocum. 4. He was the 31st American president. 5. Benjamin Disraeli, Earl of Beaconsfield. 6. William the Conqueror. 7. Sir Robert Walpole. 8. Queen Margrethe. 9. Jesse James. 10. Waterproof cloth. 11. Fled to USSR. 12. Cetewayo. 13. Mark Twain. 14. Beatrix Potter. 15. Famous ballet stars.

SPORT & LEISURE

1 David Beckham is famous for scoring a goal from the halfway line. Who was the goalkeeper?

2 Who was the captain of the English Rugby Union team in 1998?

3 What athletic event did Sally Gunnell win in 1993, setting a new world record?

4 In 1998 what Welshman played cricket for England?

5 What part of a cycling race would you expect Jean Paul Van Poppel to come into his element?

6 Complete the name of the boxer: Thomas ... Hearns.

7 What is the nickname of Huddersfield Town FC?

8 What is the least distance from the ditch that a 'long jack' can be in bowls?

9 Who won the Wimbledon women's doubles title with Steffi Graf in 1988?

10 What country is West Ham footballer Eyal Berkovic from?

11 What sport do you associate Henry Cecil with?

12 How many points do you need to win a set in volleyball (providing you are two points clear of your opponent)?

13 What sport do you watch at the Henley Royal Regatta?

14 Who play football at the Cellnet Riverside Stadium?

15 Which side do you always serve from first in a game of tennis?

GENERAL KNOWLEDGE

1 Which knighted author wrote a famous novel about Kenilworth in Warwickshire?

2 Why were the first London policemen called 'peelers'?

3 Proverbially, what is just 'skin deep'?

4 What is Cumberland sauce?

5 What do flags flying at half mast indicate?

6 What were, or are, the Gnomes of Zurich?

7 From the Bible what name do we give to the social outcast who takes care of a man who had been mugged and beaten and whose plight had been ignored by others?

8 A magnum is a measure of wine equivalent to how many bottles?

9 What is the name of the local public house in *Coronation Street*?

10 What did George Cruikshank do?

11 How many is a baker's dozen?

12 What is a façade?

13 Which English artist gave his name to devices or contraptions that are absurdly complex in design?

14 Where is Britain's unknown soldier buried?

15 In which Scottish village was the TV series *Dr Finlay's Casebook* based?

443

SCIENCE & NATURE

1 What is the chemical symbol for Copper?

2 Which elephant has the larger ears: African or Indian?

3 What are the four dimensions?

4 Is it true that Scandinavian lemmings commit mass suicide?

5 What element does the chemical symbol K represent?

6 What is the record life-span of the domestic cat: (a) 28 years, (b) 36 years or (c) 40 years?

7 What happens to phosphorus on contact with the air?

8 If a bee stings you, how will it affect the bee?

9 If your doctor told you that you had coryza, what would you be suffering from?

10 What is the record life-span of the domestic dog: (a) 28 years, (b) 30 years or (c) 32 years?

11 A drug which makes a patient insensitive to pain, touch or temperature is called a what?

12 What number does the Roman numeral 'C' represent?

13 Will two magnets with their North poles facing attract or repel?

14 How high can a flea jump approximately: (a) 12.5cm (4.9"), (b) 15cm (5.9") or (c) 20cm (7.9")?

15 The study of the processes of life in animals and plants is called what?

ENTERTAINMENT

1. Jeff and Beau Bridge's father appeared in many films including *Airplane*. What is his name?

2. Who replaced Gary Moore as lead guitarist of Thin Lizzy in the early 1980s?

3. Who starred in the film *The Lavender Hill Mob*?

4. What is the registration plate of 'Lady Penelope's' pink car in the TV programme *Thunderbirds*?

5. Which movie star's real name was Frank James Cooper?

6. If Paul Weller was the lead singer and Bruce Foxton was the bassist, who was the drummer?

7. Who starred in the films *The Deer Hunter* and *Cape Fear*?

8. Guns n' Roses covered which movie theme?

9. The cartoon show, *Top Cat* was based on which old TV Show?

10. Who, in 1998, performed the 'Ballad of Tom Jones'?

11. In which film did Katharine Hepburn and Spencer Tracy star as husband and wife lawyers?

12. What did it have to be for Fairground Attraction?

13. Who starred in the film *On the Waterfront*?

14. What is Cliff Richard's real name?

15. Who commenced each episode of a TV series with the words 'Evenin' All'?

HISTORY

1   President Abraham Lincoln represented which political party?

2   In which year did Abraham Lincoln become president of the US?

3   In which year did the American Civil War break out?

4   Where did the first military action in the American Civil War take place?

5   How many states belonged to the Confederacy at the start of the American Civil War?

6   Which one of the following states was not a member of the Confederacy: Alabama, Florida, Kentucky, Tennessee, Texas?

7   Who was president of the Confederate States?

8   Who was offered command of the Union forces by President Lincoln but declined it and went on to fight for the South?

9   Which Confederate general's heroic stand at the first Battle of Bull Run ensured a victory for the South and won him his nickname?

10   In which year did the Battle of Gettysburg take place?

11   Which heavily fortified town in the state of Mississippi was considered the key to the Mississippi River and defied several Union attempts to take it before surrendering in 1863?

12   Who was placed in overall command of the Union armies in 1864?

13   Who led Union troops on a march 'from Atlanta to the sea' in 1864?

14   Where did Robert E. Lee sign the surrender of Southern forces that effectively brought the Civil War to an end?

15   What was abolished by the 13th Amendment to the US Constitution in 1865?

FAMOUS PEOPLE

1 Which US poet was known as 'the nun of Amherst'?

2 A malapropism is an instance of the unintentional, but ridiculous, confusion of words. The word 'malapropism' comes from 'Mrs Malaprop' in the play *The Rivals*, written by which dramatist?

3 Who wrote the plays *A Doll's House* and *Ghosts*?

4 The first man to swim 100 metres in under a minute became a film star in the 1930s and 1940s. Who was he?

5 How did Malcolm Little become better known?

6 Which writer described advertising as 'the rattling of a stick inside a swill bucket'?

7 Which composer wrote the operas *Rigoletto* and *La Traviata*?

8 Who was chancellor of West Germany from 1969 to 1974?

9 With which artist did Pablo Picasso co-found the cubist movement in 1908?

10 Who discovered the first anti-rabies vaccine?

11 How many times was William Gladstone prime minister?

12 Who wrote, 'Property is theft'?

13 Which US painter developed the style known as 'action painting'?

14 What feat did Louis Blériot accomplish on 25 July 1909?

15 What nationality was the composer Frédéric Chopin?

SPORT & LEISURE

1. How many players are there in a netball team?

2. What sport did Katarina Witt perform in?

3. In what sport would you use a pommel horse?

4. Jeremy Guscott presents the TV show *The Gladiators*, but what sport is he famous for playing?

5. What football team play at The Dell?

6. When would you wear the yellow jersey on the Tour de France?

7. Who won an Olympic sprint gold medal in 1988 but had it taken away for taking performance enhancing drugs?

8. What is aikido?

9. Who are nicknamed 'The Bluebirds' in football?

10. What county cricket team does Darren Gough play for?

11. A game of table tennis is won by the first player to reach how many points?

12. Joe Frazier only lost to two boxers in his professional career. Who were they?

13. In chess, when can a pawn move diagonally?

14. Which son of a Swindon builder had 1,138 winners by the time he retired from horse racing in 1985?

15. Who did Leeds pay Charlton £2.6 million for?

GENERAL KNOWLEDGE

1 What is a 'Lent lily' better known as?

2 According to the 'language of flowers', what does the peony signify?

3 Which city is famous for its Temple of Artemis?

4 'Rule by the people as a whole' is called what?

5 What is the square root of nine?

6 Which word, beginning with 'ante-', means 'to date, before true time'?

7 When was the 'Glorious First of June'?

8 Who was the Boston Strangler?

9 Which Jewish festival is also known as the 'Feast of Lights'?

10 What is the name of the young girl who plays a leading part in *Peter Pan*?

11 In which century was tea first brought to England?

12 What is Albert sauce?

13 From which language do the words 'duet', 'piano' and 'soprano' originate?

14 What is the size of A4 paper?

15 Which character is the exploited clerk to 'Scrooge' in *A Christmas Carol* by Charles Dickens?

SCIENCE & NATURE

1   What is a John Dory?

2   The phonograph was invented by Edison, but who invented the gramophone?

3   A copperhead is a type of: (a) rattlesnake or (b) eagle?

4   The Pole Star or North Star is sometimes called what?

5   What animal is the domestic form of the polecat?

6   Who was Archimedes?

7   What is the name of the dog- or fox- like wild creatures similar to wolves?

8   What odourless, inflammable gas was discovered in 1766 by Henry Cavendish?

9   What kind of animal could be described as a 'Large White'?

10 The condensing steam engine was invented by which famous Scotsman in 1765?

11 A group of rhinoceroses is called: (a) a crash, (b) a ring or (c) a horn?

12 Alfred Nobel, who founded the Peace Prize, invented what in 1866?

13 What does a koala bear feed on?

14 What is the name given to very high-pitched sounds above 20,000 khz?

15 What is a marmoset?

ANSWERS

15. A small South American monkey.
12. Dynamite. 13. Eucalyptus leaves. 14. Ultrasound.
7. Jackals. 8. Hydrogen. 9. A breed of pig. 10. James Watt. 11. (a) A crash.
flat discs. 3. (a) Rattlesnake. 4. Polaris. 5. The ferret. 6. Greek mathematician.
1. A fish of the mackerel family. 2. Emile Berliner, who invented a recorder/player of

ENTERTAINMENT

1   Brothers Jake and Elwood liked which kind of music?

2   The heavy metal band Saxon have never had a top ten hit. True or False?

3   Which leader of the Labour Party played himself in *Rockets Galore*?

4   Who starred with Jan Francis in the TV comedy series *Just Good Friends*?

5   Name two film stars who have been married at least eight times.

6   Who had a number seven hit with 'Shout It To The Top' in October 1984?

7   Omar Sharif is famed in a field other than acting. What is it?

8   What did East 17 ask in December 1994?

9   Who starred in the film *The Heiress*?

10 Which major international female artist started her career as lead singer of the Sugarcubes?

11 Which American Senator played himself in *The Candidate*?

12 What was the name of Prince's band on the album 'Parade'?

13 What was the name of the frog who compered *The Muppet Show*?

14 Which 1985 film, starring David Bowie and Patsy Kensit, flopped disastrously?

15 From which film and stage show did the song 'Climb Every Mountain' come?

451

HISTORY

1 Babar (or Babur) (1483 to 1530) was the first emperor of which dynasty in India?

2 In which century did the English set up their first trading post in India?

3 Which two European nations were the chief rivals to the English for trade with India in the early years?

4 Which company was first responsible for trade with India and later for administering British possessions in India until 1858?

5 In which year did the atrocity known as the 'Black Hole of Calcutta' take place?

6 Who commanded the British forces that defeated the Nawab of Bengal at the Battle of Plassey in 1757?

7 In which year did the Indian Mutiny (Sepoy Mutiny) begin?

8 In the residency of which town were a small garrison of British troops and civilians besieged for nearly five months during the mutiny?

9 Benjamin Disraeli proclaimed Queen Victoria as what in 1876?

10 What Indian political movement was founded in 1885?

11 Mohandas K. Gandhi's policy of 'Satygraha' involved what kind of protest against British rule?

12 In which Indian city were over 400 people killed in 1919 when troops fired on protesters?

13 Who became leader of a 'Provisional Indian Government' in Japanese-occupied Burma during World War II?

14 Who was the leader of the Muslim League in India in the run-up to independence and the first governor-general of Pakistan?

15 In which year did India become independent of Britain?

FAMOUS PEOPLE

1 Who wrote *Uncle Tom's Cabin*?

2 Who is the only one of the four US presidents carved on Mt Rushmore to have been president in the 20th century?

3 Which Scottish architect and designer, a leading exponent of art nouveau, designed the Glasgow School of Art?

4 What was the name of the German engineer who designed and built the first car to be driven by an internal-combustion engine?

5 Who did Lady Caroline Lamb describe as 'mad, bad, and dangerous to know'?

6 When was the first test-tube baby born?

7 Who was the English conductor who founded the annual Promenade Concerts in London?

8 Who did Gore Vidal describe in 1981 as 'a triumph of the embalmer's art'?

9 What was H. H. Munro's pen name?

10 Who was the ballet impresario who founded the 'Ballets Russes' in Paris?

11 What relation is the painter Lucian Freud to the psychotherapist Sigmund Freud?

12 Who was forced to refuse the Nobel Prize for literature in 1958 under pressure from the Soviet authorities?

13 Who wrote the play *Pygmalion*?

14 Which economist wrote *The Affluent Society* in 1958?

15 Who were the co-authors of *The Communist Manifesto*?

ANSWERS

1. Harriet Beecher Stowe. 2. Theodore Roosevelt. 3. Charles Rennie Mackintosh. 4. Karl Benz. 5. Lord Byron. 6. 1978. 7. Henry Wood. 8. Ronald Reagan. 9. Saki. 10. Sergei Diaghilev. 11. Grandson. 12. Boris Pasternak. 13. George Bernard Shaw. 14. John Kenneth Galbraith. 15. Karl Marx and Friedrich Engels.

SPORT & LEISURE

1 Sheikh Mohammed is involved in what sport?

2 What country does famous goalkeeper Bruce Grobbelaar come from?

3 Who is the well known snooker player from Malta?

4 What kind of bowler is Pakistan's Saqlain Mushtaq?

5 Which dog won both the English and Irish Derbies in 1998?

6 What country do Brann Bergen play football in?

7 In March 1996 who did the England Rugby team beat 18–9?

8 In which city was Johann Cruyff born?

9 Who won the first Benson & Hedges Cup, in 1972?

10 Who are 'The Eagles' in football?

11 Ian Woosnam is famous for playing which sport?

12 The techniques used in sambo wrestling originated in which country?

13 What are ferrules on a fishing rod?

14 What name is given to the Japanese art of flower arranging?

15 Who are 'The Railwaymen' in football?

GENERAL KNOWLEDGE

1   What are the three Rs?

2   Samson, a judge of Israel, possessed what great gift?

3   Of which country is Baghdad the capital?

4   Who was the author of the 'Noddy' books?

5   What number, according to *The Hitch Hiker's Guide to the Galaxy*, is the answer to the ultimate question of life, the universe and everything?

6   Name two well known plays by Terence Rattigan.

7   Where were 'ten green bottles'?

8   Poseidon is another name for Neptune. True or false?

9   Whose favourite expression was 'Exterminate! Exterminate!'

10 What is the third book of the Bible?

11 In which year were yellow and red cards introduced for misdemeanours in the English football league?

12 What is Bezique?

13 When was the single European currency, the euro, introduced?

14 If a foreign car displayed the letters RO, what would its country of origin be?

15 Name the capital of Iceland.

1. Reading, writing and arithmetic. 2. Enormous strength. 3. Iraq. 4. Enid Blyton. 5. 42. 6. *Flare Path*, *French Without Tears*, *While the Sun Shines*, *The Winslow Boy*. 7. Standing on the wall. 8. True. 9. The 'Daleks'. 10. Leviticus. 11. 1976. 12. A card game which originated in France. 13. 1 January 1999. 14. Romania. 15. Reykjavik.

SCIENCE & NATURE

1 Who was responsible for the special theory of relativity?

2 Mulberry leaves are the favourite food of which insect?

3 The science of directing a craft or a vehicle from place to place is called what?

4 What is a gecko, and what is peculiar about it?

5 Argent is another name for what?

6 Why is a rattlesnake able to rattle?

7 What does the prefix 'kilo-' mean?

8 The ladybird is a kind of beetle. True or false?

9 What does a sextant measure?

10 What number does the Roman numeral 'X' represent?

11 Who won the Nobel prize for chemistry in 1990?

12 Which planet is the Morning Star?

13 A mammal with heavy armour plates on its body is called what?

14 What is craniology?

15 What is the difference between a frog and a toad?

ANSWERS

1. Albert Einstein. 2. The silkworm, the caterpillar of the silkmoth. 3. Navigation. 4. The smallest reptile, measuring just over 1cm (0.4"). 5. Silver. 6. It has horny rings on its tail, which it shakes. 7. A thousand. 8. True. 9. Latitude. 10. Ten. 11. Elias Cory. 12. Venus. 13. An armadillo. 14. The study of skulls. 15. A frog hops or leaps along and a toad walks.

ENTERTAINMENT

1 What was film star 'Herbie'?

2 *Blockbuster's* Bob Holness started life as a session musician and played saxophone on Gerry Rafferty's 1978 hit 'Baker Street'. True or false?

3 Who starred in the 1927 silent film *Sunrise*?

4 Which band recorded the albums 'In Utero' and 'Nevermind'?

5 In which county was Tim Brooke-Taylor born?

6 In Tony Hancock's *The Blood Donor* who played the doctor?

7 Which TV sitcom features a dog called 'Eddie' and a home help called 'Daphne'?

8 Which British band were on 'Hope Street' in 1995?

9 What creature was the star of the *Free Willy* series of movies?

10 Which British entertainer had top ten hits in the 1950s with 'Singing The Blues', 'Butterfingers', 'Water Water' and 'Little White Bull'?

11 Mark Hamill played which character in the film *Star Wars*?

12 What was the name of Sigue Sigue Sputnik's missile?

13 Who starred in the film *Independence Day*?

14 What was the first number one hit for The Rolling Stones?

15 Which film star began her career in Czechoslovakia under the name 'Hedy Kiesler'?

457

HISTORY

1 In which year did German troops reoccupy the Rhineland as part of the repudiation of the terms of the Treaty of Versailles?

2 Who was British Foreign Secretary in the government headed by Neville Chamberlain from 1938–40?

3 Who on the German side negotiated the non-aggression pact of 1939 between Germany and the Soviet Union?

4 What was the name of the sophisticated defensive system built in eastern France between the wars to repel a possible German attack?

5 Who was commander-in-chief of the British expeditionary force in France at the time of the German invasion in 1940?

6 Who became head of the French government in 1940 and negotiated the country's surrender to Germany?

7 Which town became the capital of the part of France that was not under German occupation after 1940?

8 Where, in 1941, was Hitler's deputy Rudolf Hess captured by the Allies?

9 In which year did the German attack on the Soviet Union take place?

10 Who became prime minister of Japan in 1941 and was dictator of the country until he resigned in 1944?

11 Why did the Japanese attack Pearl Harbor in December 1941?

12 What was the unique feature of the Battle of the Coral Sea in May 1942?

13 Who commanded the German Afrika Korps from 1940 to 1943?

14 Who commanded the British forces at the Battle of El Alamein in November 1942?

15 In which Russian city was the German Sixth surrounded and forced to surrender in January 1943?

1. 1936. 2. Lord Halifax. 3. Joachim von Ribbentrop. 4. The Maginot Line. 5. Lord Gort. 6. Marshal Pétain. 7. Vichy. 8. In Scotland – he had flown there alone, apparently in an effort to broker a peace agreement. 9. 1941. 10. General Hideki Tojo. 11. In order to destroy the US Pacific fleet. 12. It was a naval battle fought entirely by carrier-based aircraft, the ships of the opposing fleets never coming into contact with each other. 13. General Erwin Rommel. 14. General Bernard Montgomery. 15. Stalingrad.

FAMOUS PEOPLE

1 'He was not only a bore; he bored for England': Whose opinion of Anthony Eden was this?

2 Who wrote *Herzog* and *Humboldt's Gift*?

3 Who played 'Fleur' in the 1960s TV series *The Forsyte Sage*?

4 Who was the Scottish chemist and physicist who invented the vacuum flask?

5 Who did Gerald Ford succeed as US vice-president in 1973?

6 Which British writer won the Nobel Prize for literature in 1983?

7 Which Irish nationalist's political career was ruined by the scandal over his adultery with Kitty O'Shea in 1890?

8 United Artists was founded in 1919 by the film director D. W. Griffith, the actors Charlie Chaplin and Douglas Fairbanks and an actress. Who was she?

9 Who was elected the first president of the modern republic of Turkey in 1934?

10 Who designed the three-wheeled electric car, the C5?

11 Who wrote *The Second Sex* (1949)?

12 How is the actor David Daniel Kominski better known?

13 Who was commander-in-chief of the Confederate forces during the American Civil War?

14 What nationality was the sculptor Alberto Giacometti?

15 Who is the subject of the 1956 film *Reach for the Sky*?

ANSWERS

1. Malcolm Muggeridge. 2. Saul Bellow. 3. Susan Hampshire. 4. James Dewar. 5. Spiro Agnew. 6. William Golding. 7. Charles Stewart Parnell. 8. Mary Pickford. 9. Kemal Atatürk. 10. Clive Sinclair. 11. Simone de Beauvoir. 12. Danny Kaye. 13. Robert E. Lee. 14. Swiss. 15. Douglas Bader.

SPORT & LEISURE

1   Which cricketer has taken the most test wickets of all time?

2   Which Italian football team did Jimmy Greaves play for?

3   What event does athlete Nick Buckfield compete in?

4   Where would you play the game Baccarat?

5   Who did Henry Cooper fight on 18 June 1963?

6   What football team does Patrick Viera play for?

7   In what sport would you compete for the America's Cup?

8   When was curling first introduced as a proper Olympic event?

9   What football club is Alan Sugar the chairman of?

10 What sport do you associate Jack Rowell with?

11 On a Monopoly board, what colour is The Strand?

12 Alan Lamb and Robin Smith played cricket for England, but in what country were they born?

13 What country does footballer Robert Prosineck play for?

14 What horse recorded the fastest ever Grand National time in 8 minutes and 47.8 seconds?

15 Who were the losing finalists of the 1994 football World Cup?

GENERAL KNOWLEDGE

1 In which poem do 'slithy toves' originate?

2 The 'Abominable Snowman' is also known as?

3 Which proverb do we use to say that we should not judge a thing by its attractive golden appearance?

4 The water carrier represents which sign of the Zodiac?

5 In which year was the first Benson & Hedges Cup held?

6 What is the name given to the informal version of French that contains a large number of English words?

7 In *A Christmas Carol* by Charles Dickens, who does Scrooge receive a visit from?

8 What is chilli con carne?

9 According to the Bible, who refused to accept the truth of the resurrected Christ until he had actually seen and touched Christ's body for himself?

10 In the year 1752, what date followed 2 September?

11 In which British city would you find a lake called the Serpentine?

12 What did Alexander of Macedon and Alfred, King of England, have in common?

13 According to tradition, how many lives does a cat have?

14 What was nicknamed 'The Thunderer'?

15 Who wrote the children's novel *Emil and the Detectives*?

SCIENCE & NATURE

1 What is *The Lancet*?

2 A bongo is a type of antelope or a small tropical lizard?

3 What did the Montgolfier Brothers achieve in 1783?

4 A genet is a cat-like creature which purrs like a kettle boiling. True or false?

5 What very light metal was discovered in 1827 by Hans Christian Oersted?

6 Are there foxes which can fly?

7 What are Saturn's rings made of?

8 What is another name for the pumpkin?

9 The wreck of which famous liner was located and photographed in 1985?

10 Are bats really blind?

11 A machine for altering the voltage of alternating current is called what?

12 Are there lizards which can fly?

13 Who invented the vacuum flask?

14 If a racehorse and a greyhound raced, which would win?

15 What is measured by the quire?

1. A medical magazine. 2. It's an antelope. It's also called a bushbuck. 3. The first successful balloon flight. 4. True. 5. Aluminium. 6. No. The animal called a flying-fox is a bat. 7. Lumps of ice-covered rocks. 8. Squash. 9. *The Titanic*. 10. Some have very poor vision, but none are known to be totally blind. 11. A transformer. 12. Yes. In Malaysia there are some, also called flying-dragons. 13. James Dewar in 1885. 14. The racehorse. 15. Paper.

ENTERTAINMENT

1   Who starred in the film *Dances with Wolves*?

2   Name Donna Summers' only UK number one hit.

3   Which long running television show features a pub called 'The Rovers Return'?

4   Who is the only Conservative prime minister to have a UK top ten hit?

5   Who replaced Jon Pertwee in TV's *Doctor Who*?

6   Which TV programme, featuring 'Scottie' and 'Bones', was set in space and became a long series of major films?

7   Who starred as T. E. Lawrence in the epic *Lawrence of Arabia*?

8   Barbara Dickson was in the charts with 'I Know Him so Well' in 1985. From which show did this song come?

9   Ronan is the lead singer with which Irish boy band?

10   Who starred in the film *Brief Encounter*?

11   Of which progressive rock band was 'Fish' the original lead singer?

12   Which sports commentator was replaced by Sue Barker as host of *A Question of Sport*?

13   Which Soft Cell song appeared in the charts once in 1981, twice in 1982, once in 1985 and once in 1991?

14   Which controversial cartoon series features characters called 'Kyle', 'Kenny', 'Stan' and 'Cartman'?

15   Who starred in the film *Ghost*?

HISTORY

1 Where did Roosevelt and Churchill meet at a conference in January 1943 to plan Allied strategy in the latter part of World War II?

2 Who designed the Wellington bomber and the bouncing bomb used in the Dambusters raid in 1943?

3 In which year did the massacre in the Warsaw ghetto take place?

4 Where did the greatest tank battle of World War II take place in July 1943?

5 Where did Allied landings take place in July 1943?

6 Where did Churchill, Roosevelt and Stalin meet for a conference in November 1943?

7 In which month and year did the Allied landings in Normandy take place?

8 What was the code name used for the operation to invade Normandy?

9 Who was supreme commander of the Allied invasion force?

10 Who planted a bomb in an attempt to assassinate Hitler in July 1944?

11 The first of what type of weapon was used against London in September 1944?

12 Where did the German army begin a counter-offensive on the western front in December 1944?

13 Whom did Hitler nominate as his successor before committing suicide in April 1945?

14 In which month of which year was the first atomic bomb dropped on Japan?

15 Which American general accepted the surrender of Japan on behalf of the Allies in September 1945?

ANSWERS

1. Casablanca. 2. Barnes Wallis. 3. 1943. 4. Kursk in Russia. 5. Sicily. 6. Teheran. 7. June 1944. 8. Operation Overlord. 9. General Dwight D. Eisenhower. 10. Claus von Stauffenberg. 11. V-2 rocket (The V-1s had begun to land a few months previously). 12. In the Ardennes. 13. Admiral Karl Doenitz. 14. August 1945. 15.General Douglas Macarthur.

FAMOUS PEOPLE

1 Whose sermon on national apostasy in 1833 is considered to have inspired the Oxford Movement?

2 Which US novelist won the Nobel Prize for literature in 1993?

3 Who built the first motorcycle?

4 Who said: 'A riot is at bottom the language of the unheard'?

5 Who was premier of the USSR from 1964 to 1980?

6 Which philosopher and mathematician was an active pacifist during World War I and later took a leading role in the anti-nuclear movement?

7 Which British explorer commanded three expeditions to the Antarctic, during the first of which he located the South Pole in 1909?

8 Who was poet laureate between John Masefield and John Betjeman?

9 What instrument did Miles Davis play?

10 Which English architect and town planner designed Regents Park and Regent Street in London and rebuilt the Brighton Pavilion in oriental style?

11 Who was president of the US from 1952 to 1961?

12 Which French writer wrote the pamphlet 'J'accuse' in 1898 in support of Alfred Dreyfus?

13 What was the stage name of Erich Weiss?

14 What is the name of the English surgeon who introduced the use of antiseptics?

15 Which newspaper proprietor served as Minister of Aircraft Production in Churchill's cabinet during World War II?

ANSWERS

1. John Keble. 2. Toni Morrison. 3. Gottlieb Daimler. 4. Martin Luther King. 5. Aleksei Kosygin. 6. Bertrand Russell. 7. Ernest Henry Shackleton. 8. Cecil Day Lewis. 9. Trumpet. 10. John Nash. 11. Dwight D. Eisenhower. 12. Emile Zola. 13. Harry Houdini. 14. Joseph Lister. 15. Lord Beaverbrook.

SPORT & LEISURE

1   How many World Opens did squash player Jansher Khan win?

2   What shape is a rugby ball?

3   With which Formula 1 racing team did Nigel Mansell win the World Championship?

4   In what year did Kieran Perkins break the 400, 800 and 1,500 metres swimming world records?

5   Who took over from Michael Atherton as England cricket captain?

6   What is the racquet used in lacrosse called?

7   What team did American football legend Dan Marino play for between 1983 and 1997?

8   Steve Bull is a hero at which football club?

9   What activity is the descent of a steep slope, or vertical drop, by a rope secured above?

10 Juan Antonio Samaranch is the president of what committee?

11 Mark Todd and Ian Stark are known for competing in which sport?

12 Who was Alan Shearer's strike partner at Blackburn Rovers?

13 Where were the 1998 Commonwealth Games held?

14 Who became the first jump jockey to break 200 victories in a season?

15 Which iron is the niblick?

1. Eight. 2. Oval. 3. Williams Renault. 4. 1994. 5. Alec Stewart. 6. A crosse. 7. Miami Dolphins. 8. Wolverhampton Wanderers. 9. Abseiling. 10. IOC (International Olympic Committee). 11. Three Day Eventing. 12. Chris Sutton. 13. Kuala Lumpur. 14. Peter Scudamore. 15. No. 9.

GENERAL KNOWLEDGE

1 In which English county is the holiday resort of Morecambe?

2 Who was Sheridan Morley's father?

3 What is the name of the Dutch graphic artist who is well known for his drawings that distort perspective and deceive the eye?

4 What is abalone?

5 Which pocket-sized monthly magazine was first published in America in 1922?

6 What is the literal meaning of the word 'karaoke'?

7 Who wrote the novel *Catch 22*?

8 What does ROM stand for in computing?

9 Proverbially, where does charity begin?

10 Which theatre in London was originally called the Waldorf?

11 What is the name of the pessimistic donkey in the *Winnie the Pooh* stories?

12 In what place do Muslim people worship?

13 Who wrote the novel *The Prime of Miss Jean Brodie*?

14 What did the 'Owl and the Pussycat' go to sea in?

15 What was the profession of Lancelot (or 'Capability') Brown?

1. Lancashire. 2. Robert Morley. 3. M. C. Escher. 4. A mollusc, like the sea snail, with a flat, oval shell. 5. *Reader's Digest*. 6. Empty orchestra. 7. Joseph Heller. 8. Read Only Memory. 9. At home. 10. The Strand. 11. 'Eeyore'. 12. A mosque. 13. Muriel Spark. 14. A beautiful pea green boat. 15. Landscape gardener.

SCIENCE & NATURE

1 How many different kinds of beetle are there: (a) 50,000, (b) 100,000 or (c) 250,000?

2 What is the diameter of Saturn's widest ring: (a) 200,000 miles or (b) 170,000 miles?

3 What kind of animal is said to screech?

4 What is a megalomaniac?

5 Caviar is obtained from a fish. Which one?

6 How many bones does an adult human being have?

7 What is unique about the Komodo dragon lizard?

8 What number does the Roman numeral 'L' represent?

9 Which dinosaur had a series of heavy plates along its back?

10 Who discovered the metal titanium in 1791?

11 Are there bats that suck human blood?

12 What does a Geiger counter measure?

13 Where did the kiwi fruit originate?

14 What is the name of the fault in the Earth's crust that extends through the length of California?

15 A drongo is: (a) a fool, (b) a songbird or (c) a fish?

ENTERTAINMENT

1 Who starred in the film *Annie Hall*?

2 All Saints had their first hit in March 1998. What was the song?

3 Which TV sitcom features characters called 'Ross', 'Chandler' and 'Phoebe'?

4 In which year was Roy Kinnear born?

5 Who starred in the film *Goldfinger*?

6 Name the TV comedy set around a hapless unit of the Home Guard in World War II.

7 Who was lead singer with 1980s chart toppers Culture Club?

8 From which film and stage show did the song 'I Got Rhythm' come?

9 With which double A-side single did Jasper Carrot have his only chart success, reaching number five in August 1975?

10 Ruby Keeler, Mary Pickford, Norma Shearer and Fay Wray were not American born. From which country did they originally come?

11 In 1998, which US teen band was made up of Taylor, Isaac and Zac?

12 Which character was played by Robin Williams in the 1992 Disney film *Aladdin*?

13 Which TV sci-fi series featured characters including 'Villa' 'Servalan' and 'ORAC'?

14 Which film star first became famous for his role in the TV show *Moonlighting*?

15 Which member of Take That left the band to pursue a solo career in July 1995?

1. Woody Allen and Diane Keaton. 2. 'Never Ever'. 3. *Friends*. 4. 1934. 5. Sean Connery and Honor Blackman. 6. *Dad's Army*. 7. Boy George. 8. *Girl Crazy*. 9. 'Funky Moped/Magic Roundabout'. 10. Canada. 11. Hanson. 12. The genie. 13. *Blake's Seven*. 14. Bruce Willis. 15. Robbie Williams.

HISTORY

1 Whom did Henry II succeed as king of England in 1154?

2 Margaret, 'the Maid of Norway', queen of Scotland, drowned in 1290 while sailing from Norway to marry which future king of England?

3 The Habsburg family that provided a dynasty of Holy Roman Emperors were known for which hereditary physical peculiarity?

4 Who ordered the artist painting his portrait to paint him 'warts and all'?

5 What part of a building became subject to tax in Britain in 1695 and remained so until 1851?

6 As part of his drive to westernize Russia inwardly and outwardly, Tsar Peter the Great imposed a tax on which aspect of his nobles' personal appearance?

7 What was peculiar about the relationships between the Hanoverian kings of Britain and their eldest sons and heirs?

8 Michael Barclay de Tolly was a general of which army during the Napoleonic Wars?

9 The Count of Las Cases wrote and published (1821–23) an account of which ruler's last years?

10 Which American engineer patented the first elevator in the 1850s?

11 Which famous sailing ship, still in existence, was built and launched in 1869?

12 What happened 'on the last Sabbath day of 1879' and, according to the Scottish poet William McGonagall, 'will be remembered for a very long time'?

13 In which year did the 'Jack the Ripper' murders take place in London?

14 Who succeeded James Callaghan as prime minister in 1979?

15 Whose plays include *The Bald Prima Donna* and *Rhinoceros*?

1. King Stephen. 2. King Edward II. 3. The Habsburg lip. 4. Oliver Cromwell. 5. The windows. 6. Their beards. 7. They all hated each other. 8. The Russian army. 9. Napoleon Bonaparte's (the 'Memorial of Saint Helena'). 10. E. G. Otis. 11. *The Cutty Sark*. 12. The Tay bridge disaster (the collapse of the railway bridge across the River Tay in Scotland which led to the loss of ninety lives when a train plunged into the river). 13. 1888. 14. Margaret Thatcher 15. Eugène Ionesco.

FAMOUS PEOPLE

1   Who wrote *Madame Bovary*?

2   Which former slave founded the Tuskegee Institute in Alabama as a training college for black teachers?

3   Which economist, the leading exponent of monetarism, was awarded the Nobel Prize for economics in 1976?

4   As a commentator on the Boat Race in 1949 who said, 'I can't see who's ahead – it's either Oxford or Cambridge'?

5   Of which style of art was Roy Lichtenstein a pioneer?

6   Which German philosopher was noted for his doctrine of the *Übermensch* (superman)?

7   Who wrote the poems *The Love Song of J. Alfred Prufrock* and *The Four Quartets*?

8   Who founded the British Union of Fascists in the 1930s?

9   Which US writer said: 'There are no second acts in American lives'?

10 The book *French Provincial Cooking* helped introduce Mediterranean cuisine to Britain in the 1960s. Who wrote it?

11 What was the name of the Soviet military leader who defeated the Germans at Stalingrad in 1943?

12 Who founded the South African Students' Organization in 1968?

13 What did Jacques Yves Cousteau and Emil Gagnan invent in 1943?

14 Who was the US physicist who was the director of the Los Alamos laboratory (1943–45) that designed and built the first atomic bomb?

15 Who said, 'History is more or less bunk'?

1. Gustave Flaubert. 2. Booker T. Washington. 3. Milton Friedman. 4. Barnes Wallis.
5. Pop Art. 6. Friedrich Wilhelm Nietzsche. 7. T. S. Eliot. 8. Oswald Mosley.
9. F. Scott Fitzgerald. 10. Elizabeth David. 11. Georgi Zhukov. 12. Steve Biko.
13. The aqualung. 14. J. Robert Oppenheimer. 15. Henry Ford.

SPORT & LEISURE

1   Which English football team did Brian Roy play for?

2   Elvis Stojko competed for Canada in what sport?

3   What cricket player became a bishop in the Church of England?

4   In what sport might you win a penalty corner?

5   Stan Flashman was the chairman of what football club?

6   If you were fishing would you catch a black bass in salt water or fresh water?

7   How high off the ground is the crossbar on Rugby goalposts?

8   How high is the front wall in a squash court?

9   Kelly Slater is famous for what sport?

10 For which distance did swimmer Alexander Popov hold the world record?

11 Steve Bull is the hero of what football club?

12 How many times have Britain won the Admiral's Cup in yachting?

13 In which country did the martial art of tae kwon do originate?

14 How many times did 'Red Rum' win the Grand National?

15 What kind of game is Keno?

472

GENERAL KNOWLEDGE

1   Who wrote the *Thomas the Tank Engine* stories?

2   What instrument did Niccolo Paganini play?

3   According to the Bible, what was the name of the paradise created for Adam and Eve?

4   St Michael was the patron saint of whom?

5   In American slang, what is a shamus?

6   What was a 'doughboy'?

7   In biology, what is the term given to the ability of an organism to replace one of its parts if it is lost?

8   What does 'in the buff' mean?

9   What do the initials UAE stand for?

10 Which daily newspaper was first published on 7 October 1986?

11 What proverb, originating from blacksmiths, means that we should not try to do too much at once?

12 How does the Archbishop of Canterbury sign himself?

13 What is the SI unit of electric current?

14 Who, in ancient times, were Shem, Ham and Japheth?

15 From which language does the word 'ombudsman' come?

SCIENCE & NATURE

1 'Yin' and 'Yang' are expressions used in what kind of treatment?

2 Crabs, lobsters and shrimps all have the same number of legs. How many?

3 What did Sir Frederick Banting and J. J. R. MacLeod discover in 1922?

4 The dragonfly has one sense better developed than any other insect. Which?

5 What proportion of air is nitrogen?

6 Which is the tallest and thickest kind of grass?

7 What can be measured in joules?

8 In one day, a mole can burrow: (a) 25 metres, (b) 50 metres or (c) 100 metres?

9 Which is the second largest planet?

10 The peach is a member of the rose family. True or false?

11 What are the two digits used in the binary system of calculation?

12 A rabbit can run at 35 miles an hour. True or false?

13 Edwin Land invented what kind of camera in 1947?

14 What is a group of hedgehogs called?

15 How many carats are there in pure gold?

1. Acupuncture. 2. Ten. 3. Insulin. 4. Its eyesight. 5. Four-fifths. 6. Bamboo. 7. Energy. 8. (c) 100 metres. 9. Saturn. 10. True. 11. 0 and 1. 12. True. 13. The Polaroid. 14. An array. 15. 24.

ENTERTAINMENT

1 Tom Cruise starred in a film based on a John Grisham novel. What was the film?

2 What band does Jarvis Cocker front?

3 Which TV character lived at 23 Railway Cuttings, East Cheam?

4 Who starred in the film *Blade Runner*?

5 In September 1996, Mariah Carey reached number three with 'Endless Love'. Which male soul singer dueted with her on this track?

6 Which B movie featured salad vegetables intent on murder?

7 Which famous cartoon cat was always trying to eat 'Tweetie-Pie'?

8 What do the songs 'Back Home', 'This Time We'll Get It Right' and 'World in Motion' have in common?

9 In which film did the furry creatures called 'mogwais' appear?

10 Which former Australian soap star's debut single was 'Torn'?

11 What morning show has been hosted by Chris Evans, Mark Little and Keith Chegwin?

12 What was Take That's final single?

13 Which controversial late night show was hosted by Terry Christian?

14 Who or what was 'Flipper'?

15 In 1976, which international singing star had her first UK hit reaching number seven with 'Jolene'?

HISTORY

1. What did Lord Nelson lose in 1794 in an attack on the town of Calvi in Corsica, his arm or his eye?

2. Where did mutinies in the Royal Navy take place in 1797?

3. According to the poet Charles Wolfe, 'Not a drum was heard, not a funeral note' at the funeral of which British general of the Peninsula War in 1809?

4. Which 19th-century king of France was known as 'the Citizen King'?

5. George Cadbury, the British chocolate manufacturer and social reformer, and John D. Rockefeller, the American oil magnate and philanthropist, were both born in the same year. Was it (a) 1839, (b) 1849 or (c) 1859?

6. Who gave birth to her seventh child under chloroform in 1853, thus ensuring its acceptance as an anaesthetic?

7. The sewers of London were modernized during the 1850s in order to combat which disease?

8. According to the music-hall composer George William Hunt, 'We don't want to fight, but by jingo if we do/We've got the men, we've got the ships, we've got the money too'. Against which foreign power was the 'jingoism' of 1878 directed?

9. In which country was Leon Trotsky living when he was assassinated on Stalin's orders in 1940?

10. Which king of Egypt abdicated in favour of his son in 1952?

11. Who was the first president of the Republic of Egypt?

12. Whom did Dwight D. Eisenhower twice defeat in the presidential elections of 1952 and 1956?

13. In which year did John Profumo resign from the British government after a sex scandal?

14. Who shot and killed Lee Harvey Oswald, the presumed asssassin of president J. F. Kennedy?

15. In which year was Dr Martin Luther King assassinated?

476

FAMOUS PEOPLE

1. Which singer did Diana Ross play in the 1972 film *Lady Sings the Blues*?

2. What was the name of the envoy to the archbishop of Canterbury held hostage in Lebanon from 1987 to 1991?

3. How was William Joyce better known during World War II?

4. Which historian's five-volume *History of England* was published between 1849 and 1861?

5. Which American linguist was also known for his outspoken opposition of American involvement in Vietnam?

6. Which fashion designer created the 'little black dress'?

7. By what name did Josip Broz become better known?

8. Who wrote *Testament of Youth* in 1933?

9. Which British prime minister presided over 'the night of the long knives' in 1962, sacking a third of his Cabinet?

10. What artistic movement was launched by André Breton in 1924?

11. Who was the first woman in space?

12. Who was the British minister of education 1967–70 who was responsible for founding the Open University?

13. Which artist's works include a set of 65 etchings called *The Disasters of War* (1810–14)?

14. *On Liberty* was written in 1859 by which philosopher and economist?

15. Who became the world's first female prime minister in 1960?

ANSWERS

1. Billie Holiday. 2. Terry Waite. 3. Lord Haw-Haw. 4. Thomas Babington Macaulay. 5. Noam Chomsky. 6. Coco Chanel. 7. Tito. 8. Vera Brittain. 9. Harold Macmillan. 10. Surrealism. 11. Valentina Tereshkova. 12. Jennie Lee. 13. Francisco de Goya. 14. John Stuart Mill. 15. Sirimavo Bandaranaike of Sri Lanka.

SPORT & LEISURE

1   Which jockey overcame cancer to win the 1981 Grand National?

2   Wet flies, dry flies, nymphs and streamer flies are all used in what sport?

3   In what game would you use a shot called a 'boast'?

4   In tennis, what score is called 'deuce'?

5   What is skeet shooting?

6   How many dice do you use in a game of Backgammon?

7   What famous football city is seven miles away from Aintree racecourse?

8   What sport is Prince Charles famous for playing?

9   Where is horse racing's William Hill Sprint Championship held?

10 What country won the men's doubles table tennis title at the 1988 and 1992 Olympics?

11 What Italian football team did Asprilla and Zola play for?

12 What is the maximum width of a Rugby Union pitch?

13 Whose ear did Mike Tyson bite during a boxing match?

14 What club have Trevor Francis, David Pleat and Ron Atkinson managed?

15 When was bobsledding first incorporated into the winter Olympics?

GENERAL KNOWLEDGE

1 Which book of the Bible begins 'In the beginning was the Word'?

2 If your birthday was 5 April, what star sign would you be?

3 Proverbially, what is in the eye of the beholder?

4 What is meant by 'Dutch courage'?

5 Who wrote the play *Happy Days* in 1961?

6 What is a Bath bun?

7 In which English county is the holiday resort of Bournemouth?

8 What does the name of the city Philadelphia mean?

9 In Greek mythology, who was condemned to hold up the heavens on his shoulders for his lifetime?

10 What was the name of the early Australian coach and mail company?

11 Of which country is Berne the capital?

12 Which politician is known as 'Tarzan'?

13 From which play by Shakespeare does the expression 'Brave New World' come?

14 In which year was legionnaire's disease first described?

15 Who wrote *The Tale of Peter Rabbit*?

479

1. *The Gospel of John.* 2. Aries. 3. Beauty. 4. Courage with the aid of strong liquor. 5. Samuel Beckett. 6. A rich, rather sweet, bun. 7. Dorset. 8. City of brotherly love. 9. Atlas. 10. Cobb and Co. 11. Switzerland. 12. Michael Heseltine. 13. *The Tempest.* 14. 1976. 15. Beatrix Potter.

SCIENCE & NATURE

1 What is a bandicoot?

2 How long does it take light from the Sun to reach the Earth?

3 Which animal is the deadly enemy of snakes and rats?

4 What is controlled by a rheostat?

5 Birds have more neck-bones than giraffes. True or false?

6 Which is the largest tree in the world?

7 What is the name given to a fox's tail?

8 Pewter is an alloy of which two metals?

9 Apes have one special difference from monkeys?

10 What is xenophobia?

11 What was a quagga?

12 What was, or is, a blimp?

13 What is the only venomous snake native to Britain?

14 What is gunpowder?

15 What is unusual about the lungfish?

ANSWERS

1. A small insect-eating marsupial. 2. About eight minutes. 3. The mongoose. 4. Electric current. 5. True. 6. A sequoia in California is over 80 metres tall and has a girth of 30 metres. 7. A brush. 8. Tin and lead. 9. Apes have no tails. 10. A fear of anything or anybody foreign. 11. A type of zebra. 12. A non-rigid balloon or airship. 13. The viper, or adder. 14. A mixture of 75 per cent saltpetre, 15 per cent charcoal powder and 10 per cent sulphur. 15. It is able to breathe air.

ENTERTAINMENT

1   In which year was the 'Dulux' dog born?

2   Which TV show was created by Gene Roddenberry?

3   In March 1980, The Jam entered the chart at number one with which song?

4   Who starred in the remake of *The Avengers*?

5   In 1998 Jazzy Jeff and The Fresh Prince released a single called 'Lovely Day'. By what name is The Fresh Prince better known?

6   Exactly how many parts did Alec Guinness play in the film *Kind Hearts and Coronets*?

7   Who had hits in the late 1960s with 'Californian Dreamin'', 'Monday, Monday', and 'Dedicated to the One I Love'?

8   What film starred Will Smith and Tommy Lee Jones as alien hunters?

9   Which game show host coined the catchphrases, 'Nice to see you, to see you nice' and 'Let's have a look at the old scoreboard'?

10 Who recorded the album 'What's the Story, Morning Glory'?

11 When were the Oscars first held: (a) 1928, (b) 1932 or (c) 1936?

12 Rod Stewart's 'Sailing' was used for a BBC TV series about which ship?

13 In early children's television, who was 'Little Weed'?

14 Who starred in the film *Who Framed Roger Rabbit*?

15 Name Michael Jackson's sister who has had a top ten hit with 'The Best Things in Life are Free'.

ANSWERS

1. 1975. 2. *Star Trek*. 3. 'Going Underground'. 4. Uma Thurman, Ralph Fiennes. 5. Will Smith. 6. Eight. 7. Mama and the Papas. 8. *Men in Black*. 9. Bruce Forsyth. 10. Oasis. 11. (a) 1928. 12. HMS *Ark Royal*. 13. The plant that sat between puppets 'Bill and Ben'. 14. Bob Hoskins. 15. Janet Jackson.

HISTORY

1 Who was the last Plantagenet king of England?

2 Constantine XI was the last emperor of what?

3 Which was the last English possession in France, surrendered by Queen Mary I?

4 Who was the last Roman Catholic Archbishop of Canterbury?

5 2 September 1752 was the last day of what in Britain?

6 Who was the last king of Britain who was also Elector of Hanover?

7 Who was the last Holy Roman Emperor?

8 Whose last words were 'Please open the shutter to let in more light', usually given simply as 'More light!'?

9 Whose last novel *The Mystery of Edwin Drood* was left unfinished at his death in 1870?

10 At which battle did General Custer make his last stand?

11 Whose last resting place is in the Matopo Hills in present-day Zimbabwe?

12 Which philosopher's last resting place is inside a glass case in University College, London?

13 In which year did the last tram run in London?

14 Which was the last state of the US to be admitted to the Union?

15 In which year were the last pound notes used in Britain before ceasing to be legal tender?

1. King Richard III. 2. The Byzantine Empire. 3. Calais. 4. Reginald Pole under Mary Tudor. 5. Dating by the Julian calendar. 6. King George III. 7. Francis II (HRE 1792-1806). 8. The German poet Johann Wolfgang Goethe. 9. Charles Dickens. 10. The Battle of the Little Bighorn. 11. Cecil John Rhodes'. 12. Jeremy Bentham's. 13. 1952. 14. Hawaii (as of 1998), the 50th state, admitted in August 1959 some six months after Alaska. 15. 1988.

ANSWERS

FAMOUS PEOPLE

1   Who wrote *The Naked Ape*?

2   Which US film actress had a life-jacket named after her?

3   Who said: 'The meek shall inherit the earth but not the mineral rights'?

4   Which 19th-century mathematician designed an 'analytical engine' that was a forerunner of the computer?

5   How did Agnes Gonxha Bojahiu become better known?

6   Who became president of Pakistan in 1978?

7   What was the name of the spacecraft in which Yuri Gagarin became the first human in space?

8   *Appalachian Spring* and *Clytemnestra* are works by which choreographer?

9   Who wrote the novel *On the Road*?

10 Of which country was Daniel Ortega president between 1985 and 1990?

11 Which architect said that 'a house is a machine for living in'?

12 Whose paintings include *A Cornfield with Cypresses* and *A Starry Night*?

13 Who created the cartoon characters 'Charlie Brown' and 'Snoopy'?

14 Which composer wrote the operas *The Flying Dutchman* and *Lohengrin*?

15 In which city was Christopher Columbus born?

ANSWERS

1. Desmond Morris. 2. Mae West. 3. Jean Paul Getty. 4. Charles Babbage. 5. Mother Teresa. 6. Mohammad Zia ul-Haq. 7. *Vostok 1*. 8. Martha Graham. 9. Jack Kerouac. 10. Nicaragua. 11. Le Corbusier. 12. Vincent Van Gogh. 13. Charles Schulz. 14. Richard Wagner. 15. Genoa.

SPORT & LEISURE

1 Where do Norwich City play their home games?

2 How many cards are there in a pack?

3 If you were watching the Green Bay Packers what sport would you be watching?

4 How long is a full length snooker table?

5 Which is the only club outside of Britain that Ian Rush has played for?

6 What team did Manchester United buy Henning Berg from?

7 'Blue Gill' and 'Crappies' are found in what hobby?

8 What colour caps do jockeys riding for H. J. Joel wear?

9 Which sport takes place in a *velodrome*?

10 Ronnie O'Sullivan is famous for which sport?

11 What sides did Aston Villa striker Paul Merson play for before his present club?

12 Which cricketer is famous for scoring six sixes in one over?

13 The athlete Renate Stecher represented which country?

14 How many service boxes are there on a squash court?

15 What country does Newcastle footballer Keith Gillespie play for?

GENERAL KNOWLEDGE

1 Who plays 'Mr Bean' in the comedy series of that name?

2 What is a sorbet?

3 In *Gulliver's Travels*, 'Gulliver's' second set of adventures takes place where?

4 What did American Express introduce in 1891?

5 Who wrote the drama *Hedda Gabler*?

6 The Bull represents which sign of the Zodiac?

7 Which was the last battle fought on British soil?

8 Name the Beatles' manager who died in 1967.

9 According to the Bible, where was a tower built to reach to the heavens?

10 Which country did 'Paddington Bear' come from?

11 What kind of fruit is a seville?

12 What is the Army equivalent of an Air Chief Marshal?

13 Who was the captain of HMS *Bounty*, in which the seamen and petty officers mutinied?

14 To which part of the USA does Dixieland refer to?

15 What is the code number for 'James Bond'?

ANSWERS

1. Rowan Atkinson. 2. A water ice. 3. Brobdingnag. 4. Travellers' cheques. 5. Henrik Ibsen. 6. Taurus. 7. Culloden. 8. Brian Epstein. 9. Babel. 10. Peru. 11. Orange. 12. General. 13. William Bligh. 14. The southern states. 15. 007.

SCIENCE & NATURE

1   What does 'Eureka!' mean?

2   How big is Britain's largest ant: (a) about half an inch (1.3cm), (b) about a third of an inch (0.8cm) or (c) about a quarter of an inch (0.6cm)?

3   Who invented instant coffee?

4   A female donkey is called: (a) a jenny, (b) a jill or (c) a doe?

5   What is a monomaniac?

6   Which is the world's most poisonous snake?

7   What did Henry Ford invent which helped build his Model T Ford more quickly and cheaply?

8   What is a polliwog?

9   Joseph Priestley discovered one of the most important of gases in 1774. What was it?

10 Would a green rag upset a bull if you waved it?

11 In 1913, Nathaniel Wales invented a now indispensable kitchen storage device. What was it?

12 Which is the smallest mammal in the world?

13 In 1891, two Frenchmen decided to place the engine of their motor-car in what new position?

14 What is the offspring of a male horse and female donkey called?

15 What is the name of a negatively-charged particle that exists in an atom?

ENTERTAINMENT

1 From which film and stage show did the song 'If I Were A Rich Man' come?

2 'You Can't Hurry Love' was the first solo UK number one for which male singer and drummer?

3 If it was Friday and five o'clock what used to be on BBC TV?

4 What nationality is Manfred Mann?

5 Which movie star was the 'Girl with the Million Dollar Legs'?

6 Who was Dick Dastardly's canine sidekick?

7 Billy Joel has only had one UK number one written about his then wife, Christie Brinkley. What was the song called?

8 Who wrote the book on which the film *The Godfather* was based?

9 What show starred the 'Fonz' and 'Mr Cunningham'?

10 In 1994, Whigfield went straight in at number one with which song?

11 On which author's book was the film *Get Shorty* based?

12 Which clay characters found themselves with *The Wrong Trousers* and had *A Grand Day Out*?

13 Paul Young's debut solo hit reached number one in June 1983. Name the song.

14 Which father and daughter appeared in *Tiger Bay* and *The Truth About Spring*?

15 Who directed the 1976 film *Jaws*?

1. *Fiddler on the Roof*. 2. Phil Collins. 3. *Crackerjack*. 4. South African.
5. Betty Grable. 6. 'Mutley'. 7. 'Uptown Girl'. 8. Mario Puzo. 9. *Happy Days*.
10. 'Saturday Night'. 11. Elmore Leonard. 12. Wallace and Gromit.
13. 'Wherever I Lay My Hat (That's My Home)'. 14. Sir John and Hayley Mills.
15. Steven Spielberg.

HISTORY

1. Which island became a dependency of Norway in the 9th century and was ceded to Scotland in 1266?

2. In which city was the suffragette Emmeline Pankhurst born?

3. Where was Edith Cavell working when World War I broke out?

4. Where in the world is the most tea consumed?

5. In which county was William Caxton born?

6. During the 1980s and 1990s, which dictator ruled Iraq?

7. What is special about a catamaran?

8. On what day is pumpkin pie traditionally eaten in the US?

9. Who wrote *Revelations of Divine Love?*

10. Two-thirds of the world's oranges are produced by six nations. Name three of them.

11. What was Dorothy Parker's maiden name?

12. The ski resort of St Moritz is in which country?

13. Gypsies can be called by what other name?

14. In 1939 which country did Hitler invade?

15. Red sky at night is whose delight?

1. Isle of Man. 2. Manchester. 3. She was a nurse in Brussels. 4. Ireland. 5. Kent. 6. Saddam Hussein. 7. It is a boat with two hulls. 8. Thanksgiving Day. 9. Julian of Norwich. 10. US, Brazil, Mexico, Spain, Italy, Israel. 11. Rothschild. 12. Switzerland. 13. Romanies or travellers. 14. Poland. 15. Shepherds'.

FAMOUS PEOPLE

1 Who was Franklin Delano Roosevelt?

2 In July 1906 a Frenchman was pardoned and his prison sentence quashed. Name him.

3 Who was Kemal Atatürk?

4 In October 1822, Dom Pedro became emperor of which South American country?

5 In 1399, what was Richard II the first English king to do?

6 What is the name of the famous British queen who fought against the Romans?

7 Which famous black leader was assassinated on 4 April 1968, in Memphis, Tennessee?

8 Aleksei Leonov was the first person to do what?

9 Who was married at the Château de Candé, Touraine, on 3 June 1937?

10 Which governor-general in India was impeached for alleged corruption?

11 By what name is Siddhartha Gautama better known?

12 In October 1986 which head of state visited China on a seven-day visit?

13 Who was the Black Prince?

14 Which American general was relieved of his command during the Korean War?

15 Two people were crowned together on 11 April 1689? Who were they?

ANSWERS

1. He was the 32nd American president. 2. Alfred Dreyfus. 3. The founder and builder of modern Turkey. 4. Brazil. 5. Abdicate. 6. Boudicca. 7. Martin Luther King. 8. Walk in space. 9. The Duke of Windsor and Wallis Simpson. 10. Warren Hastings. He was acquitted. 11. Buddha ('the Enlightened'). 12. HM the Queen. 13. Edward, Prince of Wales. 14. General Douglas MacArthur. 15. William III and Mary II.

SPORT & LEISURE

1   The Derby is run on which English racecourse?

2   Nigel Mansell won the World Drivers' Championship for which Formula 1 team?

3   Monica Seles was injured in a German tennis tournament and was out of tennis for over a year. What was the incident?

4   Which football team has played in four FA Cup Finals, and lost all of them?

5   Which NBA basketball team is based in Phoenix?

6   Skoal Bandit, Zakspeed and Lotus have what in common?

7   For which athletics event is Colin Jackson famous?

8   Mr Frisk set a record time during the Grand National in which year?

9   In which sport is Alison Fisher one of the leading female players?

10 In 1977 why did Nottingham Forest vote a Millwall player, Jon Moore, as their player of the year?

11 What does the green jersey signify in the Tour de France?

12 With which sport do you associate the Boston Red Socks?

13 In the 1998 England v South Africa test at Headingley, who was the man of the match?

14 The Air Canada Silver Broom is awarded in which sport?

15 Which two countries have hosted the football World Cup twice?

490

GENERAL KNOWLEDGE

1. What does cack-handed mean?
2. There are several sections of an orchestra: woodwind, percussion and strings are three, what is the fourth?
3. If you were 'in the altogether', what would you be?
4. Monapia was the ancient name for which island?
5. In cockney rhyming slang, what does 'pen and ink' mean?
6. What line follows, 'And did those feet in ancient time'?
7. Stories about 'Lord Snooty' and his pals appeared in which publication?
8. Piccadilly Railway station is in which city?
9. Vitamin D helps bone formation and keeps teeth healthy. True or false?
10. Who wrote *The Adventures of Huckleberry Finn*?
11. What is now the official name of the former Cambodia?
12. Which anniversary does a copper or pottery wedding celebrate?
13. A numismatist studies what two things?
14. Dublin stands on which river?
15. If Bill Brewer, Jan Stewer and Peter Gurney were the first three going somewhere, where would that be?

491

SCIENCE & NATURE

1   Which ancient people invented paper?

2   A pug is what kind of animal?

3   What is the correct name for 'laughing gas'?

4   A group of turtles is called: (a) a bale, (b) a turn or (c) a shell?

5   Neptune has three moons. True or false?

6   Which is the only bird in the world which can hover?

7   What metal is produced from the mineral bauxite?

8   What is the larva of a butterfly or moth called?

9   How many legs does a lobster have?

10 Where is the Sea of Tranquillity?

11 Woofers and tweeters are part of what system in the home?

12 The smell of skunk's fluid can be detected half a mile away. True or false?

13 A mixture of chalk powder and boiled linseed oil is better known by what name?

14 Does a concave mirror or lens bend inwards or outwards?

15 For how many days can a camel go without water?

ENTERTAINMENT

1   For which Olympic Games did Whitney Houston record the song 'One Moment in Time'?

2   What is the name of the family with whom 'Paddington Bear' lived?

3   In the mid-1990s, did 'Boombastic' by Shaggy reach number one?

4   What was the name of Olivia Newton-John's character in the original *Grease* film?

5   Who reached number one in the 1960s with 'Make It Easy on Yourself' and 'The Sun Ain't Gonna Shine Anymore'?

6   Which TV series did David Hasselhof star in after *Night Rider*?

7   Michael Caine, Gary Cooper and Marlene Dietrich all started their careers as film extras. True or false?

8   Can you name one of Ringo Starr's hits of the early 1970s?

9   Michael Parkinson was savaged, during one of his chat shows, by whom?

10   Who were Petra and Goldie?

11   The Italian star Rossano Brazzi was a boxing champion. True or false?

12   With which band did Michael Hutchence perform?

13   'Baldrick' was the loyal, but dopey, servant to which character?

14   Is Dannii Minogue younger or older than her sister Kylie?

15   Who claimed to go nearly mad making a film alongside a cartoon rabbit?

493

HISTORY

1 Who wrote *A Vindication of the Rights of Man*?

2 What was the profession of H. L. Mencken?

3 Abyssinia is the former name of which country?

4 The Great Lakes flow into which river?

5 What is the name of the English decorative style that was fashionable from about 1800–30 and was influenced by the French Empire style?

6 Which nationality was the composer Sergei Rachmaninov?

7 Who was assassinated on 22 November 1963?

8 The biggest and busiest McDonald's is in: (a) New York, (b) Paris, (c) Moscow or (d) London?

9 Which is the longest river entirely in England?

10 Florence Nightingale was a nurse during which war?

11 What was Nelson's flagship called?

12 Who founded the Society of Friends?

13 Which airport handles more international aircraft than any other airport in the world?

14 If we say someone is in hot water, what do we mean?

15 The thistle is the national symbol of which country?

FAMOUS PEOPLE

1   Which king of England was called The Lionheart?

2   Princess Mary of Teck was married to whom?

3   General de Gaulle was the leader of which country?

4   Name the former British king who died in Paris in 1972.

5   Who is George Herbert Walker Bush?

6   Imre Nagy of Hungary was executed in 1958. Who was he?

7   Which English monarch died at Richmond Palace in 1603?

8   Who was Simón Bolívar?

9   Who succeeded King William IV when he died in 1837?

10 Pizarro founded which major city in Peru in 1535?

11 Which king of England acknowledged that he had at least 20 illegitimate children?

12 In the English parliament who led the campaign against the slave trade?

13 A US Naval officer was the first to reach the North Pole in April 1909. Who was he?

14 Over whom was Saladin victorious in 1187?

15 Which future king and queen of the United Kingdom were married on 10 March 1863?

SPORT & LEISURE

1 The race horse Shergar was kidnapped and has never been seen again. In which year?

2 The Peterborough Pirates play which sport?

3 A Rugby League ball is smaller than a Rugby Union ball. True or false?

4 Petanque originated in which country?

5 Who were Manchester United playing when David Beckham scored from his own half during the first game of the 1996–97 season?

6 UK surfers congregate at the River Severn to ride what?

7 A cricket bail is how long: (a)7 cm (2.8"), (b) 10cm (3.9") or (c) 11cm (4.3")?

8 In golf, an eagle is how many holes under par?

9 What other sport is regularly played at Lord's Cricket Ground?

10 Where were the Olympic Games held in 1906?

11 Chris Eubank is usually accompanied by what music when he enters the boxing arena?

12 In Japanese, judo means 'the gentle way'. True or false?

13 Which city is home to American football team the Redskins?

14 In 1998 Taine Randell succeeded who as captain of the All Blacks?

15 Where was the first football World Cup held?

ANSWERS

1. 1983. 2. Ice hockey. 3. True. 4. France. 5. Wimbledon. 6. The bore. 7. (c) 11cm (4.3"). 8. Two. 9. Real Tennis. 10. Athens. 11. 'Simply) The Best' by Tina Turner. 12. True. 13. Washington. 14. Sean Fitzpatrick. 15. Montevideo, Uruguay.

GENERAL KNOWLEDGE

1 Victoria railway stations can be found in three cities in the world. Two of them are London and Bombay. Where is the other?

2 A yegg is: (a) an American safe-breaker, (b) a young Scottish calf or (c) a kind of hiccup?

3 The novel *Rebeccca* was written by whom?

4 In a pack of cards, the queen of Clubs looks to her left. True or false?

5 What is the language spoken in Catalonia, Spain?

6 What does an astronomer study?

7 A diplomatic envoy who represents his own head of state in a foreign country is known as a what?

8 What was the title of David Niven's biographical book?

9 An American soldier would go to the PX or post exchange, where would an English soldier go?

10 Who is the female 'James Bond' created by Peter O'Donnell?

11 The Little Mermaid in Copenhagen·is a memorial to whom?

12 What is the male version of the equine term 'dam'?

13 'Be prepared' is the motto of which group of people?

14 Istanbul is the modern name for which ancient city?

15 What was the nickname of ex-US president Richard Nixon?

1. Manchester. 2. (a) an American safe breaker. 3. Daphne du Maurier. 4. True. 5. Catalan. 6. The stars. 7. An ambassador. 8. *The Moon's a Balloon*. 9. The NAAFI. 10. 'Modesty Blaise'. 11. Hans Christian Andersen. 12. Sire. 13. The Scouts. 14. Byzantium. 15. 'Tricky Dicky'.

SCIENCE & NATURE

1 A radio signal was sent across the Atlantic for the first time in which year?

2 What is the correct name for a young swan?

3 Which has the most calories: butter or margarine?

4 The average house fly lives: (a) about 20 days, (b) about one day or (c) about a week?

5 What is nickel silver?

6 White admiral, apollo, and Camberwell beauty are all types of what?

7 Hydrocyanic acid is also called what?

8 Which bird is able to swim the fastest?

9 The teeth of a rodent never stop growing. True or false?

10 What is the study of aircraft and flying called?

11 Where would you find the vestibular system?

12 What kind of fruit is a Blenheim orange?

13 Cotton manufacturing factories were opened for the first time in 1641. In which town or city?

14 How much do the world's heaviest coconuts weigh?

15 Maize is really a special kind of grass. True or false?

498

1. 1905. 2. A cygnet. 3. They have about the same. 4. (a) about 20 days. 5. An alloy of copper, nickel and zinc. 6. Butterfly. 7. Prussic acid. 8. The penguin. 9. True. 10. Aeronautics. 11. In the (inner) ear. 12. An apple. 13. Manchester. 14. 18 kg. 15. True.

ENTERTAINMENT

1 During the filming of *Twister*, a Boeing 707 was used to generate some of the high winds necessary for the plot? True or false?

2 With which band was Bryan Ferry the lead singer?

3 From which film do the songs 'I Wanna Be Like You' and 'Bear Necessities' come?

4 Who wrote the TV shows *The Liver Birds*, *Butterflies* and *Bread*?

5 In 1992, who reached number one with 'Would I Lie To You?'?

6 What was the name of the cabin boy in *Captain Pugwash*?

7 Which English film actor was born Laruska Mischa Skikne?

8 'Reach Out (I'll Be There)' was the only UK number one hit for the Temptations? True or false?

9 Who was the sister of film star Joan Fontaine?

10 'Prince Charming' and 'Stand and Deliver' were both number ones for Adam and the Ants. What was their third number one?

11 What was the name of the TV series in which Tony Curtis and Roger Moore starred?

12 Who starred as a pool player in the film *The Hustler*?

13 With whom did Debbie Gibson re-record the *Grease* song, 'You're The One That I Want' in 1993?

14 'Dylan', 'Brian' and 'Dougal' were some of the stars of which TV show?

15 With which band was Steve Marriot the lead singer?

1. True. 2. Roxy Music. 3. *Jungle Book*. 4. Carla Lane. 5. Charles and Eddie. 6. Tom Laurence Harvey. 8. False. It was a number one for the Four Tops. 9. Olivia de Havilland. 10. 'Goody Two Shoes'. 11. *The Persuaders*. 12. Paul Newman. 13. Craig McLachlan. 14. 'The Magic Roundabout'. 15. The Small Faces.

SECTION TWO

GENERAL KNOWLEDGE

1   Where is Traitors' Gate?

2   St Matthew is the patron saint of whom?

3   In a pack of cards, which way does the King of Hearts look; to his left, or to his right?

4   What is a Peach Melba?

5   What is sauce lyonnaise?

6   What is taramasalata?

7   What nationality was Brother Jonathan?

8   What is known as the 'devil's bedpost'?

9   What are croutons?

10 What was the name of the early Australian coach and mail company?

11 St Michael is the patron saint of whom?

12 If you go back 20 years or so, who would measure something in picas?

13 The jolly swagman went 'Waltzing Matilda'. What was a matilda?

14 Can you eat acorns?

15 St Nicholas is the patron saint of whom?

ANSWERS

1. The Tower of London. 2. Accountants and bankers. 3. To his right. 4. Peach halves with ice-cream and raspberry sauce. 5. A sauce with white wine and onions. 6. A Greek 'dip' dish of smoked-fish or roe paste with olive oil, etc. 7. An American. 8. The four of clubs playing-card. 9. Small pieces of toast fried in butter. 10. Cobb and Co. 11. Grocers. 12. A printer. A pica is one-sixth of an inch. 13. The swagman's roll containing his blanket. 14. Yes, but they are better served up as food for pigs. 15. Children.

SCIENCE

1   What is chalcedony?

2   A lightning conductor was invented by which American statesman in 1752?

3   Edward Bevan invented an ingenious window-blind, and patented it in 1769. What was it?

4   What can be measured in joules?

5   What is an aqueduct?

6   What is putty made of?

7   What does a micrometer measure?

8   What is a hovercraft?

9   James Hargreaves invented a machine for the textile industry in 1764. What was it?

10 Daniel Rutherford discovered one of the most important of gases in 1772. What was it?

11 Which gem was produced artificially in 1955?

12 The study and art of printing is called what?

13 Calcium carbonate is more familiarly known as what?

14 What kind of clock was invented in 1656 by Christian Huygens?

15 Sir John Harington designed and installed what sanitary device in 1589?

NATURAL HISTORY

1 Fireflies are nocturnal beetles. True or false?

2 Is the blackberry a member of the rose family?

3 A group of hares is called: (a) a down (b) harrow (c) a brace?

4 The largest-known sea anemone measures: (a) 1 foot (b) 2 feet (c) 3 feet?

5 What is another name for the blackberry?

6 What kind of animal could be described as a Karakul?

7 In one day, a mole can burrow: (a) 25 yards (b) 50 yards (c) 100 yards?

8 What is another name for sorrel?

9 A mongoose is a mammal whose favourite food is what?

10 What is the name given to the largest European deer?

11 Wheat is really a special kind of grass. True or false?

12 What is a mango?

13 A cosset is a young lamb, true or false?

14 What is a group of antelope called?

15 What is cuckoo-spit?

GEOGRAPHY

1   In which country is the River Ebro?

2   Can you name all of the 'Ridings' in Yorkshire?

3   What is the name of the city formerly called Danzig?

4   Where and what is 'Scotland Yard'?

5   In which country would you find the town of Bruges?

6   Where and what is 'Tiffany's'?

7   Saint Pierre and Miquelon, off Newfoundland, belongs to which country?

8   Where is the Dogger Bank?

9   Where is Capitol Hill?

10 The Brenner Pass, through the Alps, helps connect which two countries?

11 What is the capital of Argentina?

12 Monapia was the ancient name for which island?

13 Until 1974, Bangladesh was part of which country?

14 What is the status of the Maldive Islands?

15 Which city is on the River Senne?

ENGLISH LANGUAGE

1   In cockney rhyming slang, what does 'Cain and Abel' mean?

2   What does 'cack-handed' mean?

3   What, in Australia, was or is a 'brumby'?

4   What is the difference between the words 'alter' and 'altar'?

5   What is meant by the slang, 'Ackers'?

6   What is wrong with this sentence: He was not all together pleased at the news?

7   What is the boot of a car called in the United States?

8   What is the name for someone who studies birds?

9   What is a diphthong?

10   What are examples of diphthongs?

11   What is a bowler hat called in America?

12   What does an American mean by a 'teeter-totter'?

13   What is the name for someone who studies the art of clock-making?

14   Which single word means both 'more than one leaf' and 'departs'?

15   What would one be if one were described as a 'county' person?

1. Table. 2. Originally, left-handed, but later, just plain clumsy. 3. An untamed wild horse. 4. 'Alter' means 'to change' and 'altar' is a block or table used in church services. 5. Money. 6. It should read: He was not altogether pleased at the news. 7. The trunk. 8. Ornithologist. 9. Two vowels pronounced together so as to make a new, combined sound. 10. OU as in 'house', OI as in 'hoist'. 11. A derby hat. 12. A seesaw. 13. Horologist. 14. Leaves. 15. Ostentatiously upper-class.

SPORT

1   In which sport would you find, Fenders, Mothers, Sheets and Reefs?

2   Who is the only man to have played both Cricket and Rugby Union for England at ful international level?

3   Which member of the Royal Family has won an Olympic Medal?

4   Which player traditionally throws the ball in at a Rugby Union line out?

5   In snooker, if there are two reds left and I clear the table gaining the maximum points available, how many points have I scored?

6   Who are the only team from outside the USA to win Baseball's World Series?

7   Who won the 1997 Grand National Steeplechase?

8   Who won the 1997 Coca Cola Cup?

9   With which team did Nigel Mansell make his Formula One debut?

10 Who was captain of the victorious England Cricket team for the 1997 Sharjah one day tournament?

11 On which English race course is the Derby run?

12 How many Gold medals did Michelle Smith win for Eire, in the 1996 Olympic Games?

13 Who captained the South African cricket team in 1998?

14 Which team did Chelsea beat to win the 1998 European Cup Winners Cup Final?

15 By what name are Bradford's Rugby league team known?

ANSWERS

1. Sailing. 2. Alistair Hignall. 3. The Princess Royal (Princess Anne). 4. The Hooker. 5. 43. 6. The Toronto Blue Jays. 7. Lord Galeen. 8. Leicester City. 9. Lotus. 10. Adam Hollioake. 11. Epsom. 12. Three. 13. Hansie Cronje. 14. Stuttgart. 15. The Bulls.

HISTORY

1   Who was Lady Jane Grey?

2   What was the name of the socialist society found by George Bernard Shaw and Sidney and Beatrice Webb?

3   What did the name Baader-Meinhof refer to in the 1960's?

4   What was the Ottoman Empire?

5   Who did Kaiser Wilhelm II dismiss in 1890, an event that became known as, 'dropping the pilot'?

6   What momentous event occurred off the Falkland Islands, in 1914?

7   Who was Dag Hammarskjöld?

8   What was started by the British attack on Rommel's line on 23rd October, 1942?

9   What is a Cypriot?

10 Which famous British statesman died on 24th January, 1965?

11 What disaster overtook the Grand Hotel, Brighton, during a Conservative Party conference in 1984?

12 Constantine II (1964-1967) was the last monarch of which country?

13 What did Admiral Horthy become in 1920?

14 Who was Chiang Kai-shek?

15 King Edward VII opened which major museum at South Kensington on 26th June, 1909?

CINEMA AND TV

1 Which famous actor starred in both *Some Like It Hot* and *The Odd Couple?*

2 Who starred in the film *Tom Jones?*

3 In which film did Sylvester Stallone play in goal while Pele and Michael Caine were on the pitch?

4 Who shared the lead with Maggie Smith in the film *A Room with a View?*

5 Who starred in the film *The Sound of Music?*

6 This ex-member of Monty Python directed films like *Brazil* and *The Fisher King*. Who is he?

7 Which well-known actress played herself in *Airport 75?*

8 Jeff and Beau Bridge's father appeared in many films including *Airplane*. What is his name?

9 Terence Stamp, Anthony Newley and Laurence Harvey all turned down a part in the 1966 film which made Michael Caine a star. What was the film?

10 Which movie star's real name was Frank James Cooper?

11 The cartoon show, *Top Cat,* was based on which old T.V. Show?

12 Who starred in the film *On the Waterfront?*

13 Brothers, Jake and Elwood, liked which kind of music?

14 Name two film stars who have been married at least eight times.

15 Who starred in the film *The Heiress?*

ANSWERS

1. Jack Lemmon. 2. Albert Finney. 3. *Escape To Victory.* 4. Denholm Elliot. 5. Julie Andrews. 6. Terry Gilliam. 7. Gloria Swanson. 8. Lloyd Bridges. 9. *Alfie.* 10. Gary Cooper. 11. Sgt. Bilko. 12. Marlon Brando, Lee J. Cobb, Karl Malden. 13. Blues music; they were The Blues Brothers. 14. Zsa Zsa Gabor, Georgia Holt, Stan Laurel, Mickey Rooney, Lana Turner. 15. Olivia de Havilland.

POPULAR MUSIC

1 Which 1970's pop icon had alter-egos known as Ziggy Stardust and Aladdin Sane?

2 Name the controversial lead singer with Pulp?

3 Who won the Best Male Artist Award in the 1998 BRITs?

4 In 1988 who sang, 'Don't worry, be happy'?

5 Who covered, The artist formerly known as Prince's hit, 'Kiss', with The Art of Noise?

6 Which band did Phil Oakey front in the late seventies and eighties?

7 Who were 'Walking on Sunshine', when they won the 1997 Eurovision Song Contest with, 'Love Shine a Light'?

8 With which band was TV Presenter Jools Holland the keyboard player?

9 Who replaced Gary Moore as lead guitarist of Thin Lizzy in the early 1980s?

10 If Paul Weller was the lead singer and Bruce Foxton was the bassist, who was the drummer?

11 Who, in 1998, performed the 'Ballad of Tom Jones'?

12 By what name is Harry Webb better known?

13 The heavy metal band Saxon have never had a top ten hit. True or false?

14 Who had a number 7 hit with, 'Shout It To The Top' in October 1984?

15 Which major international female artist started her career as lead singer of the Sugarcubes?

LITERATURE

1 *The Corn Is Green* is a play written by which man who spoke no English until he was eight?

2 `Abandon hope, you who enter here.' Where does this phrase originate?

3 Shakespeare wrote: 'Which like the toad, ugly and venomous,' how did he continue?

4 Complete the proverb: 'Actions speak...'

5 Who was Violet Elizabeth Bott?

6 Who wrote *Tropic of Capricorn?*

7 The author of Frankenstein was married to the poet, Percy Bysshe Shelley. What was her name?

8 Who wrote *The Naked and the Dead?*

9 Complete these book titles: *The ------- and the Hearth, The Man in the ---- Mask* and *The ------ of the Baskervilles.*

10 'A little learning is a dangerous thing' is the beginning of a poem by whom?

11 In which boys' paper did the stories of Tom Merry & Co. appear?

12 In which Shakespeare play does 'Sebastian' appear?

13 Who wrote stories of Uncle Remus and Brer Rabbit?

14 'It is an ancient Mariner,/And he stoppeth one of three' is the beginning of a poem by whom?

15 'Wackford Squeers' appears in which Dickens novel?

GENERAL KNOWLEDGE

1 Before decimalisation, our coinage used the letters £, s and d. What did they mean?

2 Which word beginning with ante- means 'before marriage'?

3 Who is the patron saint of teachers?

4 Which anniversary does a pearl wedding celebrate?

5 What, in medieval times, was a groat?

6 What is ravioli?

7 Who was George Cadbury?

8 Who, in ancient times, were Shem, Ham and Japheth?

9 Who, or what, is the Old Lady of Threadneedle Street?

10 In what groups does one find a squadron?

11 What is kohlrabi?

12 The name of which famous nurse is concealed by the anagram Flit on, cheering angel?

13 Who in the world would be called a 'Jock'?

14 In a pack of cards, which way does the Queen of Spades look: to her left, or to her right?

15 What are the religious followers of Nanak called?

SCIENCE

1   What is a phobia?

2   What is the medical condition called 'myopia'?

3   What did Sir Walter Raleigh discover in Trinidad in 1595?

4   What is a satellite?

5   What colour is the gem called aquamarine?

6   The patella is another name for which bone?

7   What is measured in knots?

8   What is a Bofors?

9   What instrument did Adolphe Sax invent?

10   What does a thermometer measure?

11   What is the study of the chemistry of living organisms called?

12   Which is the second largest planet?

13   What is phosphor bronze?

14   In early times, what sort of weapon was a trident?

15   In later times, what was a Trident?

1. A fear, aversion or hatred. 2. Shortsightedness. 3. The Great Pitch Lake, the world's largest deposit of asphalt. 4. A small body, such as a moon, which orbits a planet. 5. A pale, bluish green. 6. The kneecap. 7. Speed. (Knots are often used for the speed of ships and aircraft). 8. An anti-aircraft gun. 9. The saxophone. 10. Temperature. 11. Biochemistry. 12. Saturn. 13. An alloy of copper, tin, zinc and phosphorus. 14. A three-pronged spear. 15. A ballistic missile.

NATURAL HISTORY

1 What is a baboon?

2 The leek is a plant relative of the lily. True or false?

3 What is a yak?

4 What is variously called the bêche-de-mer, the trepang or sea-slug?

5 What is a tuatara?

6 What is an abalone?

7 What sort of animal is a Bedlington?

8 Which very large animal has one, or sometimes two, horns on its snout?

9 What is an aphid?

10 What is another name for the endive?

11 What is a chamois?

12 A prairie-dog is; (a) a kind of wolf (b) a kind of ground squirrel (c) a small cat?

13 The peach is a member of the rose family. Yes or no?

14 What is dangerous about the Anopheles mosquito?

15 Could you take a mud-puppy for a walk?

1. A large type of monkey, found in Africa. 2. True. 3. A kind of Tibetan wild cattle. 4. The sea-cucumber (not a vegetable), highly prized as a delicacy by the Chinese. 5. It's a small reptile from New Zealand with a spine on its back. 6. It's an edible shellfish, sometimes called the sea-ear. 7. A breed of dog. 8. The rhinoceros. 9. It's another name for the greenfly. 10. Chicory. 11. The goat-antelope of Europe. 12. (b) a kind of ground-squirrel. 13. Yes. 14. It carries and spreads the disease of malaria. 15. No. It's a kind of salamander.

GEOGRAPHY

1 Kampuchea is now the official name of which country?

2 Which important American city stands on the Potomac river?

3 Where and what is the Serpentine?

4 Where is Ruritania?

5 The original building for one of the world's largest museums was called Montague House, London. What is it called now?

6 What is the commonest name for a pub in Britain?

7 What, in earlier times, was the main industry of Paternoster Row, London?

8 Which are the Low Countries?

9 If you 'crossed the Rubicon' where would you be?

10 Where are the Cheviot Hills? Southern or Northern England?

11 Which is the largest railway station in the United Kingdom?

12 Where is the River Kwai (made famous by the book about its bridge)?

13 Where in the world do they speak Tamil?

14 What is the capital of Algeria?

15 There is a 'Tin Pan Alley' in both London and New York. What is it?

1. Cambodia. 2. Washington. 3. It's a lake in Hyde Park, London. 4. It doesn't exist. It's fictional! 5. The British Museum. 6. The Red Lion. 7. Bookselling and publishing. 8. Belgium, the Netherlands and Luxembourg. 9. Italy. 10. Northern England. 11. Clapham Junction. 12. In Thailand. 13. Southern India and Sri Lanka. 14. Algiers. 15. The area given over to publishers and writers of popular music.

ENGLISH LANGUAGE

1 Can you name two words, sounding alike, which mean the same as this pair: twisted/kind of grain?

2 Which word, starting with M, means 'boring' or 'dull'?

3 Which word, beginning with O, means 'atrocious' or 'scandalous'?

4 Finish the proverb: 'Great oaks from...'

5 'Nether' and 'nethermost' were old ways of saying what?

6 What does 'vamoose' mean?

7 What is the difference between the prefixes 'ante' and 'anti'?

8 What is the female version of 'baron'?

9 What is the female version of 'masseur'?

10 What was a 'broad arrow'?

11 What is a jabot?

12 What is the name for someone who studies the nerves?

13 What was meant by the old word 'deem'?

14 What, originally, was a Thug?

15 Can you name a four-letter word for terror or fright?

SPORT

1   At which sport does Jane Sixsmith represent England?

2   Which former England Centre led Newcastle to the Division One title in 1998 as their Director of Rugby?

3   What is the minimum number of darts required to complete a leg from 501?

4   If I score 'Was-a-ri' in Judo, how many points have I scored?

5   Name the two Williams drivers for the 1998 Formula One season.

6   For which rally team did Colin McRae drive in 1997 & 1998?

7   Is 'The Oaks' a race for colts or fillies?

8   Who was the longest-serving England cricket captain?

9   Name Arsenal's highest ever scorer.

10 In the 1970s Brian Jacks rose to national fame due to the 'Superstars' television programme, but in which sport did he actually compete for Great Britain at international level?

11 Who was BBC TV personality of the year in 1996?

12 What incident in a German tennis tournament, meant that Monica Seles was injured and out of tennis for over a year?

13 Which European city hosts the games of the American football team known as 'Galaxy'?

14 Up until 1998 who sponsored the World Professional Snooker Championship?

15 In the Euro '96 match between Germany and England, what was the score after extra time?

HISTORY

1 Which famous London market moved from central London to a more southerly site in 1974?

2 What was the Munich Agreement of 1938?

3 Who was murdered by the Bolsheviks at Ekaterinburg in July, 1918?

4 What was the better-known name of the Russian revolutionary, Lev Davidovich Bronstein?

5 What was the Berlin Airlift?

6 What did Athelstan, King of Mercia, become in A.D. 927?

7 Where and what was Wessex?

8 Who were rescued from the Altmark ship, off Norway, in 1940?

9 The Prime Minister, Margaret Thatcher, visited which Eastern European country in March, 1987?

10 Who was Franklin Delano Roosevelt?

11 Vichy, France, was the headquarters of what during WW2?

12 Who was Ernest Bevin?

13 What was the better-known name of Joseph Vissarionovich Djugashvili?

14 In 1853, the Wellingtonia gigantea was discovered in California. What was it?

15 Which London department store opened on 15th March, 1909?

CINEMA AND TV

1 Who starred in the silent film *Sherlock, Jr.?*

2 Which comic provided the voice of the genie in Disney's first *Aladdin?*

3 Who starred in the film *Forty Ninth Parallel?*

4 How many episodes were there in the 1914 serial film *The Exploits of Elaine?*

5 Who received an Oscar for his creation of Wallace and Gromit?

6 Who starred in the film *Blow Up?*

7 Who starred in the film *The Private Life of Henry VIII?*

8 From which film did the song 'A Couple of Swells' come?

9 Who starred in the film *The Lavender Hill Mob?*

10 Who starred in the films *The Deer Hunter* and *Cape Fear?*

11 In which film did Katharine Hepburn and Spencer Tracy star as husband-and-wife lawyers?

12 Who commenced each episode of a TV series with the words 'Good Evening, All'?

13 Which leader of the Labour Party played himself in *Rockets Galore?*

14 Omar Sharif is famed in a field other than acting. What is it?

15 Which American Senator played himself in *The Candidate?* ·

ANSWERS

1. Buster Keaton. 2. Robin Williams. 3. Leslie Howard, Raymond Massey, Laurence Olivier. 4. Fourteen. 5. Nick Park. 6. David Hemmings, Sarah Miles. 7. Charles Laughton. 8. *Easter Parade*, 1948. 9. Alec Guinness, Stanley Holloway. 10. Robert De Niro. 11. *Adam's Rib* (1949). 12. P.C. Dixon, played by Jack Warner. 13. Michael Foot. 14. He is a champion bridge-player. 15. Hubert Humphrey.

POPULAR MUSIC

1 Which 1985 film, starring David Bowie and Patsy Kensit, flopped disastrously?

2 Elvis Presley's first UK hit reached number 2 in May 1956. Name the song?

3 All Saints had their first hit in March 1998. What was the song?

4 What band does Jarvis Cocker front?

5 Who reached number one in 1965 with, 'Tears', and has had top ten hits with, 'Love Is Like A violin', 'The River', and 'Promises'?

6 In Nov 1980, Motorhead reached number 15 in the UK with what song?

7 In 1989, Stock, Aitkin and Waterman teamed up with, The Christians, Holly Johnson, Paul McCartney and Gerry Marsden to record which song for charity?

8 In 1981, Soft Cell reached number 1 with, 'Tainted love'. Name the band's debut album released in the same year?

9 Which song, first released in 1957, took 29 years, 42 days to reach number 1 in Dec 1986?

10 Which all-girl band sang 'Viva forever'?

11 Which British band released their debut album, Rattus Norvegicus in 1977?

12 Pink Floyd have only had one UK number 1 single. Name the song?

13 Janet Jackson has never had a UK number 1. True or false?

14 Name one of Rolf Harris's top twenty hits other than his number 1 single, 'Two Little Boys'

15 Who was the blonde in Blondie?

LITERATURE

1   Who wrote the play *Pygmalion?*

2   The character 'Pip' appears in which book by Charles Dickens?

3   Who said: 'Dr Livingstone, I presume?'

4   Which famous children's books did Frances Hodgson Burnett write?

5   What line follows, 'There is a Lady sweet and kind, Was never face so pleased my mind;'?

6   What line follows, 'And did those feet in ancient time'?

7   'All men are created equal.' Where does this phrase originate?

8   What did Thomas Moore think 'A little learning' was?

9   'Ayesha' is a character in which famous book?

10 Who, on his desert island, said, 'I am monarch of all I survey', according to William Cowper?

11 'All the world's a stage, and all the men and women merely players.' Where does this phrase originate?

12 Who created 'Batman'?

13 Who created the gentleman cracksman 'Blackshirt'?

14 Who wrote *Catch 22?*

15 According to Noël Coward, who go out in the noon-day sun?

ANSWERS

1. George Bernard Shaw. 2. *Great Expectations*. 3. Sir Henry Morton Stanley. 4. *The Secret Garden; Little Lord Fauntleroy*. 5. 'I did but see her passing by, And yet I love her till I die'. 6. 'Walk upon England's mountains green?' 7. The American Declaration of Independence. 8. A dangerous thing. 9. She. 10. Alexander Selkirk. 11. Shakespeare's *As You Like It*. 12. Bob Kane. 13. Bruce Graeme. 14. Joseph Heller. 15. Mad dogs and Englishmen.

GENERAL KNOWLEDGE

1 Who wrote the play *Cavalcade?*

2 What is a rollmop?

3 According to the 'language of flowers', what does the asphodel signify?

4 Which anniversary does a sapphire wedding celebrate?

5 St David is the patron saint of what?

6 What is the Purple Heart?

7 What is hock?

8 Who, with his wife, was expelled from the Garden of Eden?

9 Rice paper isn't made from rice. What is it made from?

10 What is meant by 'Dutch courage'?

11 Who was the Father of English Poetry?

12 Which anniversary does an emerald wedding celebrate?

13 What kind of food is baclava?

14 According to the 'language of flowers', what does the honeysuckle signify?

15 Poseidon is another name for Neptune. True or false?

ANSWERS

1. Noël Coward. 2. A herring fillet rolled up with onion and pickled. 3. My regret follows you to the grave. 4. The forty-fifth. 5. Wales. 6. An American decoration awarded to soldiers wounded in battle. 7. A white Rhine wine. 8. Adam and Eve. 9. The pith of a plant. 10. Courage with the aid of strong liquor. 11. Geoffrey Chaucer. 12. The fifty-fifth. 13. Pastry filled with nuts and honey. 14. Generous and devoted attention. 15. True.

SCIENCE

1   What is agoraphobia?

2   What kind of signal was sent across the Atlantic for the first time in 1901?

3   What did the French clock-maker Antoine Redier invent in 1847?

4   What object in the sky is called Io and is 2,260 miles in diameter?

5   What did Percy Shaw of Yorkshire invent in 1934, which is seen on roads all over the world?

6   What is a capstan?

7   Rubella is a disease, also called what?

8   Water vapour is usually called what?

9   What gemstone is found in the Cairngorm Mountains of Scotland?

10 How many sides has an octagon?

11 What are the two digits used in the binary system of calculation?

12 What is gum arabic?

13 A high degree of mechanisation in industry is called what?

14 Which is longer, a metre or a yard?

15 What is a catamaran?

1. Fear of open spaces. 2. Radio signals. 3. The first alarm clock. 4. Jupiter's third-largest moon. 5. Cats' eyes. 6. A winding device used aboard ship for hauling in a cable or rope. 7. German measles. 8. Steam. 9. The cairngorm. It's a yellowish stone. 10. Eight. 11. 0 and 1. 12. An adhesive obtained from acacia trees. 13. Automation. 14. A metre. 15. A vessel for sailing, with two hulls.

NATURAL HISTORY

1   Which is the world's largest amphibian?

2   'George', a male mandrill (baboon) in the London Zoo, died aged (a) 40 years, (b) 45 years or (c) 48 years?

3   *Homo erectus pekinensis* was an example of whose ancestors?

4   What domestic animal could be described as a Siamese?

5   Which creature can jump one hundred times its length?

6   What is a mangel-wurzel?

7   A female horse aged four or under is called a what?

8   What fox-faced monkey-like small creatures are found almost entirely in Madagascar?

9   What is a firefly?

10   A rabbit can run at 35 miles an hour. True or false?

11   What is peculiar about the teeth of a rodent?

12   What kind of animal could be described as a Cotswold?

13   What is an oak-apple?

14   The macaw is a member of which expressive bird family?

15   What kind of animal is said to bell?

GEOGRAPHY

1 Where is the Gower Peninsula?

2 Where is the Clifton Suspension Bridge?

3 Where in England would you find the River Coquet?

4 Norfolk Island forms part of which country?

5 Which major city is on the River Avon?

6 Where is the Golden Gate Bridge?

7 The official name 'Éire' refers to which country?

8 Where is 'Sunset Boulevard'?

9 What is the modern name for the Sandwich Islands?

10 In what city is Piccadilly Railway Station?

11 'New Holland' was an early name for which country?

12 To which country do St Pierre and Miquelon belong?

13 'España' refers to which country?

14 Where in the world would you find Bondi Beach?

15 In which county are the Quantock Hills?

ANSWERS

1. South Wales, west of Swansea. 2. In Bristol, over the River Avon. 3. In Northumberland. 4. Australia. 5. Bristol. 6. In San Francisco, USA. 7. The Irish Republic. 8. Los Angeles. 9. Hawaii. 10. Manchester. 11. Australia. 12. France. 13. Spain. 14. Sydney, Australia. 15. Somerset.

ENGLISH LANGUAGE

1 What is the difference between 'kerb' and 'curb'?

2 What is one doing if one 'comes the old soldier'?

3 Harry was an aged man, although his wife was only aged 50. How is the word 'aged' pronounced?

4 What is the meaning of 'chutzpah'?

5 A waldgravine was (a) a former noblewoman in Germany, (b) an extinct type of wolf or (c) an engraver of tombstones.

6 What article of clothing is a 'deerstalker'?

7 What is the British equivalent of Zip codes?

8 What is a proscenium?

9 What does 'He didn't do a hand's turn' mean?

10 Can you make an anagram out of 'golden land'?

11 An 'apartment' to an American is what to an Englishman?

12 What happens if you are 'between the devil and the deep blue sea'?

13 A begum is (a) a kind of West Indian dance, (b) an African witch-doctor or (c) a Muslim princess.

14 What do Americans call trousers?

15 Complete this simile: 'Good in parts, like the...'

SPORT

1   For which Formula One team did Nigel Mansell win the World Drivers' Championship?

2   For which County Cricket team did Brian Lara play in the 1997 & 1998 seasons?

3   Who were Rugby Union Division One champions in the 1996/97 season?

4   Apart from Manchester United and Arsenal, up until 1999, which was the only other team to have won the Premier League?

5   Who is the only British Olympian to have won Gold Medals in three consecutive Olympic Games?

6   Name Denver's American football team.

7   Which British swimmer won the 100m Breaststroke Gold Medal in the 1980 Olympic Games?

8   With which club did Bobby Moore end his professional playing career?

9   By which name was wrestler Shirley Crabtree better known?

10 Who was the first British boxer in the 20th century to win a World Heavyweight title?

11 One of the most successful skiers of the 1990s was Alberto Tomba, what nationality is he?

12 Which sport do Birchfield Harriers take part in?

13 Who won the Golden Boot in the 1986 World Cup finals?

14 Who sponsored the 1998 Rugby League Challenge Cup Final?

15 Who won the 1997 British Touring Car Championship?

ANSWERS

1. Williams. 2. Warwickshire. 3. Wasps. 4. Blackburn Rovers. 5. Steven Redgrave. 6. Broncos. 7. Duncan Goodhew. 8. Fulham. 9. Big Daddy. 10. Lennox Lewis. 11. Italian. 12. Athletics. 13. Gary Lineker. 14. Silk Cut. 15. Alain Menu.

HISTORY

1 Who is the current Duke of Cornwall?

2 What was the Diet of Worms of 1521?

3 11 people were killed in St Peter's Fields, Manchester in 1819 What was it called?

4 In which country is the Democratic Party a major political unit?

5 Which Italian poet raised an army and seized Fiume in 1919?

6 What happened on 6th June, 1944, in Northern France?

7 Where in England did Julius Caesar first set foot?

8 Which large island country in the Indian Ocean was annexed by France in 1896?

9 How many ships were there in the Spanish Armada?
(a) 329 (b) 1,029 (c) 129

10 The slavery-abolitionist John Brown made a raid at Harper's Ferry in the United States in 1859. What was the result?

11 Who was Eamon De Valéra?

12 Who was Alexander the Great?

13 What major governing authority was abolished in England in 1986?

14 Who became leader of the Conservative Party on 10th February, 1975?

15 Following the death of King Edward VII on 6th May, 1910, who became king?

CINEMA AND TV

1 What was the name of the frog who compered The Muppet Show?

2 Who starred in the film *Ghost?*

3 Who starred in the film *Brighton Rock?*

4 From which stage show did the song 'Send in the Clowns' come?

5 Who directed the films *M.A.S.H.* and *The Player?*

6 Who starred in the film *Women in Love?*

7 Who starred in the film *Singin' in the Rain?*

8 Which singer's voice is heard in the cartoon film *The Lion King?*

9 Who or what was 'Flipper'?

10 Whose name was originally John Charlton Carter?

11 Who was the first British actor to win an Oscar?

12 Which film star first became famous for his role in the T.V. show *Moonlighting?*

13 Who starred in the silent 1924 film *The Thief of Bagdad?*

14 Who starred in the film *State Secret?*

15 Who was the first British actress to win an Oscar?

1. Kermit. 2. Whoopi Goldberg. 3. Richard Attenborough. 4. *A Little Night Music.* 5. Robert Altman. 6. Alan Bates, Glenda Jackson. 7. Gene Kelly. 8. Elton John. 9. A dolphin. 10. Charlton Heston. 11. George Arliss, who appeared in Disraeli in 1929. 12. Bruce Willis. 13. Douglas Fairbanks. 14. Douglas Fairbanks Jnr., Jack Hawkins. 15. Vivien Leigh, who appeared in *Gone With the Wind* in 1939.

POPULAR MUSIC

1 Which British band were on 'Hope Street' in 1995?

2 Which Australian singer collaborated with Nick Cave to reach number 11 with, 'Where The Wild Roses Grow'?

3 For the 1998 World Cup, two songs with the words 'Top Of The World' were released in support of the England football team. The official version was performed by England United, who performed the other?

4 Ronan is the lead singer with which Irish boy band?

5 Chris Rea has had only one UK top ten hit. Name the song?

6 Which former Australian soap star's debut single was, 'Torn'?

7 Which 1970's pop icon, played Che Guevara in the stage production of Evita, rode a 'Silver Dream Racer', and mutinied on the Bounty?

8 The Eurythmics have only had one UK number 1, name the song?

9 Who was the original lead singer with Generation X?

10 With which double A-side single did Jasper Carrott have his only chart success, reaching number 5 in August 1975?

11 Who reached number 3 in the UK with, 'My Best Friend's Girl', in 1978 and number 5 with, 'Drive' in 1984?

12 In 1997, the four piece band Aqua topped the carts with 'The Barbie Song'. What nationality are they?

13 Name the 1987 song taken to number 12 in the UK by Glen Hoddle and Chris Waddle?

14 'Mad' Richard Ashcroft is the vocalist with which UK Album chart-topping band?

15 In 1998 which two bands held a concert in Belfast to support the, 'Yes', campaign for the referendum on the Good Friday

LITERATURE

1 Who was 'Michael Henchard' in the novel *The Mayor of Casterbridge?*

2 Who created the fictional character 'Count Dracula'?

3 What is the main subject of novels by Dick Francis?

4 De Morgan wrote: 'Great fleas have...' Can you complete the phrase?

5 'Natty Bumppo' is a character created by which American author?

6 Who wrote *Lisa of Lambeth?*

7 Which writer used the letter 'Q' as a pseudonym?

8 'The best laid plans of mice and men.' Where does this phrase originate?

9 The character 'Quilp' appears in which book by Charles Dickens?

10 Who wrote *The Lord of the Rings?*

11 Who wrote *The Mask of Dimitrios?*

12 'Mike Hammer' was a fictional hero devised by whom?

13 Who was James Boswell?

14 Complete the proverb: 'Dead men...'

15 Anna Sewell wrote the book *Black Beauty*. Who or what was 'Black Beauty'?

1. He was the Mayor. 2. Bram Stoker. 3. Suspense and detective novels featuring horse-racing. 4. 'Little fleas upon their backs to bite 'em.' 5. J. Fenimore Cooper. 6. W. Somerset Maugham. 7. Sir Arthur Quiller-Couch. 8. Robert Burns: To a Mouse. 9. *The Old Curiosity Shop*. 10. J.R.R. Tolkien. 11. Eric Ambler. 12. Mickey Spillane. 13. Friend and fellow-traveller of Dr Samuel Johnson. 14. '...tell no tales'. 15. A horse.

GENERAL KNOWLEDGE

1 St Francis de Sales is the patron saint of whom?

2 What kind of stew comes from Lancashire?

3 What were 'dundrearies'?

4 What kind of food item comes from Chelsea?

5 What kind of food is a garibaldi?

6 In cooking, what does en croûte mean?

7 From where does the popular pub name, 'The Pig and Whistle' come?

8 What are Quakers?

9 If you were a printer, how many points would make an inch?

10 If your birthday was April 5th, what star sign would you be?

11 What is a Christian Scientist?

12 What is the Talmud?

13 In wartime, what was a WAAF?

14 What is a kebab?

15 What is Bezique?

SCIENCE

1   What sort of device was a Lee-Enfield?

2   Edwin Land invented what kind of camera in 1947?

3   Where in the body is the Achilles tendon?

4   What machine tool did Henry Maudslay invent in 1800?

5   What important electrical device was invented in 1825 by William Sturgeon?

6   Speaking of the weather, what is meant by 'precipitation'?

7   Which has most calories: margarine or butter?

8   What is autophobia?

9   'Mr Watson, come here, I want you.' was the first message in 1876 by whom?

10 What is the process of eating, digesting and assimilating food called?

11 What is a camera obscura?

12 Platinum takes its name from the Spanish word platina, meaning silver. True or false?

13 The science which studies the history of the Earth's crust is called what?

14 What is the study of the science of light called?

15 Between which planets is the asteroid belt situated?

ANSWERS

1. A rifle. 2. The Polaroid. 3. In the heel. 4. The precision lathe. 5. The electromagnet. 6. Any form of water falling from the clouds. 7. They have about the same. 8. A fear of making any reference to oneself. 9. Alexander Graham Bell over his telephone. 10. Nutrition. 11. A small room with a hole at the top, through which an image of an outside scene can be projected. 12. True. 13. Geology. 14. Optics. 15. Mars and Jupiter.

NATURAL HISTORY

1 What would you find in an apiary?

2 What kind of animal could be called a Suffolk Punch?

3 What is a group of hedgehogs called?

4 What is a bird of paradise?

5 What is a capuchin?

6 What is a gosling?

7 What is a prehensile tail?

8 Where would you find the eyes of a snail?

9 The barn owl's night vision is much better than ours. Is it (a) twice as good or (b) a hundred

10 What is another name for alfalfa?

11 What is a kipper?

12 Apart from being the name of a domestic animal, what else is called a 'cat'?

13 Which animal lives in a warren?

14 What is hemlock?

15 Which cat-like animal with tufted ears once roamed wild in Europe?

GEOGRAPHY

1   Where in Britain would you find an example of a bascule bridge?

2   Where in the world would you find the Gabba cricket ground?

3   Dacia is the old name for which country?

4   Where is the Isle of Thanet?

5   Where and what is Stonehenge?

6   Which city is on the Liffey river?

7   In which country would you find the Black Forest?

8   Where and what is Plinlimmon?

9   In which English county would you find the River Blackwater?

10   Where would you find the Leaning Tower?

11   In which city would you find Connolly railway station?

12   The Simplon Tunnel is between which two countries?

13   The American president James Monroe gave his name to which capital city?

14   In which American city would you find the Liberty Bell?

15   Which is the longest bridge in Britain?

1. Tower Bridge, London. 2. Brisbane, Australia. 3. Romania. 4. In Kent. It is separated from the rest of the county by the River Stour. 5. An ancient group of assembled large stones near Salisbury. 6. Dublin. 7. Germany. 8. A mountain in Wales. 9. Essex. 10. Pisa, Northern Italy. 11. Dublin. 12. Switzerland and Italy. 13. Monrovia, capital of Liberia. 14. Philadelphia. 15. The Humber Bridge, over the River Humber.

ENGLISH LANGUAGE

1   If someone said you were 'wet behind the ears', what would it mean?

2   To what object did the Earl of Chesterfield give his name?

3   What is the meaning of 'nefarious'?

4   In cockney rhyming slang, what does 'pen and ink' mean?

5   What is the skirting board in a room called in the United States?

6   What is a 'black maria'?

7   What speak, 'louder than words'?

8   What does 'feasible' mean: (a) able to be done (b) possible (c) probable?

9   What is the name for someone who studies reptiles?

10 Which word means a metal and guided?

11 Which word means mimic or ape?

12 If you were 'green about the gills' what would you be like?

13 What is a kimono?

14 What was 'Durst' an old way of saying?

15 What is the name for someone who studies animals?

SPORT

1. Where do Surrey County Cricket Club play the majority of their home games?

2. Name Phoenix's NBA Basketball team?

3. Which football team was Eric Morecambe renowned for supporting?

4. How many players are there in a Polo team?

5. Who was England's top scorer in the 1992 Olympic Hockey tournament?

6. Who scored a hat-trick against England in the 1992 European Championships?

7. Name Houston's American football team.

8. Which British cyclist who won a gold medal at the 1992 Olympic Games on a radical graphite and carbon-fibre bike?

9. Who won the 1998 Rugby League Challenge Cup?

10. In Rugby Union what can you do inside your own 22, but not outside, unless it's a penalty?

11. Which two football teams play each other in the Edinburgh derby match?

12. What sport do the Manchester Giants play?

13. For which Formula One team did James Hunt win the World Drivers' Championship?

14. What was the score in the 1998 FA Cup final, when Arsenal defeated Newcastle to take the Cup and League double?

15. Which heavyweight boxer is nicknamed, 'The Real Deal'?

ANSWERS

1. The Oval. 2. The Suns. 3. Luton Town. 4. Four. 5. Sean Kerley. 6. Marco Van Basten. 7. Oilers. 8. Chris Boardman. 9. Sheffield Eagles. 10. Kick the ball, 'out on the full,' (i.e. into touch without bouncing). 11. Heart of Midlothian & Hibernian. 12. Basketball. 13. McLaren. 14. 2-0. 15. Evander Holyfield.

HISTORY

1 President McKinley of the United States died on 14th September 1901, following what?

2 Which head of state in North America was executed in 1867?

3 Who is Valéry Giscard d'Estaing?

4 Who was Attila?

5 Which English monarch once had tea with Hitler?

6 Who was assassinated in Delhi, India, on 20th January, 1948?

7 On 1st April, 1965, the Greater London Council replaced what?

8 In what year did food rationing end?

9 Zanzibar and Pemba were ceded to Britain by Germany in 1890 in exchange for which North Sea island?

10 London and Paris were linked in 1891 by which new device?

11 Which newspaper proprietor was found dead in the sea off Tenerife in 1991?

12 Which Nazi leader landed by parachute near Glasgow, on 10th May, 1941?

13 Which Frenchman was pardoned and his prison sentence quashed in July, 1906?

14 England, had a dictator in the 1650s. Who was he?

15 How did Cardinal Wolsey die in 1530?

ANSWERS

1. Being shot and wounded eight days earlier. 2. Maximilian, Emperor of Mexico. 3. A former president of France. 4. King of the Huns. 5. Edward VIII (after his abdication). 6. Mahatma Gandhi. 7. The London County Council (LCC). 8. 1954. 9. Heligoland. 10. The public telephone. 11. Robert Maxwell. 12. Rudolf Hess, Hitler's deputy. 13. Alfred Dreyfus. 14. Oliver Cromwell. 15. After being taken ill on a journey from York to London.

CINEMA AND TV

1 Which TV sitcom features a dog called Eddie and a home help called Daphne?

2 From which musical play comes the song 'Ol' Man River'?

3 Who wrote the song 'I've Got You Under My Skin'?

4 Who starred as T.E. Lawrence in the epic *Lawrence Of Arabia*?

5 Who is Shirley MacLaine's brother?

6 *Thelma And Louise* starred which two famous actresses?

7 Which film featured John Gordon Sinclair as a boy who loses his place on the school football team to a girl?

8 Whose epitaph is: 'On the whole, I'd rather be in Philadelphia'?

9 Which actress's Oscar acceptance speech included the famous phrase, 'You like me, you really like me?'

10 Jodie Foster won an Oscar for her role in the film *The Accused*. What was the other film she won a best actress Oscar for?

11 What film featured a search for a toy only known as 'Rosebud'?

12 What Vietnam film featured helicopters attacking to the music 'The Ride Of The Valkyries'?

13 Dooley Wilson, as 'Sam' sang what in the film Casablanca?

14 Which Sci-Fi film, based on a book by Frank Herbert, featured Sting?

15 In which film did Paul Newman star as a pool player?

1. Frasier. 2. Show Boat. 3. Cole Porter. 4. Peter O'Toole. 5. Warren Beatty. 6. Susan Sarandon and Gina Davis. 7. *Gregory's Girl*. 8. W.C. Fields. 9. Sally Fields. 10. *Silence Of The Lambs*. 11. *Citizen Kane*. 12. *Apocalypse Now*. 13. 'As Time Goes By.' 14. *Dune*. 15. *The Hustler*.

POPULAR MUSIC

1 Which British entertainer had top ten hits in the 1950's with, 'Singing The Blues', 'Butterfingers', 'Water Water', and 'Little White Bull'?

2 Which band recorded, 'Three Lions', with David Baddiel and Frank Skinner for Euro 96 and the 1998 World Cup?

3 In 1976, which international singing star had her first UK hit reaching number 7 with, 'Jolene'?

4 Of which progressive rock band was Fish the original lead singer?

5 In 1998, which US teen band was made up of, Taylor, Isaac and Zac?

6 What does the M stand for in the band name, M People?

7 In which seventies teeny bop band would you have found, 'Les and Woody', singing, 'Shang-a-lang' and, 'Give A Little Love, Take A Little Love'?

8 According to Cornershop, what does, everybody need a bosom for?

9 From which British city do heavy rockers Saxon originate?

10 In 1997 & 1998 who topped the Album charts with, 'Urban Hymns'?

11 A.J., Howie, Nick, Kevin and Brian, make up which US boy band?

12 Name Jimi Hendrix's only UK number one?

13 Which group has had the most weeks on the UK chart in any one year?

14 Which midlands group had 6 number ones in the early 1970's including, 'Skweeze Me Pleeze Me', 'Coz I Luv You', and, 'Mama Weer All Crazee Now'?

15 Metallica's, 'Hero Of The Day', is dedicated to Motorhead's Lemmy. True or false?

1. Tommy Steele. 2. Lightning Seeds. 3. Dolly Parton. 4. Marillion. 5. Hanson. 6. Manchester. 7. Bay City Rollers. 8. A pillow. 9. Barnsley. 10. The Verve. 11. Backstreet Boys. 12. Voodoo Chile (slight return). 13. Oasis (134 in 1996). 14. Slade. 15. True.

LITERATURE

1   Who wrote *Autobiography of a Super-tramp?*

2   'Banquo' appears in which play by Shakespeare?

3   'The better part of valour is discretion.' Where does this phrase originate?

4   Under what name did Patrick Dannay and Manfred B. Lee write?

5   Who wrote *Tom Brown's Schooldays?*

6   What line follows 'Where the bee sucks, there suck I:'?

7   Who wrote *Confessions of an English Opium-Eater?*

8   Stories about Lord Snooty and his pals appeared in which publication?

9   Who, reputedly, said, 'Youth is wasted on the young'?

10 Andrew Lang wrote a series of 'Fairy Books'. How were they distinguished?

11 Complete the proverb: 'Don't change horses...'

12 Who wrote *The Rime of the Ancient Mariner?*

13 'When angry, count four; when very angry...' Complete Mark Twain's famous line.

14 Who wrote *The Ipcress File?*

15 What was the main occupation of John Betjeman?

1. William Henry Davies. 2. *Macbeth*. 3. Shakespeare's *Henry IV*. 4. Ellery Queen.
5. Thomas Hughes. 6. 'In a cowslip's bell I lie'. 7 Thomas de Quincey. 8. *The Beano.*
9. George Bernard Shaw. 10. By colours: thus, *The Green Fairy Book, The Yellow Fairy Book,* etc. 11. '...in midstream'. 12. Samuel Taylor Coleridge. 13. Swear. 14. Len Deighton. 15. Writing poetry.

GENERAL KNOWLEDGE

1 Which anniversary does a crystal wedding celebrate?

2 Who was the original Johnnie Walker of Scotch whisky fame?

3 What is Canasta?

4 St Jerome is the patron saint of whom?

5 St Elizabeth of Hungary is the patron saint of whom?

6 What are devils on horseback?

7 Which country's national assembly is called Congress?

8 Which are Europe's Latin languages?

9 If your surname is 'White', what might your nickname be?

10 According to the 'language of flowers', what does the quince signify?

11 St Luke is the patron saint of whom?

12 What is Islam?

13 What is a thick cream of lemon juice, lemon peel, eggs, sugar and butter called?

14 Which word, beginning with ante- means 'to date, before true time'?

15 Two 16th-century German painters, father and son, had the same name. Who were they?

SCIENCE

1 What did Erno Rubik invent in 1975?

2 What vehicle was first built in 1936 by Ferdinand Porsche in Germany?

3 What kind of animals would a zoologist study?

4 Which object in the sky is called Ganymede and is 3,270 miles in diameter?

5 Which of the planets is nearest the Sun?

6 How many carats are there in pure gold?

7 What metal is the main constituent of steel?

8 How many sides has a polygon?

9 Bronze is an alloy of which two metals?

10 How long is a cubit?

11 What is an optician?

12 The Zeppelin built in 1900 was the first successful example of what kind of craft?

13 Which object in the sky is called Titania and is about 620 miles in diameter?

14 What was the name of the probe which carried a robot to Mars in 1997?

15 A substance which destroys bacteria and prevents their growth is called a what?

543

ANSWERS

1. The Rubik cube. 2. The Volkswagen Beetle car. 3. All. 4. It is Jupiter's largest moon. 5. Mercury. 6. 24. 7. Iron. 8. Three or more sides (it's a many-sided figure). 9. Copper and tin. 10. 18 inches. 11. Someone who makes and sells optical equipment. 12. The first rigid dirigible airship. 13. It is the largest of the moons of Uranus. 14. The study of religious feasts. 15. Antiseptic.

NATURAL HISTORY

1   Oats are really a special kind of grass. True or false?

2   A female horse aged five or more is called what?

3   What is a bandicoot?

4   What is a ptarmigan?

5   A pomeranian is a breed of dog. True or false?

6   A capybara is related to the guinea-pig. True or false?

7   What breed of animal could be called a Shetland?

8   How do bats sleep?

9   Which animal lives in a drey?

10   What is a bilberry?

11   What is a mandrake?

12   What kind of animal could be termed a Thoroughbred?

13   What kind of animal is said to bellow?

14   What is a sardine?

15   How many humps does a Bactrian camel have?

ANSWERS

1. True. 2. A mare. 3. A small insect-eating marsupial. 4. A bird, a variety of mountain-dwelling grouse. 5. True. 6. True. 7. A pony. 8. Upside down. 9. A squirrel. 10. A shrub with dark-blue berries, also called the whortleberry or blueberry. 11. A poisonous plant of the potato family. 12. A racehorse. 13. A bull or an ox. 14. Any small fish of the herring family. 15. Two.

GEOGRAPHY

1   Where in the world would you find Central Park?

2   Which capital city stands on the River Vltava?

3   Dartmoor Prison was built in 1806 for what purpose?

4   What is Van Diemen's Land called today?

5   Where is St Mark's Cathedral?

6   Where in the world would you find a Magyar?

7   What, in England, was the Fosse Way?

8   To which country does Martinique belong?

9   Where is Balmoral Castle?

10 Upstream from Oxford, what is the River Thames known as?

11 Lake Titicaca is found in which two South American countries?

12 Where would you find people speaking Afrikaans?

13 Which city is on the Scottish River Tay?

14 The official name 'Deutschland' refers to which country?

15 Victoria railway stations may be found in three cities in the world. Which?

ENGLISH LANGUAGE

1   The name of which bird is associated with silliness?

2   This adjustable spanner was invented by Charles Moncke and is called what?

3   What's wrong with this sentence: One should always carry an umbrella when you go out walking here?

4   Can you name two words which sound alike and mean the same as this pair: band of singers/24 sheets of paper?

5   What exactly is a zealot?

6   What does 'Q.E.D.' mean?

7   What is the meaning of 'edifice'?

8   Name two words, sounding alike, which mean the following: use needle and thread/plant seeds.

9   In cockney rhyming slang, what does 'half-inch' mean?

10 If Fred 'went bananas' what happened?

11 If you took umbrage, would it be poisonous?

12 What's the plural of 'axis'?

13 If your surname is Clark, what might you be nicknamed?

14 How should the following sentence read: 'Help! I will drown and no one shall save me.'?

15 What does 'catchpenny' mean?

1. Cuckoo. 2. A 'monkey wrench', named after the inventor. 3. It should read: One should always carry an umbrella when one goes out walking here. 4. Choir/quire. 5. A rather fanatical follower, enthusiast or fan. 6. 'Quod erat demonstrandum'; that which was to be proved. 7. A building. 8. Sew/sow. 9. Pinch. 10. He got wildly angry. 11. No, it only means 'to feel resentment'. 12. Axes. 13. Nobby. 14. Help! I shall drown and no one will save me. 15. Cheap, trivial.

SPORT

1 Name Queens Park Rangers' home ground.

2 Name Pittsburgh's American football team.

3 What do Skoal Bandit, Zakspeed and Lotus have in common?

4 Name the British adventurer who led the successful Thrust II supersonic land speed record attempt.

5 What sport do Poole Pirates take part in?

6 What nationality was Greg Rusedski at birth?

7 Which sport played in the southern hemisphere is a cross between Rugby, American football and Gaelic football, with teams such as the Essendon Bombers and Footscray Bulldogs?

8 Where do the 'Broncos' English Rugby League team come from?

9 In Cricket, a batsman may only score a maximum of 30 leg byes in any one innings. True or false?

10 Who was the first person to break the four-minute mile?

11 What sport do the Cardiff Devils play?

12 Ice Dance champions Torvill and Dean are associated most with which piece of music?

13 The 'Buccaneers' American football team come from which US city?

14 Name West Bromwich Albion's football ground?

15 Name the five disciplines in the modern pentathlon?

HISTORY

1 Who was leader of the Labour Party immediately before Tony Blair?

2 What was the Field of the Cloth of Gold?

3 Which company opened the first supermarket in Britain, at Manor Park, East London, in 1947?

4 Which motoring organisation was started on 29th June, 1905?

5 Which American general was known as 'Old Blood and Guts'?

6 Who was Mr Five-Per-Cent?

7 Who was Simón Bolivar?

8 What happened in the Falkland Islands on 2nd April 1982?

9 Who was assassinated in Dallas in 1963?

10 King Edward III established which famous Order of chivalry in 1348?

11 Which commercial radio station began operating in October, 1973?

12 Where and what was Bechuanaland?

13 Millions of rabbits in Britain died in 1953 as a result of what?

14 Who was Jean Batten?

15 In what year did Columbus make his first major voyage?

CINEMA AND TV

1 From which film and stage show did the song 'Climb Every Mountain' come?

2 Who starred in the film *Goldfinger?*

3 Which famous actress turned down the female lead in *Gone With The Wind?*

4 Who starred in the film *Victim?*

5 Which was the first musical film with its own score?

6 The star of *Little Caesar* was born in Bucharest as Emmanuel Goldenberg. Who is he?

7 Sir John Pratt, the British diplomat, had a famous film-actor-brother. Who was he?

8 Which movie star's real name was Jane Alice Peters?

9 Who starred in the 1943 film *Shadow of a Doubt?*

10 Who starred in the film *The Baby and the Battleship?*

11 Who starred in the film *The Producers?*

12 Which two famous actors turned down the lead role in *The Godfather* that eventually went to Al Pacino?

13 Who played Bonnie in the film *Bonnie and Clyde?*

14 Which famous American comedian was born in England at Eltham, Kent?

15 Who starred in the film *Blade Runner?*

1. *The Sound of Music.* 2. Sean Connery, Honor Blackman. 3. Bette Davis. 4. Dirk Bogarde. 5. *The Broadway Melody*, 1929. 6. Edward G. Robinson. 7. Boris Karloff, whose real name was William Henry Pratt. 8. Carole Lombard. 9. Joseph Cotten. 10. John Mills, Richard Attenborough. 11. Zero Mostel, Gene Wilder. 12. Robert Redford and Warren Beatty. 13. Faye Dunaway. 14. Bob Hope. 15. Harrison Ford.

POPULAR MUSIC

1 Blockbuster's Bob Holness started life as a session musician and played saxophone on Gerry Rafferty's 1978 hit, 'Baker Street'. True or false?

2 Courtney Love is lead singer of which American band?

3 Name Donna Summers only UK number 1 hit?

4 Vanessa Mae reached number 16 in Jan 1995 with, 'Toccata And Fugue'. What instrument does she play?

5 Which US soul singer recorded the original, 'Alphabet Song', for the children series, Sesame Street?

6 '(Sittin' On) The Dock Of The Bay' was the only UK top 10 hit for which US vocalist?

7 Name Hot Chocolate's lead vocalist?

8 In which year did Bucks Fizz win the Eurovision Song Contest?

9 In which UK county does Rod Stewart have his main residence?

10 Falco is the only Austrian to top the UK chart. Which fellow Austrian was he paying tribute to, in his number 1 hit song?

11 Who reached number 1 in July 1972 with, 'Schools Out'?

12 Who was lead singer with 1980's chart toppers, Culture Club?

13 Which singer, real name Gloria Fajardo, owns 2 Cuban Hotels, lives in Miami, has a daughter called Emily and broke her back in a bus crash in 1990?

14 What do the songs, 'Back Home', 'This Time We'll Get It Right', and 'World In Motion', have in common?

15 True or False, Barry Manilow has only had 1 UK top 10 hit?

LITERATURE

1 Complete the proverb: 'Clothes do not...'

2 What had John Debrett and John Burke in common?

3 What was the most famous book from the author of *Kidnapped* and *The Black Arrow?*

4 Who wrote the play The Playboy of the Western World?

5 'Breathes there a man, with soul so dead,/Who never to himself hath said,' is the beginning of a poem by whom?

6 Who wrote the verse Matilda (told such awful lies)?

7 Who was the leading character in the novel *1984?*

8 *Pamela* was whose first novel?

9 'Blood is thicker than water'. Where does this phrase originate?

10 What historical novel did Henryk Sienkiewicz write?

11 Complete the proverb: 'Accidents will happen...'

12 Who were the Houyhnhnms in *Gulliver's Travels?*

13 Who said, 'Father, I cannot tell a lie. I did it with my little hatchet'?

14 Who wrote the novel *An American Tragedy?*

15 Who, in Russia, occupied a place similar to that of Shakespeare in England?

1. '...make the man'. 2. They both produced books of reference on the Peerage. 3. *Treasure Island.* 4. J.M. Synge. 5. Sir Walter Scott. 6. Hilaire Belloc. 7. Winston Smith.' 8. Samuel Richardson. 9. John Ray: *English Proverbs* (1670). 10. *Quo Vadis.* 11. '...in the best-regulated families'. 12. A noble race of horses who ruled humans. 13. George Washington (according to Mark Twain). 14. Theodore Dreiser. 15. Alexander Pushkin.

GENERAL KNOWLEDGE

1 If your surname is 'Murphy', what might your nickname be?

2 What is Scientology?

3 Who was the first Pope?

4 How did worsted get its name?

5 What is prosciutto?

6 Who was James Earl Carter?

7 St Eloi is the patron saint of whom?

8 St Genesius is the patron saint of whom?

9 What is vermouth?

10 What is Shintoism?

11 To the ancient Greeks and Romans who was Apollo?

12 Who was the original 'Angry Young Man'?

13 How did teddy-bears receive their name?

14 If you were born on Good Friday or Christmas Day, what special power might you have?

15 If a foreign car displayed the letters RO, what would its country of origin be?

SCIENCE

1 What did Ladislao Biro invent in 1933?

2 What machine first saw service in 1961 and was built by Unimation?

3 If something is cupreous, what does it contain?

4 What colour is a ruby?

5 What is graphite?

6 What is a facsimile?

7 Sir Joseph Swan demonstrated the use of a modern lighting object in 1878. What was it?

8 What did Samuel Morse invent in 1837?

9 How many days are there in a year?

10 Who invented the jet engine?

11 Isaac Newton discovered what in 1687?

12 What element does the chemical symbol K represent?

13 What is controlled by a rheostat?

14 What is gastritis?

15 What is 'nickel silver'?

ANSWERS

1. The ballpoint pen. 2. An early form of chemistry, much given to errors. 3. Copper. 4. Red. 5. A form of carbon, sometimes called black-lead. 6. An exact copy of a picture or other flat-surface pattern. 7. The filament electric lamp. 8. The Morse code. 9. 365 (366 in leap years). 10. Frank Whittle. 11. The force of gravity. 12. Potassium. 13. Electric current. 14. Inflammation of the stomach lining. 15. An alloy of copper, nickel and zinc.

NATURAL HISTORY

1 The flying fox is not a fox at all. What is it?

2 What sort of animal is called a terrier?

3 The lettuce is a member of the daisy family. Yes or no?

4 Can you name the very common, small, grey, many-legged garden creature sometimes called a 'leatherjacket'?

5 What is the wild Australian 'teddy-bear' called?

6 What sort of animal is a Rottweiler?

7 Parsley is a plant relative of the carrot. Yes or no?

8 Birds have more neck-bones than giraffes. True or false?

9 What is a clove?

10 Is it true that Scandinavian lemmings commit mass suicide?

11 Is it true that lemmings are rodents, like rabbits and mice?

12 What is a cayuse?

13 Which animal lives in a hive?

14 What is a tamarind?

15 What is a tamarisk?

ANSWERS

1. A bat. 2. Various breeds of dogs. 3. Yes. 4. Woodlouse. 5. The koala. 6. A breed of dog. 7. Yes. 8. True. 9. The flower-bud of the clove tree, dried and used as a spice. 10. No. It's a myth. 11. True. 12. An American term for a poor horse. 13. A bee. 14. A tropical tree which has pods filled with sweet, reddish-black pulp. 15. A small tree or shrub which grows in salt deserts or by the seashore.

GEOGRAPHY

1 Is there really such a place as 'Timbuktu'? If so, where is it?

2 In which city would you find the Gare du Nord railway station?

3 In which city would you find Grand Central railway station?

4 To which country do the Canary Islands belong?

5 Where is Hans Christian Andersen's memorial, the Little Mermaid, located?

6 Which cathedral in Britain has three spires?

7 Which submarine first sailed under the Arctic ice-cap?

8 Where did the coconut originate?

9 Where is the Chamber of Horrors?

10 Where is Exmoor?

11 What is the second highest mountain in the world?

12 The Republic of Benin is in which continent?

13 Which city is on the River Hooghly?

14 Nyasaland is a country now called what?

15 The volcano Popocatepetl is in which country?

ANSWERS

1. Yes. It is in the Mali Republic, Northern Africa. 2. Paris. 3. New York. 4. Spain. 5. In Copenhagen harbour. 6. Lichfield Cathedral. 7. The Nautilus. 8. Polynesia. 9. It's part of the Madame Tussauds waxwork show in London. 10. Somerset. 11. K2. 12. Africa. 13. Calcutta. 14. Malawi. 15. Mexico.

ENGLISH LANGUAGE

1 What have been called 'the Devil's Picture Books'?

2 What is a split infinitive?

3 In the theatrical world what is an 'angel'?

4 What does the Latin 'ad hoc' mean?

5 What is the singular form of the word 'graffiti'?

6 Who were 'the great unwashed'?

7 What are gym shoes often known as in the United States?

8 Americans refer to this item of clothing as an undershirt. What do we call it?

9 Can you name two words sounding alike which mean the same as this pair: remain/heavy measurer?

10 How much does a 'stitch in time' save?

11 What is a 'lady bountiful'?

12 Is a babu (a) a kind of monkey, (b) an Indian clerk or (c) an American child?

13 Complete this simile: 'To blush like a...'

14 What does 'machiavellian' mean?

15 What is a 'chanticleer'?

SPORT

1   Colin Jackson is famous for which athletics event?

2   If I was playing Stapleford rules, what sport would I be playing?

3   In which county is Headingley cricket ground?

4   Which snooker player is nicknamed 'The Whirlwind'?

5   Which snooker player gained the nickname, 'The Hurricane'?

6   Who managed Leeds United to a UEFA Cup place in the 1997/98 season?

7   Name Atlanta's Baseball team.

8   Which jump jockey holds the record for the most winners in a season?

9   Which British squash player finally ousted Jansher Khan as world number one in 1998?

10   In Cricket, and excluding the wicket keeper, which fielding position is usually nearest the bat?

11   How high is the net on a tennis court: 2ft 6ins, 3ft or 3ft 4ins?

12   How old was Stephen Hendry when he became Snooker's world number one?

13   Name the three events in equestrian three-day eventing?

14   In which European country was the sport of Handball invented?

15   By what name was the USA's Olympic Basketball team known in the 1996 Olympic Games?

557

HISTORY

1   What event took place in St Paul's Cathedral in July, 1981, and was seen by 700 million T.V. viewers?

2   In which year did the Gunpowder Plot take place?

3   The island of Réunion became a colony of which country in 1764?

4   Oliver Cromwell, although he became England's Head of State, was not King. What was he called?

5   Who was Alfred the Great?

6   What part of Rome became a sovereign state in 1929?

7   Who was the last Danish king of England?

8   What 'British' character was invented by John Arbuthnot in 1712.

9   Which famous magazine went on sale for the first time on 1st October, 1938?

10   In very early times, what was the status of Sussex, Essex and Kent?

11   The followers of John Wycliffe, the 14th century religious reformer, were called what?

12   Who was Chester Arthur?

13   Which British award for bravery was instituted on 23rd September, 1940?

14   What, politically speaking, was 'the Axis' before the Second World War?

15   In 1889, Lord Rosebery was elected chairman of which new London authority?

558

1. Prince Charles and Lady Diana Spencer were married. 2. 1605. 3. France. 4. The Lord Protector. 5. The King of Wessex who resisted the Danes. 6. The Vatican City. 7. Hardicanute (1019-1042). 8. 'John Bull'. 9. Picture Post. 10. They were kingdoms of England before A.D. 808. 11. Lollards. 12. 21st American president. 13. The George Cross. 14. The alliance between Germany, Italy and (later) Japan in WW2. 15. The London County Council.

CINEMA AND TV

1 What creature was the star of the *Free Willy* series of movies?

2 English gentleman and actor David Niven was born in which country?

3 Ruby Keeler, Mary Pickford, Norma Shearer and Fay Wray were not American born. From which country did they originally come?

4 Who starred in the film *Brief Encounter?*

5 Which was the first Mickey Mouse cartoon?

6 What was unusual about the film *Becky Sharp* released in 1935?

7 What morning show has been hosted by Chris Evans, Mark Little and Keith Chegwin?

8 Stanley Baker, Jack Hawkins, Michael Caine starred together in which African war film?

9 Who starred in the film *Doctor in the House?*

10 Who starred in the film *Crocodile Dundee?*

11 Michael Douglas had an affair with which actress in the film *Fatal Attraction?*

12 The Bond films were based on books written by which author?

13 Who starred in the film *The Outlaw Josey Wales?*

14 Who played the leading role in the three film versions of *The Thirty-Nine Steps?*

15 Which film has been re-made more times than any other?

ANSWERS

1. A killer whale. 2. In Scotland. 3. Canada. 4. Trevor Howard and Celia Johnson. 5. *Steamboat Willie*, 1928. 6. It was the first in three-colour Technicolor. 7. *The Big Breakfast*. 8. *Zulu*. 9. Dirk Bogarde, Kenneth More, James Robertson Justice. 10. Paul Hogan, Linda Kozlowski. 11. Glenn Close. 12. Ian Fleming. 13. Clint Eastwood. 14. 1935: Robert Donat; 1959: Kenneth More; 1978: Robert Powell. 15. *Cinderella*.

POPULAR MUSIC

1 In 1998 Jazzy Jeff and The Fresh Prince released a single called, 'Lovely Day'. By what name is, The Fresh Prince better known?

2 Which country did A-Ha come from?

3 What was the surname of Matt and Luke from Bros?

4 What is Blur's home town?

5 What was Blondie's first number 1 hit?

6 Who in the 1970's had top ten hits with, 'Billy Don't Be A Hero' and 'The Night Chicago Died'?

7 Which Peter was a founder member of Genesis?

8 'You Can't Hurry Love', was the first solo UK number 1 for which male singer and drummer?

9 In which movie did Madonna sing, 'Another Suitcase In Another Hall'?

10 Name Meatloaf's only UK Number 1?

11 Who sang the duet with Tina Turner, 'It Takes Two', which reached number 5 in Nov 1990?

12 In 1984 Prince starred in a semi-autobiographical film of what name?

13 Who had a top ten hit in Nov 1987 with 'Letter From America'?

14 Gladys Knight sang the theme song for which Bond film?

15 What links Derek And The Dominoes, The Yardbirds, Cream and Blind Faith?

LITERATURE

1 Who wrote *The Guns of Navarone?*

2 'The boy stood on the burning deck.' Where does this phrase originate?

3 Which of the following is not an author: Dickens, Molière, Goethe, Tchaikovsky?

4 Who created the fictional aristocratic detective 'Lord Peter Wimsey'?

5 *The Adventures of Huckleberry Finn* was written by whom?

6 Who wrote *The Informer?*

7 With which Arab ruler are the *Arabian Nights* much associated?

8 'If I should die, think only this of me:' is the beginning of a poem by whom?

9 Who wrote the book *Utopia* in 1516?

10 Who was Thomas Carlyle?

11 'Brevity is the soul of wit.' Where does this phrase originate?

12 What is a euphemism?

13 'Professor George Edward Challenger' appears as a character in which book by Arthur Conan Doyle?

14 'To lose one parent, Mr Worthing, may be regarded as a misfortune. To lose both looks like...' Can you finish the line?

15 Who spoke the above lines, in what play?

GENERAL KNOWLEDGE

1   What does circa or c. in connection with dates mean?

2   In ancient times, what were centaurs believed to be?

3   What is a brandysnap?

4   The Palladium in London is a variety theatre. Isn't this a Latin name?

5   What was meant by 'my old Dutch'?

6   Which word, beginning with post- means 'after dinner'?

7   Who in the world would be called a 'Limey'?

8   Who or what was Big Bertha?

9   What, applied to a person, is a 'ham'?

10 Which politician is known as 'Tarzan'?

11 Who painted the picture of a stag entitled 'Monarch of the Glen'?

12 What is an éclair?

13 The Scales represent which sign of the Zodiac?

14 Which anniversary does a cotton wedding celebrate?

15 What is an ambassador?

ANSWERS

1. About or around. 2. A race of beings half-horse, half-man. 3. A thin crisp biscuit flavoured with ginger and brandy. 4. Yes, but the original was a temple or image of the goddess Pallas. 5. A cockney expression, meaning 'my wife'. 6. Postprandial. 7. An Englishman. 8. A large gun trained on Paris during WW1. 9. An actor with more enthusiasm than ability. 10. Michael Heseltine. 11. Sir Edwin Landseer. 12. A long, light pastry with cream filling and chocolate sauce. 13. Libra. 14. The first. 15. A diplomatic envoy who represents his own head of state in a foreign country.

SCIENCE

1   The science and technology of nuclear studies is called what?

2   The study of minerals is called what?

3   How many fluid ounces are equivalent to one litre?

4   Glass is mainly composed of what?

5   What is the name given to the outer layer of skin?

6   Euclid, the Greek mathematician, is known as the father of what?

7   How long does it take light from the sun to reach the earth?

8   What everyday igniting device was invented by John Walker in 1827?

9   The first artificial dye was created in 1856 by Sir William Perkins. What colour was it?

10   How many moons does Uranus have: (a) 6, (b) 5 or (c) 4?

11   In 1926 Erik Rotheim made the first gas-propelled spray-can. It was the ancestor of what?

12   After he invented the electric battery in 1800, how did Count Alexander Volta's name become known?

13   In 1675 John Flamsteed became the first man in what job?

14   What are the four dimensions?

15   In litres, what is the capacity of the human lungs?

ANSWERS

1. Nucleonics. 2. Mineralogy. 3. 35.2. 4. Sand. 5. The epidermis. 6. Geometry. 7. About eight minutes. 8. The friction match. 9. Mauve. 10. Five. 11. The aerosol. 12. The electric measure of force, or volt, was named after him. 13. Astronomer Royal. 14. Width, depth, length and time. 15. Five litres.

NATURAL HISTORY

1   What does the word 'dinosaur' mean?

2   What is a freesia?

3   What is a tunny?

4   A coatimundi is a type of raccoon. True or false?

5   What's the name of a fox's home?

6   What kind of animal could be called a percheron?

7   What is cotoneaster?

8   What is cochineal?

9   What is a group of geese called?

10 What sort of animal is called an Aberdeen Angus?

11 What is an aspen?

12 What sort of fruit is the gean?

13 Which animal is the deadly enemy of snakes and rats?

14 Vanilla is a member of the orchid family. Yes or no?

15 Which elephant has the largest ears: African or Indian?

1. 'Huge' or 'terrible' lizard. 2. A plant of the Iris family, grown in South Africa. 3. Another name for a tuna fish. 4. True. 5. An earth. 6. A breed of horse. 7. A tree or shrub related to the hawthorn. 8. A red dyestuff made from the pulverised bodies of the Coccus insect. 9. A gaggle. 10. A breed of cattle. 11. A forest tree, also known as the trembling poplar. 12. The wild cherry. 13. The mongoose. 14. Yes. 15. African.

GEOGRAPHY

1   Where is the Statue of Liberty?

2   Where and what is Stromboli?

3   Which is the world's largest church?

4   Where is the Great Barrier Reef?

5   Where would you find the Kremlin?

6   What is the highest point in Australia?

7   Where in the world do they speak Catalan?

8   Where is Transylvania?

9   'Eesti' refers to which country?

10 Anvers is another name for which Belgian city?

11 What was previously known as Angora?

12 Which is Britain's largest lake?

13 What, in England, was Ermine Street?

14 The shamrock is the national symbol of which country?

15 Which city is on the Tiber?

ANSWERS

1. On Liberty Island, New York Harbour, USA. 2. An active volcano in Italy. 3. St Peter's, Rome. 4. Off the coast of Queensland, Australia. 5. Moscow, Russia. 6. Mount Kosciusko, 7,308ft. 7. In Catalonia, Spain. 8. Romania. 9. Estonia. 10. Antwerp. 11. Ankara, Turkey. 12. Loch Lomond, Scotland. 13. A Roman road, stretching from Beachy Head to York. 14. Ireland. 15. Rome.

ENGLISH LANGUAGE

1 Why is our 'funnybone' so called?

2 What is an 'ocker'?

3 What is the name for someone who studies coins and medals?

4 To what living thing did Leonard Fuchs, the German botanist, give his name?

5 What is a 'drongo', and how did the term originate?

6 What do we mean by the expression 'to play gooseberry'?

7 'Draw, O Caesar, erase a coward.' What is unusual about this sentence?

8 To what kind of dog did Spain give its name?

9 Which word can mean beautiful or a market?

10 A doxy is: (a) a kind of flower, (b) a breed of dog or (c) a woman of low character?

11 What is the difference between 'allusion' and 'illusion'?

12 If you were totally lumbered, what would have happened?

13 In cockney rhyming slang, what does 'daisy roots' mean?

14 What is 'to essay' an ancient way of saying?

15 Is a doge: (a) a Venetian magistrate (b) a French breed of poodle (c) a kind of judo?

1. Its correct name is the humerus. 2. An Australian know-it-all. 3. Numismatist. 4. The fuchsia plant. 5. Australian slang for a persistent failure, named after a racehorse of a similar nature. 6. To be an unwelcome third person when two people want to be alone. 7. It's a palindrome. It reads the same, letter for letter, backwards and forwards. 8. The spaniel. 9. Fair. 10. (c) a woman of low character. 11. An 'allusion' is a suggestion or reference to something; an 'illusion' is a false impression. 12. You would have been completely put upon, or taken advantage of. 13. Boots. 14. To attempt or try. 15. (a) a Venetian magistrate.

SPORT

1. If I was sitting on the 'Strip', watching the 'Christmas Tree' and revving my 'Rail', what sport would I be taking part in?

2. Which football team play at Maine Road?

3. Who captained Essex County Cricket team during the 1994 season?

4. In American Football how many points are awarded for a 'Safety'?

5. What are the three disciplines in a Triathlon?

6. If Stoke City were playing a home derby match, who would they be playing?

7. Who won the 1994 women's Rugby World Cup?

8. In which month is the Kentucky Derby run?

9. Who provided the engines for the 1998 McLaren Formula One team?

10. What do the initials MCC stand for?

11. How wide is a discus throwing circle: 2.5m, 2.7m or 3.1m?

12. Which sport was the subject of the Popplewell Report in 1985?

13. What do the initials BBBC stand for?

14. In 1990 the horse Mr Frisk set a record time in which major race?

15. In which major sporting championship does the winner receive a, 'Green Jacket?

HISTORY

1 What did Britain buy 176,602 shares of on 25th October, 1875?

2 31 people lost their lives in a fire at which London underground station in November 1987?

3 What famous mutiny, aboard which ship, took place off Tonga on 28th April, 1789?

ERM... CHARGE?

4 What headgear for men came into general use in about 1884?

5 Who was Warren Harding?

6 Which is the oldest royal residence in Britain?

7 At the Battle of Ashdown, in A.D. 871, the Danes were defeated by forces under which famous king?

8 Who was the last English monarch to lead his troops in battle?

9 Who was Woodrow Wilson?

10 Which former general became President of the French Fifth Republic in 1959?

11 Who was Madame de Pompadour?

12 What did the Boers in South Africa begin in December, 1835?

13 Who was the last monarch of Germany?

14 Who discovered the Pacific Ocean?

15 Who was the last monarch of Portugal?

568

1. Shares in the Suez Canal. 2. Kings Cross. 3. The Bounty. 4. The straw boater. 5. He was 29th American president. 6. Windsor Castle. 7. King Alfred. 8. King George II at Dettingen in 1743. 9. He was the 28th American president. 10. Charles de Gaulle. 11. The mistress of King Louis XV of France. 12. The 'Great Trek' northward from Cape Colony. 13. Wilhelm II (1888-1918). 14. Francisco Pizarro in 1513. 15. Manoel II.

CINEMA AND TV

1 Mark Hamill played which character in the film *Star Wars?*

2 Tom Cruise starred in a film based on a John Grisham novel. What was the film?

3 This cute alien was desperate to 'phone home'. What was his name?

4 Who starred in the film *Annie Hall?*

5 Who starred in the film *Hobson's Choice?*

6 Who starred in the film *Duck Soup?*

7 What is unusual about the 1995 film *Toy Story?*

8 From which film and stage show did the song 'Consider Yourself' come?

9 Who starred in the film *The Day of the Triffids?*

10 Who starred in the film *Passport to Pimlico?*

11 Who starred in the original film *To Be or Not to Be?*

12 Which movie star's real name was Frances Gumm?

13 How did the Marx Brothers acquire their names?

14 For which film did Oliver Stone win a best director Oscar in 1986?

15 From which film and stage show did the song 'Diamonds Are a Girl's Best Friend' come?

1. Luke Skywalker. 2. *The Firm.* 3. E.T. The Extra-Terrestrial. 4. Woody Allen and Diane Keaton. 5. Charles Laughton, Brenda de Banzie, John Mills. 6. The four Marx brothers. 7. It is entirely computed-generated. 8. *Oliver!* 9. Howard Keel. 10. Stanley Holloway, Margaret Rutherford. 11. Jack Benny. 12. Judy Garland. 13. They were taken from a comic strip called 'Mager's Monks'. 14. *Platoon.* 15. *Gentlemen Prefer Blondes.*

POPULAR MUSIC

1   Which band recorded the albums 'In Utero' and 'Nevermind'?

2   Who recorded the Album, 'No Jacket Required'?

3   What was the first UK top ten hit for Elton John?

4   Who is the only Conservative Prime Minister to have a UK top ten hit?

5   Hawkwind have only had one top ten hit, name it?

6   Which British artist has had the highest total of weeks on the UK chart?

7   Which non-British or American act has totalled the highest number of weeks on the UK chart?

8   In Sept 1996 the Cardigans reached number 21 with, 'Lovefool'. From what album did the track come?

9   In September 1996, Mariah Carey reached number 3 with, 'Endless Love'. Which male soul singer dueted with her on this track?

10 Which band have a lead singer called Cerys and recorded the album, 'International Velvet'?

11 What nationality were Boney M?

12 Who recorded the albums, 'Meddle and 'Wish You Were Here'?

13 In December 1993 Chaka Demus and Pliers had a number one hit with, 'Twist And Shout', who recorded the original?

14 Which American southern boogie band had hits with 'Sweet Home Alabama' and 'Freebird'?

15 Midge Ure was formerly vocalist with which 80's New Romantic band?

LITERATURE

1 The character 'Porthos' appears in which famous book?

2 Complete the proverb: 'The devil take...'

3 What sort of creatures were (a) Babar, (b) Tarka and (c) Orlando?

4 'The buck stops here'. Where does this phrase originate?

5 Who wrote *South Riding?*

6 Who created the fictional character 'The Baron', also called 'John Mannering'?

7 Who wrote *Ivanhoe?*

8 Who wrote *The Diary of a Nobody?*

9 By what name was children's author Charles Lutwidge Dodgson better known?

10 In which novel by one of the Brontë sisters does 'Cathy Earnshaw' appear?

11 Complete the proverb: 'Cast not your pearls...'

12 Who wrote *Rebecca?*

13 Who created the character 'Harry Palmer', although he is never named in the books about him?

14 Complete this line by Shakespeare: 'Friends, Romans, countrymen...'

15 Complete the proverb: 'The course of true love...'

1 *The Three Musketeers*. 2. '...the hindmost'. 3. (a) an elephant (b) an otter (c) a cat. 4. From a notice on the desk of President Truman. 5. Winifred Holtby. 6. John Creasey as 'Anthony Morton'. 7. Sir Walter Scott. 8. George Grossmith. 9. Lewis Carroll. 10. *Wuthering Heights*. 11. '...before swine'. 12. Daphne du Maurier. 13. Len Deighton. The name was only used in the films. 14. '...lend me your ears'. 15. '...never did run smooth'.

GENERAL KNOWLEDGE

1 Who is the patron saint of travellers?

2 Who, or what, is 'Ernie'?

3 What is cannelloni?

4 What is a bisque?

5 What is haggis?

6 Who painted landscapes of the Suffolk countryside?

7 Which anniversary does a lace wedding celebrate?

8 What is a bruxelloise?

9 Moses was the leader of which nation?

10 What does the name of the city Philadelphia mean?

11 What is meant by 'Dutch gold'?

12 What is consommé?

13 What kind of food item comes from Worcester?

14 What is the name of the young girl who plays a leading part in Peter Pan?

15 How does the Archbishop of York sign himself?

ANSWERS

1. St Christopher. 2. The Electronic Random Number Indicator Equipment for drawing Premium Bonds. 3. Thin rolls of pasta stuffed with meat or vegetables. 4. A creamy soup. 5. A Scottish dish made with the heart, lungs and liver of a sheep or calf. 6. John Constable. 7. The thirteenth. 8. A French sauce for asparagus. 9. Israel. 10. City of brotherly love. 11. An alloy of copper and zinc. 12. Clear meat soup. 13. Sauce. 14. Wendy. 15. His Christian name followed by Ebor.

SCIENCE

1   How fast is the earth orbiting the sun?

2   Cartography is the science of what?

3   What did Alberto Santos-Dumont build and operate in 1898?

4   What happens to phosphorus on contact with the air?

5   The scientific study of seas and oceans is called what?

6   What kind of animals would a lepidopterist study?

7   A dodecagon has how many sides?

8   Pneumonia is a disease which affects which part of your body?

9   What does a microscope do?

10 Richard Trevithick built a coach driven by what sort of power in 1801?

11 The Dead Sea contains about (a) 25% (b) 40% (c) 12% salts?

12 The science of the study of the body and its parts is called what?

13 Which is the largest tree in the world?

14 What is the colour of chlorophyll?

15 How much of an iceberg is below the surface: 25%, 45% or 85%?

1. 66,700 miles per hour. 2. Maps and map-making. 3. A cylindrical balloon with a gasoline engine. 4. It bursts into flame. 5. Oceanography. 6. Butterflies and moths. 7. Twelve. 8. Lungs. 9. Magnifies small objects. 10. Steam. 11. 25%. 12. Anatomy. 13. A sequoia in California is 275 feet tall and has a girth of 103 feet. 14. Green. 15. 85%.

NATURAL HISTORY

1   Cinnamon is a member of the laurel family. Yes or no?

2   A giant panda is a bear-like creature which feeds almost entirely on what?

3   What kind of animal is said to coo?

4   A fritillary is (a) a butterfly, (b) a kind of lily?

5   The evergreen shrub Camellia is a relative of the tea plant. True or false?

6   What is an asp?

7   What is a jackdaw?

8   A mandrill is a member of which animal family?

9   What sort of animal is called a Charolais?

10   What is the name given to a fox's tail?

11   What is the record life-span of the domestic cat: (a) 28 years, (b) 36 years or (c) 40 years.

12   Grampus is a name given to a sea mammal usually called what?

13   The elder is a member of the honeysuckle family. Yes or no?

14   An egret is (a) a kind of heron, (b) the name for a young eagle.

15   Bamboo is a kind of grass. Yes or no?

ANSWERS

1. Yes. 2. Bamboo shoots. 3. A dove. 4. Both are true! 5. True. 6. It's a general term for a venomous snake. 7. A species of crow. 8. Baboons. 9. A breed of cattle. 10. A brush. 11. 36 years. 12. A whale or a dolphin. 13. Yes. 14. It's a kind of heron. 15. Yes.

GEOGRAPHY

1   Who was the first sovereign to live at Buckingham Palace?

2   Where is the Vale of the White Horse?

3   Why is the Vale of the White Horse so called?

4   In which city is the Doge's Palace?

5   What country was the republic of Slovakia formerly part of?

6   What is the Pennine Chain?

7   Which city is on the River Orwell?

8   Byzantium is an ancient name for which city?

9   Where are the Scilly Isles?

10 The Cenotaph stands in Whitehall in London. What does 'cenotaph' mean?

11 In which city would you find Paddington railway station?

12 Where is the Golden Temple?

13 Which cathedral has the world's tallest spire?

14 Where in the world would you find the people called Lapps?

15 On which stretch of water does the Swiss city of Lausanne stand?

ANSWERS

1. Queen Victoria. 2. A valley in Oxfordshire. 3. Because it carries the image of a white horse where the turf is cut away to reveal the chalk beneath. 4. Venice. 5. Czechoslovakia. 6. A mountain range in the Midlands and North of England. 7. Ipswich. 8. Istanbul. 9. Off Land's End, Cornwall. 10. An empty tomb. 11. London. 12. Amritsar, India. 13. Ulm Cathedral, Germany. 14. In Lapland, which is spread across Norway, Sweden and Finland. 15. Lake Geneva.

ENGLISH LANGUAGE

1 'Verily' was an old way of saying what?

2 What slang term would an American use to describe a pimple?

3 Why are British policemen sometimes called 'bobbies'?

4 What does an American call a clothes-peg?

5 What is odd about the names 'sea-lion' and 'sea-horse'?

6 If you were 'in the doghouse', what would it mean?

7 What is unusual about the sentence 'King, are you glad you are king'?

8 What is the difference between 'bizarre' and 'bazaar'?

9 What is the difference between 'averse' and 'adverse'?

10 A baby's nappy is called what in the US?

11 What, in earlier times, was an 'argosy'?

12 What would a lorry in the United States be called?

13 What exactly is a 'glutton'?

14 Which word, starting with P, means ardent or zealous?

15 Which word means both 'a cash register' and 'to cultivate land'.

SPORT

1 Which county cricket team has its home at Old Trafford?

2 In 1994, which country hosted the Winter Olympics?

3 By which name is Rugby Union's William Henry Hare better known?

4 If I were to 'Serve, Dig, Spike or Set', what sport would I be playing?

5 In equestrianism, which rider with the first name Nick, won the World Cup in 1995?

6 Alison Fisher is one of the leading female exponents of which sport?

7 In which country did Pele finish his professional playing career?

8 What does 'PB' against a runner's time indicate?

9 Who, before Lynford Christie, last won an Olympic 100m gold medal for Britain?

10 What was ex-England hooker Brian Moore's occupation when not on the Rugby pitch?

11 What is the highest possible 'Out' shot in darts?

12 Name the home city for 'The 49ers', American Football team.

13 How many players are there in a Gaelic Football team?

14 How old was Brian Clough when he finished his playing career; 29, 31, 34 or 38?

15 Where is the Leander Rowing Club based?

1. Lancashire. 2. Norway. 3. Dusty. 4. Volleyball. 5. Nick Skelton. 6. Snooker. 7. USA. 8. Personal Best. 9. Alan Wells. 10. Solicitor. 11. 170. 12. San Francisco. 13. 15. 14. 29. 15. Henley-on-Thames.

HISTORY

1 Following an earthquake in London in 1580, how many people died? (a) none (b) 2 (c) 43.

2 In March, 1938, what was renamed 'Ostmark' as part of the German Reich?

3 Who was Benjamin Harrison?

4 Who was the last monarch of Italy?

5 Which French prime minister was reputed to have slept fully clothed?

6 Where and what was Northumbria?

7 The People's Palace was opened by Queen Victoria in 1887. Where was it?

8 What was the Weimar Republic?

9 What happened in August, 1914, so starting World War I?

10 Bosnia and Herzegovina was annexed by which country in 1908?

11 What body of men did Louis-Philippe of France found in North Africa in 1831?

12 When did the Channel Islands become part of England?

13 Which British monarch was bigamously married?

14 Of whom or what was St Pancras the patron saint?

15 The first issue of the Daily News newspaper appeared on 21st January, 1846. Who was the editor?

CINEMA AND TV

1 Who starred in the film *Independence Day?*

2 What films featured ewoks, droids and the Millenium Falcon spaceship?

3 Who's debut feature as a director was the film *Duel?*

4 Who starred in the film *Richard III?*

5 Who starred in the film *It's a Wonderful Life?*

6 Who starred in the film *Jaws?*

7 Which is the newest BBC radio station?

8 Three films with the words 'Shanghai', 'Rome', 'Orient' in their titles, all end with the same word. What is the word?

9 George Lansbury, a former leader of the Labour Party, had a film-actress granddaughter. Who is she?

10 Stepin Fetchit took his name from a racehorse. What was his real name?

11 Which T.V. sci-fi series featured characters including Villa, Servalan and ORAC?

12 Which controversial late night show was hosted by Terry Christian?

13 Who starred in the film *Chinatown?*

14 Which Oscar-winning actress is now a Labour M.P.?

15 Which sports commentator was replaced by Sue Barker as host of *A Question Of Sport?*

ANSWERS

1. Will Smith, Bill Pullman, Jeff Goldblum, Mary McDonnell. 2. *Star Wars.* 3. Steven Spielberg. 4. Sir Ian McKellen. 5. James Stewart, Donna Reed, Lionel Barrymore. 6. Roy Scheider, Robert Shaw, Richard Dreyfuss. 7. Radio Five. 8. Express. 9. Angela Lansbury. 10. Lincoln Theodore Monroe Andrew Perry. 11. *Blake's Seven.* 12. *The Word.* 13. Jack Nicholson, Faye Dunaway. 14. Glenda Jackson. 15. David Coleman.

POPULAR MUSIC

1 In March 1980, The Jam entered the chart at number one with which song?

2 Which member of Take That, left the band to pursue a solo career in July 1995?

3 'You're The One That I Want', and 'Summer Nights' were singles taken from which 1978 movie?

4 'With A Little Help From My friends', has been taken to number one by two different acts, name them?

5 Which group recorded the albums, 'A Day At The Races' and, 'A Night At The Opera'?

6 Who recorded the albums, 'Hergest Ridge' and 'Tubular Bells'?

7 What nationality is Bryan Adams?

8 Which group recorded the album, 'Carry On Up the Charts'?

9 Which group produced their 'Greatest Hits' before their 'Arrival' album?

10 Who were the voices behind, Derek and Clive?

11 What was Take That's, final single?

12 Which Beatle became a Travelling Wilbury?

13 Which brothers featured heavily on the soundtrack to the film, 'Saturday Night Fever'?

14 'Whisky In The Jar', was the first UK top ten hit for which Irish band?

15 Which 50's & 60's singing star, father of Kim, had hits with, 'A Teenager In Love', 'Sea Of Love', and 'Rubber Ball'?

LITERATURE

1 'Sir Percy Blakeney' appears in which famous book?

2 Who wrote *The Forsythe Saga?*

3 'The child is father of the man.' Where does this phrase originate?

4 Complete the proverb: 'Beauty is in...'

5 Which playwright, a contemporary of Shakespeare, was killed in a pub brawl?

6 Who wrote *The Woman in White?*

7 Who, according to the opening line of the book, was born in 1632 in York?

8 'David Balfour' appears in which book by R.L. Stevenson?

9 'Captain Ahab' appears in which adventure story by Herman Melville?

10 Who created the female James Bond 'Modesty Blaise'?

11 Who wrote *Puck of Pook's Hill?*

12 Of which well-known book was Boris Pasternak the author?

13 'Holden Caulfield' is a character in which book by J.D. Salinger?

14 What line follows, 'Ye mariners of England'?

15 Who was the Bard of Avon?

1. *The Scarlet Pimpernel.* 2. John Galsworthy. 3. *My Heart Leaps Up.* William Wordsworth. 4. '...the eye of the beholder'. 5. Christopher Marlowe. 6. Wilkie Collins. 7. *Robinson Crusoe.* 8. *Kidnapped.* 9. *Moby Dick.* 10. Peter O'Donnell. 11. Rudyard Kipling. 12. *Dr Zhivago.* 13. *The Catcher in the Rye.* 14. 'That guard our native seas'. 15. William Shakespeare.

GENERAL KNOWLEDGE

1   What are 'angels on horseback'?

2   Who was Sir Frank Brangwyn?

3   What is the name given to the male reproductive organ of a plant?

4   What had Shakespeare and George Washington in common?

5   What is a flapjack?

6   St Dunstan is the patron saint of whom?

7   A jeroboam is a measure of wine equivalent to how many bottles?

8   What is colcannon?

9   Who is the patron saint of Norway?

10 What are profiteroles?

11 In a pack of cards, which way does the Queen of Clubs look: to her left, or to her right?

12 Who is the reigning monarch of Japan?

13 Eros is another name for Cupid. True or false?

14 Rule by the people as a whole is called what?

15 What is a 'Scotch woodcock'?

SCIENCE

1   Where on the body would you find your occiput?

2   If your doctor told you that you had coryza, what would you be suffering from?

3   What would you use a drosometer to measure?

4   What, in ancient times, was the Philosophers' Stone?

5   What did the Russian Venera 9 space probe do?

6   What does an ammeter measure?

7   The scapula is another name for which bone?

8   What poison was used to kill the Ancient Greek thinker Socrates?

9   What colour is a topaz?

10   What does a theodolite measure?

11   Pewter is an alloy of which two metals?

12   Corundum is a mineral which produces which precious stones?

13   What colour is the stone called lapis lazuli?

14   Who was Louis Brennan?

15   A better name for frozen dew is what?

583

ANSWERS

1. The back of your head. 2. The common cold. 3. Dew. 4. A mythical stone fabled to have the power of turning base metal into gold. 5. Orbited Venus. 6. Electric current. 7. The shoulder-blade. 8. Hemlock. 9. Yellowish or bluish, although it is sometimes without colour. 10. Angles. It is used by surveyors. 11. Tin and lead. 12. Sapphires and rubies. 13. Blue with veins of gold. 14. Inventor of the monorail. 15. Frost.

NATURAL HISTORY

1   How do we get cocoa?

2   A group of crows is called: (a) a crowd (b) a murder.

3   What is a capercailzie?

4   What was a quagga?

5   What is a custard-apple?

6   What is a hazel-nut?

7   Where would you find a Red Admiral; (a) at sea (b) on a flagpole (c) in your garden?

8   Where did the cucumber originate?

9   What is an aloe?

10   What sort of animal is an ounce?

11   Freshwater eels are all born in one place. Where?

12   What is an anaconda?

13   What's the record life-span of the domestic dog: (a) 28 years, (b) 30 years or (c) 32 years?

14   Which, of all the mammals, produces the largest baby?

15   What kind of animal could be described as a Hampshire?

ANSWERS

1. It's the seed of the cacao tree, ground and powdered. 2. A murder.
3. It's a large type of grouse. 4. An extinct type of zebra. 5. A fruit with soft flesh grown in the West Indies and America. 6. The fruit of the hazel-nut bush or tree.
7. (c) In your garden. 8. Southern Asia. 9. A plant which produces a bitter-tasting substance used in medicine. 10. A snow leopard. 11. The Sargasso Sea in the Atlantic. 12. A large South American snake. 13. 28 years. 14. The blue whale.
15. A breed of sheep.

GEOGRAPHY

1 Which is the world's smallest continent?

2 Where is the original Waterloo?

3 Hokkaido is an island, part of which country?

4 What is the capital of Jordan?

5 What is the West African country, Upper Volta, now known as?

6 On which stretch of water does Geneva stand?

7 In what country are the ruined remains of the ancient city of Troy?

8 Where in the world would you find a Maori?

9 What do the Parisians call their underground railway system?

10 Heligoland once belonged to Britain and formerly to Denmark. To which country does it belong now?

11 In which city would you be likely to find a gondola?

12 Which is the highest mountain peak in England?

13 The leek is a national symbol of which country?

14 The Belgian Congo is a country now called what?

15 What was the DDR?

ANSWERS

1. Australasia. 2. In Belgium, the site of a famous victory in battle by Wellington. 3. Japan. 4. Amman. 5. Burkina Faso (meaning 'the land of upright men'). 6. Lake Geneva. 7. Turkey. 8. New Zealand. 9. The Metro, or Le Métropolitain. 10. Germany. 11. Venice. 12. Scafell Pike, Cumbria. 13. Wales. 14. Zaire. 15. The German Democratic Republic or East Germany.

ENGLISH LANGUAGE

1 What does 're-invent the wheel' mean?

2 What word, beginning with F, means copy or replica?

3 If you 'nail your colours to the mast', what does it mean?

4 Can you name two words, sounding alike, which mean the same as these phrases: grain used for food/instalment story?

5 What is a hustler, in its American sense?

6 What does the Yiddish word 'schlock' mean?

7 What weapon was named after the French town of Bayonne?

8 If you suffered from phobophobia, what would you fear?

9 What do Americans call a 'drawing pin'?

10 What is the name for words which have the same (or similar) meanings, like brief/short, difficult/hard and sly/cunning?

11 If you spent your free time doing the same thing as if you were working, what would people say you were doing?

12 Why is a 'mantelpiece' so called?

13 What is a 'pastiche'?

14 What is the male version of a 'heroine'?

15 Can you name two words, sounding similar, which mean the same as this pair: wildebeest/original.

SPORT

1 Which football club is generally accepted as the oldest in England?

2 Peter Shilton played his 1000th league game with which club?

3 Kendo is the ancient Japanese art of what?

4 A cricket umpire holds both arms straight up above his head to indicate what?

5 How often is the US Masters golf tournament held?

6 Which county did former England cricket captain Tony Greig also lead?

7 By joining, which country will turn the Five Nations Rugby Union tournament into the 'Six Nations'?

8 For what feat will the gymnast Nadia Comaneci always be remembered?

9 What is the name of New Orleans American football team?

10 In the Tour de France what does the green jersey signify?

11 In Golf, what is the term for one under par at a hole?

12 What sport do the Scottish Claymores play?

13 If you were at Goodison Park or Anfield which city would you be in?

14 Who won the 1998 Rugby Union Women's World Cup?

15 For which Italian side did 'Gazza', play?

ANSWERS

1. Notts County. 2. Leyton Orient. 3. Sword fighting. 4. Six runs. 5. Every year. 6. Sussex. 7. Italy. 8. The first perfect 10 score in a major competition. 9. The Saints. 10. Points Leader. 11. Birdie. 12. American Football. 13. Liverpool. 14. New Zealand. 15. Lazio.

HISTORY

1 Francisco Pizarro, the Spanish conqueror, overcame which people, and where, in 1533?

2 What century-long event ended after the English were defeated at Castillon in 1453?

3 Who was Richard Cobden?

4 In October, 1822, Dom Pedro became Emperor of which South American country?

5 If a country was ruled entirely by its nobility, it would be called what?

6 In Birkenhead the first of a system of transport was started in August 1860. What was it?

7 What is the surname of the Queen?

8 Which bridge was opened on 4th September 1964?

9 Who, in the 15th century, was Lambert Simnel?

10 Which venerable figure, a philosopher and member of the Order of Merit, was imprisoned in 1961?

11 What were the Pre-Raphaelites?

12 Who were the Brylcream Boys?

13 Which English monarch was never crowned?

14 On 14th January, in both 1205 and 1814, what were held on the river Thames?

15 In which city in 1921 did a mutiny take place on a Russian battleship?

CINEMA AND TV

1 What was film star Herbie?

2 Who is the actor-nephew of the film director Sir Carol Reed?

3 Who starred in the film *Dances With Wolves?*

4 How many musical items were included in the film *Fantasia?*

5 Which T.V. sitcom features characters called Ross, Chandler and Phoebe?

6 Which rock band provided soundtrack music for the film *Flash Gordon?*

7 Who starred in the film *The Sting?*

8 Who starred in the 1993 film *The Fugitive?*

9 What happened to the 1942 movie *Yankee Doodle Dandy* in 1985?

10 Which movie star's real name was Roy Scherer?

11 Whose sister Jeanne appeared with him in the film *Yankee Doodle Dandy?*

12 What was unusual about the 1932 Czech film *Extase?*

13 Who starred in the film *The Hospital?*

14 In *Murder on the Orient Express,* who played the role of Hercule Poirot?

15 Which B-movie featured salad vegetables intent on murder?

ANSWERS

1. A VW Beetle car. 2. Oliver Reed. 3. Kevin Costner, Mary McDonnell. 4. Eight. 5. *Friends.* 6. Queen. 7. Paul Newman, Robert Redford. 8. Harrison Ford. 9. It was computer-converted to full colour. 10. Rock Hudson. 11. James Cagney's. 12. It featured actress Hedy Lamarr in the nude. 13. George C. Scott, Diana Rigg. 14. Albert Finney. 15. *Attack Of The Killer Tomatoes.*

POPULAR MUSIC

1. St Winifred's School Choir reached number one in 1980 with which song?

2. 'Golden Brown' was a hit for which band?

3. What did Italian model Sabrina, sing about in 1988?

4. With which movie theme did the Central Band of the Royal Air Force reach number 18 in 1955?

5. What was the Rolling Stones' first UK number one?

6. 'Lucille' and 'Coward of the County', were number one hits for which Country and Western singer?

7. Don Mclean's 'American Pie', was his only UK number one. True or false?

8. What nationality is Manfred Mann?

9. Barry Manilow has only had one UK top ten hit. True or false?

10. Which TV Rat had a hit in 1984, with, 'Love Me Tender'?

11. Under what name did Manfred Mann release singles after 1973?

12. Who had hits in the late 1960's with, 'Californian Dreamin'', 'Monday, Monday' and 'Dedicated To The One I Love'?

13. Where is Doors singer Jim Morrison buried?

14. Who had a number 4 hit with 'I Love Rock 'n' Roll' in April 1982?

15. Was Jethro Tull a singer or a band?

LITERATURE

1 Who was Omar Khayyam?

2 Whose biographical book was *The Moon's a Balloon?*

3 Who wrote *Lost Horizon?*

4 What, according to Tennyson, are more than coronets?

5 Who is 'hero' in Shakespeare's play *Much Ado About Nothing?*

6 R. Austin Freeman's books featured the world's premier scientific detective. What was his name?

7 In which novel by W. Somerset Maugham does the character 'William Carey' appear?

8 Who said, on arriving at New York Customs: 'I have nothing to declare but my genius'?

9 Lovelace wrote: 'I could not love thee, dear, so much...' What follows?

10 Who wrote *The African Queen?*

11 'Day breaks on England down the Kentish hills', is the beginning of a poem by whom?

12 'The course of true love never did run smooth'. Where does this phrase originate?

13 How does Cleopatra kill herself in *Antony and Cleopatra?*

14 Who wrote Lady Chatterley's Lover?

15 Which novels use the French Revolution as a background?

ANSWERS

1. A Persian poet and mathematician. 2. David Niven's. 3. James Hilton. 4. Kind hearts. 5. Hero, who is a female character! 6. Dr Thorndyke. 7. *Of Human Bondage.* 8. Oscar Wilde. 9. 'Lov'd I not honour more.' 10. C.S. Forrester. 11. James Elroy Flecker. 12. Shakespeare's *A Midsummer Night's Dream.* 13. By snake-bite. She places an asp to her bosom. 14. D.H. Lawrence. 15. Dickens's *A Tale of Two Cities,* Orczy's *The Scarlet Pimpernel.*

GENERAL KNOWLEDGE

1. If something is served à la maître d'hôtel, how is it prepared?

2. Osiris was a god of ancient Egypt. What was his domain?

3. What is pesto?

4. What is a sassenach?

5. What is a doughnut?

6. Which French liqueur has a strong anise taste?

7. Which anniversary does a china wedding celebrate?

8. Who was the Beast of Bolsover?

9. Who was Edith Cavell?

10. Who, in a music-hall song, went to Crewe in mistake for Birmingham?

11. From which musical play did the song 'Some Day My Heart Will Awake' come?

12. What is saltimbocca?

13. Which British stamps were the first to be perforated?

14. Who was the Boston Strangler?

15. 'Shear you sheep in May....' (what's the next line in the verse?)

SCIENCE

1 Who has been called 'the Father of Chemistry'?

2 A drug which makes a patient insensitive to pain, touch or temperature is called a what?

3 Which famous American bridge was designed by John Roebling but completed by his son in 1886?

4 When iron oxidises, what is formed?

5 What system has replaced the carburettor in many modern cars?

6 What is a more familiar word for the umbilicus?

7 What is opsomania?

8 What is xenophobia?

9 What happens to your eyes if you sneeze?

10 For what do we use our olfactory sense?

11 What is measured by an ampère?

12 What is speleology?

13 What was the Caravelle, and where did it come from?

14 Who invented the photocopier (xerography) in 1948?

15 In London, the station 2LO began what in 1922?

NATURAL HISTORY

1 Apes have one special difference from monkeys. What is it?

2 What kind of animal is said to meow?

3 Where did the pomegranate originate?

4 What domestic animal could be described as a Burmese?

5 What was remarkable about the skeleton of Piltdown Man, found in Sussex?

6 The antlers of young deer are covered in what?

7 What is a tapir?

8 If a bee stings you, how will it affect the bee?

9 A freshwater lobster is called what?

10 What sort of animal is an ocelot?

11 What, on a horse, is a hock?

12 Animals which suckle their young are called what?

13 Has an earwig anything to do with ears?

14 What is a group of budgerigars called?

15 What is yarrow or milfoil?

1. Apes have no tails. 2. A cat. 3. Persia. 4. A cat. 5. It was a fake. 6. Velvet. 7. A smallish creature with a flexible nose. 8. The bee loses its sting, and dies. 9. A crayfish. 10. A wild American cat like a small leopard. 11. The ankle. 12. Mammals. 13. Nothing whatsoever. 14. A chatter. 15. A perennial meadow plant with very small, daisy-like flowers arranged in clusters.

GEOGRAPHY

1 Which is the largest county in England?

2 What is peculiar about the door of No. 10 Downing Street?

3 Where and what is Fontainebleau?

4 What is the French-speaking principality on the Mediterranean Sea called?

5 What is a native of Monaco called?

6 Prehistoric remains abound in the Eildon Hills in Britain. Where are these hills?

7 Which city is on the River Amstel?

8 Where and what is the Matterhorn?

9 On which river does Lisbon stand?

10 What would you find at West Point in the USA?

11 What is the capital of Ethiopia?

12 The Suez Canal is named after the town of Suez, but what lies at the other end?

13 Where in the world would you find a Liverpudlian?

14 What would you expect to find in Wall Street, New York?

15 To which country does Réunion belong?

1. North Yorkshire. 2. It cannot be opened from the outside. 3. A chateau not far from Paris, used as the summer residence for the French President. 4. Monaco. 5. A Monegasque. 6. Roxburgh, Scotland. 7. Amsterdam. 8. A famous mountain in Italy and Switzerland. 9. The Tagus. 10. The US Military Academy. 11. Addis Ababa. 12. Port Said. 13. In Liverpool. 14. Offices of financiers, brokers and bankers. 15. France.

ENGLISH LANGUAGE

1 Name two words, sounding alike, which mean the same as this pair: atmosphere/one who inherits.

2 It'll be alright on the night. What's wrong with this sentence?

3 Pagoda is a Chinese word for an Eastern temple. True or false?

4 What does dependent mean?

5 What does dependant mean?

6 Finish the proverb: 'Advice most needed is...'

7 Which word beginning with B can mean frontier or border?

8 Why were milliners so called?

9 What is the meaning of 'opulent'?

10 What is the plural of 'talisman'?

11 What is a female 'peacock' called?

12 A yegg is: (a) an American safe-breaker, (b) a young Scottish calf or (c) a kind of hiccup?

13 'Blackamoor' was an old way of saying what?

14 What would it mean if you 'got a flea in your ear'?

15 How was the word ouija (for a ouija board) derived?

SPORT

1   What was American footballer William Perry's nickname?

2   David Bedford is associated with which sport?

3   Where was the 1986 Football World Cup held?

4   What is the nickname of Wigan's Rugby League team?

5   Whilst playing which sport did Prince Charles break his arm?

6   Which Pam was Martina Navratilova's doubles partner?

7   What sport do the Boston Red Socks play?

8   Who was the first person to have been in charge of both England and Australia's football teams?

9   Which city hosted the 1972 Olympic Games?

10 Who was the first overseas manager to win the FA Cup?

11 Bob Nudd was World Champion at which sport?

12 Who was the first man to win the Embassy World Snooker Championship twice?

13 What was Mohammed Ali's original name?

14 Mick the Miller was a champion at which sport?

15 Which controversial British athlete reputedly tripped Mary Decker in the 1984 Olympics?

597

1. The Fridge. 2. Athletics. 3. Mexico. 4. Warriors. 5. Polo. 6. Shriver. 7. Baseball. 8. Terry Venables. 9. Munich. 10. Ruud Gullit. 11. Angling. 12. Steve Davis. 13. Cassius Clay. 14. Greyhound Racing. 15. Zola Budd.

HISTORY

1 Parliament passed the Stamp Act in 1765 to tax which group of people?

2 Who was Dwight David Eisenhower?

3 Who was Jomo Kenyatta?

4 Who or what were the Fenians?

5 What, politically, do Americans run for and Britons stand for?

6 Who was the first English king able to sign his name?

7 What were the Nuremberg Laws?

8 Where and what was Mercia?

9 Richard II was the first English king to do what, in 1399?

10 What document, drafted by Thomas Jefferson, was carried by the American Congress on 4th July, 1776?

11 Who wrote The Decline and Fall of the Roman Empire?

12 Which country in the Himalayas was conquered by the Gurkhas in 1768?

13 What was the Berlin Wall?

14 What sculpture did Étienne Falconet complete in 1763?

15 What innovation was part of the journey on the Glasgow-London night express on 2nd April, 1873?

CINEMA AND TV

1 Who starred in the film *The Dam Busters?*

2 To what song did the boys finally strip in *The Full Monty*?

3 Who starred in the film *One Flew Over the Cuckoo's Nest?*

4 Who starred in the film *The Wizard of Oz?*

5 In which film did Rex Harrison and Audrey Hepburn co-star?

6 In *Spice: The Movie,* who starred as the Spice Girls' manager?

7 From which film and stage show did the song 'Happy Talk' come?

8 Who starred in the film *Robin Hood, Prince of Thieves?*

9 In Monty Python's *Life Of Brian,* which python played Brian?

10 Exactly how many parts did Alec Guinness play in the film *Kind Hearts and Coronets?*

11 Which T.V. character lived at 23 Railway Cuttings, East Cheam?

12 What would you find at 84, Charing Cross Road?

13 Which father and daughter appeared in *Tiger Bay* and *The Truth About Spring?*

14 Who was America's Sweetheart?

15 From which film and stage show did the song 'Hopelessly Devoted to You' come?

POPULAR MUSIC

1 Billy Joel has only had one UK number one written about his then wife, Christie Brinkley. What was the song called?

2 Name Jean Michel Jarre's only UK top ten hit?

3 Tammy Wynette appeared with which British band on the number 2 hit, 'Justified And Ancient'?

4 Huey Lewis is Jerry Lee Lewis' nephew. True or false?

5 Who reached number one in 1975 with, 'Make Me Smile, (Come Up And See Me)'?

6 Who is the lead singer of Guns N' Roses?

7 Who has had top ten hits with, 'Come On You Reds', 'We're Gonna Do It Again', 'Move Move Move (The Red Tribe)'?

8 Which song, released around the time of his death was Elvis Presley's last UK number 1?

9 Who was the long time singing partner of Paul Simon?

10 Jimmy Sommerville started his career as lead vocalist with which band?

11 Edwin Collins was the lead singer with which 1980's band?

12 What was the Spice Girls first album called?

13 Which influential bands' members included Mo Tucker, Sterling Morrison and Lou Reed?

14 In which film did David Bowie appear alongside a cast of Jim Henson puppets?

15 Who recorded the album, 'What's The Story, Morning Glory'?

LITERATURE

1   What did the fictional character 'Phileas Fogg' achieve?

2   'Who would true valour see,/Let him come hither' is the beginning of a poem by whom?

3   Who wrote *The Water-Babies?*

4   Who said, 'It is impossible for an Englishman to open his mouth, without making some other Englishman despise him.'?

5   Who wrote the words to 'Cherry Ripe' and 'Gather Ye Rosebuds'?

6   Who wrote the original story of *The Wizard of Oz?*

7   'James Gatz' is a character in which book by F. Scott Fitzgerald?

8   Who wrote the mystery story *The Franchise Affair?*

9   'Hamelin Town's in Brunswick/By famous Hanover city;' is the beginning of a poem by whom?

10 Who wrote the play *Who's Afraid of Virginia Woolf?*

11 Which famous children's book did Beatrix Potter write?

12 The character 'Mrs Proudie' appears in which famous book?

13 Who wrote *Room at the Top?*

14 Which character in Dickens was always waiting for something to turn up?

15 The character 'Rochester' appears in which famous book?

I DESPISE YOU!

GENERAL KNOWLEDGE

1 What is meant by a 'ballpark figure'?

2 What does it signify when eight bells are sounded at sea?

3 St Anthony is the patron saint of whom?

4 Which anniversary does a steel wedding celebrate?

5 To the ancient Romans, who was Cupid?

6 What did Alexander of Macedon and Alfred, King of England, have in common?

ME, ABOMINABLE ?!

7 What is another name for the 'Abominable Snowman'?

8 Who in the world would be called 'Digger'?

9 What did Oscar Wilde's Lady Windermere carry?

10 What kind of food is an Oval Osborne?

11 In a pack of cards, which way does the Jack of Clubs look: to his left, or to his right?

12 The Twins represent which sign of the Zodiac?

13 What does 'Going Dutch' mean?

14 What is a tartare sauce?

15 The lemon-sole is not a sole, but a relative of what?

ANSWERS

1. A rough estimate. 2. The end of a watch of four hours. 3. Grave-diggers. 4. The eleventh. 5. The god of love. 6. They were both known by the title 'The Great'. 7. The Yeti. 8. An Australian. 9. A fan. 10. A kind of biscuit. 11. To his right. 12. Gemini. 13. Each person paying for themselves at a meal. 14. A mayonnaise dressing with chopped pickles, olives, capers etc. 15. The plaice.

SCIENCE

1 Why might one 'get a lift' from what Elisha Otis invented in 1853?

2 The biological study of cells and their functions is called what?

3 What was, or is, a blimp?

4 What nationality was the astronomer Copernicus?

5 What makes up just over 27% of the Earth's crust?

6 What was a ZX81 an early example of?

7 When is Halley's Comet likely to be seen from Earth again: 2062, 2012, 2001?

8 Cupronickel is an alloy of which two metals?

9 What important communication line was laid across the ocean in 1858?

10 What is a taxidermist?

11 Will two magnets with their North poles facing attract or repel?

12 Which is longer, one and a half kilometres or a mile?

13 What colour is a moonstone?

14 What does a speedometer measure?

15 Who were the two Sir William Braggs?

1. It was the passenger elevator. 2. Cytology. 3. A non-rigid balloon or airship. 4. Polish. 5. Silicon. 6. Home computer. 7. 2062. 8. Copper and nickel. 9. The transatlantic cable. 10. A person practised in the art of preparing, stuffing and mounting skins. 11. Repel. 12. A mile. 13. White. 14. Speed. 15. Physicists, father and son.

NATURAL HISTORY

1 How far can a frog jump?

2 What is a mite?

3 Which is the world's largest crab? Does it measure (a) 12 inches across (b) 10 inches across (c) 8 inches across?

4 What kind of animal is said to bray?

5 What ape is known to local people as 'man of the forest'?

6 What is unusual about the lungfish?

7 Which is the largest bird in the world?

8 What is chicory?

9 What sort of flavour does a Blenheim Orange have?

10 What kind of animal is said to 'low'?

11 What is pepper?

12 How high can a flea jump approximately: (a) 5 inches (b) 6 inches (c) 8 inches?

13 What does the name 'dachshund' mean?

14 How many bones are there in a swan's neck: (a) 12 (b) 23 (c) 32?

15 What is a Keeshond?

1. About ten feet. 2. In the animal sense, a very tiny spider-like creature. 3. 12 inches across. It's the giant spider crab of Japan. 4. An ass or donkey. 5. The orang-utan. 6. It is able to breathe air. 7. The ostrich. 8. A plant whose leaves are used in salads, and whose roots are ground to mix with coffee. 9. Apple flavour - it's an apple! 10. A cow. 11. The pungent dried berries of the pepper plant, usually powdered. 12. 8 inches. 13. Badger-hound. 14. (b) 23. 15. A breed of dog.

GEOGRAPHY

1 How many states are there in Australia?

2 Where and what is Dunkery Beacon?

3 What is the capital of the Ukraine?

4 Cologne is a city now known by another name. What is that name?

5 The Gold Coast is the old name for which country?

6 To which real river did the song Ol' Man River refer?

7 Where in England would you find the Farne Islands?

8 If a car displayed the letters TR, what would be its country of origin?

9 Verulamium was the name given by the Romans to what?

10 In which London street would you find the Hilton and Dorchester hotels and Grosvenor House?

11 Where and what is 'The Pentagon'?

12 Which country regards Land of My Fathers as its anthem?

13 Where and what is the Mull of Kintyre?

14 What is meant by the Six Counties?

15 What is the capital of Thailand?

ENGLISH LANGUAGE

1 What is the name for someone who studies the stars?

2 What would be your condition if you found yourself in 'Queer Street'?

3 To what did a watchmaker, Christopher Pinchbeck give his name?

4 What does an American call a jumble sale?

5 What does the word 'sceptic' mean?

6 What does 'pro tem.' stand for?

7 What was a 'doughboy'?

8 Which word, beginning with R, means to dwell or to inhabit?

9 What, in the United States, is a 'hobo'?

10 What is another name for an American 'dime'?

11 What is the name for someone who studies handwriting?

12 What is the meaning of 'larboard'?

13 What is a 'highball', as known to Americans?

14 What was a 'spiv'?

15 Where would you be if you were in an American 'hoosegow'?

SPORT

1 Name Minnesota's American Football team.

2 Who sponsors the traditional curtain raiser to Wimbledon, at Queens Club?

3 How many players are there in a Ryder Cup team?

4 How many hulls does a catamaran have?

5 With which sport do you associate Tony Jarrett?

6 Which sport did Nigel Mansell move to after leaving Formula One?

7 Who sponsored Jaguar's successful challenge at Le Mans?

8 Name the odd one out: Pike, Chub, Roach, Pouting.

9 What nationality is tennis player Gabriella Sabatini?

10 Which football team plays its home games at The Valley?

11 Who was the first man to defeat Frank Bruno in a world title fight?

12 In which sport are players awarded Brownlow Medals?

13 Who was man-of-the-match in the 1998 England v South Africa test at Headingley?

14 Which tennis player has won more women's singles titles than any other, and in 1984 set the longest winning streak of 74 victories?

15 For which Club did England star Graeme Le Saux play during the 1997/98 season?

607

1. Vikings. 2. Stella Artois. 3. Twelve. 4. Two. 5. Athletics (110m Hurdles). 6. Indy Car Racing. 7. Silk Cut. 8. Pouting is a sea fish. 9. Argentinian. 10. Charlton Athletic. 11. Tim Witherspoon. 12. Australian Rules Football. 13. Mark Butcher. 14. Martina Navratilova. 15. Chelsea.

HISTORY

1 What was CND, launched in 1958?

2 The Treaty of Paris was signed in 1763. What was its purpose?

3 Which of King Henry VIII's wives outlived him?

4 In 1964 rival gangs of young people began rioting and making disturbances at seaside towns. What did they call themselves?

5 The Rotherhithe tunnel under the Thames was opened in: (a) 1830 (b) 1843 (c) 1850?

6 In Delhi, India, on 1st January, 1877, Queen Victoria was proclaimed what?

7 When King William IV died in 1837, who succeeded him to the throne?

8 Who became commander-in-chief of the American forces in 1775?

9 What were the Huguenots?

10 Which London authority was abolished in 1988?

11 Women campaigners for the vote were known as what in 1906?

12 What caused 43 people to be killed in north-eastern England in 1916?

13 Who was Perkin Warbeck?

14 When were Premium Bonds first introduced: (a) 1956 (b) 1960 (c) 1970?

15 The Atlantic Charter was issued by Churchill and Roosevelt in 1941. What did it proclaim?

1. The Campaign for Nuclear Disarmament. 2. To cede Canada and other territories to Britain. 3. Catherine Parr. 4. Mods and rockers. 5. (a) 1843. 6. Empress of India. 7. Queen Victoria. 8. George Washington. 9. French Protestants. 10. The Inner London Education Authority (ILEA). 11. Suffragettes. 12. A raid by the Zeppelin airship L15. 13. A pretender to the English throne. 14. (a) 1956. 15. The Four Freedoms.

CINEMA AND TV

1 Who starred in the 1927 silent film *Sunrise?*

2 From which film and stage show did the song 'I Could Have Danced All Night' come?

3 Who starred in the film *Modern Times?*

4 Name the only film outing for George Lazenby as James Bond?

5 Which actor turned down three major parts that made Humphrey Bogart famous, including the lead role in *Casablanca?*

6 Who starred in the film *The Night of the Hunter?*

7 Name the T.V. comedy set around a hapless unit of the Home Guard in World War Two?

8 Who starred in the film *An American in Paris?*

9 Who starred in the film *M*A*S*H?*

10 Who was Batman in the film *Batman Forever?*

11 Who played The Penguin in the film *Batman Returns?*

12 Which long-running television show features a pub called 'The Rover's Return'?

13 Which series of films set in a rowdy girls' school starred Alastair Sim?

14 Who starred in the film *All That Heaven Allows?*

15 In which film did the furry creatures called mogwais appear?

POPULAR MUSIC

1. Rod Stewart's, 'Sailing', was used for a BBC TV series about which ship?

2. Which American singer's first UK number one was, 'Only The Lonely'

3. What nationality are folk singers, Foster and Allen?

4. The Moody Blues are best known for their song, 'Nights In White Satin', but what was their only UK number 1 single?

5. Which band asked us to 'Rock The Casbah' and wondered, 'Should I Stay Or Should I Go'?

6. Which three piece band were Ginger Baker and Jack Bruce members of?

7. With which band did Liza Minnelli collaborate on her 1989, 'Results', album?

8. Mother and Son band, Lieutenant Pigeon reached number 1 in September 1972, with which song?

9. What nationality were the band, Kraftwerk?

10. In July 1982, Wavelength, recorded their only hit, 'Hurry Home'. What major event was the inspiration for the song?

11. In 1980 Marti Webb reached number 3 with, 'Take That Look Off Your Face'. From which musical did the song come?

12. Which Foo Fighter was originally the drummer in Nirvana?

13. Paul Young's debut solo hit reached number 1 in June 198 3 Name the song.

14. Who was the lead vocalist with the Undertones?

15. Which US female vocal group was always reputed to be Prince Charles' favourite Pop act?

LITERATURE

1 Who wrote *Anna of the Five Towns?*

2 Who said: 'Give me a lever long enough, and I will move the World.'

3 Who wrote *The Manchurian Candidate?*

4 In which Shakespeare play does 'Proteus' appear?

5 Which famous children's book did Kenneth Grahame write?

6 'I must go down to the sea again...' Can you recite the next line of Masefield's poem?

7 Who wrote *A Dance to the Music of Time?*

8 Don't count your chickens before they are hatched. Where does this phrase originate?

9 Who wrote *All Quiet on the Western Front?*

10 What line follows 'Listen, my children, and you shall hear'?

11 Who wrote *Tom Jones?*

12 *No Orchids for Miss Blandish* was written by whom?

13 'Sidney Carton' is a character in which book by Charles Dickens?

14 What were the words that would open Ali Baba's magic cave?

15 According to Alexander Pope, in what does, 'Hope springs eternal'?

1. Arnold Bennett. 2. Archimedes. 3. Richard Condon. 4. *Two Gentlemen of Verona.* 5. *The Wind in the Willows.* 6. 'To the lonely sea and the sky'. 7. Anthony Powell. 8. *Don Quixote*, by Cervantes. 9. Erich Maria Remarque. 10. 'Of the midnight ride of Paul Revere'. 11. Henry Fielding. 12. James Hadley Chase. 13. *A Tale of Two Cities.* 14. 'Open sesame'. 15. The human breast.

GENERAL KNOWLEDGE

1 What famous landmark stands on the site of Tyburn Tree in London?

2 Westminster Abbey is over 500 feet long. Yes or no?

3 What group of people are found in an orchestra?

4 What is meant by 'Dutch nightingales'?

5 What can be grouped into fleets?

6 In what place do Jewish people worship?

7 What is ratatouille?

8 The Goat represents which sign of the Zodiac?

9 What is mornay?

10 According to the 'language of flowers', what do oak leaves signify?

11 In which year did Britain join the EEC?

12 Whose statue stands in front of Wesley's Chapel in City Road, London?

13 What kind of food product is aioli?

14 What is chow mein?

15 Samson, a judge of Israel, possessed what great gift?

SCIENCE

1 What is gunpowder?

2 The blue dye called indigo comes from what?

3 What, in WW2, was a Stuka?

4 The study of the processes of life in animals and plants is called what?

5 What was first built from a stack of zinc and copper discs sandwiched between cardboard discs soaked in acid?

6 What is the art and practice of cultivating the land called?

7 Radio waves are reflected back to Earth by what?

8 What is an antidote?

9 What is an alloy?

10 What illuminating experience first occurred in London in 1810?

11 Hydrocyanic acid is also called what?

12 Which is the smallest planet?

13 The sternum is another name for which bone?

14 Who was Anthony Fokker?

15 What can an insulator not do?

NATURAL HISTORY

1. Which is the original native to Britain, the grey or the red squirrel?

2. The harvestman is a spider-like creature with very long legs. True or false?

3. What is another name for the thrift plant?

4. What kind of animal is said to whinny?

5. Which dog is sometimes called an alsatian?

6. A chipmunk is: (a) a type of squirrel (b) a kind of ape.

7. What are capers?

8. What kind of animal is said to hoot?

9. What is a globe artichoke?

10. What is an albatross?

11. About how many kinds of poisonous snake are there?

12. Are there such things as sea serpents?

13. What is the only venomous snake native to Britain?

14. What is a sloe?

15. Does a centipede have a hundred legs?

GEOGRAPHY

1 Cawnpore is a former name for which city?

2 Where in the world would you find a Dyak?

3 'Oxon' is another name for where?

4 The maple is the national symbol of which country?

5 Which English city is known familiarly as 'Brum'?

6 How many 'Royal Boroughs' are there in Britain, and what are their names?

7 Where and what is Watling Street?

8 Which country owns Easter Island?

9 Which city is on the River Foyle?

10 In which country can the Sphinx be found?

11 Where is Port Sunlight, and what made it famous?

12 In the United States, what is Amtrak?

13 Saint Lazare railway station will be found in which city?

14 Where is the Shwe Dagon Pagoda?

15 What is the capital of Canada?

ENGLISH LANGUAGE

1 What is a 'moonlighter'?

2 If an American offered to 'come by', what would you expect him to do?

3 What's the plural of 'dwarf'?

4 Whose motto is 'Be Prepared'?

5 What is meant by the word 'Unwitting'?

6 To an American, what is a 'John Hancock'?

7 What would you get in America if you asked for a 'vest'?

8 What should you ask for if you were looking for a toilet in America?

9 What, according to the magazine Private Eye, are 'hackettes'?

10 What is a consonant?

11 What is a vowel?

12 In European politics, what does the acronym CAP stand for?

13 What kind of flower was named after its grower, Dr Alexander Garden?

14 How did the word 'fan', meaning an enthusiast, come into being?

15 What does the old-fashioned term 'To fare' mean?

SPORT

1   In which city is the annual World Professional Snooker Championship held?

2   Who captained the Scottish Rugby Union team during it's 1990 Grand Slam victory?

3   Which race was won 14 times by Mike Hailwood?

4   Which Chinese game involves 144 tiles divided into six suits?

5   In which sport do you refer to the pitch as a Gridiron?

6   What is the maximum score possible in one game of Ten Pin Bowling?

7   In which sport would you compete for the Air Canada Silver Broom?

8   Which sport features banderillas, veronicas, muletas and picadors?

9   Which is larger: the United States or British golf ball?

10 How many hits are allowed on one side of the net in Volleyball?

11 June Croft is associated with which sport?

12 How many lanes are there in an Olympic-sized swimming pool?

13 Which stick and ball game uses the largest pitch?

14 By what name is footballer Edson Arantes do Nascimento better known?

15 Which is the first 'Classic' of the English Horse racing season?

ANSWERS

1. Sheffield. 2. David Sole. 3. Isle of Man TT. 4. Mah Jong. 5. American Football. 6. 300. 7. Curling. 8. Bull Fighting. 9. US. 10. Three. 11. Swimming. 12. Eight. 13. Polo. 14. Pele. 15. The 1000 Guineas.

HISTORY

1 Which famous ship, sunk in 1545, was lifted from the seabed in 1982?

2 Which queen was discovered to be bald at the time of her execution?

3 What was laid beneath the sea between Dover and Calais in 1850?

4 Who was Lyndon Baines Johnson?

5 Under what name is the former Elizabeth Bowes-Lyon now known?

6 What have these people in common: Julius Caesar; Abraham Lincoln; Mahatma Gandhi?

7 What instrument of destruction was invented in 1777 by David Bushnell?

8 What office did Archbishop Makarios assume in December 1959?

9 Who in the English parliament led the campaign against the slave trade?

10 What did Albert Schweitzer found in Lambaréné, French Equatorial Africa?

11 May Day became a Bank Holiday in which year?

12 The first British colour supplement was published by what newspaper in 1962?

13 The Dorset labourers in Tolpuddle, Dorset, were punished for what action?

14 When was the last time we had an earthquake in Britain?

15 Who was Roald Amundsen?

ANSWERS

1. The Mary Rose. 2. Mary, Queen of Scots in 1587. 3. The first submarine telegraph cable. 4. He was the 36th American president. 5. The Queen Mother. 6. They were all assassinated. 7. The torpedo. 8. He became the first president of Cyprus. 9. William Wilberforce. 10. A hospital to combat sleeping sickness and leprosy. 11. 1978. 12. The Sunday Times. 13. Forming a trade union. 14. In 1984, on 19th July, in Gwynedd. 15. Norwegian explorer who was first to reach the South Pole.

CINEMA AND TV

1 What was the name of the first James Bond film to feature Pierce Brosnan in the lead role?

2 Who starred in the film *The Way to the Stars?*

3 Who, in the movies, was the 'Brazilian Bombshell'?

4 Who starred in the film *Northwest Frontier?*

5 Who starred in the film *If...?*

6 Which T.V. programme, featuring 'Scottie' and 'Bones', was set in space and became a long series of major films?

7 From which film and stage show did the song 'Some Enchanted Evening' come?

8 Who starred in the film *The Guns of Navarone?*

9 What was controversial about the 1915 silent movie *The Birth of a Nation?*

10 Which two brothers acted in the film *The Falcon's Brother?*

11 Which famous cartoon cat was always trying to eat 'Tweetie-Pie'?

12 What was unusual about the language used in the 1965 film *Incubus*, starring William Shatner?

13 From which film and stage show did the song 'I Got Rhythm' come?

14 Which T.V. cop show featured a bald detective played by Telly Savalas?

15 Who starred in the film *Mildred Pierce?*

619

1. *Goldeneye.* 2. John Mills. 3. Carmen Miranda. 4. Kenneth More, Lauren Bacall. 5. Malcolm McDowall, David Wood, Richard Warwick. 6. *Star Trek.* 7. *South Pacific.* 8. Gregory Peck, David Niven. 9. It featured the Ku Klux Klan. 10. George Sanders and Tom Conway. 11. Sylvester. 12. It is Esperanto. 13. *Girl Crazy.* 14. *Kojak.* 15. Joan Crawford.

POPULAR MUSIC

1. In 1989 who recorded the album, 'Like A Prayer'?

2. Who was the lead singer with Tubeway Army?

3. In 1992, Witney Houston reached number 1 with, 'I Will Always Love You', from which movie does the song come?

4. Who in the 1970's had top 10 hits with, 'Love Is Life', 'You Sexy Thing' and 'So You Win Again'?

5. Who reached number 1 in December 1986 with, 'Caravan Of Love'?

6. In 1991, Iron Maiden had their first UK number 1 with, 'Bring your Daughter To The Slaughter', but what was their first top ten hit?

7. Name Michael Jackson's sister who has had top ten hits with, 'The Best Things In Life Are Free', 'Let's wait awhile' and 'What Have You Done For Me Lately'?

8. Which band's biggest-selling album was 'Pills, Thrills And Bellyaches'?

9. In 1957, Harry Belafonte reached number one with, 'Mary's Boy Child'. Who recorded a cover version in 1978 which also reached number 1?

10. In 1994 Whigfield went straight in at number 1 with which song?

11. 'Ballroom Blitz', 'Blockbuster' and 'Teenage Rampage', were all hits for which 1970s UK band?

12. From which album do Shakespeare's Sister's hits, 'Stay', 'You're History', and 'I Don't Care', come?

13. Who hit number one in 1992 with 'Ebeneeezer Goode'?

14. Who had hits in the 1970's, with his brothers, his sister and on his own, recording songs such as, 'Puppy Love', 'Crazy Horses', and 'Young Love'?

15. Who hit number 4 in 1982 with, 'Maid of Orleans'?

ANSWERS

1. Madonna. 2. Gary Numan. 3. The Bodyguard. 4. Hot Chocolate. 5. The Housemartins. 6. 'Run To The Hills'. 7. Janet Jackson. 8. Happy Mondays. 9. Boney M. 10. 'Saturday Night'. 11. Sweet 12. 'Hormonally Yours' 13. Shamen. 14. Donny Osmond. 15. Orchestral Manoeuvres in the Dark.

LITERATURE

1 Who was Sir Max Beerbohm?

2 The character 'Caliban' appears in which Shakespeare play?

3 What was truly remarkable about the American author Helen Adams Keller?

4 Arthur Mee was the editor of a famous reference work. What was it called?

5 Who wrote *Lorna Doone?*

6 Complete the proverb: 'Brevity is...'

7 'Yet each man kills the thing he loves.' From where does this phrase originate?

8 In which Shakespeare play does 'Regan' appear?

9 Name the two main characters who sailed aboard the *Hispaniola*.

10 'And did those feet in ancient time/Walk upon England's mountains green?' is the beginning of a poem by whom?

11 In which book by Evelyn Waugh does 'Guy Crouchback' appear?

12 In which part of England is the novel *Lorna Doone* based?

13 In what languages did these authors write: (a) Dante (b) Maxim Gorki (c) Betjeman (d) André Gide?

14 Who wrote *The Good Companions?*

15 Who first employed the word 'sleuth', to mean a detective?

621

1. A critic and caricaturist. 2. *The Tempest*. 3. She was blind and deaf. 4. *The Children's Encyclopaedia*. 5. R. D. Blackmore. 6. ...the soul of wit. 7. Oscar Wilde: *The Ballad of Reading Gaol*. 8. *King Lear*. 9. Long John Silver and Jim Hawkins. 10. William Blake. 11. *Men at Arms*. 12. Exmoor. 13. (a) Italian (b) Russian (c) English (d) French. 14. J.B. Priestley. 15. The author, Angus Bethune Reach, in his book, *Clement Lorimer*, used the expression 'sleuthhound', in 1848.

GENERAL KNOWLEDGE

1   How wide are the clock faces on the Clock Tower at Westminster: 23 feet, 25 feet or 30 feet?

2   Who is the patron saint of tax-collectors?

3   What is a Chateaubriand?

4   Which word, beginning with post- means 'after death?'

5   How much was a pennyweight?

6   What is a Battenburg?

7   Which theatre in London was originally called the Waldorf?

8   What is lasagne?

9   Friday is named after Frigga, the German goddess of married love. True or false?

10 What is the word for a group of angels?

11 Of what group does one find a posse?

12 Which herb looks like parsley but has a slight taste of aniseed?

13 Who was the painter of the famous Laughing Cavalier?

14 Who is the patron saint of scholars?

15 In which city, apart from London, would you find Soho?

ANSWERS

1. 23 feet. 2. St Matthew. 3. A thick grilled fillet steak. 4. Post-mortem. 5. 24 grains. 6. A cake with squares of pink and yellow sponge. 7. The Strand. 8. Flat pasta cooked with tomatoes, cheese or meat. 9. True. 10. A host. 11. Cowboys, constables, police. 12. Chervil. 13. The Dutch portrait painter, Frans Hals. 14. St Bridget. 15. Birmingham.

SCIENCE

1 The phonograph was invented by Edison, but who invented the gramophone?

2 What event was the Bell X1 connected with?

3 Aerophobia is: (a) a fear of draughts (b) a fear of flying?

4 Phonetics is the study of what?

5 What is gun-metal?

6 Who is regarded as the pioneer of modern computers?

7 The science of the study of animal life is called what?

8 What does Eureka! mean?

9 What was a V2?

10 Herpetology is the study of what?

11 What's the record weight for a hailstone: (a) 2 lb, (b) 3 lb, (c) 4 lb?

12 Aeronautics is the study of what?

13 What was pioneered by Joseph Lister?

14 What was broadcast by radio for the first time in 1900?

15 What is hypochondria?

ANSWERS

1. Emile Berliner, who invented a recorder/player of flat discs. 2. Breaking the sound barrier. 3. It's both. 4. Speech and the sounds made by the voice. 5. An alloy of copper, tin and zinc. 6. Charles Babbage. 7. Zoology. 8. I have found it! 9. A long-distance weapon in the form of a rocket. 10. Reptiles. 11. (a) 2 lb. 12. Aircraft and flying. 13. Antiseptic surgery. 14. The human voice. 15. An abnormal belief that one is ill, usually with an imaginary illness.

NATURAL HISTORY

1 What kind of animal is a kite?

2 What is a shaddock?

3 How big is a newly-born kangaroo?

4 What is an amphibian?

5 What is a gudgeon?

6 How much do the world's heaviest coconuts weigh?

7 What is a John Dory?

8 A group of badgers is called: (a) a bark (b) a sete?

9 How big is Britain's largest ant: (a) about half an inch, (b) about a third of an inch or (c) about a quarter of an inch?

10 What is a group of leopards called?

11 Can any mammals lay eggs?

12 What kind of animal could be described as a Cheviot?

13 What was originally called the love apple?

14 A zebu is a kind of zebra. True or false?

15 The brush-tailed rat-kangaroo is a rodent found in Africa. True or false?

624

1. A hawk. 2. A fruit related to the orange and lemon, and resembling the grapefruit. 3. About two centimetres long. 4. A creature which needs to return to water to breed, such as frogs, toads, salamanders. 5. An easily-caught freshwater fish, like a small carp. 6. 18kg. 7. A fish of the mackerel family. 8. A sete. 9. About a third of an inch. 10. A leap. 11. Yes, the platypus and the spiny anteater or echidna. 12. A breed of sheep. 13. The tomato. 14. False. It's a kind of African domestic cattle. 15. False. It's a marsupial found in Australia.

GEOGRAPHY

1   What does the Monument in London commemorate?

2   Whose country retreat is the house called Chequers?

3   Where in the world do they speak Swahili?

4   On which stretch of water does Chicago stand?

5   Which river forms part of the border between England and Scotland?

6   Where in the world do they speak Faroese?

7   Where and what is Mount Etna?

8   Where is the Palace of Topkapi?

9   What was known in early times as 'Cathay'?

10 What have the county of Surrey, the country of Jamaica and the county of Yorkshire in common?

11 Where and what was Mercia?

12 Sauchiehall Street is in which British city?

13 The Chiltern Hills spread over two counties. Which are they?

14 Which river forms a border between Devon and Cornwall?

15 Which country regards Scots Wha Hae as its anthem?

ANSWERS

1. The place where the Great Fire started. 2. The Prime Minister. 3. East Africa.
4. Lake Michigan. 5. The Tweed. 6. The Faroe Islands, between Scotland and Norway.
7. An active volcano in Italy. 8. In Istanbul, Turkey. It is now a museum. 9. China.
10. They all have cities called Kingston. 11. An ancient kingdom of Britain, in what is now the Midlands. 12. Glasgow. 13. Oxfordshire, Buckinghamshire. 14. The Tamar.
15. Scotland.

ENGLISH LANGUAGE

1   What does the phrase, 'Apple-pie order' mean?

2   What's wrong with this sentence: Our cat always licks it's paws after a meal?

3   If you were playing checkers in America, what would you be doing?

4   What is the name for someone who studies mankind?

5   What is the name for someone who studies or collects postage-stamps?

6   What is the difference between adventitious and adventurous?

7   A peon is: (a) a flower (b) a labourer in Spain (c) a comedian.

8   What does 'carry a torch' mean?

9   What would it mean if you 'cast pearls before swine'?

10   A 'shambles' is a real mess, but what was it originally?

11   What modern term replaces the word, 'Methinks'?

12   What does 'compos mentis' mean?

13   What is a 'ham', theatrically-speaking?

14   What does 'Twain' mean?

15   What is a 'chipolata'?

1. Everything neat and in its place. 2. It should read: Our cat always licks its paws after a meal. 3. You'd be playing draughts. 4. Anthropologist. 5. Philatelist. 6. The first means 'accidental' and the second means 'venturesome'. 7. (b). 8. To be in love with someone. 9. That you offered something of value to someone who could not understand its value. 10. A butcher's slaughterhouse. 11. I think. 12. Sane, in one's right mind. 13. An actor who overacts, and lacks real ability. 14. Two. 15. A small sausage.

SPORT

1 Who is the only man to have won World Titles at both motor cycle and car racing?

2 Which sporting figure re-enacted Hannibal's crossing of the Alps for charity?

3 Which football club formerly played their home games at The Baseball Ground?

4 With which team did Damon Hill begin his Formula One career?

5 Who was the, 'Crafty Cockney', winner of the World Professional Darts Championship in 1980?

6 Which US baseball star married Marilyn Monroe?

7 Which sporting star was kidnapped in 1983, never to be seen again?

8 Which team always leads the Olympic parade?

9 What is New Zealand's Rugby League team known as?

10 In which sport are the balls made of crystallate?

11 In which sport would you compete for a Lonsdale Belt?

12 Which sports commentator had a Private Eye column named after him for his amusing commentary mistakes?

13 Which steeplechase course contains the notorious hazards, The Chair and Beachers Brook?

14 Which two disciplines are common to both men's and women's gymnastics?

15 Which is the only city to have hosted the Commonwealth Games twice?

ANSWERS

1. John Surtees. 2. Ian Botham. 3. Derby County. 4. Williams. 5. Eric Bristow. 6. Joe DiMaggio. 7. Shergar. 8. Greece. 9. The Kiwis. 10. Snooker. 11. Boxing. 12. David Coleman. 13. The Grand National course at Aintree. 14. Floor and Vaulting horse. 15. Edinburgh.

HISTORY

1   Who was William McKinley?

2   What street conveyance appeared in London for the first time in 1861?

3   Of which country was King Farouk the sovereign from 1936?

4   Which monarch this century was almost sixty when he was crowned?

5   To be in prison is sometimes referred to as being 'in the clink'. Why?

6   What was unique about the founding of the town of Jamestown in Virginia?

7   What kind of performer was Charles Blondin?

8   Where and when did the Great Fire of London start?

9   Which famous consort of an English King sold oranges outside the Theatre Royal in London?

10 When was the state of war (World War II) with Germany formally declared at an end?

11 Which famous black leader was assassinated on 4th April 1968, in Memphis, Tennessee?

12 Which pianist became the first Prime Minister of the new state of Poland after the First World War?

13 What did 75,000 Londoners die of during 1665?

14 Which major newspaper closed down for almost a year in 1978?

15 The Kingdom of Serbs, Croats and Slovenes was established in 1919. What was it eventually called?

CINEMA AND TV

1 Which film star began her career in Czechoslovakia under the name 'Hedy Kiesler'?

2 Which T.V. show was created by Gene Roddenberry?

3 Who starred in the film *The Courtneys of Curzon Street*?

4 Who starred in the film *The Bank Dick*?

5 Who starred in the 1969 film *Goodbye, Mr Chips*?

6 Which film actor was known as 'The Duke'?

7 Who starred in the film *North by Northwest*?

8 Which controversial cartoon series features characters called Kyle, Kenny, Stan and Cartman?

9 What T.V. programme is abbreviated to the letters TOTP?

10 Who starred in the film *Lawrence of Arabia*?

11 Who played 'Dorothy Michaels' in the film *Tootsie*?

12 From which film and stage show did the song 'If I Ruled the World' come?

13 Who turned down the role of Indiana Jones in *Raiders of the Lost Ark*?

14 Who starred in the silent film *Safety Last*?

15 What did actress Frances McDormand do in 1996?

1. Hedy Lamarr. 2. *Star Trek*. 3. Anna Neagle, Michael Wilding. 4. W.C. Fields. 5. Peter O'Toole, Petula Clark. 6. John Wayne. 7. Cary Grant, Eva Marie Saint. 8. *South Park*. 9. *Top Of The Pops*. 10. Peter O'Toole, Alec Guinness, Anthony Quinn, Jack Hawkins, Omar Sharif. 11. Dustin Hoffman. 12. Pickwick. 13. Tom Selleck. 14. Harold Lloyd. 15. Win a best actress Oscar for her role in *Fargo*.

POPULAR MUSIC

1   Who recorded the theme song for the 1988 Los Angeles Olympics?

2   Who released, Vindaloo in support of the English football team in 1998?

3   In the mid 70's David Soul had a string of top ten hits. T.V. viewers were more familiar with him as whom?

4   Can you name the lead singer of Madness?

5   In the early 1970's Judy Collins entered the UK chart 8 times with the same song. Name the song?

6   Where do the band Del Amitri come from?

7   In 1979 the Dickies reached number 7 with a cover of a children's TV programme theme song. What was the song?

8   What was the Doors' only UK top ten hit?

9   Which band had hits with 'Hombug' and 'A Whiter Shade Of Pale?'

10   Which band's first album was 'Pablo Honey'?

11   Who entered, 'Ooh Aah...Just A Little Bit', in the 1996 Eurovision Song Contest?

12   Who entered the chart in June 1998 with, 'Lost In Space'?

13   In 1988, a beer commercial gave The Hollies their second UK number 1. Can you name the song?

14   What was Michael Jackson's first solo UK number 1?

15   In 1981, Joe Dolce had his one and only UK hit which reached number one. What was the song?

LITERATURE

1   Sir John Tenniel was the illustrator of which children's books?

2   In which Shakespeare play does 'Titania' appear?

3   Complete the proverb: 'Ask no questions...'

4   'Farewell to the Land where the gloom of my glory' is the beginning of a poem by whom?

5   'Svengali' appears in which play by George Du Maurier?

6   Who wrote *Jitterbug Perfume* and *Even Cowgirls Get The Blues*?

7   'Oh East is East, and West is West, and never the twain shall meet.' From where does this phrase come?

8   In which Shakespeare play does 'Rosalind' appear?

9   Who had nothing to offer but 'blood, toil; tears and sweat'?

10 Complete the proverb: 'Catch not at the shadow...'

11 Complete the proverb: 'Books and friends should be...'

12 Who wrote *Rumpole of the Bailey?*

13 Complete the proverb: 'Better an egg today...'

14 When thrown to the lions, who was spared because of his previous kindness?

15 Who wrote *The Darling Buds of May?*

1. *Alice's Adventures in Wonderland* and *Through the Looking Glass*.   2. *A Midsummer Night's Dream*.   3. '...and be told no lies'.   4. Lord Byron.   5. *Trilby*.   6. Tim Robbins.   7 Kipling, *The Ballad of East and West*.   8. *As You Like It*.   9. Winston Churchill.   10. '...and lose the substance'.   11. '...few but good'.   12. John Mortimer.   13. '...than a hen tomorrow'.   14. Androcles.   15. H.E. Bates.

GENERAL KNOWLEDGE

1 What is a madeleine?

2 St Peter is the patron saint of whom?

3 Who was Alexander the Great?

4 What is kedgeree?

5 From the gastronomic point of view, what is a legume?

6 St Cecilia is the patron saint of whom?

7 St Stephen is the patron saint of whom?

8 What is bouillabaisse?

9 Which is London's largest park?

10 What is toad in the hole?

11 What do O.J. Simpson's initials stand for?

12 St David is the patron saint of whom?

13 Who was the 'Brown Bomber'?

14 What is Albert sauce?

15 Who in the world would be called a 'Kraut'?

SCIENCE

1   What colour is a sapphire?

2   What is a monomaniac?

3   Seismology is the study of what?

4   What is argon?

5   Palaeontology is the study of what?

6   What is nychtophobia?

7   In which country is it believed that gunpowder was invented?

8   Who was Archimedes?

9   What is Alpha Centauri?

10   What is a masochist?

11   What is the name of the nearest star?

12   Who invented the miner's safety-lamp?

13   What does 'dirigible' mean?

14   What substance is fermented to make alcohol?

15   What is impetigo?

ANSWERS

1. Blue. 2. Someone who has an enormous liking for one subject. 3. Earthquakes. 4. A gas, of which the atmosphere contains about 1%. 5. Animal and plant fossils. 6. A fear of the dark. 7. China. 8. Greek mathematician. 9. The third brightest star in the sky. 10. Someone who derives pleasure from being ill-treated or hurt by others. 11. Proxima Centauri. 12. Sir Humphry Davy. 13. The word means 'something that can be directed', and is normally used as a name for an airship or navigable balloon. 14. Sugar. 15. A contagious skin disease, mainly of the face and hands.

NATURAL HISTORY

1 The potato is a member of the nightshade family. Yes or no?

2 What is a herbivore?

3 A copperhead is a type of: (a) rattlesnake (b) eagle?

4 A dik-dik is a small East African bird. True or false?

5 What is the correct name for the insect called 'daddy-long-legs'?

6 What was the dodo?

7 What is a cassowary?

8 What large animal is usually found in large African rivers, and whose name means 'river-horse'?

9 What sort of animal is a Dandie Dinmont?

10 What is a calabash?

11 What is an insectivore?

12 What sort of animal is a schnauzer?

13 What is the general name given to creatures like snakes, lizards, crocodiles and tortoises?

14 What sort of animal is a saluki?

15 What is a cucumber?

ANSWERS

1. Yes. 2. A plant-eating animal. 3. (a) a rattlesnake. 4. False. It's a small antelope. 5. The crane-fly. 6. An extinct flightless bird once found on Mauritius. 7. A large, flightless bird of Australia, similar to the ostrich and emu, but smaller. 8. The hippopotamus. 9. A breed of dog. 10. A large, melon-shaped fruit of the calabash tree. 11. An insect-eating mammal, like a mole or a shrew. 12. A breed of dog. 13. Reptiles. 14. A breed of dog. 15. The fruit of a creeping plant with bristly lobed leaves.

GEOGRAPHY

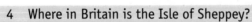

1 In the old days, lawbreakers were hanged at Tyburn Tree, London. What marks the spot now?

2 What is the current name of the country formerly known as Tripolitania?

3 What is the Indian name for India?

4 Where in Britain is the Isle of Sheppey?

5 What is the mistral?

6 Who, in 1859, first crossed Niagara Falls on a tightrope?

7 Who usually lives at No. 11, Downing Street, London?

8 Which is the largest gulf in the world?

9 The Alps cover land areas in which five countries?

10 Ashby-de-la-Zouch, according to a once-popular song, is a little English town by the sea. Is that true?

11 Where is the Bridge of Sighs?

12 How many countries are members of the United Nations: (a) 185, (b) 197 or (c) 301?

13 What was the old name for the Republic of Vanuatu in the Pacific?

14 Which is the largest forest in Britain?

15 The Mont Cenis Pass is between which two countries?

ENGLISH LANGUAGE

1   If you 'weigh anchor', what are you doing?

2   A British soldier would go to the NAAFI. Where would an American soldier go?

3   What, in earlier times, was an article of clothing called a boa?

4   What is an android?

5   What is an 'ebb tide'?

6   What is a chaparral?

7   What is a twill?

8   What is a twerp?

9   What is the term sci-fi short for?

10   What is a moron?

11   What is a clique?

12   What is 'flim-flam'?

13   What is cavalry?

14   What do 'aught' and 'ought' mean?

15   What is a scene if it is picturesque?

1. Raising the anchor from the water, ready to sail away. 2. The PX or post exchange. 3. A scarf of feathers. 4. A robot in human form. 5. A receding tide. 6. A dense, tangled, brushwood. 7. A woven fabric showing diagonal lines. 8. A slang term for someone contemptible: either stupid, a cad, or both. 9. Science fiction. 10. A feeble-minded person. 11. An exclusive group of persons. 12. A trick or deception, also idle meaningless talk. 13. A group of horse-soldiers. 14. Anything. 15. Attractive and interesting.

SPORT

1 What did Britain buy 176,602 shares of in 25th October, 1875?

2 31 people lost their lives on an escalator at which London underground station in November, 1987?

3 What famous mutiny, aboard which ship, took place off Tonga, on 28th April, 1789?

4 What headgear for men came into general use in about 1884?

5 Who was Warren Harding?

6 Which is the oldest royal residence in Britain?

7 At the Battle of Ashdown, in A.D. 871, the Danes were defeated by forces under which famous king?

8 What 'British' character was invented by John Arbuthnot in 1712.

9 Who was Woodrow Wilson?

10 Which former general became President of the French Fifth Republic in 1959?

11 Who was Madame de Pompadour?

12 What did the Boers in South Africa begin in December, 1835?

13 Who was the last monarch of Germany?

14 Who discovered the Pacific Ocean?

15 Who was the last monarch of Portugal?

1. Shares in the Suez Canal. 2. Kings Cross. 3. The Bounty. 4. The straw boater. 5. He was 29th American president. 6. Windsor Castle. 7. King Alfred. 8. 'John Bull'. 9. He was the 28th American president. 10. Charles de Gaulle. 11. The mistress of King Louis XV of France. 12. The 'Great Trek' northward from Cape Colony. 13. Wilhelm II (1888-1918). 14. Francisco Pizarro in 1513. 15. Manoel II.

HISTORY

1 Who were the Chindits?

2 In 1947, what did Prince Philip become?

3 Which northern Australian city was bombed by the Japanese in 1942?

4 Who or what in Spain was the Falange?

5 What happened to Cardinal Karol Wojtyla on 16th October, 1978?

6 Which queen bathed every three months, 'whether she needed to or not'?

7 How did Sir Francis Drake die?

8 Which building in Stratford-upon-Avon was destroyed by fire in 1926?

9 Which British political party came to an end in 1990?

10 What was the Maginot Line?

11 What did Benito Mussolini found in 1917?

12 Which American city became the 'Motor Capital' of the world from 1903 onwards?

13 Who or what was the Klu Klux Klan?

14 George Carey is Archbishop of Canterbury. How many preceded him?

15 Was Rotten Row, London every really rotten?

CINEMA AND TV

1 Who starred in the film *Lassie Come Home?*

2 In the film *Too Much Too Soon,* Errol Flynn played the part of another real actor. Who?

3 Who was known as 'the First Lady of the Screen'?

4 From which film and stage show did the song 'If I Were a Rich Man' come?

5 What naughty word did Emma Dunn utter in the 1932 US film *Blessed Event?*

6 Who starred in the film *Yankee Doodle Dandy?*

7 Who kissed 16-year-old Petula Clark in the 1949 film *Don't Ever Leave Me?*

8 Who starred in the film *Carmen Jones?*

9 Who turned down the role of Ghandi in the film of the same name?

10 Who starred in the remake of *The Avengers?*

11 Who was born Israel Baline in 1888 in Temun, Siberia?

12 Who starred in the 1996 film *Twister?*

13 Which film featured a selection of ghosts and a giant marshmallow man terrorising a city?

14 Who starred in the film *Enter The Dragon?*

15 Who hosts the long-running radio series, *I'm Sorry I Haven't A Clue?*

639

1. Roddy McDowell, Dame May Whitty, Elsa Lanchester, Edmund Gwenn. 2. John Barrymore. 3. Norma Shearer. 4. *Fiddler on the Roof.* 5. Damn. 6. James Cagney. 7. Jimmy Hanley. 8. Dorothy Dandridge, Pearl Bailey, Harry Belafonte. 9. Sir Alec Guinness. 10. Uma Thurman, Ralph Fiennes. 11. Irving Berlin. 12. Helen Hunt, Bill Paxton. 13. *Ghostbusters.* 14. Bruce Lee. 15. Humphrey Littleton.

POPULAR MUSIC

1. Which ex-member of Yazoo released the album 'Alf'?

2. For what was Mungo Jerry's number one hit, 'In The Summer Time' used in the summer of 1996?

3. Complete the missing band member: 'Crosby, Stills, Nash and...'?

4. Who recorded England's official song for Italia '90 (World in Motion)?

5. With which song did the New Seekers reach number one in December 1971?

6. Who said 'ullo John got a new motor?', in 1984?

7. Who had number one hits in the 60's with 'Apache', 'Telstar', and 'Foot Tapper'?

8. Who sang the 'Leader of the Pack' in 1965?

9. In the mid 1990's who topped the charts with 'Oh Carolina', and 'Boombastic'?

10. Who featured on the re-recording of Smokie's 'Living Next Door To Alice' in May 1995?

11. With which song did Buddy Holly achieve his only UK number 1 single?

12. Which band reached number 1 with 'Rock Around The Clock' in 1955?

13. Which band did Kurt Cobain front?

14. Skunk Anansie have had a string of hits in the UK. Their name derives from Jamaican folk lore. What creature is a Skunk Anansie?

15. Which part of the UK do Runrig come from?

LITERATURE

1 Who wrote *The Faerie Queene?*

2 *The Magus* and *The Collector* are books by which British author?

3 *The Halfpenny Marvel* was a boys' weekly, introducing a famous detective in its first issue. Who?

4 In which Shakespeare play does 'Prospero' appear?

5 'Doctor Aziz' appears in which book by E.M. Forster?

6 Who adopted a pen-name made up of the word 'yes' in French and Russian?

7 Who wrote *The L-Shaped Room?*

8 Complete the proverb: 'A bad workman always...'

9 David Copperfield was the favourite book of which author?

10 Who said, 'a woman is only a woman, but a good cigar is a smoke'?

11 What was the better-known pseudonym of Samuel Langhorne Clemens?

12 'The female of the species is more deadly than the male.' Where does this phrase originate?

13 'Inspector Bucket' appears in which book by Charles Dickens?

14 'Bottom' is a character from which Shakespeare play?

15 Who wrote the play *Death of a Salesman?*

GENERAL KNOWLEDGE

1 According to the 'language of flowers', what does the snowdrop signify?

2 Who is the patron saint of television?

3 What is euchre?

4 What is coleslaw?

5 What kind of food item comes from Melton Mowbray?

6 In the year 1752, what date followed 2nd September?

7 What is an agnostic?

8 What instrument did Niccolo Paganini play?

9 Which anniversary does a silk and fine linen wedding celebrate?

10 What is a referendum?

11 What is the Koran?

12 What is a male swan called?

13 Who, or what, in London, is the 'Old Bill'?

14 What is Dogget's Coat and Badge?

15 To the ancient Romans, who was Jupiter?

1. Hope. 2. St Clare. 3. A card game. 4. A cabbage salad. 5. Meat pies. 6. 14th September. The calendar had changed and 11 days were omitted. 7. Someone who believes that man cannot know whether God exists or not. 8. The violin. 9. The twelfth. 10. A national vote on a particular issue. 11. The sacred book of Islam. 12. A cob. 13. The Metropolitan Police. 14. A prize annually awarded to Thames watermen. 15. The god ruling all gods and men.

SCIENCE

1 What is horticulture?

2 A protusion, or rupture in a weak place on the body is called a what?

3 Who invented nylon?

4 As a measure, how long is a chain?

5 Which head of state in Israel was a biochemist?

6 The scientific study of crystals is called what?

7 What is beryl?

8 What is antimony?

9 What name is given to the shape of an ordinary round tin can?

10 Who invented instant coffee?

11 As a measure, how long is a hand?

12 What is metrology?

13 The Pole Star or North Star is sometimes called what?

14 What electrical communication system was invented in 1839?

15 What sort of shuttle was invented for the weaving industry by John Kay in 1733?

1. The art of gardening. 2. Hernia. 3. Wallace H. Carothers. 4. 22 yards. 5. Chaim Weizmann. 6. Crystallography. 7. A precious stone: varieties of it are emerald and aquamarine. 8. A hard, brittle element of metallic appearance. 9. Cylinder. 10. The Nestle Company of Switzerland in 1937. 11. Four inches. 12. The science of weights and measures. 13. Polaris. 14. The telegraph. 15. A flying shuttle.

NATURAL HISTORY

1 Which is Britain's largest meat-eating wild animal?

2 What is an adder?

3 What is the name given to pouched animals?

4 A condor is a type of: (a) puma (b) vulture?

5 A female donkey is called: (a) a jenny (b) a jill (c) a doe?

6 What animal is the domestic form of the polecat?

7 Rye is really a special kind of grass. True or false?

8 A dog sweats through its paws. True or false?

9 What is a sea-horse?

10 What is a group of bears called?

11 What is the tallest animal of all?

12 What sort of animal is a pointer?

13 What is, or was, a unicorn?

14 What sort of animal is a tigon?

15 The onion is a member of the lily family. Yes or no?

ANSWERS

1. The badger. 2. Another name for the viper. 3. Marsupials. 4. A type of vulture. 5. A jenny. 6. The ferret. 7. True. 8. True. 9. A small fish with a prehensile tail and a head something like that of a horse. 10. A sloth. 11. The giraffe. 12. A dog. 13. It never existed, but was believed to be a horse-like animal with a single horn on its forehead. 14. The offspring of a lion and a tigress. 15. Yes.

GEOGRAPHY

1 Where is the Orange River?

2 Where and what is Manhattan?

3 Which is Scotland's longest river?

4 The daffodil is the national symbol for which country?

5 The chrysanthemum is the national symbol for which country?

6 Lusitania is the old name for what?

7 England has two Newcastles. One is 'upon Tyne'. What is the other?

8 What is the old country of Bohemia now called?

9 Burma is now called what?

10 Where and what was Lyonesse?

11 Where and what was Bernicia?

12 Where does the River Thames rise?

13 What is the capital of Iceland?

14 What is the name of the underground railway system in Rome?

15 Where would you find an Elephant and Castle?

ANSWERS

1. South Africa. 2. It's an island at the centre of New York City. 3. The Tay. 4. Wales. 5. Japan. 6. Portugal. 7. Newcastle-under-Lyme, Staffordshire. 8. The Czech Republic. 9. Myanmar. 10. A mythical 'lost' land connecting Cornwall and the Scilly Isles. 11. An ancient kingdom in northern England between the Tyne and the Forth. 12. In the Cotswold Hills. 13. Reykjavik. 14. La Metropolitana. 15. In South London; it's a major junction, and formerly the name of a pub.

ENGLISH LANGUAGE

1 What word, beginning with C, can mean dogma or doctrine?

2 To an American, what is a 'hunky'?

3 What does 'to wax' mean?

4 What does 'to wane' mean?

5 The city of Damascus gave its name to what?

6 What does 'ten bucks' mean to an American?

7 What is the name for someone who studies plants?

8 If your surname is Miller, what might you be nicknamed?

9 Can you make a one-word anagram out of 'no more stars'?

10 What, in the United States, is a 'mortician'?

11 What is wrong with the phrase, 'One should always do his best'?

12 What does the acronym WMO mean?

13 What was, or is, a 'grass widow'?

14 Who or what was a 'quisling'?

15 What do Americans call pants?

No, not quizling darling...

ANSWERS

1. Creed. 2. A foreigner, especially one from middle Europe. 3. To grow or increase. 4. To shrink or decrease in size. 5. The cloth called 'damask'. 6. Ten dollars. 7. Botanist. 8. Dusty. 9. Astronomer. 10. An undertaker. 11. It should read, 'One should always do one's best'. 12. World Meteorological Organisation. 13. A woman whose husband is much occupied outside and apart from the domestic scene. 14. A wartime traitor (after Vidkun Quisling, the Norwegian traitor). 15. You'd ask for underpants.

SPORT

1 From which country does Tae Kwon Do originate?

2 Name the four competition swimming strokes?

3 How many players are there in a Water Polo team?

4 Who was the youngest man ever to win a singles title at Wimbledon?

5 What is the height of a Badminton net: 4ft 9ins, 5ft 1in, 5ft 4ins or 5ft 9ins?

6 In TT motorcycle racing, what does TT stand for?

7 Name Detroit's American football team?

8 In Rugby Union, how many players are linked together in a scrum?

9 Who was the English goalkeeper who could not stop the 'Hand of God'?

10 In show jumping how many faults are awarded for a refusal?

11 Over which course is the Champion Hurdle run?

12 What is the shortest men's high hurdle distance in the Olympic Games?

13 In which sport would you take part in sprints and pursuits, on a track, marked with a Red Printer's line, a Stagers line and a Blue band?

14 In which sport would you compete in the Biennial World Championships in slalom, tricks and jumps events?

15 Malcolm Cooper is a British double Olympic Gold medallist at which sport?

ANSWERS

1. Korea. 2. Freestyle, Butterfly, Breaststroke, Backstroke. 3. Seven. 4. Boris Becker. 5. 5ft 1in. 6. Tourist Trophy. 7. Detroit Lions. 8. 16. 9. Peter Shilton. 10. Three. 11. Cheltenham. 12. 110m. 13. Cycling. 14. Water Skiing. 15. Small Bore Rifle Shooting.

HISTORY

1 What opened between Paddington and Farringdon Street, London, on 10th January, 1863?

2 Who were Eva Duarte Péron and Maria Estela Péron?

3 Who was the original Nosey Parker?

4 Pizarro founded which major city in Peru in 1535?

5 In 1982, the destroyer HMS Sheffield was sunk by an Exocet missile fired by which nation?

6 Who were the greatest political enemies of late 19th-century England?

7 Which was the first monarch of the House of Tudor?

8 Which public figure made her first journey by rail on 13th June, 1842?

9 Which British prime minister was awarded the Nobel Prize for Literature?

10 What happened at Chernobyl, USSR, in April, 1986?

11 In 1972, 40,000 British Asians were expelled from which East African country and by whom?

12 Who was Engelbert Dollfuss, and how did he meet his end?

13 Who was Grover Cleveland?

14 When did Eva Perón of Argentina die?

15 Which was the first state of the USA.

CINEMA AND TV

1   Who starred in the film *Invasion of the Body Snatchers?*

2   Which four sister actresses appeared in the film *The Story of Alexander Graham Bell?*

3   Which American drama about oil barons included Sue Ellen, Bobby and Miss Ellie amongst its cast?

4   Who starred in the film *Badlands*?

5   Which movie was based on the life of middleweight boxer Jake La Motta?

6   Who played Hutch in *Starsky And Hutch?*

7   Who starred in the film *Grease?*

8   Which was the first British film to win an Oscar?

9   Who starred in the film *Double Indemnity?*

10 Which football hardman starred in the 1998 film, *Lock, Stock and Two Smoking Barrels?*

11 Who starred in the film *Lethal Weapon?*

12 Who starred in the 1925 silent film *The Big Parade?*

13 What famous T.V. doctor did both Tom Baker and Jon Pertwee play?

14 Which movie star was the 'Girl With the Million-Dollar Legs?'

15 What was the name of the 8ft tall yellow canary in the T.V. show *Sesame Street?*

1. Donald Sutherland, Brooke Adams, Leonard Nimoy, Jeff Goldblum. 2. Polly Ann, Georgianna, Loretta Young, and Elizabeth Jane Young, better known as Sally Blane. 3. *Dallas*. 4. Martin Sheen and Sissy Spacek. 5. *Raging Bull*. 6. David Soul. 7. John Travolta, Olivia Newton-John. 8. *The Private Life of Henry VIII*, in 1934. 9. Fred MacMurray, Barbara Stanwyck. 10. Vinnie Jones. 11. Mel Gibson, Danny Glover. 12. John Gilbert. 13. *Dr. Who*. 14. Betty Grable. 15. Big Bird.

POPULAR MUSIC

1   Queens', 'Bohemian Rhapsody' was at number 1 for longer than any other single in the UK. True or false?

2   Who in the 1970's, did, 'The Jukebox Jive', with their, 'Sugar Baby Love'?

3   With whom did Elton John record his first UK number 1, 'Don't Go Breaking My Heart'?

4   What nationality are The Crash Test Dummies?

5   Who reached number 3 in February 1980 with, 'Turning Japanese'?

6   Which band won a 'Brit' award, then handed it back when it was discovered that they mimed all their records?

7   Which group rescheduled their 1998 UK tour for tax reasons?

8   China Crisis only had one UK top ten hit, name the song?

9   Which band features Peter Buck as its lead guitarist?

10   With whom did UB40 record their number one hit, 'I Got You Babe'?

11   The Thompson Twins were a duo. True or false?

12   Which Beatle had hits in the early 1970's with, 'It Don't Come Easy', 'Back Off Boogaloo' and 'You're Sixteen'?

13   Whose songs include 'Tangled Up In Blue', 'All Along The Watchtower' and 'Masters Of War?

14   Who reached number one in 1992 with, 'Deeply Dippy'?

15   Which Welshman had top ten hits in 1981, with, 'This Old House', 'Green Door', and 'You Drive Me Crazy?

LITERATURE

1 'I wandered lonely as a cloud' is the beginning of a poem by whom?

2 By what name is Jean-Baptiste Poquelin better known?

3 'For fools rush in where angels fear to tread.' Where does this phrase originate?

4 What was the name of the capital of King Arthur's kingdom?

5 Who wrote the play *The School for Scandal*?

6 Complete Shelley's line: 'If winter comes, can ——— be far behind?'

7 Who wrote *Love in a Cold Climate*?

8 Who wrote *The Grapes of Wrath*?

9 Who wrote *Breakfast at Tiffany's*?

10 According to Tennyson, 'In Spring a young man's fancy' does what?

11 The character 'Mrs Doasyouwouldbedoneby' appears in which famous story?

12 Which was Shakespeare's last play?

13 What had John Evelyn in common with Samuel Pepys?

14 Who created the villain 'Dr Fu Manchu'?

15 Who wrote *My Idea Of Fun*?

1. William Wordsworth. 2. Molière. 3. *An Essay on Criticism*. (Pope). 4. *Camelot*. 5. Richard Brinsley Sheridan. 6. Spring. 7. Nancy Mitford. 8. John Steinbeck. 9. Truman Capote. 10. 'Lightly turns to thoughts of love'. 11. *The Water Babies*. 12. *Henry VIII*, written with the assistance of John Fletcher. 13. They were both diarists. 14. Sax Rohmer. 15. Will Self.

GENERAL KNOWLEDGE

1 What is couscous?

2 Who is the reigning monarch of Spain?

3 St Agatha is the patron saint of whom?

4 The American cartoonist Chester Gould conceived which character?

5 Which day is the Muslim Sabbath?

6 A Frenchman referring to 'trèfles, carreaux, piques, et coeurs' would be speaking of what?

7 According to the 'language of flowers', what does the veronica signify?

8 Sir William Alexander Smith founded what boys' organisation?

9 Some extra books to the Bible are called the Apocrypha. How many are there?

10 Whose capital is Edinburgh (apart from Scotland!)?

11 What is nougat?

12 What does the Beaufort Scale measure?

13 Who was 'Tricky Dicky'?

14 Which tribal chieftain in Europe became president and later, king of his country?

15 What is a prune?

SCIENCE

1   An expert in codes and ciphers would be called what?

2   What important navigational device did John Bird invent in 1757?

3   What is an insecticide?

4   Who was Sir Richard Arkwright?

5   How many moons does the planet Jupiter have: (a) 12 (b) 10 (c) 8?

6   What did Henry Ford invent which helped build his Model T Ford more quickly and cheaply?

7   What is a vacuum?

8   What is the difference between a biretta and a beretta?

9   What was the name of the first manned spacecraft?

10 What is the name for a unit of heat?

11 In which year did Marie Curie win a Nobel Prize?

12 Christopher Latham Sholes invented what was called 'a literary piano' in 1870. What was it?

13 What is 'white metal'?

14 What odourless, inflammable gas was discovered in 1766 by Henry Cavendish?

15 What is Canopus?

ANSWERS

1. A cryptologist. 2. The sextant. 3. A substance which kills insects. 4. Inventor and industrial leader. 5. Twelve. 6. The modern production assembly line. 7. A space containing absolutely nothing. 8. The first is a cap worn by a priest, and the second is a small pistol. 9. Vostok 1. 10. A therm. 11. 1911. 12. The first practical typewriter. 13. An alloy of lead, tin, antimony and copper. 14. Hydrogen. 15. The second brightest star in the sky.

NATURAL HISTORY

1   What is a wallaby?

2   What kind of animal is said to grunt?

3   Rice is really a special kind of grass. True or false?

4   What is a juniper?

5   Which of the following animals belongs to the Equidae family; zebra, wild ass or horse?

6   What is an octopus?

7   Which is the world's most poisonous snake?

8   Is it true that elephants are afraid of mice?

9   What kind of animal is said to caw?

10 What is a locust?

11 Which bird has the widest wing-spread known as a span?

12 What is another name for veronica?

13 What sort of animal is a Sealyham?

14 What is the name of the dog- or fox-like wild creatures similar to wolves?

15 What was a cockatrice?

GEOGRAPHY

1 How many Scilly Isles are there: 14, 40 or 140?

2 On which river does New Orleans stand?

3 What did Florentine navigator, Amerigo Vespucci, give his name to?

4 What is the capital of Afghanistan?

5 Which town lies at the very centre of Australia?

6 The Great St Bernard Pass is between which two countries?

7 Where in the world do they speak Navajo?

8 Where in the world would you find the Catacombs?

9 What exactly are the Catacombs?

10 Which Belgian city stands where the River Schelde flows into the sea?

11 To whom do the Virgin Islands belong?

12 Which city is on the Rio de la Plata river?

13 What, in London, is known as the 'Ally Pally'?

14 Where would you find Hadrian's Wall?

15 Andorra is 175 square miles in area. True or false?

ENGLISH LANGUAGE

1   What does an American mean by a 'faucet'?

2   How many sides does a polygon have?

3   What's the male version of a 'sorceress'?

4   What is a back-bencher?

5   What is the plural of 'roof'?

6   What does the old word 'Tarry' mean?

7   Which word has replaced 'Wont'?

8   What are the two meanings of digest?

9   'Any one of us could be right'. 'Anyone of us could be right'.
    Which of these two sentences is correct?

10 What does the acronym, RAC stand for?

11 What is the phrase, 'Live on, Time, emit no evil' an example of?

12 What was a zoot-suit?

13 What would you do with a 'black velvet'?

14 What does an American call a 'dinner jacket'?

15 A leading person in sport is named after what playing-card?

SPORT

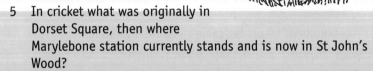

1　In Luge Tobogganing do competitors travel feet or head first?

2　Name Boston's NBA Basketball team?

3　What is the aim of a Puissance show jumping event?

4　Who is the youngest man ever to play football for England at full international level?

5　In cricket what was originally in Dorset Square, then where Marylebone station currently stands and is now in St John's Wood?

6　In Rounders, what is awarded if the bowler delivers three 'no-balls'?

7　At which sporting event would you have a 'Barrel Man', hold a 'Cinch', have a 'Hang-up' and sit in a 'Shute box'?

8　At which racetrack is the 2000 Guineas run?

9　Name the variant of Lawn Bowls predominantly played in the North of England?

10　What is the official distance for a Marathon?

11　Name Maclaren's two drivers for the 1998 season?

12　What is the sport of Modern Pentathlon supposed to be mimicking?

13　Over which course is the Prix de l'Arc de Triomphe run?

14　Name Toronto's Baseball team?

15　Which footballer was credited with the 'Hand of God' in the 1986 World Cup?

ANSWERS

1. Feet first. 2. Celtics. 3. To jump higher than anyone else. 4. Michael Owen. 5. Lord's Cricket Ground. 6. Half-Rounder. 7. Rodeo. 8. Newmarket. 9. Crown Green Bowls. 10. 26miles 385yds (42.2km). 11. Mikka Hakkinen & David Coulthard. 12. The journey of a Kings messenger through enemy territory. 13. Longchamps. 14. Blue Jays. 15. Diego Maradona.

HISTORY

1 Who was the last monarch of Russia?

2 The disputes in Cyprus are largely due to the quarrels between which two peoples?

3 What disaster caused the Tay Bridge, Scotland, to collapse in December, 1879?

4 How long did King Edward VIII reign: (a) 10 months (b) 7 months (c) 14 months?

5 The foundation stone of which great bank was laid in August, 1732?

6 What mode of transport came to London in 1836?

7 What, in 1858, was the Miracle of Lourdes?

8 In 1856, the trekking Boers in South Africa set up an independent republic called what?

9 A German banker, whose first names were Meyer Amschel, founded a famous company in Frankfurt. What was his surname?

10 In 1894, what innovation in shipping routes was opened in Lancashire?

11 Which national newspaper did Sir Arthur Pearson found in 1900?

12 Who were the Desert Rats?

13 Who was the legendary Prester John?

14 Which daily newspaper went on sale in 1896 at a price of fid (a halfpenny)?

15 What was the Black Hole of Calcutta?

CINEMA AND TV

1 From which stage show did the song 'I'm Forever Blowing Bubbles' come?

2 What film starred Will Smith and Tommy Lee Jones as alien hunters?

3 Who starred in the film *The Godfather*?

4 How much did Jim Rockford charge as a private investigator in *The Rockford Files*?

5 Who starred in the film *Red River*?

6 From which film and stage show did the song 'Indian Love Call' come?

7 If it was Friday and five o'clock, what used to be on BBC TV?

8 What was noteworthy about the 1926 silent film *The Black Pirate*?

9 From which film and stage show did the song 'It Ain't Necessarily So' come?

10 What part did Jerry Lacey play in the film *Play It Again, Sam*?

11 Who starred in the film *The Card*?

12 Which movie star was 'The Hunk'?

13 What or who was 'Genevieve' in the film of the same name?

14 In which Disney film did two dogs share spaghetti at an Italian café?

15 Who directed the film *Mississippi Burning*?

659

1. The US production, *The Passing Show* of 1918. 2. *Men In Black*. 3. Marlon Brando.
4. 200 dollars a day plus expenses. 5. John Wayne, Montgomery Clift. 6. *Rose Marie*.
7. *Crackerjack*. 8. It was in Technicolor. 9. *Porgy and Bess*. 10. Humphrey Bogart.
11. Alec Guinness. 12. Victor Mature. 13. A vintage car. 14. *The Lady And The Tramp*.
15. Alan Parker.

POPULAR MUSIC

1   What nationality is singer Bjork?

2   Who's top ten hit's include, 'Animal Nitrate' and 'Film Star'?

3   Who reached number 1 in the 1960's with, 'Make It Easy On Yourself' and 'The Sun Ain't Gonna Shine Anymore'?

4   Simon Le Bon was lead singer with which New Romantic band?

5   Barbra Streisand's number 1 hit, 'Evergreen', was the theme song from which film?

6   Which band did John Lydon (Aka Johnny Rotten) form after the break up of the Sex Pistols?

7   American band, The Presidents of the United States of America, once played the Democratic convention in support of the real President, Bill Clinton. True or false?

8   Bobby 'Boris' Pickett and the Crypt-Kickers reached number 3 in 1973 with which tongue-in-cheek horror song?

9   Which Michael Jackson video did Lenny Henry record a spoof of for the BBC in 1983?

10   Who reached number 2 in 1970 and number 8 in 1991 with, 'All Right Now'?

11   Who sang, 'Things Can Only Get Better', in 1994?

12   Which cockney singer had top ten hits in the 1960's with, 'A picture Of You', 'That's What Love Will Do' and 'It Only Took A Minute'?

13   Who recorded, 'Who Killed Bambi', on the flip side of the Sex Pistol's, 'Silly Thing'?

14   'The Bomb! (These Sounds Fall Into My Mind)' was a number 5 hit in 1995 for which Producer/artist/group?

15   Smokey Robinson reached number 1 in 1981 with, 'Being With You'. He had previously held that position with, 'Tears Of A Clown', as the front man of which band?

LITERATURE

1 'When I consider how my life is spent' is the beginning of a poem by whom?

2 Who wrote *Gigi?*

3 Who, in 1974, said, 'It will be years – and not in my time – before a woman will...become Prime Minister'?

4 Who wrote *Farewell, My Lovely?*

5 Complete the proverb: 'Cut your coat...'

6 Which children's book did Richard Adams write?

7 'Bilbo Baggins' is a character in which two books?

8 Who wrote *I Robot?*

9 Who wrote the classic novel *Madame Bovary?*

10 How did Lord Acton complete this line: 'Power tends to corrupt, and absolute power ...'

11 Who originated the phrase, 'Big Brother is watching you'?

12 Which novel by Charles Dickens was left unfinished?

13 What was the occupation of Johann Christoph Friedrich von Schiller?

14 The character 'Sexton Blake' had an American counterpart. Name him.

15 Complete the line, 'Laugh, and the world laughs with you, weep...'

1. John Mitton. 2. Colette. 3. Margaret Thatcher. 4. Raymond Chandler. 5. '...according to your cloth'. 6. *Watership Down.* 7. *The Hobbit* and *Lord of the Rings.* 8. 'And your hair has become very white.' 9. Gustave Flaubert. 10. Corrupts absolutely. 11. George Orwell in his book (1984). 12. *The Mystery of Edwin Drood.* 13. He was a German playwright and poet. 14. Nick Carter. 15. 'and you weep alone.'

GENERAL KNOWLEDGE

1   A German referring to 'Herzen, Schellen, Grün und Eicheln' would be speaking of what?

2   What Italian artist was also an architect, philosopher, poet, composer, sculptor and mathematician?

3   To what did Buncombe, North Carolina, give its name?

4   Mercury is another name for the messenger of the gods Hermes. True or false?

5   What did Catherine II of Russia and Peter I of Russia have in common?

6   How old is the card game of Whist?

7   Which is the holy city of Hindus?

8   If something is held 'in camera', what does it mean?

9   What is béarnaise?

10   What is the Devil's Picture-book?

11   Composed of what group does one find a bevy?

12   Who was Sir Stafford Cripps?

13   What animal's name do the Chinese give to the year 1999?

14   Thursday is named after Thor, the German god of thunder. True or false?

15   Sunday is named after the Sun. True or false?

ANSWERS

1. German playing-cards with Hearts, Bells, Leaves and Acorns as suits. 2. Leonardo da Vinci. 3. Bunkum, or nonsense. 4. True. 5. They were both known by the title 'The Great'. 6. It dates from the eighteenth century. 7. Benares. 8. With the public as a whole excluded. 9. A sauce made with egg-yolks, butter, shallots, tarragon and vinegar. 10. A pack of playing-cards. 11. Girls, beauty, larks, quails, swans. 12. British Labour statesman and Chancellor of the Exchequer. 13. The year of the Hare. 14. True. 15. True.

SCIENCE

1 What was the Tin Lizzie, introduced in the USA in 1908?

2 What is oreology?

3 Pneumatic machines are driven by what?

4 The study of living things in relation to their environment is called what?

5 What was, or is, a quadrant?

6 What is agate?

7 What is anthrax?

8 Nitrogen is the main constituent of air. True or false?

9 The science relating to the flow of fluids is called what?

10 What was the aircraft called which had a rotary wing and was flown before the first helicopter?

11 An advanced system of electric lighting was invented in 1840 by Sir William Grove. What was it?

12 What device, valuable to miners, did Sir Humphry Davy invent in 1815?

13 The study of matter and energy is called what?

14 Joseph Priestley discovered one of the most important of gases in 1774. What was it?

15 The condensing steam engine was invented by which famous Scotsman in 1765?

663

NATURAL HISTORY

1 A male horse aged five or more is called a what?

2 What do ruminant animals do?

3 What is a cuttlefish?

4 A group of rhinoceroses is called a crash, a ring or a horn?

5 What sort of animal is a corgi?

6 What is another name for the heartsease?

7 What is a yew?

8 Would a green rag upset a bull if you waved it?

9 What record does the humming-bird, about 5cm long, hold?

10 What is sesame?

11 The capybara is the largest rodent in the world, and comes from...?

12 A group of partridges is called: (a) a covey (b) a pride.

13 What film cartoon character chased Tweetie-Pie?

14 What sort of animal is a caracal?

15 What is scarlet pimpernel?

GEOGRAPHY

1 Which city is on the Tigris river?

2 Which is the world's largest waterfall?

3 What is the Sirocco?

4 'Auld Reekie' is a familiar name for which city?

5 Which is the largest island in the world?

6 What would you find at Princeton, Dartmoor, in Devon?

7 What is British Honduras now called?

8 What mysterious objects are to be found on Easter Island in the Pacific?

9 Caledonia was the name given by the Romans to what?

10 What was known to the Romans as 'Cambria'?

11 Which is the tallest building in Britain?

12 Where in the world would you find a Mancunian?

13 What is the Dardanelles?

14 After Paris, which is the largest French-speaking city?

15 Canton is a former name for which Chinese city?

1. Baghdad. 2. Boyoma Falls, Congo. 3. A hot wind which blows from the Sahara over the North Mediterranean coasts. 4. Edinburgh. 5. Greenland, 840,000 sq.m. 6. Dartmoor Prison. 7. Belize. 8. Huge stone statues of human heads. 9. Scotland. 10. Wales. 11. Canary Wharf Tower, in east London. 12. In Manchester. 13. A narrow strait in Turkey which divides Europe and Asia. 14. Montreal, Canada. 15. Guangzhou.

ENGLISH LANGUAGE

1 What is a quid pro quo?

2 Can you name two words sounding alike which mean the same as this pair of phrases: song of praise/male of 'her'?

3 Can you make a Gilbert and Sullivan title out of the anagram 'name for ship'?

4 What were 'bright young things'?

5 What is the meaning of 'prognosticate'?

6 In American English, what is a shnook?

7 A limousine is a kind of car, but what does the word actually mean?

8 What happens if 'you cut off your nose to spite your face'?

9 What does an American mean by a 'realtor'?

10 What does the word 'pianoforte' mean?

11 What is the difference between a scholar and a pupil?

12 A valise, to an American, is what to a Briton?

13 What is a tram called in the United States?

14 What was a 'gentleman's gentleman'?

15 How did the word lampoon originate?

1. 'Something for something'; a kind of retaliation. 2. Hymn/him. 3. HMS Pinafore. 4. Upper-class socialites of the 1920s and 1930s. 5. To foretell. 6. Someone completely put upon, and totally naïve. 7. A cloak. 8. You do something in anger which is actually going to do you more harm. 9. An estate agent. 10. A piano, but the word originally means 'soft and strong'. 11. A scholar is a learned person; a pupil is someone being taught. 12. A suitcase. 13. A streetcar. 14. A high-class valet. 15. From the Old French word lampon, meaning a kind of drinking song.

SPORT

1   How many players are there on an, 'Aussie Rules' football team?

2   How long is an American football pitch?

3   On what surface is the game of, 'Bandy', played?

4   Which is usually smaller, a Rugby League ball or a Rugby Union ball?

5   Which sport would I be taking part in if I were competing in, The Scottish Six Days Trial?

6   Starting in Paris, where does the world famous rally finish?

7   Where do the, 'Mets', Baseball team come from?

8   Over which course is the St Leger run?

9   Which Arsenal Goalkeeper missed the 1973 FA Cup Final, due to a broken leg, and later became a commentator first on the BBC, then ITV?

10   Wayne Gretzky having scored more than 2000 points in under 850 games, is regarded as one of the greatest exponents of which sport?

11   In Netball what do the initials WD stand for?

12   In the mid-1980s, the Birmingham super prix was raced, Monte Carlo style around the streets of the city. What class of cars were raced?

13   When was the MCC founded: 1787, 1790, 1801 or 1821?

14   How many players are there in an outdoor Field Hockey team?

15   How heavy is a Hammer in athletics: 12lb, 14lb, 16lb or 18lb?

ANSWERS

1. Eighteen. 2. 100yds. 3. Ice. 4. Rugby League Ball. 5. Motorcycle Trials Riding. 6. Daker. 7. New York. 8. Doncaster. 9. Bob Wilson. 10. Ice Hockey. 11. Wing Defence. 12. Formula 3000. 13. 1787. 14. Eleven. 15. 16lb.

HISTORY

1 Which European country overthrew its monarchy and became a republic on 5th October, 1910?

2 Gold diggers in Ballarat, Australia, died in a clash with troops in 1854. What was the conflict called?

3 During the last war, what was an 'Anderson'?

4 What started in California in 1848?

5 The early Roman historian Flavius Josephus, wrote a history of which people?

6 Who was married at the Château de Candé, Touraine, on 3rd June, 1937?

7 Who was Aristophanes?

8 The cousin of the American president Theodore Roosevelt also became president. Who was he?

9 Who was Yuri Alekseyevich Gagarin?

10 What was unique about HMS Dreadnought, launched by the Queen in 1960?

11 Which English queen is said to have had six fingers on one hand?

12 Which queen of England was bald at the age of 31?

13 On 2nd July, 1858, Disraeli and Gladstone felt unwell in House of Commons. Why?

14 What did the Jameson Raid into the Transvaal on 29 December, 1895, lead to?

15 What is the Bayeux Tapestry?

CINEMA AND TV

1 Who directed and starred in the film *Citizen Kane?*

2 What British city was *The Full Monty* set in?

3 Who starred in the film *The Colditz* Story?

4 In which cartoon film is the kingdom of Pepperland attacked by the Blue Meanies?

5 Which game show host coined the catchphrases, 'Nice to see you, to see you nice' and 'Let's have a look at the old scoreboard'?

6 What show starred the 'Fonz' and Mr Cunningham?

7 Who starred in the film *The African Queen?*

8 Who played Princess Leah in the *Star Wars* trilogy?

9 From which film and stage show did the song 'Oh, What a Beautiful Mornin'' come?

10 Who won the best actress Oscar for her role in *Dead Man Walking?*

11 The part of a famous film comedian was played by Buddy Doyle in *The Great Ziegfeld.* Who?

12 From which film and stage show did the song 'Ol' Man River' come?

13 Which actor needed to lose his dirty raincoat to star in *A Woman Under the Influence?*

14 What film featured a malevolent computer called HAL?

15 The part of which actress was played by Faye Dunaway in *Mommie Dearest?*

POPULAR MUSIC

1   Which Cockneys had top ten hits with, 'Rabbit', 'Ain't No Pleasing You', and 'Snooker Loopy'?

2   Who recorded the album, 'Mr Bad Guy'?

3   Who recorded the album, 'Joshua Tree'?

4   Which feline band had top ten hits with, 'Runaway Boys', and 'Rock This Town'?

5   What type of music did, The Specials, The Beat, and Selector, play?

6   In 1998 which band implored Scotland's football team, 'Don't Come Home Too Soon'?

7   What was Madness's first top ten hit?

8   Which Hawaiian reached number 1 in Jun 1988 with, 'Nothing's Gonna Change My Love For You'?

9   What is the best selling single of all time?

10 The Bluebells reached number 1 with which song over 8 years after it's first release?

11 Which group recorded 11 number 1 hits in a row between 1963-1966?

12 What nationality is heavyweight singer Demis Roussos?

13 Who was the lead vocalist with Roxy Music?

14 Which band was Ozzy Osbourne the lead singer of?

15 In 1982 Musical Youth reached number 1 with, 'Pass The Dutchie'. What is a 'Dutchie'?

ANSWERS

1. Chas & Dave. 2. Freddie Mercury. 3. U2. 4. The Stray Cats. 5. Ska 6. Del Amitri 7. 'One Step Beyond'. 8. Glen Medeiros. 9. 'Candle In The Wind 97' (Elton John). 10. 'Young At Heart'. 11. The Beatles. 12. Greek. 13. Bryan Ferry. 14. Black Sabbath. 15. A Jamaican cooking pot.

LITERATURE

1   Complete the proverb: 'Circumstances...'

2   William Harrison Ainsworth wrote many books with titles like *Jack Sheppard* and *Windsor Castle*. Name two more.

3   'Margot Beste-Chetwynde' appears in which book by Evelyn Waugh?

4   'He thought he saw an Elephant,/That practised on a fife:' is the beginning of a poem by whom?

5   *A Journey to the Centre of the Earth* was written by which author?

6   Who wrote *The Red Badge of Courage?*

7   In which Shakespeare play does the 'Duke Orsino' appear?

8   What was the name of the fictional Australian half-caste detective?

9   What line follows, 'Shall I compare thee to a summer's day?'

10 Who wrote *Nineteen Eighty-Four?*

11 Who wrote *Black Narcissus?*

12 Who created 'Philip Trent', appearing in the book *Trent's Last Case?*

13 For what form of verse was this author also famed?

14 What line follows, 'Tiger! Tiger! burning bright'?

15 What line follows, 'The rich man in his castle'?

1. '...alter cases'. 2. *Guy Fawkes*, *The Tower of London*, *Old St Paul's*. 3. *Decline and Fall*. 4. Lewis Carroll. 5. Jules Verne. 6. Stephen Crane. 7. *Twelfth Night*. 8. Inspector Napoleon Bonaparte. 9. 'Thou art more lovely and more temperate.' 10. George Orwell. 11. Rumer Godden. 12. E.C. Bentley. 13. The invention of the nonsense rhymes called 'clerihews'. 14. 'In the forests of the night'. 15. 'The poor man at his gate'.

GENERAL KNOWLEDGE

1   In a pack of cards, which way does the Jack of Diamonds look, to his left, or to his right?

2   What is a vol au vent?

3   Which close relative of the onion has a similar, but more delicate flavour?

4   Which anniversary does a golden wedding celebrate?

5   What is the sixth sign of the Zodiac?

6   What, as a game, is Chemin de Fer?

7   Which anniversary does an iron or sugar-candy wedding celebrate?

8   What was a 'doughboy'?

9   What was a 'mae-west'?

10 Who in the world would be called a 'Pom' or 'Pommie'?

11 The Crab represents which sign of the Zodiac?

12 What is the Society of Friends?

13 St Jude is the patron saint of what?

14 What is a macaroon?

15 Which word, beginning with post- means 'someone who studies after graduating'.

SCIENCE

1　In 1891, two Frenchmen decided to place the engine of their motor-car in what new position?

2　In 1913, Nathaniel Wales invented a now-indispensable kitchen storage device. What was it?

3　Brass is an alloy of which two metals?

4　Biology is the study of what?

5　What does 'argentine' mean?

6　The science and technology of extracting metals from their ores is called what?

7　With what device are Paul Nipkow and John Logie Baird associated?

8　George Graham invented a device for regulating clocks in 1721 What was it?

9　Alfred Nobel, who founded the Peace Prizes, invented what in 1866?

10　What does WWW stand for?

11　Duralumin is an alloy of which three metals?

12　What is ammonia?

13　What did Samuel Colt invent in1836?

14　What machine for easier travel took its modern form in 1878?

15　In Roman numerals, what is D?

1. In the front of the car. 2. The refrigerator. 3. Copper and zinc. 4. Living things. 5. Of, or like, silver. 6. Metallurgy. 7. Television. 8. A compensating pendulum. 9. Dynamite. 10. World Wide Web. 11. Aluminium, copper and magnesium. 12. A pungent compound of nitrogen and hydrogen. 13. The revolver. 14. The safety bicycle, invented by H.J. Lawson. 15. 500.

NATURAL HISTORY

1 Is it possible for a bird to have teeth?

2 What kind of animal could be described as a Yorkshire White?

3 What is an onager?

4 Which creature lives in an eyrie?

5 What is another name for the filbert?

6 What is an alligator?

7 What is a crab-apple?

8 What is a spaniel?

9 What is the name for an insect-eating animal covered with sharp spines?

10 What is a prawn?

11 What is vanilla?

12 What is a mussel?

13 What is a polliwog?

14 What is a bittern?

15 What kind of animal could be described as a Large White?

GEOGRAPHY

1 What is the United States' busiest airport?

2 What is Britain's second most populous city?

3 Havana is the capital of which country?

4 Aix-la-Chapelle is the French name for the German city of..........?

5 Where in the world would you find Buenos Aires?

6 'België' or 'Belgique' refers to which country?

7 In New York City, streets are divided into East and West by what avenue?

8 The rose is the national symbol for which country?

9 Which city is on the River Seine?

10 What would you expect to find in The Temple, London?

11 Which English county, having been 'abolished', is now 'alive' again?

12 What is the country of Siam now called?

13 What is the Wash, and where is it?

14 What is the tallest structure in the United Kingdom?

15 What is the Bosphorus?

1. O'Hare Airport. 2. Birmingham. 3. Cuba. 4. Aachen. 5. Argentina. 6. Belgium. 7. Fifth Avenue. 8. England. 9. Paris. 10. Lawyers' offices. 11. Rutlandshire. 12. Thailand. 13. A large, shallow bay on the coast of Norfolk and Lincolnshire. 14. The IBA mast in Lincolnshire. 15. A narrow strait which joins the Black Sea to the Sea of Marmora.

ENGLISH LANGUAGE

1 What was 'parlous' an old way of saying?

2 If you 'led someone up the garden path', what would it mean?

3 A sepoy: is (a) a cuttle-fish (b) an Indian soldier (c) a kind of skin disease.

4 A matelot is: (a) sailor (b) a skin eruption (c) a thin carpet?

5 What does ad.lib. stand for?

6 What well-known drink was originally called 'usquebaugh'?

7 What is another word for gnome or goblin?

8 If you were asked to act in loco parentis, what would you have to do?

9 What does 'I trow' mean?

10 Which word can mean both 'sound of a clock' and 'a type of flea or nit'?

11 What is a 'beefeater'?

12 While we in Britain 'form a queue', what do Americans do?

13 What is a series of misfortunes better known as?

14 What does 'p.m.' stand for?

15 If, in earlier times, you 'took the King's shilling', what did you do?

SPORT

1   In Lawn Bowls what is the target ball known as?

2   In which country did the sport of Petanque originate?

3   Which equestrian sport is broken down into, Trotting and Pacing events, where the drivers sit on lightweight carts and the horses are not permitted to gallop?

4   Where is the King George VI Chase run?

5   How many players are there in an outdoor Handball team?

6   Who was the bowler that was hit for six sixes by Sir Garfield Sobers in one over?

7   What is the diameter of a netball net: 15ins, 16ins, 17ins or 18ins?

8   In which sport would you use a half-butt, a spider and an extended spider?

9   Which football team plays its home games at Upton Park?

10 At the Olympics, in which sport would you compete in the Trap and Skeet events?

11   In Judo, which is higher; an Orange, Blue or Green belt?

12 If Sabre and Foil are two of the disciplines, what is the third?

13 What wood is a cricket bat traditionally made from?

14 From which sport does the phrase, 'take a raincheck', come?

15 What is the maximum number of jumps to be negotiated, in the show jumping phase of a three-day event?

ANSWERS

1. The Jack. 2. France. 3. Harness Racing. 4. Kempton Park. 5. Eleven. 6. Derek Nash. 7. 15ins. 8. Snooker. 9. West Ham United. 10. Clay Target shooting. 11. Blue. 12. Épée (Fencing). 13. Willow. 14. Baseball. 15. 12.

HISTORY

1   Who were the Plantaganets?

2   Which group of people were set legally free in the British Empire in August, 1834?

3   How many kingdoms in England were there before A.D. 808 ?

4   Who was the last English monarch to die in battle?

5   In the Monte Bello islands, 1952, the first British experiment of what kind of object took place?

6   Which ex-movie actor became the 40th US president?

7   At the second Battle of Ypres, 1915, what deadly weapon was used for the first time?

8   Which famous steamship made her maiden voyage in April, 1838?

9   What, in connection with the motor-car, was begun on 1st January, 1904?

10 Who was taken hostage in Beirut in January, 1987?

11 Which country did the United States bomb in 1986 in retaliation for terrorist activities?

12 Who or what were the Blackshirts in Britain?

13 What historical event took place in the United States from 1861–1865?

14 Who was called 'the wisest fool in Christendom'?

15 In what year did the first motor-bus appear in London: (a) 1880 (b) 1899 (c) 1901?

CINEMA AND TV

1 Who starred in the film *The Blue Lamp?*

2 Who was the female lead in the film *Top Gun?*

3 Which film actress was born in Brussels, and was the daughter of a Dutch baroness?

4 When were the Oscars first held: 1928, 1932 or 1936?

5 From which film and stage show did the song 'America' come?

6 What was the first programme to be shown on Channel 4?

7 What is wrong with the cartoon film character Gerald McBoing Boing?

8 Who starred in the film *Mission Impossible?*

9 From which film and stage show did the song 'Big Spender' come?

10 Who starred in the 1939 film *The Four Feathers?*

11 Which American 'black-face' singer was born in St Petersburg?

12 Who is Emilio Estevez's father?

13 Name the ex-Blue Peter presenter who hosted *The Money Programme?*

14 Who starred in the film *Show Boat?*

15 Who was Dick Dastardly's canine sidekick?

679

1. Jack Warner. 2. Kelly McGillis. 3. Audrey Hepburn. 4. 1928. 5. *West Side Story*. 6. *Countdown*. 7. He's a small boy who can only produce the sound 'boing-boing'. 8. Tom Cruise, Jon Voight. 9. *Sweet Charity*. 10. John Clements, Ralph Richardson. 12. Martin Sheen. 13. Valerie Singleton. 14. Irene Dunne, Allan Jones, Paul Robeson. 15. Muttley.

POPULAR MUSIC

1 Where did the band, The Long Pigs, get their name?

2 Who reached number 1 in 1957 with, 'Great Balls Of Fire'?

3 John Lennon reached number 1 in July 1969 with, 'Give Peace A Chance'. Under the name of which band did he record the song?

4 In 1984 who sang, 'Girls Just Want To Have Fun'?

5 In August 1992 K.D. Lang recorded, 'Crying', which reached number 13. With whom did she record the song?

6 Jamiroquai entered the top 10 with, 'Stillness In Time', in which year?

7 Which British band had top ten hits in the 1980's with, 'Ghosts' and 'I Second That Emotion'?

8 Which was the first Beatle to have a solo number 1?

9 Rolf Harris's number 1 hit, 'Two little boys', was released in 1969. When was the song written; 1903, 1921, 1950 or 1968?

10 Name INXS's lead singer who tragically died in 1997

11 With which band did Stephen Jones reach number 3 in 1996 singing, 'You're Gorgeous'?

12 In the Beatles, which instrument did Paul McCartney usually play?

13 If Sting was the bassist, and Andy Summers was the guitarist, who was the drummer?

14 Who was the lead singer with Punk band The Damned?

15 Who performed the lead vocals on the Sex Pistols', 'No One Is Innocent' which reached number 7 in July 1978?

LITERATURE

1 Who wrote *The Scarlet Letter?*

2 'Clyde Griffiths' was the leading character in which book by Theodore Dreiser?

3 Who created the fictional detective 'Inspector French'?

4 Who created the fictional gentleman adventurer 'Bulldog Drummond'?

5 Complete the line: 'O what tangled web we weave, when first we...'

6 Complete Browning's line: 'God's in his heaven...'

7 Who was Sir John Betjeman?

8 Who wrote the poem 'The Dong with a Luminous Nose'?

9 Who was the young heroine found in Eleanor Hodgman Porter's children books?

10 The character 'Mr Pecksniff' appears in which book by Charles Dickens?

11 In which Shakespeare play does the character 'Portia' appear?

12 Which famous children's book did Arthur Ransome write?

13 What was mysterious about the diary of Samuel Pepys?

14 Where and what was 'Shangri-la'?

15 The character 'Dolly Varden' appears in which famous book?

GENERAL KNOWLEDGE

1   What food is junket?

2   Which anniversary does a silver wedding celebrate?

3   If your surname is 'Clark', what might your nickname be?

4   Who was the great love of Dante Alighieri?

5   Who ranks higher, a marquess or an earl?

6   What group of objects is described as a flotilla?

7   What is a dolma?

8   What was, or is, an Annie Oakley?

9   What is scrumpy?

10   Which anniversary does an ivory wedding celebrate?

11   What group of objects can be described as a crew?

12   What kind of food item comes from Banbury?

13   Who was Britain's monarch before Queen Elizabeth II?

14   What group is often described as a fifteen?

15   Who was Konrad Adenauer?

1. Curds, mixed with cream, sweetened and flavoured. 2. The twenty-fifth. 3. Nobby. 4. Beatrice. 5. A marquess. 6. Ships. 7. A vine or cabbage leaf with savoury stuffing. 8. A free ticket for a circus or theatre. 9. Cider made from small, sweet apples. 10. The fourteenth. 11. Sailors or aircraft staff. 12. Cake. A kind of mince pie. 13. George VI. 14. A rugby team. 15. A German statesman.

ANSWERS

SCIENCE

1 What is a circumference?

2 The tibia is another name for which bone?

3 What machine with remarkable powers of balance was invented in 1852 by Léon Foucault?

4 What is the name of a negatively-charged particle that exists in an atom?

5 Sterling silver is pure silver plus a tiny percentage of what?

6 What is pharmacology?

7 What kind of instrument is a bowie?

8 Toxicology is the study of what?

9 How many planets are there?

10 What kind of animals would an hippologist study?

11 Iodine takes its name from the Greek word iodes, meaning violet. True or false?

12 Astronomy is the study of what?

13 What is claustrophobia?

14 What is the name given to very high-pitched sounds above 20,000khz?

15 What is an airship?

ANSWERS

1. The distance all the way round a circle. 2. The shin-bone. 3. The gyroscope. 4. Electron. 5. Copper. 6. The science of drugs. 7. A knife. 8. Poisons. 9. Nine. 10. Horses. 11. True. 12. The stars. 13. Fear of confined spaces. 14. Ultrasound. 15. A power-driven dirigible aircraft, lighter than air.

NATURAL HISTORY

1   Is it true that an ostrich will stick its head in the sand when in danger?

2   To what plant did the botanist Leonard Fuchs give his name?

3   What is chlorophyll?

4   What is the alligator pear also known as?

5   Which fish has a curling, prehensile tail?

6   What sort of animal is a pug?

7   A pinniped is a paddle-footed animal. Can you name one example?

8   What is a guava?

9   A kid is: (a) any young creature (b) a young goat.

10   Brachiosaurus, a dinosaur, weighed about 75 tons when alive. Is this a record?

11   What is a shrike?

12   Where does an animal live if it is arboreal?

13   Mulberry leaves are the favourite food of which insect?

14   What are animals with backbones called?

15   The rhesus is found in India, where it is very destructive. It is a member of what animal family?

1. No. It's untrue. 2. The fuchsia. 3. The green colouring matter in plants. 4. The avocado. 5. The sea horse. 6. A breed of dog. 7. Seals, sealions, walruses. 8. A tropical plant with yellow, pear-shaped fruit. 9. A young goat. 10. Yes. 11. A bird with a hooked bill, short wings and a long tail. 12. In trees. 13. The silkworm, the caterpillar of the silkmoth. 14. Vertebrates. 15. Monkeys.

GEOGRAPHY

1 Which Mediterranean island lies close to a smaller island called Gozo?

2 In which city would you find Red Square?

3 Which country's name means 'land of silver'?

4 The St Gotthard Tunnel, Switzerland, is remarkable as what?

5 Where in the world do they speak Tagalog?

6 What is Stansted?

7 The name 'Iberia' refers to which area?

8 Copenhagen is the capital of which country?

9 Where in the world do they speak Pidgin?

10 Where and what is Santorini?

11 The official name 'Ísland' refers to which country?

12 What is the capital city of Norway?

13 What are 'antipodes'?

14 Which is the highest mountain peak in Britain?

15 Where in England is 'The Golden Mile'?

ENGLISH LANGUAGE

1. In American English, what is a prat?

2. What is the female version of 'colt'?

3. What is the difference between 'already' and 'all ready'?

4. It will be a real problem if you upset this vehicle! Name the vehicle.

5. What does an American mean by 'suspenders'?

6. What is a bandana?

7. The city of Florence gave its name to which coin?

8. To what material did the town of Mosul give its name?

9. What would you ask for in the United States, if you wanted to buy a pair of tights?

10. What is the name for someone who studies fish?

11. How many objects are in a 'baker's dozen'?

12. If you were 'like putty' in someone's hands, what would you be?

13. What does the rhyming slang 'Lord Mayor' mean?

14. What is the name for someone who studies codes and ciphers?

15. What is Interlingua?

1. The buttocks or bottom. Hence pratfall in the theatre. 2. Filly. 3. The first means 'before, and by the time mentioned' and the second, 'everyone ready'. 4. The apple-cart. 5. Braces. 6. A large coloured handkerchief of silk or cotton. 7. The florin. 8. Muslin. 9. Pantie hose. 10. Ichthyologist. 11. 13. 12. Easily influenced. 13. Swear. 14. Cryptologist. 15. An artificial language.

SPORT

1 Over which course is the Whitbread Gold Cup run?

2 What is the second most expensive property in the British version of Monopoly?

3 Who won the British Open Golf Tournament in 1985?

4 In Rugby, who feeds the ball in to the scrum?

5 For which sport is Joe Montana famous?

6 Which football team play at, 'The Dell'?

7 Where do the Seahawks American Football team come from?

8 Over which course is the Grand National run?

9 What sport do the Sheffield Eagles play?

10 How many players are there in a Netball team?

11 How high is a Volleyball net: 2.22m, 2.32m, 2.40m or 2.43m?

12 With what sport do you associate Miguel Indurain?

13 In Rallying, why was the Audi Quattro revolutionary?

14 What CC, are the majority of Speedway motorcycles?

15 Where do surfers in the UK congregate to, 'Ride the bore'?

ANSWERS

1. Sandown Park. 2. Park Lane. 3. Sandy Lyle. 4. Scrum Half. 5. American Football. 6. Southampton. 7. Seattle. 8. Aintree. 9. Rugby League. 10. Seven. 11. 2.43m. 12. Cycling (especially the Tour de France). 13. First Rally car with permanent four-wheel drive. 14. Two. 15. The River Severn.

HISTORY

1 What is the C.I.A.?

2 What historic tragic event took place in Marseilles in October 1934?

3 On 4th November, 1605, who was arrested in the vaults of the Houses of Parliament?

4 Which king acceded to the throne of England on Boxing Day, 1135?

5 In 1931, the United States adopted what as its national anthem?

6 Which ship left England in December 1787 under the command of Captain William Bligh?

7 Who arrived back in Spain from America in 1493?

8 Who was the only English pope?

9 Who was the last Saxon king of England?

10 Who was St Augustine?

11 Which large museum in London opened in 1759?

12 What took the place of the Daily Herald, which ceased publication on 14th September, 1964?

13 Wat Tyler and John Ball were leaders of what rebellion in 1381?

14 Who was Harry S. Truman?

15 What happened to the Shah of Iran in 1979?

CINEMA AND TV

1   What was memorable in the film *A Night to Remember?*

2   Who starred in the film *The Graduate?*

3   Which three movie stars received their first screen kisses when aged 14?

4   Which actor won an Oscar in a film in which he never spoke?

5   Who played the sadistic dentist in *Little Shop Of Horrors?*

6   From which stage show did the song 'I'm Just Wild About Harry' come?

7   In early children's television, who was 'Little Weed'?

8   *Gregory's Girl* was a film made by which British director?

9   Who starred in the 1938 film *The Adventures of Robin Hood?*

10   Which story of two composers netted director, Milos Forman his second best director Oscar?

11   From which film and stage show did the song 'Sixteen Going on Seventeen' come?

12   What T.V. show featured a Boston bar where, 'everybody knows your name'?

13   Who starred in the film *Beverly Hills Cop?*

14   Who wrote the book on which the film, *The Godfather* was based?

15   From which film and stage show did the song 'Stranger in Paradise' come?

689

POPULAR MUSIC

1 What was Madonna's first UK number one hit?

2 Who had top ten hits with 'Lovin Things' and 'Ob-la-di Ob-la-da'?

3 In 1975 who sang 'Love Me Love My Dog'?

4 Who had top ten hits with 'Runaway', 'Hey Little Girl' and 'Little Town Flirt'?

5 Who released the album 'Don't Look Back' in 1978?

6 Who was the lead singer and rhythm guitarist with The Shadows?

7 Terry Hall sang with The Specials before forming which group?

8 As a spin-off single from which TV series did, Paul Shane and the Yellowcoats reach number 36 in 1981?

9 Who performed the theme to the Bond film, Live And Let Die?

10 Who released the album 'New Boots And Panties'?

11 Who was the lead singer with The Clash?

12 Who was 'Glad All Over' to be number one in 1963, but were in 'Bits And Pieces' to only make number two in 1964?

13 Charles and Eddie reached number one with which song in 1992?

14 Who recorded the album 'Penthouse and Pavement'?

15 Who had hits in 1991 with 'Promise Me', 'Holding On' and 'Woman To Woman'?

LITERATURE

1   'I will arise and go now, and go to Innisfree,' is the beginning of a poem by whom?

2   Who wrote *The Informer?*

3   Who wrote the book *John Halifax, Gentleman,* which appeared in 1857?

4   'Lizzie Borden took an axe...' What did she do then?

5   Complete the proverb: 'The child is father...'

6   According to Samuel Johnson, what is Patriotism?

7   Who were Athos and Aramis?

8   'I must go down to the seas again' begins a poem by whom?

9   Who wrote *The Pumpkin Eater?*

10 Who created the ex-convict and cracksman character 'Boston Blackie'?

11 Complete the proverb: 'Between two stools...'

12 Who wrote *The Pilgrim's Progress?*

13 What was unusual about the character 'Rebecca' in the book of that name?

14 Who wrote *Don Quixote?*

15 What line follows, 'When icicles hang by the wall,'?

1. W. B. Yeats. 2. Liam O'Flaherty. 3. Mrs Craik, also known as Dinah Maria Mulock. 4. 'And gave her mother forty whacks'. 5. '...to the man'. 6. The last refuge of a scoundrel. 7. Two of the Three Musketeers. 8. John Masefield. 9. Penelope Mortimer. 10. Jack Boyle. 11. '...you fall to the ground'. 12. John Bunyan. 13. She never appears. 14. Miguel de Cervantes. 15. 'And Dick the shepherd blows his nail'.

GENERAL KNOWLEDGE

1   What was called an 'Albert'?

2   The Bull represents which sign of the Zodiac?

3   Who composed 'The Planets'?

4   Rule by officialdom is called what?

5   According to the 'language of flowers', what does the bay leaf signify?

6   In a pack of cards, which way does the Jack of Hearts look, to his left, or to his right?

7   St Sebastian is the patron saint of whom?

8   Is a pantechnicon a large van?

9   Who was the first-ever murder victim?

10   St Isidore is the patron saint of whom?

11   Which word, beginning with post- means 'those coming after'?

12   Who is the reigning monarch in Denmark?

13   St Apollonia is the patron saint of whom?

14   Which anniversary does a paper wedding celebrate?

15   What is black pudding?

ANSWERS

1. A heavy type of watch chain. 2. Taurus. 3. Gustave Holst. 4. A bureaucracy. 5. 'I change but in death'. 6. To his left. 7. Athletes. 8. It is now, but originally it was a building housing artistic works in Belgrave Square, London. 9. Abel, who was murdered by his brother, Cain. 10. Farmers. 11. Posterity. 12. Queen Margaret II. 13. Dentists. 14. The second. 15. A kind of sausage made from pigs' blood.

SCIENCE

1   The study and treatment of diseases of the mind is called what?

2   The science and study of radioactive materials is called what?

3   'Muscular rheumatism' is also called what?

4   What kinds of animal would an ichthyologist study?

5   What does a seismometer measure?

6   What is Sirius?

7   Gabriel Fahrenheit used mercury in 1714 for his invention. What was it?

8   What useful and accurate timepiece did John Harrison invent in 1735?

9   What is myxomatosis?

10 An advancement in making textiles was announced in 1883 by Sir Joseph Swan. What was it?

11 What did Charles Goodyear invent in 1839?

12 The science of directing a craft or a vehicle from place to place is called what?

13 What is geodesy?

14 What does Moh's Scale measure?

15 What laboratory aid was named after its inventor, Robert Bunsen?

1. Psychiatry 2. Radiochemistry. 3. Fibrositis. 4. Fishes. 5. The strength of earthquakes. 6. The brightest star in the sky. 7. The mercury thermometer. 8. The ship's chronometer. 9. A disease of rabbits. 10. The first synthetic fibre. 11. Vulcanised rubber. 12. Navigation. 13. The study and measurement of the earth on a large scale. 14. Different levels of hardness in minerals. 15. The Bunsen burner.

NATURAL HISTORY

1   The caribou is an American variety of what sort of deer?

2   What is another name for belladonna?

3   Which is the smallest mammal in the world?

4   What sort of animal is a Pomeranian?

5   What is the name of the tiny rodent with long hind legs, which hops like a kangaroo?

6   What is a chive?

7   Is it true that marsupials are only found in and around Australia?

8   What does a koala feed on?

9   Which is the most dangerous fish in the world?

10   What sort of animal is a husky?

11   What is a medlar?

12   Hessian, or sacking, is made from which plant?

13   Which reptile is able to change its colour?

14   What is orris-root?

15   What sort of animal is a boxer?

GEOGRAPHY

1 What does 'Mediterranean' mean?

2 Kilauea and Mauna Loa are volcanoes in what country?

3 Where would you find 'Spaghetti Junction'?

4 Where are the Royal Botanic Gardens, and how are they better known?

5 Whereabouts would you find the River Yarrow?

6 On which island is the State of Brunei?

7 Yucatan is a region of which country?

8 Where is Lake Katrine?

9 'Frisco' is a nickname for which city?

10 Where and what is Mount Erebus?

11 What city in Northern Ireland stands on the River Lagan?

12 What is the name of the London Underground line which is colour-coded yellow on maps?

13 Which is the most populous city in Canada?

14 What is the longest river in the world?

15 Which British territory is famous for its apes?

1. The middle of the land or earth. 2. Hawaii. 3. On the motorway near Birmingham. 4. Kew Gardens. 5. In the border region between England and Scotland. 6. Borneo. 7. Mexico. 8. In central Scotland. 9. San Francisco. 10. An active volcano in Antarctica. 11. Belfast. 12. Circle Line. 13. Toronto. 14. The Amazon. 15. Gibraltar.

ENGLISH LANGUAGE

1 What does an American mean by 'notions'?

2 What happens when you 'buttonhole' someone?

3 What does 'mens sana in corpore sano' mean?

4 What were once referred to as 'Hatches, Matches and Despatches'?

5 An emir is: (a) an extinct bird (b) a University student (c) a Muslim chieftain?

6 What does 'N.B.' stand for?

7 If someone is 'tarred with the same brush' as yourself, what does it mean?

8 What's wrong with this: We voted for a new chairman, and the bulk of the votes went to Joe Harris.

9 What would have happened, in earlier times, if you were 'shanghaied'?

10 Which is the correct spelling: (a) hiccough (b) hiccup (c) hickup?

11 How do we get the word 'posh'?

12 Finish the proverb: 'Accidents will happen in...'

13 When an American keeps to the sidewalk, what would he be doing?

14 Jean Nicot, French diplomat, gave his name to what drug?

15 What does 'obsequious' mean?

1. Haberdashery; miscellaneous small items, like pins, needles, cotton. 2. You detain that person in conversation. 3. 'A sound mind in a sound body'. 4. Births, Marriages and Deaths: the personal column announcements in The Times. 5. (c) a. 6. 'Nota bene'; note well. 7. He would have the same faults and qualities as you. 8. It should be: We voted for a new chairman, and the majority of the votes went to Joe Harris. 9. You were kidnapped, often to serve aboard a ship. 10. (b) hiccup. 11. From the old P & O shipping line, which used the initials to denote the preferred cabins Port side Out, Starboard Home. 12. '...the best regulated families'. 13. Staying on the pavement. 14. Nicotine. 15. Dutiful, to the point of fawning.

SPORT

1. Which three football teams were promoted to the Premiership in 1997 only to be relegated the following year?

2. What is the technical term for making a sail smaller, whilst it's still attached to the mast?

3. On what course is golf's U.S. Masters played?

4. Name Cincinnati's American football team?

5. Which sport do the London Towers play?

6. In cricket, what is the maximum length of a Test Match?

7. Which sport was played at the Olympic Games in 1900, where the French collected all six Gold medals, but was never again an Olympic sport?

8. Jill Hammersley and Carl Prean are known for playing which sport?

9. What two skills are combined in the sport of Orienteering?

10. Name three events in a heptathlon?

11. In Netball, what do the initials WA stand for?

12. Which Football team plays at Craven Cottage?

13. Over which course is the Irish Derby run?

14. Where is Golf's 'Royal and Ancient Club' based?

15. How long is a cricket bail: 8cm, 7cm, 10cm or 11cm?

ANSWERS

1. Barnsley, Bolton and Crystal Palace. 2. Reefing. 3. Augusta National. 4. Bengals. 5. Basketball. 6. Five days. 7. Croquet. 8. Table Tennis. 9. Running & Map Reading. 10. 100m hurdles, Shot put, High jump, 200m, Long jump, Javelin & 800m. 11. Wing Attack. 12. Fulham. 13. The Curragh. 14. St Andrew's, Scotland. 15. 11cm.

HISTORY

1 Who was Valentina Vladimirovna Tereshkova?

2 Who was Michael Collins?

3 London's first railway terminus opened on 20th July, 1837. What was it called?

4 In which year did Papua New Guinea become independent of Australia?

5 Who was David Ben Gurion?

6 What was a 'clippie'?

7 Who was Llewelyn ap Gruffydd, or Llewelyn the Great?

8 Which British national newspaper went on sale for the first time on 7th October, 1986?

9 When did the first election for the European Parliament take place?

10 The population of Malta is reputed to be descended from which ancient people?

11 In the Vietnam War, what was the name of the North Vietnam communist forces?

12 In France, on 7th April, 1795, what measuring unit was made official?

13 Mother Teresa received the Order of Merit from whose hands in 1983?

14 In 1886, the longest railway tunnel in Britain to date, opened. What was its name?

15 Who was the Supreme Commander of the Allies at the end of World War One?

ANSWERS

CINEMA AND TV

1 Who played the part of Clark Gable in *Gable and Lombard?*

2 Who starred in the film *Rebel Without a Cause?*

3 Name the 'Road' films starring Crosby, Hope and Lamour.

4 In *Terms Of Endearment*, what was Jack Nicholson's character's previous occupation?

5 What wheelchair-bound actor was once *Superman?*

6 Who starred in many roles in the film *Kind Hearts and Coronets?*

7 Who played the part of Al Jolson in *The Jolson Story?*

8 Who starred in the 1933 film *King Kong?*

9 Which movie star was 'The Iron Butterfly'?

10 Which actor retired from acting in the movies at the age of four?

11 Who directed the film *Bridge on the River Kwai?*

12 Who wrote, produced, directed and starred in the film *Yentl?*

13 Who starred in the film *Who Framed Roger Rabbit?*

14 On which author's book was the film *Get Shorty* based?

15 Which British child actor is now an advertising executive?

ANSWERS

1. James Brolin. 2. James Dean. 3. ...to Hong Kong, ...to Morocco, ...to Rio, ...Singapore, ...Utopia. 4. An astronaut. 5. Christopher Reeve. 6. Dennis Price, Alec Guinness, Valerie Hobson. 7. Larry Parks. 8. King Kong himself, and Robert Armstrong, Fay Wray and Bruce Cabot. 9. Jeanette MacDonald. 10. Baby Le Roy (LeRoy Winebrenner), after about a dozen films, in 1936. 11. Sir David Lean. 12. Barbra Streisand. 13. Bob Hoskins. 14. Elmore Leonard. 15. Freddie Bartholomew, who became a vice-president of Benton & Bowles.

POPULAR MUSIC

1   Frankie goes to Hollywood's first 3 hits reached number 1, the first being, 'Relax' and the second, 'Two Tribes'. What was the third?

2   Name the Four Tops' only UK number 1?

3   What was unusual about the music of The Flying Pickets?

4   Which TV series was Joe Fagin's, 'That's Living Alright' the theme to?

5   Which musician and songwriter is the link between Depeche Mode, Yazoo and The Assembly?

6   Which new wave band's only top 10 hit was, 'Do Anything You Want To Do'?

7   Which area of London do the band East 17 come from?

8   Who recorded top ten hits with, 'Boogie Wonderland', 'After The Love Has Gone' and 'September'?

9   Thereze Bazar and David Van Day, who made up duo, 'Dollar', were originally part of which group?

10 Max Bygraves has never had a UK number 1. True or false?

11 In 1990, Donovan scored a minor hit with a re-recording of, 'Jennifer Juniper' billed as, Singing Corner meets Donovan. Who were, Singing Corner?

12 Boyzone's first UK top 10 hit was, 'Love Me For A Reason'. Who recorded the original?

13 In May 1986 who reached number 1 with, 'The Chicken Song'?

14 In 1980, 'Slodgenessabounds', recorded which drinkers' lament?

15 What nationality was Plastic Bertrand?

LITERATURE

1   Who wrote *The Lord of the Flies?*

2   Complete the proverb: 'The darkest hour...'

3   Who wrote *The Seven Pillars of Wisdom*?

4   Complete the proverb: 'Distance lends...'

I'M MORE EQUAL THAN YOU...

5   Who wrote *The Horse Whisperer*?

6   Who wrote *Schindler's Ark?*

7   The twin brothers Peter and Anthony Shaffer are famed as what?

8   'All animals are equal, but some animals are more equal that others'. Where does this phrase originate?

9   The fictional character 'The Saint' was created by whom?

10 Who wrote *The Hitchhikers Guide To The Galaxy?*

11 Complete the proverb: 'Don't have too many...'

12 Who wrote *Crime and Punishment?*

13 What, according to Bulwer Lytton, 'is mightier than the sword'?

14 Complete the proverb: 'Cleanliness is...'

15 Frederick Marryat wrote a story along the lines of the *Swiss Family Robinson*. It was called.....?

701

GENERAL KNOWLEDGE

1 What, in Switzerland, are rappen?

2 What is baba au rhum?

3 The name of which naval hero is concealed by the anagram Honor est a Nilo?

4 St Raphael is the patron saint of whom?

5 What is an eclair?

6 Which anniversary does a bronze or electrical appliance wedding celebrate?

7 The Fishes represent which sign of the Zodiac?

8 What is a Mormon?

9 How did damask come to be named?

10 What does a Tarot pack of 78 cards comprise?

11 Jews who in early times settled in Spain and Portugal are called what?

12 If you suffered from ombrophobia, what would you fear?

13 What is gazpacho?

14 Who was Jean-Baptiste Corot?

15 Of what group does one find a sheaf?

SCIENCE

1 What is the lightest metal?

2 The letters EPNS on cutlery stand for what?

3 What sort of cloud is a nimbus?

4 What is an alternator?

5 What is an icosahedron?

6 What, in WW2, was a Hurricane?

7 Archaeology is the study of what?

8 Which transparent wrapping material was invented by Jacques Brandenburger in 1908?

9 What is the name given to the calendar at present used internationally?

10 The longest side of a right-angled triangle is called what?

11 Factories for the manufacture of what were opened for the first time in Manchester in 1641?

12 What was a Luger?

13 What is dermatology?

14 Who was responsible for the special theory of relativity?

15 Who, in 1888, invented the Kodak camera?

ANSWERS

1. Lithium. 2. Electro-plated nickel silver. 3. A rain cloud. 4. A kind of electric generator which produces alternating current. 5. A solid figure with twenty faces. 6. A British fighter aircraft. 7. Human history and prehistory through human remains and antiquities. 8. Cellophane. 9. The Gregorian. 10. The hypotenuse. 11. Cotton. 12. A pistol. 13. The science of the treatment of the skin. 14. Albert Einstein. 15. George Eastman.

NATURAL HISTORY

1   What is the name give to an animal defined as a small type of llama and whose wool is prized?

2   The parsley plant is a plant relative of hemlock. True or false?

3   How many different kinds of snakes are there: (a) hundreds (b) thousands (c) dozens?

4   What is a beagle?

5   What is a marmoset?

6   Garlic is a plant relative of the lily. True or false?

7   What sort of animals are known as 'anthropoids'?

8   Is there, or was there, ever a white elephant?

9   What sort of animal is a serval?

10 A small mouse-sized creature with a slightly bushy tail is called what?

11 The radish is a member of the cabbage family. Yes or no?

12 What is a vixen?

13 The shaddock was an early form of which fruit?

14 What is the offspring of a male horse and female donkey called?

15 What, in early times, was a turnspit?

ANSWERS

1. Alpaca. 2. True. 3. About 2,400 species. 4. A breed of dog. 5. A small South American monkey. 6. True. 7. Man-like apes. 8. No. The closest colouring is a kind of darkish pink! 9. A long-legged, short-tailed African wild cat. 10. A dormouse. 11. Yes. 12. A female fox. 13. The grapefruit. 14. A hinny. 15. A small dog placed in a revolving wire cage to turn the meat on a roasting spit.

GEOGRAPHY

1 Which country was awarded the George Cross in 1942?

2 Which is the largest salt-water lake or inland sea?

3 In which county would you find the Cotswold Hills?

4 The 'Palace of Westminster' is the official title of which famous building?

5 Where in the world is Saab airport?

6 In 1935, a US aviator named James Angel crash-landed in Venezuela, discovering what?

7 The Hanging Gardens of Babylon, in Iraq were regarded as what?

8 What is familiarly known as the 'V and A'?

9 For what, historically, is Pitcairn Island famed?

10 Which is Britain's smallest colony?

11 Where in the world do they speak Letzeburgesh?

12 Which major river flows through Brazil?

13 The American capital, Washington, is in 'D.C.' What does that stand for?

14 What is the highest mountain in the continent of Africa?

15 The Andaman Islands, in the Indian Ocean are part of which country?

ENGLISH LANGUAGE

1 What was 'To wot' an old way of saying?

2 Which word means 'similar to' and 'to think well of'.

3 Can you name two words, sounding alike, which mean the same as this pair: work to a dough/want?

4 What does 'queasy' mean?

5 What is molasses, as understood by Americans?

6 What would you ask for in the United States, if you wanted a pair of knickers?

7 To what do the slang terms, 'wonga' and 'wedge' refer?

8 What does an American call rubbish?

9 What is the female version of 'hart'?

10 Which word, beginning with A, is another word for aspect or look?

11 If you have a secret idea held in reserve, what would you have up your sleeve?

12 In cockney rhyming slang, what does 'Barnet Fair' mean?

13 What is the Ship of the Desert?

14 What would you mean if you said to someone 'mea culpa'?

15 How do we get the word nark, meaning a 'police informer'?

1. To know. 2. Like. 3. Knead/need. 4. Sick, inclined to vomit. 5. Treacle. 6. Panties. 7. Money. 8. Trash. 9. Hind. 10. Appearance. 11. An ace. 12 Hair. 13. A camel. 14. You would mean 'it's my fault'. 15. It comes from the Romany (Gipsy) word nak, meaning 'nose'.

ANSWERS

SPORT

1. In American football, which player scores, 'the point after'?

2. Which Italian footballer missed the deciding penalty to give Brazil victory in the 1994 World Cup Finals?

3. Which game is faster, Rugby Fives or Eton Fives?

4. In Tennis, name the four Grand Slam events?

5. In Squash, which ball is slowest, a red dot, a blue dot or a yellow dot?

6. Name the famous snooker and billiards playing brothers who dominated the games in the middle of this century?

7. In which sport would you use, a Do, a Shinai, a Kote and a Hakama?

8. How old was Mike Tyson when he won his first World Heavyweight title?

9. Which football team plays its home matches at, 'The Hawthorns'?

10. Which form of skiing was the first to be organised competitively?

11. Between 1920 and 1928, this great swimmer won five Olympic swimming golds and set 67 World Records. He later became more famous as Tarzan. Who was he?

12. When was the Oxford and Cambridge boat race first contested: 1815, 1821, 1829 or 1840?

13. In the Tour de France, what is signified by a red polka dot jersey?

14. Over which course is 'The Oaks' run?

15. Who won the first Rugby Union World cup in 1987?

707

1. The Kicker. 2. Roberto Baggio. 3. Rugby Fives. 4. Wimbledon and the Australian, French and US Opens. 5. Yellow dot. 6. Joe and Fred Davis. 7. Kendo. 8. Twenty. 9. West Bromwich Albion. 10. Ski Jumping. 11. Johnny Weissmuller. 12. 1829. 13. King of the Mountains. 14. Epsom. 15. New Zealand.

HISTORY

1 What was the Stern Gang in Palestine?

2 Who was the last king of Scotland?

3 Sir Oswald Mosley was expelled from which political party in 1931?

4 On 10th February, 1840, at the Chapel Royal, St James's, London, a marriage took place between whom?

5 Which king of England acknowledged that he had at least 20 illegitimate children?

6 The death of Ruth Ellis in 1955 marked what?

7 What did the Soviet Union do between 1979 and 1989?

8 What happened to Rufus, son of William I, while hunting in the New Forest?

9 What disaster struck Lynmouth, Devon, in August, 1952?

10 Which former British monarch became Governor of the Bahamas in 1940?

11 What was Irgun Zvai Leumi, and what did it do in July, 1946?

12 What was the General Belgrano, and what happened to it in May, 1982?

13 In King Arthur, a place called Caerleon is mentioned. What is this place known as today?

14 Where and what was Bernicia?

15 Who was John Cabot?

CINEMA AND TV

1 Who starred in the film *Anna Karenina?*

2 Who starred in the film *Pygmalion?*

3 Which actress and singer married a French film director, and now lives near Paris?

4 Who starred in the film *Dr Strangelove?*

5 Which film, starring Jack Hawkins, dealt with the problems of a deaf child?

6 Which American child star became a leading diplomat?

7 Who starred in the film *Destry Rides Again?*

8 Which clay characters found themselves with *The Wrong Trousers* and had *A Grand Day Out?*

9 Who starred in the 1931 film *Dracula?*

10 What was the name of the actor who played a Vulcan who was Captain Kirk's second-in-command?

11 In *Roxanne,* what unusual physical feature did Steve Martin's character possess?

12 Who starred in the film *The Manchurian Candidate?*

13 Which actor gives a brilliant performance in the film *A Place in the Sun?*

14 Who starred in the film *The Grapes of Wrath?*

15 Who starred in the film *Raging Bull?*

709

POPULAR MUSIC

1. Which Pink Floyd album featured a prism and refracted light on the cover?

2. With whom did Robert Palmer record, 'I'll Be Your Baby Tonight'?

3. Who reached number 6 in 1981 with, 'Reward'?

4. What nationality are the Isley Brothers?

5. Which film did Cliff Richard star in with Una Stubbs and Melvyn Hayes?

6. Which film featured Go West's, 'King Of Wishful Thinking' on the soundtrack?

7. Bryan Adams' '(Everything I Do), I Do It For You' featured in which film?

8. What nationality are Ace of Bass?

9. In 1982, which alphabetical group had top ten hits with, 'The Look Of Love', 'Poison Arrow' and 'All Of My Heart'?

10. Adam and the Ants had three number one hits, 'Goody Two Shoes', 'Stand And Deliver' being two. What was the third?

11. Who is the lead singer with Bad Manners?

12. Which Australian clocked up the most weeks in the UK chart for the year 1988?

13. With which group did Diana Ross record a large number of her hits?

14. In 1974/75 The Wombles were achieving great chart success. Who was the, vocalist, arranger, producer and inspiration behind the act?

15. Who was the lead singer with 'The Who'?

LITERATURE

1 Complete the proverb: 'Curses, like chickens...'

2 Who is the current Poet Laureate?

3 Under what name was Eric Arthur Blair better known?

4 Who wrote *The Information?*

5 Who said, 'There's a sucker born every minute'?

6 Who wrote *Lucky Jim?*

7 Who wrote *Anna Karenina?*

8 Which well-known comedian has written a number of novels including *Stark* and *Gridlock?*

9 In which play by Shakespeare does 'Desdemona' appear?

10 Which juvenile magazine was started in 1879 to counter the 'blood and thunder' novelettes?

11 Complete the proverb: 'Desperate diseases...'

12 Who wrote *The Constant Nymph?*

13 The Bible says, 'Life for life, eye for eye, tooth for tooth...' What follows?

14 Who wrote *The Go-Between?*

15 Complete the proverb: 'Don't make a mountain...'

711

1. '...come home to roost'. 2. Ted Hughes. 3. George Orwell. 4. Martin Amis. 5. Phineas T. Barnum. 6. Kingsley Amis. 7. Leo Tolstoy. 8. Ben Elton. 9. *Othello.* 10. *The Boy's Own Paper.* 11. '...must have desperate remedies'. 12. Margaret Kennedy. 13. Hand for hand, foot for foot. 14. L.P. Hartley. 15. '...out of a molehill'.

GENERAL KNOWLEDGE

1 The Lion represents which sign of the Zodiac?

2 St Vitus is the patron saint of whom?

3 Is it true that Mormons are allowed several wives?

4 If your surname is 'Miller', what might your nickname be?

5 Of whom was Noël Coward speaking when he referred to 'Aunt Edna'?

6 The fava, or Windsor bean is better known as what?

7 Which word, beginning with post- means 'in the afternoon'?

8 What kind of food item comes from Yorkshire?

9 Name the first three who went to Widecombe Fair!

10 Name the second three who went to Widecombe Fair!

11 How was 'mayonnaise' named?

12 To the ancient Romans, who was Mars?

13 What is a paella?

14 What kind of food is a custard-cream?

15 Which musical play featured the song 'Climb Ev'ry Mountain'?

ANSWERS

1. Leo. 2. Comedians. 3. It was true, but the practice is no longer allowed.
4. Dusty. 5. A fictional audience character, typical of those attending matinees.
6. The broad bean. 7. Post-meridian (usually shortened to p.m.). 8. Pudding.
9. Bill Brewer, Jan Stewer, Peter Gurney. 10. Peter Davy, Dan'l Whidden, Harry Hawk.
11. It was first used at the port of Mahón, Minorca, and named after it. 12. The god
of war. 13. A dish of meat with saffron rice and seafood. 14. A kind of sandwich
biscuit with a centre layer of cream. 15. The Sound of Music.

SCIENCE

1 What are hailstones?

2 Who was Alfred Adler?

3 To whom was Sir Max Mallowan the archaeologist married?

4 What does 'aerofoil' mean?

5 What unit of measure is equivalent to 1.76 pints?

6 What pioneer of photography was born in Evershot in 1800?

7 What is anthomania?

8 Scaly debris under the skin on the hair is called what?

9 Who was Sigmund Freud?

10 In computer language, what is a byte?

11 The science of building massive structures is called?

12 What handy cooking device was invented by Frenchmen, Denis Papin, as long ago as 1675?

13 William Lee invented the stocking frame in 1589, the first example of what machine?

14 What did Sir Alexander Fleming discover?

15 Argent is another name for what?

ANSWERS

1. Hard balls of ice which fall during thunderstorms. 2. An Austrian psychiatrist. 3. Agatha Christie. 4. A body so shaped that it receives lift when it travels through the air. 5. A litre. 6. William Fox Talbot. 7. An overpowering desire for and love of flowers. 8. Dandruff. 9. Psychiatrist, founder of psychoanalysis. 10. Eight bits. 11. Civil engineering. 12. The pressure cooker. 13. Knitting machine. 14. Penicillin. 15. Silver.

NATURAL HISTORY

1 What is the most that an elephant can weigh: (a) 3 tons (b) 5 tons (c) 7 tons?

2 What is a group of lions called?

3 What is another name for honeysuckle?

4 What is a leech?

5 A galago is a small large-eyed animal like a small monkey. What is it also called?

6 What sort of animal is a retriever?

7 What is a cicada?

8 A basilisk is a type of lizard. True or false?

9 A group of turtles is called: (a) a bale (b) a turn (c) a shell?

10 What is woad?

11 The cauliflower is a plant relative of the cabbage. True or false?

12 What is a gecko, and what is peculiar about it?

13 A gecko in the West Indies is the smallest what of its kind?

14 What is a citron?

15 What is a buzzard?

GEOGRAPHY

1   Which British cities have underground railways?

2   Whereabouts is Nova Scotia?

3   Rhodesia is the old name for where?

4   Which is the hottest place in the world?

5   Which fictional character is said to have lived at 221b Baker Street, London?

6   Which is the deepest lake in the world?

7   Where is Beachy Head?

8   What first occurred in London on 18th December, 1890?

9   What is the capital city of Finland?

10 Which island group includes Fuerteventura and Lanzarote?

11 What is the capital of China?

12 Who lives at Lambeth Palace, London?

13 Which express American train ran between Cincinnati and New Orleans?

14 The cities of Kyoto and Nara are in which country?

15 What is the Gota opened in Sweden in 1832?

ANSWERS

1. London, Liverpool, Tyne and Wear, and Glasgow. 2. Canada. 3. Zimbabwe. 4. Death Valley, California, 120°F. 5. Sherlock Holmes. 6. Baikal, Siberia, is 5,371 feet deep. 7. A headland on the south coast near Eastbourne. 8. The opening of the first underground electric railway in the world. 9. Helsinki. 10. The Canary Islands. 11. Beijing. 12. Archbishop of Canterbury. 13. The Chattanooga Choo-Choo. 14. Japan. 15. A canal.

ENGLISH LANGUAGE

1 What's the plural of 'chateau'?

2 What does R.S.V.P. stand for?

3 Which single word means someone who expects the best will happen?

4 What does the German word 'Kaiser' mean?

5 What, in the 1920s, was a 'bootlegger' in the United States?

6 What does 'at a loose end' mean?

7 If you want to play draughts with an American, what would he call the game?

8 What happens if you 'send someone to Coventry'?

9 Which word, beginning with A, means forbear or refrain?

10 Which word, beginning with R, means abominable or disgusting?

11 What are 'darbies'?

12 Which word, beginning with M, means meek or unpretentious?

13 There are nine possessive pronouns. Name three.

14 Which word, beginning with E, can mean elongate or stretch?

15 What was 'To ween' an old way of saying?

SPORT

1   The 'Yankees' baseball team comes from which city?

2   In Rugby Union who competes for the Calcutta Cup?

3   The Hennessy Gold Cup is run over which race course?

4   From where does the sport of Pelota originate?

5   What other sport is regularly played at Lord's Cricket Ground?

6   Who was the number two driver for Ferrari's Formula One team in the 1997 & 1998 seasons?

7   What calibre rifles are used in the Biathlon, Nordic Skiing event?

8   In a four man Bobsleigh, where does the, 'brakeman' sit?

9   In championship darts from what score do competitors start each leg?

10 In Judo if the Referee says, 'Hajime!', what should you do?

11 In cycling who wears the yellow jersey?

12 In which year did Rhythmic Gymnastics first appear in the Olympic Games?

13 In an Olympic Discus competition, how many throws is each contestant allowed?

14 For which Formula 1 team was Ayrton Senna driving, when he was killed?

15 Which 1970s Chelsea player reputedly became the object of Raquel Welch's desire, after she watched him play at Stamford Bridge?

ANSWERS

1 New York. 2. Scotland and England. 3. Newbury. 4. The Basque region of Spain. 5. Real Tennis. 6. Eddie Irvine. 7. .22. 8. At the rear. 9. 501. 10. Start fighting. 11. The Race Leader. 12. 1984. 13. Six. 14. Williams. 15. Peter Osgood.

HISTORY

1 Where would you look for the site of ancient Carthage?

2 What post did Gaelic scholar, Dr Douglas Hyde take in June, 1938?

3 Who was the last Viceroy of India?

4 John George Diefenbaker was prime minister of which country?

5 What was the League of Nations?

6 Who was 'Bloody Mary'?

7 Who was the famed American John Brown?

8 Which Royal person in Britain died of typhoid fever on 14th December, 1861?

9 Who met whom in Ujiji, Africa, on 10 November, 1871?

10 The first meeting of which international peace body was held in Paris in 1920?

11 Which French ruler was reported to be afraid of cats?

12 Which American senator was fatally wounded in Los Angeles on 5th June, 1968?

13 What became the name of the territory administered by the British South Africa Company?

14 Which notorious Australian bushranger was hanged at Melbourne in 1880?

15 What historical event took place in England from 1642 to 1646?

CINEMA AND TV

1   The Italian star Rossano Brazzi was a sports champion. In what field?

2   The US character actress Marie Blake was sister of which famous singing star of Hollywood?

3   Who, in the movies, was the 'It Girl'?

4   Who starred in the film *Sunset Boulevard?*

5   Which radio show featured the characters Eccles and Bluebottle?

6   Who played the part of George Raft in *The George Raft Story?*

7   *Bananas, Sleeper* and *Love and Death* were films made by which New York-based director?

8   From which film and stage show did the song 'Summertime' come?

9   Which film starred Johnny Depp as an eccentric B-movie director?

10   Who starred in the film *Road to Morocco?*

11   In the *Dixon of Dock Green* TV series, who needed to be raised from the dead?

12   Which movie actor started out named Malden Sekulovich?

13   What was the name of the sequel to the film *Jurassic Park?*

14   Who starred in the film *Ghostbusters?*

15   From which film and stage show did the song 'There's No Business Like Show Business' come?

ANSWERS

1. He was featherweight boxing champion of Italy. 2. Jeanette MacDonald. 3. Clara Bow. 4. William Holden, Gloria Swanson. 5. *The Goon Show.* 6. Ray Danton. 7. Woody Allen. 8. *Porgy and Bess.* 9. Ed Wood. 10. Bing Crosby, Bob Hope, Dorothy Lamour. 11. P.C. Dixon. In the film *The Blue Lamp,* he was shot dead. 12. Karl Malden. 13. *The Lost World.* 14. Bill Murray, Dan Aykroyd. 15. *Annie Get Your Gun.*

POPULAR MUSIC

1   Which Kenyan vocalist enjoyed chart success in the 1970s and 1980s with, 'The Last Farewell' and 'The Skye Boat Song'?

2   T'Pau enjoyed chart success in the late 1980's with, 'Heart And Soul' and 'China In Your Hand'. Which TV series gave the band its name?

3   With whom did the Beachboys, re-release, 'Fun Fun Fun', in March 1996?

4   In the early 1960's, who had UK number 1's with, 'You Don't Know', and 'Walking Back To Happiness'?

5   Which hard rock band released the album, 'Break Like The Wind' featuring collaborations with Cher and Jeff Beck?

6   What sporting event helped Luciano Pavarotti reach number 1 with 'Nessun Dorma'?

7   With whom did Van Morrison record, 'When God Shines His Light', in 1989?

8   Who recorded the best-selling album, 'Jagged Little Pill'?

9   With whom did Craig McLachlan re-record the *Grease* song, 'You're The One That I Want', in 1993?

10 Louise was formerly with which all-girl band?

11 Which band's first full vocal song 'Firestarter', reached number one in 1996?

12 Which actor/singer has had considerable chart success, as well as playing Oz in 'Auf Wiedersehen Pet', and writing and starring in the TV drama, Crocodile Shoes?

13 Which band was Alison Moyet half of in 1983?

14 Who had top ten hits in the early 1970's with 'All The Young Dudes', 'All The Way From Memphis' and 'Roll Away The Stone'?

15 What was the charge when singer, Mark Morrison was arrested?

1. Roger Whittaker. 2. Star Trek. 3. Status Quo. 4. Helen Shapiro. 5. Spinal Tap. 6. Italia 90 World Cup. 7. Cliff Richard. 8. Alanis Morissette. 9. Debbie Gibson 10. Eternal. 11. Prodigy. 12. Jimmy Nail. 13. Yazoo. 14. Mott the Hoople. 15. Possession of a Stun Gun.

LITERATURE

1   What happened to the character 'Jack Griffin' in a novel by H.G. Wells?

2   Who was Honoré de Balzac?

3   Complete the proverb: 'As well be hanged for a sheep...'

4   Complete the proverb: 'Conscience does make...'

5   According to Voltaire, 'God is always on the side' of what?

6   'Daisy Buchanan' appears in which novel by F. Scott Fitzgerald?

7   Who wrote *The Time Machine?*

8   What 'desert island' story was written by R.M. Ballantyne?

9   Who wrote *A Passage to India?*

10 John Milton wrote: 'And did those feet in ancient time...?' how did he continue?

11 A.E.W. Mason wrote a book about courage and cowardice. Can you name it?

12 Complete the proverb: 'Blessed is he who expects nothing...'

13 Rupert Brooke wrote, 'Stands the Church clock at ten to three?' How did he continue?

14 Who wrote *Tristram Shandy?*

15 The Wesley brothers, Charles and John wrote hymns. How many? (a) 1,100 (b) 550 (c) 5,500

GENERAL KNOWLEDGE

1 Who was the Yorkshire Ripper?

2 Who invented the lawnmower?

3 What is a 'romany rye'?

4 What kind of food item comes from Bakewell?

5 A legume with flat, dishlike seeds is called what?

6 Who was Honoré de Balzac?

7 St Lawrence is the patron saint of whom?

8 What kind of food was known as a 'wally'?

9 Which Sunday newspaper was first issued on 28th January, 1990

10 What did Mrs Mary Baker Eddy found?

11 What are gnocchi?

12 Who is the reigning prince of Luxembourg?

13 St Fiacre is the patron saint of whom?

14 According to the 'language of flowers', what does the peony signify?

15 What suits are found in a traditional pack of Tarot cards?

SCIENCE

1　Linus Yale invented what device in 1865?

2　What sort of vehicle was a Sherman?

3　Who invented milk chocolate?

4　What kind of animals would an entomologist study?

5　What is toxiphobia?

6　What are an A340 and a 767?

7　In 1901 Alva J. Fisher invented and developed the first domestic machine of this kind, electrically powered. It was what?

8　What is mycology?

9　What is bone china?

10　Who invented the fountain pen?

11　Oil of vitriol is an old name for which chemical?

12　The study of the atmosphere and the weather is called what?

13　What does a sextant measure?

14　What did Christopher Cockerell invent?

15　What is Jacques-Yves Cousteau famed for?

ANSWERS

1. The cylinder lock. 2. A military tank. 3. Daniel Peter, Switzerland, 1875. 4. Insects. 5. A fear of being poisoned. 6. Modern jet airliners. 7. The washing machine. 8. The study of fungi. 9. An imitation porcelain containing bone ash. 10. Lewis Waterman in 1884. 11. Sulphuric acid. 12. Meteorology. 13. Latitude. 14. Hovercraft. 15. Underwater exploration.

NATURAL HISTORY

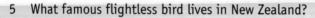

1   What are the two kinds of rats found in Britain?

2   What sort of animal is a Kerry Blue?

3   Which fish is faster - the sailfin or the guppy?

4   The fig is a member of the mulberry family. Yes or no?

5   What famous flightless bird lives in New Zealand?

6   What kind of animal could be described as a Landrace?

7   Which is the world's fastest mammal?

8   What is a crowberry?

9   What is a bustard?

10   Which mammals have the shortest life?

11   What is a tuna?

12   Which is the only bird in the world which can hover?

13   Which plant is called 'queen-of-the-meadows'?

14   Why is a rattlesnake able to rattle?

15   A group of goldfinches is called: (a) a charm (b) a guild.

724

GEOGRAPHY

1 Which continent contains more than 50% of the world's population?

2 Constantinople is the old name for where?

3 Where is the River Tamar?

4 What island was known as Van Diemen's Land?

5 The 7th Earl of Shaftesbury is commemorated by which central London statue?

6 Where is the driest place on Earth?

7 What are the Ellice Islands called now?

8 Which town is geographically nearest the centre of England?

9 Where in the world is Richmond airport?

10 Which town traverses two major rivers in Berkshire?

11 What is the capital of Brazil?

12 What, in ancient times, stood at the harbour of Alexandria, Egypt?

13 What are the names of the four main Channel Islands?

14 Why was the character 'Paddington Bear' so called?

15 What is the currency used in India?

ENGLISH LANGUAGE

1 To an American, what is the difference between a jalopy and a junker?

2 To what drink did the city of Geneva give its name?

3 A scattermouch is (a) a native of Asia Minor (b) a buffoon (c) a large four-wheeled wagon.

4 Which word, beginning in E, means raise or uplift?

5 How did the expression 'to eat humble pie' originate?

6 Can you name two words, sounding alike, which mean: 'male child' and 'floating anchor'?

7 What do the letters 'ad lib.' stand for?

8 What is the female version of 'stag'?

9 What does 'eldritch' mean?

10 What is a 'gringo'?

11 What is a 'poncho'?

12 What is meant by 'Strine'?

13 Which word, beginning with P, means toxin or venom?

14 What did people do when they were 'streaking'?

15 Would you be prosecuted if you 'went off in a high dudgeon'?

SPORT

1 In Golf, what is the term used for two under par at a hole?

2 Where did the 1992 summer Olympics take place?

3 After retiring from international competition, which British shot putter made his name by winning international, 'Strong Man', competitions?

4 Which Scottish footballer is the only player to have scored 100 goals in both the English and Scottish football leagues?

5 How many players are there in a Baseball team?

6 With which sport do you associate Carl Fogarty?

7 What six-a-side sport starts with a 'face-off'?

8 In which sport would you compete for the Davis Cup?

9 Which sport was ruled by the Hambledon Club, from Halfpenny Down in the 1700s?

10 Which country do the, 'Socceroos', represent?

11 Who won the 1986 World Cup?

12 In 1998 what colour was a McLaren Formula 1 Car?

13 With which sport do you associate Laura Davies?

14 What nationality is tennis star Mark Philippoussis?

15 By what score did the England Rugby Union team lose the first test against Australia, on their 1998 tour, (their heaviest defeat in 150 years)?

1. Eagle. 2. Barcelona. 3. Geoff Capes. 4. Kenny Dalglish. 5. Nine. 6. Motor Cycling. 7. Ice Hockey. 8. Tennis. 9. Cricket. 10. Australia. 11. Argentina. 12. Silver. 13. Golf. 14. Australian. 15. 76-0.

HISTORY

1   Who, in WW2, was Bomber Harris?

2   In 1867, Quebec, Ontario, New Brunswick and Nova Scotia united to form what?

3   Approximately how old was Henry VI when he came to the throne?

4   Where and what was Lidice?

5   Which English monarch was excommunicated by the Pope in 1570?

6   Which British monarch spoke no English?

7   Who was the first British monarch to live in Buckingham Palace?

8   Who was imprisoned on Devil's Island on 22nd December, 1894?

9   Which historic document was published by Marx and Engels in February, 1848?

10 When did decimal coinage replace the old pounds, shillings and pence?

11 Who said, "A modest little man, with much to be modest about", and who was he referring to?

12 Who was Richard Milhous Nixon?

13 What was first dropped on 6th August, 1945?

14 What was the name of the tax paid by the Britons to keep out Danish invaders?

15 Which governor-general in India was impeached for alleged corruption?

ANSWERS

1. Sir Arthur Harris, Marshal of the RAF. 2. The Dominion of Canada. 3. Ten months. 4. A mining village, in Czechoslovakia, totally destroyed by the Nazis as a punishment. 5. Queen Elizabeth I. 6. King George I. 7. Queen Victoria. 8. Alfred Dreyfus. 9. The Communist Manifesto. 10. On 15th February, 1971. 11. Winston Churchill said this about Clement Attlee. 12. He was the 37th American president. 13. The atom bomb over Hiroshima. 14. Danegeld. 15. Warren Hastings. He was acquitted.

CINEMA AND TV

1 Which movie star was the 'Man You Love to Hate'?

2 How many times has *Doctor Jekyll and Mr Hyde* been filmed: (a) 24 (b) 43 (c) 46?

3 About whom was this remark made: 'Most of the time he sounds like he has a mouth full of wet toilet paper'?

4 Who starred in the film *Vertigo?*

5 What event was the film *Dog Day Afternoon* about?

6 Who starred in the film *Zulu Dawn?*

7 Who devised the T.V. series *Grange Hill* and *Brookside?*

8 From which stage show did the song 'Wand'rin' Star' come?

9 Who, in movies and television, was the 'Meanest Man in the World'?

10 Exactly what was *The Titfield Thunderbolt* in the 1952 film?

11 Which spoof picture of a terrible heavy metal band featured their albums, 'Smell The Glove' and 'Shark Sandwich'?

12 Who starred in the film *The Railway Children?*

13 Which veteran chat show host was savaged by Rod Hull and Emu?

14 Which oriental actor played alongside Peter Sellers in the *Pink Panther* films?

15 Who starred in the 1989 film *Henry V?*

1. Erich von Stroheim. 2. (c) 46. 3. Marlon Brando. 4. James Stewart. 5. A failed bank robbery. 6. Burt Lancaster, Peter O'Toole. 7. Alec Guinness, Joan Greenwood. 8. *Paint Your Wagon.* 9. Jack Benny. 10. A train. 11. *This Is Spinal Tap.* 12. Dinah Sheridan, Bernard Cribbins, Jenny Agutter. 13. Michael Parkinson. 14. Burt Kwok. 15. Kenneth Branagh, Derek Jacobi, Brian Blessed.

POPULAR MUSIC

1   Name Kylie's younger sister who's also had chart hits?

2   Who was the bass player with The Rolling Stones?

3   Which actor and singer reached number one in 1956 with 'Memories Are Made Of This'?

4   In 1976 Laurie Lee and the Dipsticks' reached number four with 'Convoy GB'. Name the hairy Disk Jockey who made up half the act?

5   In which year was Elvis Presley number 1 in the UK chart with, 'All Shook Up'; 1951, 1957, 1959 or 1962?

6   Who released the album, 'All Mod Cons'?

7   Which singer, who's real name was Jerry Dawsey, reached number one in 1967 with 'Release Me' and 'The Last Waltz'?

8   Which singer married Whitney Houston?

9   What nationality were the group, Hothouse Flowers?

10 With which band was Buddy Holly the lead singer?

11 'I'm Into Something Good' was a debut hit for which British band?

12 What was the name of Jimi Hendrix's best-known band?

13 Which band were originally called Composition Of Sound?

14 Pete Best was the original drummer with which group?

15 With whom did Gabrielle record 'If You Ever' in 1996?

LITERATURE

1 Who, in *Treasure Island,* was Captain Flint?

2 Which famous children's book did L.M. Montgomery write?

3 Complete Oliver Cromwell's line: 'Put your trust in God and...'

4 Complete the proverb: 'As you make your bed...'

5 Who wrote *Lolita?*

6 The character 'Topsy' appears in which famous book?

7 Who wrote the play *The Second Mrs Tanqueray?*

8 Robert Browning wrote: 'Oh, to be in England...' How did he continue?

9 The character 'Emma Roualt' appears in which famous French book?

10 'Age cannot wither her, nor custom stale her infinite variety'. Who is the line about?

11 In which Shakespeare play do 'the three Witches' appear?

12 Who wrote *Babbitt?*

13 The character 'Sergeant Troy' appears in which famous book?

14 How does the following limerick continue: There was a young lady named Bright / Whose speed was faster than light?

15 Which Durrell had a brother called Gerald?

1. The parrot. 2. Anne of Green Gables. 3. 'Keep your powder dry'.
4. '...so you must lie in it'. 5. Vladimir Nabokov. 6. *Uncle Tom's Cabin.*
7. Sir Arthur Pinero. 8. 'Now that April's there'. 9. *Madame Bovary.*
10. Cleopatra, according to Shakespeare. 11. *Macbeth.* 12. Sinclair Lewis. 13. *Far From the Madding Crowd.* 14. She set out one day / In a relative way / And returned home the previous night. 15. Lawrence Durrell.

GENERAL KNOWLEDGE

1   Which anniversary does a china wedding celebrate?

2   What is a sorbet?

3   What is an atheist?

4   Which 19th-century event is concealed by the anagram I require love in a subject?

5   St Valentine is the patron saint of whom?

6   Which European princess had children named Albert, Caroline and Stephanie?

7   How many deadly sins are there?

8   Which anniversary does a coral wedding celebrate?

9   Who is the patron saint of wine-growers?

10 The river Medway runs through Kent. What is a man born east of it called?

11 Who would be taking the advice 'vamp till ready'?

12 Who is Ken Dodd?

13 Which architect designed Waterloo Bridge and the present Anglican Cathedral in Liverpool?

14 St Augustine is the patron saint of whom?

15 What is doner kebab?

SCIENCE

1 What is meant by the 'occult sciences'?

2 How many sides has a heptagon?

3 A land region devoid of water is called what?

4 What does an altimeter measure?

5 What are cantilever, beam and cable-stayed types of?

6 Saturn is the only planet that has rings around it. True or false?

7 What was the R101?

8 What is the familiar name for sodium bicarbonate?

9 What is a dodecahedron?

10 What is alabaster?

11 What is phobophobia?

12 Who invented the centigrade thermometer?

13 What is a rectangle?

14 Pollenosis is a name for a common complaint, usually called what?

15 What is a billion?

NATURAL HISTORY

1 The avens plant is also called what?

2 What is a ratel?

3 What sort of animal is called a Shorthorn?

4 The ancestors of horses and rhinoceroses were very alike. What does this prove?

5 Which is the largest British butterfly?

6 A booby is a kind of sea-bird. True or false?

7 What is another name for the sycamore?

8 A gavial is a water reptile - a long slender version of what?

9 Chives are members of the lily family. Yes or no?

10 How big is the biggest spider: (a) about 7 inches overall (b) about eight inches overall (c) about ten inches overall?

11 What kind of animal could be described as a Berkshire?

12 Do sea birds drink salt sea-water?

13 Is an ant-lion a large ant?

14 What is jute?

15 The ladybird is a kind of beetle. True or false?

GEOGRAPHY

1 Where in London is 'Poets' Corner'?

2 What kind of people would go sailing in a dhow?

3 What are the Gilbert Islands in the Pacific now called?

4 There are four Ben Lomonds: two in Australia, one in the US and one in Scotland which is the tallest of the four. True or false?

5 Which cathedral in the United Kingdom has the tallest spire?

6 What country is the Pacific island of Luzon part of?

7 The term 'Kypros' or 'Kibris' refers to which country?

8 Which is the world's longest railway tunnel?

9 Where are the Atlas Mountains?

10 What is meant by 'Asia Minor'?

11 Where would you find Derwent Water?

12 Where is the River Dove?

13 What is the deepest part of the Atlantic Ocean called?

14 The term 'Österreich' refers to which country?

15 How long is the Eurotunnel?

ANSWERS

1. In Westminster Abbey. 2. The Arabs. 3. Kiribati. 4. False. The Scottish mountain is the lowest. 5. Salisbury Cathedral. 6. The Philippines. 7. Cyprus. 8. The Simplon, 12. miles. 9. Algeria, North Africa. 10. The part of Turkey in Asia. 11. It's a lake in the Lake District, Cumbria. 12. In Staffordshire and Derbyshire. 13. Puerto Rico Trench. 14. Austria. 15. 31 miles.

ENGLISH LANGUAGE

1 An ayah is: (a) an Indian nurse (b) a Mediterranean boat (c) a Malayan knife?

2 When an American refers to the 'hood' of his car, what does it mean?

3 What is a sombrero?

4 What would a fanlight in your hall be called by an American?

5 What happens if you, 'go off the deep end'?

6 What is wrong with this phrase: 'The freshly cleaned ladies' toilet'?

7 Which is the only possessive pronoun which takes an apostrophe?

8 What's the difference between emigrate and immigrate?

9 What is another word for motto or saying?

10 What is the meaning of the acronym DPP?

11 What is the name for someone who studies the sound of words?

12 What is the female version of 'gander'?

13 What does an American mean by a 'derby' hat?

14 'King Arthur telephoned his wife every day'. This is patently untrue, but what is the name for this sort of phrase?

15 What happens if you 'chance your arm'?

SPORT

1 Edgbaston is the home ground of which County cricket team?

2 Name Sheffield Wednesday's football ground?

3 Which former striker and Gladiators host was accused of match fixing?

4 What happened to Colombian defender Andres Escobar when he returned home after scoring an own goal to put his team out of the 1994 World Cup?

5 How long is a squash racket's handle: 27ins, 29ins, 30ins or 32ins?

6 With which sport do you associate Canadians, Gasper & Benoit?

7 True or false in the 1900 Olympic Games, live birds were used in the pigeon shooting contest?

8 From which country does Muki boxing come?

9 If you were a Juryo entering a Basho, which sport would you be taking part in?

10 In total how many players are permitted in an Ice Hockey team?

11 How many points are awarded for a Drop Goal in Rugby League?

12 Which saloon car racing team did Nigel Mansell drive for as a guest in 1998?

13 Which British football team play their home games at Carrow Road?

14 Who won the 1997 US Masters golf tournament?

15 In which sport do you have a square wicket and a bat shaped like a frying pan?

HISTORY

1   By what name is Siddhartha Gautama better-known?

2   What was the surname of King Edward VII?

3   Who was George Lansbury, and what publication did he start in 1919?

4   Who was the last of the Plantagenet kings?

5   What in the 1930s, was the Anschluss?

6   What international document was signed on 11th November, 1918?

7   Who conquered Mexico for Spain?

8   In 1922, Benito Mussolini led a march on Rome. What was the result?

9   Who is James Earle Carter?

10 Who was Muhammed Ali Jinnah?

11 Who was Calvin Coolidge?

12 In 1945, the 15th August was celebrated as VJ Day. What was that?

13 What or who was Vidkun Quisling?

14 Who was the oldest British monarch when they died?

15 What was Buchenwald, Germany, notorious for during the Second World War?

CINEMA AND TV

1 What silent movie great starred in *The Freshman?*

2 What T.V. series did David Hasselhof star in before *Baywatch?*

3 Name four films whose title starts with the word Top?

4 Who starred in the film *Saturday Night and Sunday Morning?*

5 Fleago, Bingo, Drooper and Snorky were who?

6 What T.V. police drama starred Jack Lord and was set on a beautiful set of islands?

7 Who starred in the film *To Kill a Mockingbird?*

8 What was the name of the cowboy toy in the film *Toy Story?*

9 Who directed in the film *The Searchers?*

10 Which famous soul singer took a starring role in one of the *Mad Max* films?

11 Who starred in the film *The Fallen Idol?*

12 Name the two films for which Tom Hanks won best actor Oscars?

13 Who directed the films *The Lost Weekend* and *The Apartment?*

14 Who starred in the 1927 film *The Jazz Singer?*

15 Which French actor and singer was the following remark made about, 'A great artiste, but a small human being'?

739

POPULAR MUSIC

1 In 1995, who recorded the album 'Different Class'?

2 Which 1991 Alan Parker film depicted the forming of a fictitious Dublin Soul band, and featuring reworked versions of classic Soul songs?

3 What band was lead by Steve Marriot?

4 Which group is associated with Australian, Nick Cave?

5 Name Blue Oyster Cult's only hit single released in 1978?

6 In August 1995, the media whipped up competition between Blur's 'Country House' and Oasis' 'Roll With It'. Which Single sold the most copies?

7 In 1992 who recorded the album '0898'?

8 What was the Beatles' first single to hit the Charts in 1962?

9 Who recorded her only number one hit with Nielson's 'Without You'?

10 Who had top ten hits with 'Heaven Is A Place On Earth', 'I Get Weak' and 'Leave A Light On'?

11 In 1995 who recorded the album 'Paranoid and Sunburnt'?

12 In the early 1970's which family was David Cassidy a member of?

13 Who's first solo album release was called 'Faith'?

14 Which female singer recorded 'Unforgettable' with her dead father in 1991?

15 Which cartoon characters dueted with Cher, singing 'I Got You Babe' in 1994?

1. Pulp. 2. The Commitments. 3. The Small Faces. 4. The Bad Seeds. 5. '(Don't Fear) The Reaper'. 6. Blur's 'Country House'. 7. Beautiful South. 8. 'Love Me Do'. 9. Mariah Carey. 10. Belinda Carlisle. 11. Skunk Anansie. 12. The Partridge Family. 13. George Michael. 14. Natalie Cole. 15. Beavis and Butt-head.

LITERATURE

1   Dikrán Kuyumjian is better known as whom?

2   Complete the proverb: 'The quality of mercy is not...'

3   Complete the proverb: 'A cat may...'

4   Who wrote *Whisky Galore?*

5   According to the old recitation, to the north of which city is the Chinese idol?

6   Who wrote *Death on the Nile?*

7   Complete the Shakespearean line: 'A rose by any other name would...'

8   According to Edward Lear, in what did the Jumbies go to sea?

9   Which newspaper would you buy if you were an actor?

10 Who was François-Eugène Vidocq?

11 Who wrote *Far From the Madding Crowd?*

12 Dashiell Hammett created a husband-and-wife team named 'Nick and Nora Charles' What was the name of the book?

13 Agatha Christie created 'Hercule Poirot'. What was the name of her other major detective?

14 In which work by Dylan Thomas does the character 'Captain Cat' appear?

15 'Fagin' is a character in which book by Dickens?

GENERAL KNOWLEDGE

1 Which anniversary does a copper or pottery wedding celebrate?

2 The Ram represents which sign of the Zodiac?

3 What were, or are, the Gnomes of Zurich?

4 Which word, beginning with post- means 'published after the death of the composer or author'?

5 Indian ink didn't come from India. Where does it come from?

6 Who is the patron saint of sailors?

7 Dutch clocks didn't come from Holland. Where do they come from?

8 What is lobscouse?

9 Who, on stage in 1937, did the Lambeth Walk?

10 What does the abbreviation NATO stand for?

11 St Hubert is the patron saint of whom?

12 Which kind of bridge is largely played nowadays: Auction or Contract?

13 Which spacecraft was the first to land on Mars?

14 Tuesday is named after Tiw, or Tyr, the German god of the rules of war. True or false?

15 Who invented jeans?

SCIENCE

1   An important medical preventive system was invented in 1796 by Edward Jenner. What was it?

2   What aerial device was invented by André-Jacques Garnerin in 1802?

3   What is varicella another name for?

4   Which medical procedure involves the use of many needles all over the body?

5   What is a bathyscape?

6   What is acoustics?

7   What is a chiropodist?

8   What is measured by the gallon?

9   What is humidity?

10 Stainless steel is an alloy of which metals?

11 What is measured by a watt?

12 Who was Isambard Kingdom Brunel?

13 What is an ammonite?

14 What does the prefix 'kilo-' mean?

15 The femur is another name for which bone?

ANSWERS

1. Vaccination. 2. The parachute. 3. Chicken-pox. 4. Acupuncture 5. A diving vessel for underwater exploration. 6. The science of sound. 7. One who practises in, and deals with, ailments of the feet. 8. Liquid. 9. The amount of moisture in the atmosphere. 10. Iron, chromium and nickel. 11. Power. 12. Inventor and engineer. 13. An extinct mollusc with a coiled shell. 14. A thousand. 15. The thigh bone.

NATURAL HISTORY

1   What is cassava?

2   What is an iguana?

3   What sort of animal is a Saint Bernard?

4   The lory is a member of which very noisy family of birds?

5   What is the name for the large South American cat with leopard-like spots?

6   What sort of animal is a chihuahua?

7   What is a caterpillar the larva of?

8   Is the horn on a rhinoceros similar to a tusk on an elephant?

9   What is a more familiar name for the cavy?

10 A group of ants is called an angle or a colony?

11 What is the name for the large, spotted wild cat, smaller than a tiger?

12 What sort of animal is a Doberman pinscher?

13 What is a young kangaroo called?

14 A mammal with heavy armour plates on its body is called what?

15 What kind of animal is said to gobble?

ANSWERS

1. A plant whose roots produce a pleasant-tasting starch. 2. A large, tree-dwelling lizard. 3. A breed of dog. 4. The parrots. 5. The jaguar. 6. A breed of dog. 7. A moth or butterfly. 8. No. A rhinoceros horn is made of compacted hair. 9. The guinea-pig. 10. A colony. 11. The leopard. 12. A breed of dog. 13. A joey. 14. An armadillo. 15. A turkey.

GEOGRAPHY

1 The old country of Babylonia is now called?

2 Which major American city stands on the Hudson river?

3 Camulodunum was the ancient name for which Essex city?

4 What is the capital of India?

5 Where is Bermuda?

6 Provençal is a language spoken in which part of the world?

7 How many people live on the Scilly Isles: 25, 250 or 2,500?

8 In which city would you find Waverley railway station?

9 In which country does the Mekong river end?

10 Where and what is Sandringham?

11 What language is spoken in the Channel Isles?

12 What was Sri Lanka previously known as?

13 What is Abyssinia now called?

14 In which country is the town of Rotarua?

15 Persia is the old name for which country?

1. Iraq. 2. New York City. 3. Colchester. 4. New Delhi. 5. In the West Indies. 6. Southern France. 7. About 2,500. 8. Edinburgh. 9. Vietnam. 10. It's a royal residence in Norfolk. 11. English, and a dialect of French called Jerseyaise. 12. Ceylon. 13. Ethiopia. 14. New Zealand. 15. Iran.

ENGLISH LANGUAGE

1 Can you give another word, beginning with S, for hygienic or antiseptic?

2 Complete this simile: 'To turn up like a bad...'

3 What is the name for someone who studies the origin of words?

4 Which of these three spellings is correct: (a) desicated, (b) desiccated or (c) dessicated?

5 Which word, beginning with H, means infidel or pagan?

6 What is the difference between 'yolk' and 'yoke'?

7 If someone says 'the ball is in your court', what does it mean?

8 What's the male version of a 'maidservant'?

9 Which of the following words is misspelled: Sythe, paralel, conquerer?

10 What's the male version of an 'usherette'?

11 Which word, starting with N, can mean armada or fleet?

12 Which word, starting with A, means detached or reserved?

13 What was 'Thenceforth' an old way of saying?

14 What is meant by a persona non grata?

15 What is the female version of 'boar'?

1. Sanitary or sterile. 2. '...penny'. 3. Etymologist. 4. (b) desiccated. 5. Heathen. 6. The first means 'the yellow part of an egg', and the second is a kind of wooden collar for oxen. 7. You are responsible. 8. Manservant. 9. All of them. They should be scythe, parallel, conqueror. 10. Usher. 11. Navy. 12. Aloof. 13. From that time onwards. 14. Someone who is not in favour or not welcome. 15. Sow.

SPORT

1   Which British swimmer won a breaststroke gold medal in the 1980 Olympics?

2   With which sport do you associate Mary Peters?

3   What do, Chris Waddle, Stuart Pearce and Paul Ince have in common?

4   Name Washington's American football team?

5   Which Scottish defender suffered the indignity of Paul Gascoigne lobbing the ball over his head to then chip it into the goal, during Euro 96?

6   With which sport do you associate David Bryant?

7   Which British sports personality of the year gained notoriety for swearing while collecting the trophy from the Princess Royal?

8   With which athletic event do you associate Sergei Bubka?

9   Which England football manager was controversially portrayed as a turnip by the tabloid press?

10   Great Britain have won the Olympic Hockey gold medal three times. True or false?

11   Which British entrepreneur owns the London Broncos Rugby League team?

12   Who captained England's Grand Slam, winning team in 1980?

13   With which sport do you associate the, 'Cresta Run'?

14   In which country is the Paul Ricard racing circuit?

15   Name Miami's American football team?

HISTORY

1 Which driverless, computer-run railway began operating on 30th July, 1987?

2 What was the occupation of Adolf Hitler's father?

3 What is the Orange Order?

4 11 Victoria Crosses were awarded as a result of an action which took place against Zulus in 1879. What was it?

5 Which king of England is believed to have had 23 children?

6 Who was James Garfield?

7 Which head of state visited China on a 7-day visit in October, 1986?

8 What was the Lusitania?

9 Which future British monarch was born on 9th November, 1841?

10 What was the Spanish Inquisition?

11 What was the Comintern?

12 Who were the Bolsheviks?

13 In 1933 in Germany, all political parties except one were banned. Which one?

14 Who was the fattest of all British monarchs?

15 Who was 'the Lady with the Lamp'?

CINEMA AND TV

1   Prince Charles is credited with having described someone as, 'Terribly nice one minute, and well, not so nice the next.' Who was he talking about?

2   What comic-book character did Buster Crabbe play?

3   What animal follows the landlord Jack Lemmon in *Under the Yum Yum Tree?*

4   Which film featured Kevin Costner and Whitney Houston in lead roles?

5   In the film *Turner and Hooch,* who was Hooch?

6   Who starred in the film *Caesar and Cleopatra?*

7   Who starred in the film *My Darling Clementine?*

8   In the film *Pulp Fiction,* what was a Quarterpounder with cheese in France called?

9   Which movie star's real name was Ruth Elizabeth Davis?

10 Which movie star's real name was Ruby Stevens?

11 Who has been married to Frank Sinatra and Woody Allen?

12 Who starred in the film *Home Alone?*

13 Who played the ambitious, smalltown T.V. star in the film *To Die For?*

14 Who played the name part in the film *Alfie?*

15 Which cartoon show featured Thelma and Shaggy amongst others?

1. Frank Sinatra. 2. Flash Gordon. 3. A cat. 4. *The Bodyguard.* 5. A big dog. 6. Claude Rains and Vivien Leigh. 7. Henry Fonda, Linda Darnell. 8. A Royale. 9. Bette Davis. 10. Barbara Stanwyck. 11. Mia Farrow. 12. Macauley Culkin, Joe Pesci, Daniel Stern. 13. Nicole Kidman. 14. Michael Caine. 15. *Scooby Do.*

POPULAR MUSIC

1 Which group, 'Lost That Lovin' Feeling'?

2 Who recorded the album 'Stanley Road' in 1995?

3 Who sang 'I Feel Good' and 'Sex Machine' and was known as 'the hardest working man in showbusiness'?

4 Which guitarist recorded a version of the US National Anthem in the late 60's, on his left-handed 'Strat'?

5 What links the bands Genesis and Mike And The Mechanics

6 'One Day In Your Life' was the first number one for which US mega star?

7 Which actress and singer featured Neil Kinnock in her pop video during his General Election Campaign?

8 Who walked 'On The Bright Side Of The Road' looking for his 'Brown-eyed Girl', saying 'Baby Please Don't Go'?

9 What was the title of Bjork's second album?

10 Who recorded the album 'Wild Wood' in 1993?

11 Elvis Costello And The Attractions had their first top ten hit in 1979. What was the song?

12 Who was the lead singer with Thin Lizzy?

13 Which blues singer has a cherished guitar called 'Lucille'?

14 Who recorded the albums, 'No Need To Argue' and 'Everybody Else Is Doing It, So Why Can't We?'?

15 Michael Crawford has only entered the Chart twice. On both occasions with different versions of the same song. Can you name the song?

1. Edwin Collins. 2. Paul Weller. 3. James Brown. 4. Jimi Hendrix. 5. Mike Rutherford (he's a member of both bands). 6. Michael Jackson. 7. Tracey Ullman. 8. Van Morrison. 9. 'Post'. 10. Paul Weller. 11. 'Oliver's Army'. 12. Phil Lynott. 13. B.B. King. 14. The Cranberries. 15. The Music Of The Night.

LITERATURE

1   According to Keats, what is the, 'Season of mists and mellow fruitfulness?'

2   Robert Burns wrote, 'Wee, sleekit, cow'rin', tim'rous beastie...' How did he continue?

3   'Captain Dobbin' appears in which book by Thackeray?

4   Genius, according to Thomas Edison, is, 'One percent inspiration and...'

5   Who wrote *The World According To Garp?*

6   'Sir Toby Belch' appears in which play by Shakespeare?

7   The character 'Clara Peggoty' appears in which book by Charles Dickens?

8   In which Shakespeare play does 'Shylock' appear?

9   Who wrote *The Sportswriter?*

10 'Full fathom five thy father lies;' is the beginning of a poem by whom?

11 Which American author wrote *The Scarlet Letter?*

12 In which books will you find the characters Zaphod Beeblebrox and Ford Prefect?

13 Complete the proverb: 'Children should be seen...'

14 Complete the line: 'Some are born great, some achieve greatness, and some...'

15 Complete the proverb: 'Burn not your house...'

ANSWERS

1. Autumn. 2. 'O what a panic's in thy breastie!' 3. *Vanity Fair.* 4. '99 percent perspiration'. 5. Gustave Flaubert. 6. *Twelfth Night.* 7. *David Copperfield.* 8. *The Merchant of Venice.* 9. Richard Ford. 10. William Shakespeare. 11. Nathaniel Hawthorne. 12. *The Hitch-Hiker's Guide* series by Douglas Adams. 13. '...and not heard'. 14. 'Have greatness thrust upon them'. 15. '...to fright the mouse away'.

GENERAL KNOWLEDGE

1 What is the name given to the beam placed above a window or door?

2 In what place do Hindu people worship?

3 What did George Cruikshank do?

4 Turkish baths weren't started in Turkey. Where were they started?

5 In the Army who is more senior, a Major or a Colonel?

6 Which day is the Jewish Sabbath?

7 Who was Aubrey Beardsley?

8 Who was Karl Benz?

9 To the ancient Romans who was Venus?

10 What are *marrons glacés*?

11 Who in the world would be called 'Taffy'?

12 What is an 'idiot board'?

13 Who is the patron saint of sculptors?

14 What anniversary does a leather wedding celebrate?

15 In ancient times what was King Midas's big problem?

ANSWERS

1. Lintel. 2. A temple. 3. He was a caricaturist and illustrator of books. 4. The Near East. 5. Colonel. 6. Saturday. 7. A black and white artist. 8. German maker of an early car. 9. The goddess of love. 10. Chestnuts coated with sugar. 11. A Welshman. 12. A card used in a television studio to prompt an actor. 13. St Claude. 14. The third. 15. Everything he touched turned to gold.

SCIENCE

1 Hepatitis is inflammation of what?

2 Which weather-measuring instrument was invented in 1643 by Torricelli?

3 What object in the sky is called Triton, and is about 1,680 miles in diameter?

4 The study of the minute structure of tissues and organs is called what?

5 What is enteritis?

6 Which planet is the Morning Star?

7 Who invented saccharine?

8 What is dipsomania?

9 André-Marie Ampère gave his name to what?

10 What is pyrophobia?

11 In Roman numerals, what is M?

12 Mothers could not survive without Walter Hunt's invention in 1849. What was it?

13 What is a rhomb?

14 What is the familiar name for sodium carbonate?

15 The Silver Ghost, introduced in 1906, was the first example of what by a famous company?

ANSWERS

1. The liver. 2. The barometer. 3. It is Neptune's largest moon. 4. Histology. 5. Inflammation of the intestines. 6. Venus. 7. C.H. Fahlberg, who discovered it by accident when working on something else. 8. An almost overpowering desire for alcoholic drink. 9. The ampere, a unit of electric current. 10. Fear of fire. 11. 1,000. 12. The safety-pin. 13. An equilateral parallelogram. 14. Washing soda. 15. The first car by Rolls-Royce.

NATURAL HISTORY

1. Jasmin is a plant relative of the olive. True or false?

2. The Caffer cat, found originally in Egypt, was the ancestor of what?

3. What is a cygnet?

4. In Britain what is unusual about the stag beetle?

5. What is saffron?

6. What colour is a lobster when it's alive in the water?

7. What sort of animal is a Samoyed?

8. What domestic animal could be described as a Manx?

9. In the movies, what was Blondie and Dagwood's dog called?

10. What kind of animal is said to howl?

11. What is a leveret?

12. What is an auk?

13. What is gorse?

14. How many legs can a centipede have; (a) more than 300 (b) more than 200 (c) more than 100?

15. What is a basenji?

ANSWERS

1. True. 2. The domestic cat. 3. A young swan. 4. It's our heaviest beetle. 5. A yellow-coloured pigment obtained from the saffron crocus. 6. A bluish-grey. It only turns red when it's cooked. 7. A breed of dog. 8. A cat. 9. Daisy. 10. A wolf. 11. A young hare. 12. A diving bird of the northern seas, usually black and white. 13. A wild shrub with yellow flowers and very sharp spines. 14. More than 300. 15. A breed of dog.

GEOGRAPHY

1   We call this place Leghorn; what do the Italians call it?

2   Where is the Forest of Dean?

3   Eboracum was the name given by the Romans to which city?

4   The Mont Blanc vehicular tunnel is between which two countries?

5   Where in the world do they speak Frisian?

6   To which country does Madeira belong?

7   What is the capital of Poland?

8   Where is the Sphinx?

9   Where is the Caledonian Canal?

10   What was remarkable about the Temple of Artemis at Ephesus?

11   Where is the Kariba Dam?

12   The official language of Andorra is Spanish. True or false?

13   The Battle of Hastings wasn't fought in Hastings at all. Where was it fought?

14   Where does the Rhine river rise?

15   What is the capital of Romania?

ENGLISH LANGUAGE

1   What was an 'albert'?

2   What word, beginning with E, means costly or dear?

3   What does the old word 'Caitiff' mean?

4   Can you name two words, sounding alike, which mean the same as this pair: male offspring/heavenly body?

5   What two words, sounding alike, mean 'entire' and 'hole-making tool'?

6   'Don't buy a pig in a poke', goes the advice. What was a 'poke'?

7   A tiro is; (a) a South American fish (b) a novice (c) a circular building in a park?

8   What is a *magnum opus*?

9   What is the meaning of the abreviation, ATC?

10   Which women, in earlier times, were known as 'The Fishing Fleet'?

11   What was meant by the phrase, 'to ken'?

12   What does an American mean by 'dry goods'?

13   Who or what was a 'nippy'?

14   What is the name for someone who studies the history of words?

15   What is the female version of 'buck'?

1. A short watch-chain fastened to a waist-coat pocket. 2. Expensive. 3. Coward. 4. Son/Sun. 5. All/awl. 6. A poke was a sack or bag, in which animals were sold in the market-place. 7. (b) a novice. 8. A great work of literature. 9. Air Traffic Control. 10. Young women who went out to India in search of husbands. 11. To know. 12. Drapery and linen products. 13. A waitress in Lyons's tea shop during the 1920s and 1930s. 14. Lexicologist. 15. Doe.

SPORT

1. What was Nigel Benn's fighting nickname?

2. What music usually accompanies Chris Eubank as he enters the boxing arena?

3. Name Green Bay's American football team?

4. With which sport do you associate Peekaboo Street?

5. Which England goalkeeper had a premature end to his career when he injured an eye in a car accident?

6. In the 1997/98 season who did Mohammed Al Fayed appoint as Director of Football at Fulham?

7. Which Formula One driver also owned an airline?

8. Which former Tottenham player captained Germany during the 1998 World Cup?

9. Which horse is buried at the Aintree winning post?

10. Who won the 1998 European Cup Winners Cup?

11. In 1998 which County Cricket team did Robin Smith captain?

12. With which county is the family name Cowdrey synonymous?

13. In which year did Virginia Wade win the Wimbledon singles title?

14. Who captained the England Rugby Union team during their 1998 tour of the southern hemisphere?

15. What nationality is the athlete Haile Gebresilassie?

HISTORY

1   Who was the Black Prince?

2   Who were the Aztecs?

3   After the collapse of the French government, who became head of state of France in July, 1940?

4   What did the 1763 Peace of Paris end?

5   What was the Louisiana Purchase?

6   What was the name of the famous son of Philip II of Macedonia?

7   Who was Aristotle?

8   During the American Civil War what happened in Appomattox, Virginia on 9th April, 1865?

9   On 13th January, 1898, Émile Zola used a newspaper to publish his famous open letter *J'accuse*. What cause provoked the writing of the letter ?

10 What were the Nuremberg Trials held in 1945-1946?

11 The first screw-propelled iron transatlantic steamship made her maiden voyage in 1845 . What was she called?

12 Who was the first King of Scots?

13 Which well-known New York bridge was designed by the father but built by the son of the Roebling family?

14 The National Viewers and Listeners Association against 'bad taste' was founded in 1965 by whom?

15 10,000 people died of what 1854 epidemic in London?

CINEMA AND TV

1 Which movie star was the 'Mexican Spitfire'?

2 Who, in show business, was 'Ol' Blue Eyes'?

3 Which film featured Mr Black and Mr Pink?

4 Who directed the film in question three?

5 Who starred in the film *Midnight Cowboy*?

6 How many Marx Brothers spent *A Night at the Opera*?

7 The film *The Gold Rush* shows Charlie Chaplin eating his boots. Was this a fake?

8 Who starred in the film *Back to the Future*?

9 Which movie star's real name was Byron Elsworth Barr?

10 Who starred in the film *Letter from an Unknown Woman*?

11 Which fictional character has been used most in films?

12 Which American president appeared in the movie *Bedtime for Bonzo*?

13 Which British TV star has held a 'Swap Shop' a 'House Party' and is a bit of a 'Telly Addict?

14 From which film did the song 'Nice Work If You Can Get It' come?

15 From which film did the song 'Be a Clown' come?

1. Lupe Velez. 2. Frank Sinatra. 3. *Reservoir Dogs*. 4. Quentin Tarantino. 5. Dustin Hoffman, Jon Voight. 6. Four. 7. In a sense: the boots were made of liquorice. 8. Michael J. Fox and Christopher Lloyd. 9. Gig Young. 10. Joan Fontaine, Louis Jourdan. 11. Sherlock Holmes, in about 200 films. 12. Ronald Reagan. 13. Noel Edmonds. 14. *A Damsel in Distress*, 1937. 15. *The Pirate*, 1948.

POPULAR MUSIC

1   Who reached number one in 1976 with 'Don't Cry For Me Argentina'?

2   Who performed the title song to Dudley Moore's film Arthur?

3   Which combined Australian and New Zealand band reached number 7 in 1992 with 'Weather With You'?

4   Which actor did Madonna marry on a cliff top?

5   Which US band had top ten hits in 1982 with 'I'm A Wonderful Thing Baby', 'Stool Pigeon' and 'Annie I'm Not Your Daddy'?

6   Which female American singer won two Grammies with 'All I Wanna Do' in 1995?

7   Who had top ten hits with 'Joe Le Taxi' and 'Be My Baby' as well as appearing in Chanel perfume adverts?

8   The Heartbreakers' recording career has spanned nearly twenty years, with great success in the United States. Yet they have never made the UK top ten. Name their lead vocalist?

9   In 1960 Johnny Preston reached number one with a song about a Red Indian love story. Can you name the song?

10 Who was The Who's original drummer who died from a drugs overdose.

11 Who recorded the album 'Kissing Gate' in 1993?

12 Who went straight in at number one in June 1998 with their debut single 'C'est La Vie'?

13 Which band had albums, 'New World Record', 'Eldorado' and 'Out Of The Blue'?

14 Who re-recorded his 1974 number one single 'Kung Fu Fighting' in 1998 with Bus Stop?

15 'The Whole Of The Moon' and 'The Return Of Pan' were hits for which Irish band led by Mike Scott?

LITERATURE

1   What sort of fictional character was 'Jules Maigret'?

2   Who wrote *Moby Dick?*

3   Complete the proverb: 'Catch your bear...'

4   From which Shakespeare play does the quotation, 'All the world's a stage' come?

5   'Up the airy mountain,/Down the rushy glen' is the beginning of a poem by whom?

6   Who is the main character in Arthur Conan Doyle's *The Lost World?*

7   Who wrote The Castle of Otranto?

8   Who was the great adversary of Robin Hood?

9   Who wrote *Fahrenheit 451?*

10 The character 'Augustus Snodgrass' appears in which famous book?

11 Who wrote *Call of the Wild?*

12 'John Gilpin was a citizen/Of credit and renown' is the beginning of a poem by whom?

13 Complete the proverb: Advice when most needed...

14 'Reggie Fortune' is a fictional detective created by whom?

15 The character 'Bill Sikes' appears in which book by Charles Dickens?

GENERAL KNOWLEDGE

1   What kind of food item is associated with Bombay?

2   Who was Jean Renoir's father?

3   How many is a baker's dozen?

4   Who was Jesus?

5   What is the Trinity?

6   In a pack of cards, which way does the Jack of Spades look, to his left, or to his right?

7   According to the 'language of flowers', what does the jasmine signify?

8   Which daily newspaper was first published on 7th October, 1986?

9   What anniversary does a tin wedding celebrate?

10 Why is a bowler hat so called?

11 What is a pizza?

12 A clutch is composed of what items?

13 In British movies and on stage, which actress was famed for her portrayal of eccentric elderly ladies?

14 What is *paté de fois gras*?

15 Who is the patron saint of secretaries?

ANSWERS

1. Duck. It's not a duck at all, but a kind of fish. 2. Auguste Renoir.
3. Thirteen. 4. Christians believe he was the Son of God, and part of the Trinity.
5. The belief that God, Jesus and The Holy Spirit are all one. 6. To his left.
7. Amiability. 8. The Independent. 9. The tenth. 10. It was first sold by the hatters,
Thomas and William Bowler. 11. An open pie of bread dough, with various toppings.
12. Eggs. 13. Margaret Rutherford. 14. Goose liver paté. 15. St Cassian.

SCIENCE

1   In 1769 Nicholas-Joseph Cugnot built a tractor driven by what sort of power?

2   What's the medical term for loss of memory?

3   What is ailurophobia?

4   What is chlorine?

5   What is ophthalmology?

6   The art of making motion pictures is called what?

7   Whitcomb Judson, in 1892, invented something that avoided the use of buttons. What was it?

8   What did King C. Gillette invent in 1895?

9   What is craniology?

10 Which man and wife discovered radium in 1898?

11 What is pomology?

12 The study of the properties of substances and their interaction is called what?

13 The square of the hypotenuse is equal to the sum of the squares on the other two sides. What is this?

14 The science of the mind is called what?

15 What was a V1?

ANSWERS

1. Steam. 2. Amnesia. 3. A fear of cats. 4. A gas. 5. The science of the eye; its study, and its diseases. 6. Cinematography. 7. The zip fastener. 8. The safety-razor. 9. The study of skulls. 10. Pierre and Marie Curie. 11. The study of fruit-growing. 12. Chemistry. 13. The famous theorem of Pythagorus, Greek philosopher. 14. Psychology. 15. A flying bomb in the form of a pilotless aircraft.

NATURAL HISTORY

1   What is a boa?

2   Gorillas, chimpanzees, and orang-utans are all what?

3   The hyacinth is a plant relative of the lily. True or false?

4   What is the difference between a frog and a toad?

5   Are there any mammals able to fly?

6   Is an ant-lion an insect or a mammal?

7   What is a cowrie?

8   Which insect makes a loud chirping sound?

9   Which common, everyday creature has eight eyes?

10   The kestrel is also known as a what?

11   How many legs does a lobster have?

12   A mastodon was an early example of a what?

13   What domestic animal could be described as a tabby?

14   What sort of animal is called an Ayrshire?

15   The hamster is a small animal native to which areas?

ANSWERS

1. A snake that kills by squeezing its prey to death. 2. Apes. 3. True. 4. A frog hops or leaps along and a toad walks. 5. Yes, bats. 6. An insect. 7. The shell of a mollusc, used by some early peoples as money. 8. The cricket. 9. The spider. 10. A windhover. 11. Eight. 12. An elephant. 13. A cat. 14. A breed of cattle. 15. Asia and eastern Europe.

GEOGRAPHY

1 What is Formosa now called?

2 What was remarkable about the Temple of Zeus at Olympia?

3 What is Etna, and where is it?

4 Which two countries form the island of Hispaniola?

5 What is the name of the stretch of water that lies between Australia and Papua New Guinea?

6 Which is the world's oldest republic?

7 The official name 'Misr' refers to which country?

8 What is the capital of Japan?

9 Where in the world do they speak Coptic?

10 Where in Spain is the Alhambra Palace?

11 What is the capital of the Sudan?

12 Which is the largest lake in the United Kingdom?

13 Where and what is Wookey Hole?

14 Which is Britain's longest river?

15 How many bridges are there across the River Thames?

765

ENGLISH LANGUAGE

1   How did we acquire the word 'pram'?

2   What word, beginning with B, means bold or courageous?

3   A snob is (a) a shoemaker (b) a kind of linen cap (c) a kind of door-handle.

4   What is a 'malapropism'?

5   Can you name two words, sounding alike, which mean the same as this pair: take by theft/metal?

6   What is, or was, 'cheesecake'?

7   What does 'buckshee' mean?

8   What do the Americans mean by a 'freeway'?

9   What was a 'flapper'?

10   Which group were known as 'The Few'?

11   What is the difference between 'balmy' and 'barmy'?

12   Can you name two words, sounding alike, which mean the same as this pair: a market/price for rail ticket?

13   How did the 'doily' get its name?

14   What does 'e.g.' stand for?

15   Can you suggest a palindrome for 'Eve'?

1. It's a shortened form of 'perambulator'. Perambulate means to walk or travel. 2. Brave. 3. (a) a shoemaker. 4. A failed attempt to sound 'educated', as in 'The threat of nuclear war was a real deterrent' (instead of deterrent). 5. Steal/steel. 6. A pin-up picture of a film star or other semi-clad female. 7. Something which turns up, free of charge. 8. A motorway. 9. A voguish, somewhat high-spirited young woman of the 1920s. 10. Allied fighter pilots during the Battle of Britain in 1940. 11. The first means 'mild and pleasant' and the second 'silly or foolish'. 12. Fair/fare. 13. It was first made by a famous haberdasher named Doyley or d'Oyley. 14. Exempli gratia: 'for example'. 15. Madam I'm Adam.

SPORT

1   With which sport do you associate Michael Doohan?

2   In American football how many yards do you have to gain, in order to achieve a 'First down'?

3   With which sport do you associate the Searle brothers?

4   Who scored for England in the 1966 World Cup final, apart from Geoff Hurst?

5   Judo, in Japanese, means, 'the Gentle way'. True or False?

6   With which sport do you associate Jesper Parnevik?

7   Name Warrington's Rugby League team?

8   What nationality is three-day eventer, Mark Todd?

9   With which sport do you associate Armand de la Cuevas?

10 Which sport is famous for being played at the 'Guards Club'?

11 Name Utah's NBA Basketball team?

12 Which of the following is not a coarse fish, Chub, Dace, Grayling, Carp?

13 With which sport do you associate David Campese?

14 Who scored England's opening goal in the 1998 World Cup?

15 Who sponsored Rugby League's Super League in 1998

1. Motor Cycling. 2. Ten. 3. Rowing. 4. Martin Peters. 5. True. 6. Golf. 7. Wolves. 8. New Zealand. 9. Cycling. 10. Polo. 11. The Jazz. 12. Grayling. 13. Rugby Union. 14. Alan Shearer. 15. JJB.

HISTORY

1 Who in 1895 set sail from Boston on the first solo round-the-world voyage?

2 What experiment took place in Monte Bello islands, off northwest Australia, in 1952?

3 In which war were the Boers in South Africa victorious at Magersfontein, on 11 December 1899?

4 A purpose-built supermarket was opened in Croydon in August, 1950, by which company?

5 When were Life Peerages introduced?

6 What did the heroine Grace Darling do in 1838?

7 Which Soviet president visited the Queen at Windsor in 1989?

8 To which president was Eleanor Roosevelt married?

9 What was the name given to Oliver Cromwell's soldiers?

10 Who landed on Pitcairn Island in 1790?

11 Who defeated whom at the Battle of Flodden Field in 1513?

12 Egbert was the first English king to be converted to what?

13 Who was Nikita Sergeyevich Khrushchev?

14 What happened to the MP Spencer Perceval in 1812?

15 In which London underground station did fire break out in 1987?

CINEMA AND TV

1   Who starred in the film *Mr Smith Goes to Washington*?

2   The film *The Women* in 1939 had an all-women cast. How many women were involved; (a) 64 (b) 97 (c) 5?

3   Which movie star's real name was Dawn Evelyeen Davis?

4   Who played Seymour in the film *Little Shop Of Horrors*?

5   Which film, made in 1963, used an all-boy cast?

6   What was unusual about the original version of the 1924 silent film *Greed*?

7   Who wrote the book on which the film *2001: A Space Odyssey* was based?

8   What is the connection between *Austin Powers: International Man Of Mystery* and *Wayne's World*?

9   Who starred in the film *Psycho*?

10 Who starred in the film *The Best Years of Our Lives*?

11 Which movie star was the 'Oomph Girl'?

12 Who starred in the film *Great Expectations*?

13 Which movie star is the 'Professional Virgin'?

14 Who starred in the film *Taxi Driver*?

15 Who starred in the film *The Constant Husband*?

POPULAR MUSIC

1   Who recorded the 1987 album 'Now That's What I Call Quite Good'?

2   Who is Led Zeppelin's lead singer?

3   What was the title of 'Take That's' first album?

4   Which Quentin Tarantino film sound track featured 'Jungle Boogie' by Kool and the Gang?

5   Which band will be best remembered for 'Love Shack' and 'Rock Lobster'?

6   Which super model featured on Bon Jovi's 'Please Come Home For Christmas' video in 1994?

7   Name Madonna's 1998 album?

8   Name Natalie Imbruglia's debut album.

9   What nationality is Enya?

10   On which Beatles album would you find 'Helter Skelter', 'Dear Prudence' and 'Back In The USSR'?

11   Name Radiohead's third album featuring the tracks, 'Paranoid Android' and 'Karma Police'?

12   Name Rod Stewart's 1998 'Covers' album?

13   Which 1998 movie sound track features Puff Daddy singing Led Zeppelin and The Wallflowers performing David Bowie's 'Heroes'?

14   Which musical legend reached number three in the US album chart in June 1998 (soon after his death) with 'In The Wee Small Hours'?

15   Who released the album 'Pilgrim' in 1998?

770

LITERATURE

1. The character 'Captain Rawdon' appears in which book by Charles Dickens?

2. Who wrote *Barchester Towers*?

3. What author became most famous for his nonsense verse and limericks?

4. In which book by Thomas Hardy does 'Angel Clare' appear?

5. Complete the proverb: 'The devil finds work...'

6. 'Though I've belted you and flayed you, By the livin' Gawd that made you,' wrote Kipling. What was the next line?

7. Complete Kipling's line: 'God of our fathers, known of old...'

8. Who wrote *Les Misérables*?

9. Who wrote *The Third Man*?

10. Who wrote *A Farewell to Arms*?

11. Who often accompanied, and was usually baffled by, Hercule Poirot on his investigations?

12. Who wrote *The Ginger Man*?

13. Complete the proverb: 'Don't count your chickens...'

14. James Dixon, a lecturer in history, appears as a character in which book by Kingsley Amis?

15. How old was the title character in the book *Lolita*?

ANSWERS

1. *Bleak House*. 2. Anthony Trollope. 3. Edward Lear. 4. *Tess of the D'Urbervilles*. 5. '...for idle hands to do'. 6. 'You're a better man than I am, Gunga Din!' 7. '...Lord of our far-flung battle-line'. 8. Victor Hugo. 9. Graham Greene. 10. Ernest Hemingway. 11. Captain Hastings. 12. J.P. Donleavy. 13. '...before they are hatched'. 14. *Lucky Jim*. 15. 12.

GENERAL KNOWLEDGE

1 What is a prairie oyster?

2 Which American President was the last to be impeached?

3 What is a facade?

4 If you are a red-headed Australian, what might your nickname be?

5 What is gingerbread?

6 What is a 'blockbuster'?

7 What is abalone?

8 Which vitamin helps bone formation and keeps teeth healthy?

9 Which sign of the Zodiac represents the Virgin?

10 What is 'bubble and squeak'?

11 Who is the patron saint of workers?

12 What creature is sometimes known as 'Devil's Fingers'?

13 What are blinis or blintzis?

14 What word, beginning with ante-, means 'a small room leading to another'?

15 What is cribbage?

1. A raw egg with vinegar and other condiments. 2. Richard Nixon. 3. The front of a building. 4. Bluey. 5. A cake flavoured with ginger and treacle. 6. A great success, as of a book, film or stage show. 7. A mollusc, like the sea snail, with a flat, oval shell. 8. Vitamin D. 9. Virgo. 10. A mashed, fried mixture of cabbage and potato. 11. St Joseph. 12. The starfish. 13. Russian thin, stuffed pancakes. 14. Anteroom. 15. A card game for a varying number of players.

SCIENCE

1 Violet, indigo, blue, green, yellow, orange and red are the colours of what?

2 What is Gallophobia?

3 Barthelemy Thimonnier invented the 'girls' best friend' in 1830. What was it?

4 Quicksilver is an ancient name for what substance?

5 What did the underwater robot Jason help discover?

6 Who invented the waterproof macintosh?

7 What is an adhesive?

8 What's another name for an Air-Cushioned Vehicle?

9 What did Samuel Christian Friedrich Hahnemann found?

10 How many sides has a tetragon?

11 What is measured in decibels?

12 The sugar in milk is called what?

13 What long-distance signalling system was introduced in 1794?

14 What is *The Lancet*?

15 What does a barometer measure?

NATURAL HISTORY

1 The world's largest reptile, a crocodile of the Far East, is how long; (a) 12 feet (b) 14 feet (c) 16 feet?

2 What is a group of dolphins called?

3 What is cinnamon?

4 When is a snake not a snake?

5 What is arrowroot?

6 Give an example of a mammal which lives in the sea.

7 What kind of animal could be called a hackney?

8 Which sea creature has eyes at the ends of its 'arms'?

9 What is variously known as a dace, dare or dart?

10 What is the difference between a panther and a leopard?

11 What is a cranberry?

12 What is a wryneck?

13 What is krill?

14 A bongo is a type of antelope or a small tropical lizard?

15 Barley is really a special kind of grass. True or false?

ANSWERS

1. 16 feet long. 2. A school. 3. The spicy bark of a tree found in Sri Lanka. 4. When it's a blind snake, which is actually a legless lizard. 5. A kind of starchy substance made from a plant of the same name. 6. Whale, porpoise, seal, sealion. 7. A breed of horse. 8. The starfish. 9. A small river fish. 10. There isn't any! 11. A red acid berry growing on an evergreen shrub. 12. A small bird like a woodpecker with a habit of twisting its neck. 13. Small crustaceans such as shrimps, forming the main diet of whales. 14. It's an antelope. It's also called a bushbuck. 15. True.

GEOGRAPHY

1 The thistle is the national symbol of which country?

2 Which city is on the River Manzanares?

3 What are the Trossachs?

4 Which island's capital is Nuuk?

5 If you bought a pack of cards, and found the suitmarks to be hearts, leaves, bells and acorns, where might you be?

6 Where is Lundy Island?

7 What is the largest city in New Zealand?

8 The diameter of each dial on the Big Ben clock tower is; (a) 10 feet (b) 31 feet (c) 23 feet?

9 Where and what is Mauritius?

10 Which is the 'Land of the Rising Sun?'

11 Where and what is Maxim's?

12 What is the capital of the Russian Federation?

13 What stands on the rocks off Plymouth in Devon?

14 What is the capital of Greece?

15 Which is the world's smallest sovereign state?

ANSWERS

1. Scotland. 2. Madrid. 3. A wooded valley in central Scotland. 4. Greenland. 5. In a German-speaking country. 6. In the Bristol Channel. 7. Auckland. 8. (c) 23 feet. 9. An island republic in the Indian Ocean. 10. Japan. 11. A famous restaurant in Paris. 12. Moscow. 13. The Eddystone Lighthouse. 14. Athens. 15. The Vatican City.

ENGLISH LANGUAGE

1 What might you be nicknamed if your surname was Murphy?

2 What single word means 'a prophet of doom'?

3 What is the term for a man who has two wives at the same time?

4 What one word can mean 'a place where money is kept' and 'sloping ground'?

5 What does 'hindermost' mean?

6 What would a 'light-fingered' person have a tendency to do?

7 What is the female version of the equine term, 'sire'?

8 What is a female 'fox' called?

9 What is a 'bastion'?

10 What are words like 'Hooray!, Hey!, Gosh!' called?

11 What is a Canuck?

12 What is, or was, an Anzac?

13 What is the difference in meaning between continuous and continual?

14 What kind of confection is called 'cotton candy' in America?

15 What word means beast or brute?

SPORT

1 What nationality the is golfer Tom Lehman?

2 In which sport would you compete for the Curtis Cup?

3 What is the term used to describe a female horse less than four years old?

4 At which weight did boxer Chris Eubank make a comeback in 1998?

5 Who captained Glamorgan County Cricket team during their championship winning season, 1997?

6 With which sport do you associate John Francome?

7 Name San Diego's American football team?

8 What number did Paul Gascoigne usually wear for England?

9 How many points is a free throw in basketball worth if scored?

10 In Judo, apart from throwing your partner or pinning him to the ground, how do you score points?

11 In the 1970s which brand of cigarettes became synonymous with the Lotus Formula One team.

12 Which County Cricket team plays the majority of their home games at the Oval?

13 With which sport do you associate Robert Fox?

14 Which football club plays its home games at the Riverside?

15 Who provided the engines for William's F1 team, during their triumphant 1996 season?

1. American. 2. Golf (Women's). 3. Filly. 4. Cruiserweight. 5. Matthew Maynard. 6. Horse Racing. 7. Chargers. 8. Eight. 9. One. 10. By gaining a submission. 11. JPS. 12. Surrey. 13. Modern Pentathlon. 14. Middlesborough. 15. Renault.

HISTORY

1 What, in Nazi Germany, was the SS?

2 Who succeeded James Callaghan as leader of the Labour Party in November, 1980?

3 Six experimental objects were installed in London by the Post Office in 1855. What were they?

4 Which American general was relieved of his command during the Korean War?

5 Who was British Prime Minister for a total of over 20 years?

6 Where and what was Deira?

7 Who was Bonnie Prince Charlie?

8 Who was proclaimed Empress of India on 1st January, 1877?

9 Korea was annexed by which country in 1910?

10 Who was Herbert Hoover?

11 In what year were identity cards abolished in Britain?

12 Which was the last monarch of the House of Tudor?

13 Since he spoke no English, how did George I communicate with Sir Robert Walpole?

14 In London, 1946, the first assembly of which international body took place?

15 What happened in September, 1939, that started World War II?

CINEMA AND TV

1 Was Joyce Grenfell English or American?

2 Which English film actor was born Laruska Mischa Skikne?

3 Which gentlemanly English actor was brought up speaking only German?

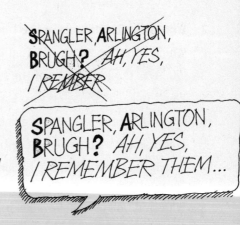

4 Who starred in the film Carve Her Name with Pride?

5 What was unique about the Nestor Film Studio on Sunset Boulevard?

6 Who starred in the film Wonder Man?

7 What was unique about the film The World, the Flesh and the Devil?

8 Which was the first full-length talking film?

9 Who starred in the film The Citadel?

10 Which movie star's real name was Spangler Arlington Brugh?

11 Which movie star's real name was Robert Taylor?

12 Who is Larry Hagman's mother?

13 Who starred in the film Force of Evil?

14 Who starred in the film Home at Seven?

15 How are the film actors Dana Andrews and Steve Forrest connected?

POPULAR MUSIC

1 Who took the title role in the film Buster?

2 Which super model was married to Rod Stewart?

3 Who was the lead singer of the Pretenders?

4 Who's only Christmas hit was 'Last Christmas'?

5 Who's daughter recorded 'These Boots Were Made For Walking'?

6 Who was the lead singer of the Undertones?

7 Which Canadian guitarist's backing bands have included The International Harvesters, The Blue Notes and Crazy Horse

8 Who said 'You're Unbelievable' in 1990?

9 Who had top ten hits with 'War', 'Contact' and 'H.A.P.P.Y. Radio'?

10 Who recorded the album 'Listen without Prejudice'?

11 Who was labelled the 'New Dylan' and went on to write and sing rock anthems like 'Born To Run' and 'Born In The USA?

12 'Sheena Is A Punk Rocker' was the first UK hit for which US Punk band?

13 After which 1982 advertising campaign did John Lee Hooker chart with 'Boom Boom'?

14 Which singer starred in the film The Young Ones?

15 Who reached number one in 1996 with 'Killing Me Softly' and 'Ready Or Not'?

LITERATURE

1 What was the fate of the author Erskine Childers, who wrote *The Riddle of the Sands*?

2 Complete the proverb: 'Constant dripping...'

3 Complete this line by Charles Kingsley: 'For men must work...'

4 Who was the author of *King Solomon's Mines, She* and *Allan Quatermain*?

5 Who said: 'I am on the side of the angels'?

6 In which play does Captain Hook appear?

7 Which author introduced the character Dr Fu Manchu?

8 Complete the line of Richard Lovelace, 'Stone walls do not a prison make...'

9 What, according to Phineas T. Barnum, is born every minute?

10 'Fear no more the heat of the sun/Nor the furious winter's rages;' is the beginning of a poem by whom?

11 In which book are Becky Sharp and Amelia Sedley friends?

12 Who wrote *The Tenant of Wildfell Hall*?

13 Complete the proverb: 'Better be a fool...'

14 'Not a drum was heard, not funeral note' begins a poem by whom?

15 'In Xanadu did Kubla Khan/A stately pleasure-dome decree:' is the beginning of a poem by whom?

GENERAL KNOWLEDGE

1   What anniversary does a flower or fruit wedding celebrate?

2   What is galantine?

3   To the ancient Greeks who was Pluto?

4   If you suffered from theophobia, what would you fear?

5   Which popular French drink contains wormwood oil?

6   What is a fondue?

7   Rule by a privileged class is called what?

8   Who invented the crossword puzzle?

9   St John of God is the patron saint of whom?

10 In which religion is the god Brahma found?

11 What is the name given to a lake of sea water bounded by a coral reef?

12 What anniversary does a ruby wedding celebrate?

13 What is a kipper?

14 What food comes from Eccles in Lancashire?

15 St Augustine of Hippo is the patron saint of whom?

SCIENCE

1 Who invented the Diesel engine in 1892?

2 What is solder made of?

3 Which is the most abundant metal on earth?

4 Which metal has the chemical symbol, Sn?

5 What is kleptomania?

6 If a car is described as a coupé, what is it like?

7 Ants use an acid to sting. What's it called?

8 Hydrogen, combined with oxygen, makes what?

9 Botany is the study of what?

10 What is gutta-percha?

11 What does a telescope do?

12 What did the Montgolfier Brothers achieve in 1783?

13 What is the more common name for sodium chloride?

14 What kind of weapon is a Gatling?

15 What is the exosphere?

ANSWERS

1. Rudolf Diesel. 2. It's an alloy of tin and lead. 3. Aluminium. 4. Tin. 5. A morbid desire to steal and hide things. 6. It has two doors and a sloping roof. 7. Formic acid. 8. Water. 9. Plants. 10. A material like rubber made from the latex of trees in Malaysia. 11. Magnifies distant objects. 12. The first successful balloon flight. 13. Salt. 14. A machine-gun. 15. The outermost part of the Earth's atmosphere.

NATURAL HISTORY

1   What is a potto?

2   Which wild small rodent with long ears once was native only to Spain and North Africa?

3   What are cashews?

4   What is the name of the South American fruit shaped like a pine-cone?

5   What is the difference between a tortoise and a turtle?

6   A female rat can give birth to how many young at a time; (a) 8 (b) 12 (c) 20?

7   The scarab, or dung-beetle, was sacred to which people?

8   What is another name for the mountain ash?

9   Does an elephant drink through its trunk?

10 A cross between a she-ass and a stallion is called what?

11 What sort of creature is a bunting?

12 What is a snail?

13 A genet is cat-like creature which purrs like a kettle boiling. True or false?

14 Celery is a plant relative of the carrot. Yes or no?

15 What is the world's largest mammal?

ANSWERS

1. A lemur found in West Africa. 2. The rabbit. 3. Kidney-shaped nuts from an American tree. 4. A pineapple. 5. A tortoise lives on land; a turtle lives in water. 6. 20. 7. The ancient Egyptians. 8. The rowan. 9. No. It sucks up water with its trunk and squirts it into the mouth. 10. A hinny. 11. A small, seed-eating finch-like bird which can be quite tame. 12. A gastropod, like a slug, but with a shell. 13. True. 14. Yes. 15. The blue whale.

GEOGRAPHY

1   What is the national language of Brazil?

2   What are the Dolomites and where are they?

3   What is the capital of the Isle of Man?

4   Amsterdam is the capital of which country?

5   Where in Europe is the 'Blue Grotto?'

6   Who lives at the Mansion House, London?

7   Where would you find 'The Shambles'?

8   Nyasaland is the old name for where?

9   Britain is unusually warm considering its latitude. Why?

10 Where is the Forest of Arden?

11 What contains about 70% of the entire planet's fresh water?

12 Which major port stands on the Douro river?

13 Is there really such a place as 'Lambeth Walk?'

14 Where are the Goodwin Sands?

15 Where and what is the 'Old Bailey'?

ANSWERS

1. Portuguese. 2. They are part of the Alps, and are in Italy. 3. Douglas. 4. The Netherlands. 5. Capri, in Italy. 6. The Lord Mayor of London. 7. York. 8. Malawi. 9. Because the islands are warmed by the currents from the Gulf Stream. 10. Warwickshire. 11. Antarctica (frozen in its ice). 12. Oporto. 13. Yes, it's a street in Lambeth, London. 14. At the Straits of Dover. 15. The Central Criminal Court, London.

ENGLISH LANGUAGE

1   What does 'doughty' mean?

2   How did the word galvanise originate?

3   What, in earlier times, was an object called a 'churchwarden'?

4   If you were clever enough to translate the name of the composer Giuseppe Verdi into English, what could it be?

5   Can you name two words, sounding alike, which mean the same as this pair of phrases: giving a security/bundle of soft goods?

6   What word, beginning with P, means trade or vocation?

7   What would you be doing in cockney rhyming slang if you were having a 'butcher's'?

8   If you believe 'that's the way the cookie crumbles', what are you in effect doing?

9   Finish the proverb: 'He who excuses himself...'

10 What is 'gasoline'?

11 Why do prisoners say 'in stir' for prison?

12 What is an acronym?

13 What does the acronym NATO mean?

14 Which is the correct spelling: 'license; licence'.

15 In French, what is *le magasin*?

1. Brave. 2. It was named after the inventor Luigi Galvani. 3. A long, clay pipe. 4. Joe Green or Greens. 5. Bail/bale. 6. Profession. 7. A look. From 'butcher's hook'. 8. Accepting things the way they are. 9. '...accuses himself'. 10. The American word for 'petrol'. 11. It is a gypsy word, shortened from stirpen, meaning prison. 12. A word formed from the initials of a phrase. 13. (North Atlantic Treaty Organisation). 14. Both are correct. The first is the verb, the second is the noun. 15. A shop.

SPORT

1 True or false, the Tour de France always takes place exclusively within France?

2 What always goes to the FA Cup final but never appears?

3 In the mid 1980's F1 team, Zakspeed were sponsored by cigarette manufacturer, West. What did the team paint on the side of the cars to beat tobacco advertising bans?

4 Which football team's official nickname is, 'The Lillywhites'?

5 Which day of the week is 'Ladies day' at Royal Ascot?

6 In which sport might you use the controversial 'Great Big Bertha', or 'Ti Bubble 2'?

7 What nationality is the tennis star Martina Hingis?

8 If I was throwing my ball with a 'chistera', against the wall of the 'cancha', what sport would I be playing?

9 What sport do the Washington Bullets play?

10 In which year was the America's Cup won for the first time by a boat not from the United States?

11 With which sport do you associate John Parrott?

12 Who won the 1997 FA Cup?

13 How many American footballers per team are allowed on the field at any one time?

14 What material are boules made from?

15 In athletics what is the maximum permitted amount of wind assistance that can be received for a record to stand?

HISTORY

1 Which well-known Irish political party was founded in Dublin in 1905?

2 When was the first Labour government formed?

3 Which future king and queen of the United Kingdom were married on 10th March, 1863?

4 Above whose head did a sword, suspended by a hair, hang?

5 Who opened his first shelter for abandoned children in Stepney, London, in 1867?

6 Ambassadors accredited to the Court of St James go to which country?

7 In March, 1837, which new Australian city was named after the then Prime Minister?

8 When did Britain change to decimal currency?

9 Who was the last Emperor of Austria?

10 Henry V of England defeated the French in 1415. What was the battle?

11 Which general, in early times, used elephants to cross the Alps?

12 What happened in at Scapa Flow, Scotland, in June, 1919?

13 Who was the first English monarch to be addressed as 'Your Majesty'?

14 Who was Kemal Atatürk?

15 Debate in the House of Lords was televised for the first time in what year?

CINEMA AND TV

1   Which African president played an African chief in the film *Sanders of the River*?

2   Which double act starred in the 1929 silent film *Big Business*?

3   Which two film stars starred in the TV show *The Persuaders*?

4   From which film did the song 'Jeepers Creepers' come?

5   Exactly what, or who, was 'Jeepers Creepers'?

6   Who starred in the film *Nashville*?

7   What did James Cagney do to Mae Clarke's face in the film *The Public Enemy*?

8   Which movie star's real name was Bernard Schwartz?

9   Who starred in the film *City Lights*?

10 Who provided the voices in the cartoon film *Animal Farm*?

11 What memorable part did Sessue Hayakawa play in a David Lean film of 1957?

12 Who starred in the film *Meet Me In St Louis*?

13 Who starred in the film *Batman* in 1966?

14 Who starred in the 1973 film *American Graffiti*?

15 Which film featured a mermaid played by Darryl Hannah?

ANSWERS

1. Jomo Kenyatta. 2. Laurel and Hardy. 3. Roger Moore and Tony Curtis. 4. *Going Places*, 1938, sung by Louis Armstrong. 5. It was a racehorse. 6. Ned Beatty, Karen Black. 7. Pushed a grapefruit into it. 8. Tony Curtis. 9. Charlie Chaplin, Virginia Cherrill. 10. Maurice Denham. 11. Colonel Saito in *Bridge on the River Kwai*. 12. Judy Garland, Margaret O'Brien. 13. Adam West, Cesar Romero, Burgess Meredith. 14. Richard Dreyfuss and Ron Howard. 15. *Splash*.

POPULAR MUSIC

1. 'You Were Made For Me', 'I'm Telling You Now' and 'I Understand' were all top ten hits for which UK group?

2. Which car company used Brian May to sing 'Everything we do, is driven by you'?

3. Apart from Oasis, who was in the top ten in December 1995 with 'Wonderwall'?

4. Who was the front man with Rock band, Rainbow?

5. Who developed the trade mark of crying on stage whilst singing 'Just Walking In The Rain' in the 1950's?

6. With which group was Lionel Richie the lead singer?

7. Which instrument did Jazz musician Buddy Rich play?

8. Who, in the 60's had hits with 'Twenty Four Hours From Tulsa' and 'Something's Gotten Hold Of My Heart'?

9. With whom did Iggy Pop record 'Well Did You Evah' in 1991?

10. Who had a UK top ten hit with Kenny Rogers, singing, 'Islands In The Stream' in 1983?

11. Which car company told us to, 'Search For The Hero Inside Yourself' courtesy of M People?

12. In 1981, with whom did Lionel Richie record 'Endless Love'?

13. Which was Cliff Richard's first UK number one hit?

14. Which instrument did Benny Green play?

15. What nationality were Men At Work?

LITERATURE

1 The character 'Passepartout' appears in which famous book by Jules Verne?

2 Who wrote *The Jungle Book*?

3 In which book by Anthony Trollope does 'Obadiah Slope' appear?

4 Who wrote the play *Under Milk Wood*?

5 Complete the proverb: 'Charity covers a...'

6 Complete the proverb: 'Birds of a feather...'

7 'Sam Spade' was a fictional private detective conceived by whom?

8 Which famous children's book did E. Nesbit write?

9 Louisa May Alcott wrote which book in three weeks?

10 In which book by Daphne du Maurier does the character 'Mrs Danvers' appear?

11 'This is the way the world ends,' wrote T.S. Eliot, 'not with a bang, but...'

12 Which of the following children's books was not written by Roald Dahl; *Mathilda, Charlie and the Chocolate Factory, Junk*?

13 What line follows, 'It was a lover and his lass,'

14 Who wrote *Lord Peter Views the Body*?

15 Who wrote *Zorba the Greek*?

GENERAL KNOWLEDGE

1 What is sauerkraut?

2 What is the Army equivalent of an Air Chief Marshal?

3 What is Cumberland sauce?

4 What was the occupation of Sir Jacob Epstein?

5 What anniversary does a woollen wedding celebrate?

6 What is stroganoff?

7 Who was Sheridan Morley's father?

8 Who was Thomas Arnold?

9 What was loo, as a game?

10 What word, beginning with post-, means 'a part added to a letter after the signature'?

11 St Nicholas is the patron saint of whom?

12 In cricket who is the Twelfth Man?

13 Who was Boofy Gore?

14 To the ancient Romans who was Saturn?

15 What is meant by 'Dutch comfort'?

ANSWERS

1. Cabbage fermented with salt. 2. General. 3. A redcurrant sauce with lemons, oranges, and port wine. 4. Sculptor. 5. The seventh. 6. Thinly-cut meat, onions and mushrooms in a sour cream sauce. 7. Robert Morley. 8. Famous headmaster of Rugby school. 9. A card game with many variants. 10. Postscript. 11. Bakers. 12. The substitute. 13. 8th Earl of Arran, politician and journalist. 14. The god of agriculture. 15. Cold comfort.

SCIENCE

1 Etymology is the study of what?

2 In what year was the first American space probe successfully launched?

3 What is hydrophobia?

4 The chemical formula CO means what?

5 The first microphone was invented by Edward Hughes in (a) 1878 (b) 1898 (c) 1908?

6 Michael Faraday invented an electrical generating machine in 1831. What was it?

7 Who invented the electric razor?

8 What object in the sky is called Callisto, and is 3,000 miles in diameter?

9 What historic event involved Orville and Wilbur Wright in 1903?

10 What is ornithology?

11 What is amber?

12 What is anthracite?

13 Cobalt takes its name from the German word *Kobold*, meaning a goblin. True or false?

14 Word-blindness, and a deep-rooted difficulty in learning to read, is called what?

15 What are Saturn's rings made of?

ANSWERS

1. Words and their history. 2. 1958. 3. A fear of water, especially of drinking it. 4. Carbon Monoxide. 5. (a) 1878. 6. The dynamo. 7. Joseph Schick. 8. It is Jupiter's second-largest moon. 9. The first flight by a powered heavier-than-air aircraft. 10. The study of birds. 11. A yellow fossil resin, regarded by many as a gem. 12. A hard coal which burns with very little smoke. 13. True. 14. Dyslexia. 15. Lumps of ice-covered rocks.

NATURAL HISTORY

1   Including its tusks, how many teeth does an elephant have?

2   What is a pomegranate?

3   What sort of animal is a dalmatian?

4   Which is North America's largest meat-eating animal?

5   What is an aardvark?

6   What is another name for allspice?

7   A litter of piglets is called a farrow. True or false?

8   Mustard is a member of the cabbage family. Yes or no?

9   The banded ant-eater is a marsupial from where?

10 What's remarkable about the King's holly plant of Tasmania?

11 What kind of animal is said to cackle?

12 Brussels sprouts are plant relatives of the cabbage. Yes or no?

13 Are there foxes which can fly?

14 What is a beech?

15 What is a scorpion?

1. Four. 2. A fruit with thick, leathery skin and filled with seeds (which are not edible). 3. A breed of dog. 4. The grizzly bear. 5. A nocturnal mammal, which feeds on ants and is found in Africa. 6. Pimento. 7. True. 8. Yes. 9. Australia. 10. It's thought to be about 40,000 years old. 11. A hen. 12. Yes. 13. No. The animal called a flying-fox is a bat. 14. A common forest tree, of much value as timber. 15. A creature related to the spider with four pairs of legs.

GEOGRAPHY

1 The Balearic Islands are part of which country?

2 On which island would you have been if you had were at the original Raffles Hotel?

3 In which country would you find the town of Cuzco?

4 What large former church, now a mosque, stands in Istanbul?

5 What Palace, built by Cardinal Wolsey, stands by the Thames in Surrey?

6 Where in the world do the people speak Urdu?

7 Where in the world would you find a Walloon or Wallon?

8 Which county is known as the 'Garden of England'?

9 In which English town would you find 'The Lanes'?

10 Where and what is Alcatraz?

11 Where are the Brecon Beacons?

12 Where and what is Stromboli?

13 The River Danube flows through how many countries?

14 Where and what is Roedean?

15 What is the highest peak in the Alps?

1. Spain. 2. Singapore. 3. Peru. 4. St Sophia. 5. Hampton Court.
6. Pakistan. 7. Belgium. 8. Kent. 9. Brighton. 10. It's a former prison built on an island in San Francisco Bay. 11. South Wales. 12. It's an Italian volcano. 13. Six.
14. A famous girls' school near Brighton. 15. Mont Blanc.

ENGLISH LANGUAGE

1 We all know what an asterisk is, but what does the word actually mean?

2 Do Panama hats come from Panama?

3 What word, beginning with S, means beckon or call?

4 How many sides does a pentagon have?

5 What is the female version of 'drake'?

6 What does the acronym SNAFU mean?

7 If someone lacks the sense of '*meum et tuum*', he is likely to be a what?

8 What are (or were) 'backroom boys'?

9 Kerosene to an American, is the same thing as what to a Briton?

10 To what did Captain Charles Lynch, of Virginia, give his name?

11 What are moccasins?

12 What does this cockney expression mean: 'He has half-inched a whole lot of tomfoolery'.

13 If you 'needle' someone, what are you really doing?

14 What was a 'billycock'?

15 The windscreen of a car is called what in America?

1. A small star. 2. No, and never did. The 'palmata' hat comes from South America, made from the leaves of a plant like a palm. 3. Summon. 4. Five. 5. Duck. 6. Situation Normal, All Fouled Up. 7. A thief. The words mean 'mine and thine'. 8. Scientists or boffins. 9. Paraffin. 10. Lynching. 11. Soft shoes or slippers made of deerskin. 12. He has stolen a whole lot of jewellery. 13. Annoying them. 14. A soft felt hat with a wide brim. 15. The windshield.

SPORT

1   During cycling time trials how many cyclists are on the track at any one time?

2   How many times has Tom Watson won the US Masters Championship?

3   Which country will become the 10th Cricketing Test Nation?

4   Which football team plays their home matches at the Stadium of Light?

5   Robin Cousins and John Curry are the only British men to have won Olympic Men's Figure Skating gold medals. True or False?

6   In Ten Pin Bowling what term describes knocking ten pins down with two balls?

7   Who was the last Briton to win a singles title at Wimbledon?

8   What nationality is former Newcastle striker Faustuno Asprilla?

9   Which cricketer had the nickname 'Beefy'?

10   Who is Great Britain's delegate on the International Olympic Committee?

11   Whom did Tony Blair appoint as Sports Minister in 1997?

12   In Polo, how long does a 'Chuka' last?

13   Which sport do the West Coast Eagles play?

14   How many men form a line out in Rugby League?

15   In Euro 96 how many teams did England beat without the use of a penalty shoot-out?

ANSWERS

1. One. 2. Twice. 3. Bangladesh. 4. Sunderland. 5. True. 6. Spare. 7. Virginia Wade. 8. Colombian. 9. Ian Botham. 10. The Princess Royal. 11. Tony Banks. 12. Seven minutes. 13. Australian Rules Football. 14. None (you don't have line outs in Rugby League). 15. Two.

HISTORY

1 What was the name of the wife of King Louis XVI of France?

2 What happened in the year 971 when the body of St Swithin was moved to a cathedral?

3 Who is Gerald Ford?

4 What opened between Stockton and Darlington in September, 1825?

5 In what year was the Great Exhibition held in Hyde Park, London?

6 On 27 January, 1859, Queen Victoria became a grandmother. Who was her grandson?

7 Who was Rutherford Hayes?

8 Which Mongol conqueror succeeded his father at the age of 13?

9 Who was Bertha Krupp, and what was named after her?

10 Which area in Southern Africa became a British colony in 1813?

11 Which group of buildings, costing a million pounds, opened in Birmingham in 1964?

12 In which country is the Republican Party a major political unit?

13 Who was Field Marshal Paul von Beneckendorf und von Hindenburg?

14 In A.D. 301, Edward, son of King Edward I, was invested as what?

15 Who was the first English king to be divorced?

CINEMA AND TV

1 Who starred in the film *Lucky Jim*?

2 What makes *Snow White and the Seven Dwarfs* of historic significance?

3 Who's real name was Archibald Leach?

4 The lead role in this film was turned down by John Wayne, Paul Newman and Frank Sinatra before being taken by Clint Eastwood. Name this film?

5 Which film star became Miss Hungary in 1936, but was disqualified for being under age?

6 Who starred in the films *The Conversation* and *The French Connection*?

7 Which movie star was the 'Sweater Girl'?

8 Which film actor was born Herbert Charles Angelo Kuchacevich ze Schluderpacheru?

9 Who wore the vest and was the hero in *Die Hard*?

10 Who is the oldest winner of the best actress Oscar?

11 Who starred in the film *Stagecoach*?

12 From which film did the song 'A Fine Romance' come?

13 Who starred in the 1941 film *The Maltese Falcon*?

14 Which of these film stars began as extras; Michael Caine, Gary Cooper, Marlene Dietrich?

15 Which film star wrote the novel *Diamond Lil*?

POPULAR MUSIC

1 Which Leicester band had nine top ten singles between 1975 & 1978, all cover versions of classic rock & roll songs?

2 In 1996, PJ & Duncan, changed their names to what?

3 With whom did the Pet Shop Boys record 'What Have I Done To Deserve This', the theme to the film, 'Scandal',?

4 Which pop quiz programme, is hosted by Mark Lamarr?

5 Kylie Minogue reached number one with 'Especially For You' in collaboration with whom?

6 Ska band Madness only had one UK number one, name the song?

7 What was Madonna's first UK hit single?

8 Which rock group had eight number 1 albums between 1969 and 1979?

9 By what name is Reg Dwight better known?

10 Which long-running band replaced their famous drummer and lead singer with the singer from Stiltskin?

11 By what name is Harry Webb better known?

12 Who recorded the theme song 'Love Song For A Vampire', for the 1993 film, Dracula starring Gary Oldman and Keanu Reeves?

13 Level 42 never had a UK number 1. True or false?

14 Which Welshman has had 15 UK top ten hits, between 1965 and 1988?

15 Which comic indie band have written songs including, 'Rod Hull Is Still Alive - Why?' 'The Trumpton Riots' and 'Paintball's Coming Home'?

LITERATURE

1 Who wrote *Fear Of Flying*?

2 In which story does 'Sam Weller' appear?

3 Complete the proverb: 'Do not halloo till you're...'

4 Who wrote *The Great Gatsby*?

5 Who wrote *Cold Comfort Farm*?

6 'Tom Canty' is a character in which story by Mark Twain?

7 'I hear a sudden cry of pain!/There is a rabbit in a snare' is the beginning of a poem by whom?

8 Complete the proverb: 'A bird in hand...'

9 Who wrote *Ross Poldark*?

10 Who or what was 'Excalibur'?

11 'Superintendent Roderick Alleyn' was created by whom?

12 The Compleat Angler, or the Contemplative Man's Recreation, was written by whom?

13 Who invented the comic-strip super-sleuth 'Dick Tracy'?

14 In which Shakespeare play does Caliban appear?

15 Who wrote the fairy stories *The Cuckoo Clock*, *The Tapestry Room* and *Four Winds Farm*?

ANSWERS

1. Erica Jong. 2. *Pickwick Papers*. 3. '...out of the wood'. 4. F. Scott Fitzgerald. 5. Stella Gibbons. 6. *The Prince and the Pauper*. 7. James Stephens. 8. '...is worth two in the bush'. 9. Winston Graham. 10. King Arthur's sword. 11. Ngaio Marsh. 12. Izaak Walton. 13. Chester Gould. 14. *The Tempest*. 15. Mary Louisa Molesworth.

GENERAL KNOWLEDGE

1 Monday is named after the Moon. True or false?

2 Where in Britain would you find our oldest surviving clock?

3 What word, beginning with ante-, means 'before dinner'?

4 What is a Wiener schnitzel?

5 Who or what was Chad?

6 Who was Britain's answer to Louis Armstrong?

7 What was, or is, a billycock hat?

8 What is a Latter-Day Saint?

9 In a pack of cards, which way does the Queen of Diamonds look: to her left or to her right?

10 What anniversary does a wooden wedding celebrate?

11 What did Albert Schweitzer set up in Lambaréné?

12 What is the Army equivalent of a Lieutenant Commander in the Navy?

13 How did 'knickers' get their name?

14 A methuselah is a measure of wine equivalent to how many bottles?

15 What article of clothing is a mantilla?

SCIENCE

1   What is the Red Planet?

2   What does one measure with an anemometer?

3   What is a chinook?

4   What does 'opaque' mean?

5   What is the difference between 'inflammable' and 'flammable'?

6   The study of microscopic organisms is called what?

7   What is a Polaris?

8   Haematite is a metal ore. Which metal?

9   Which of these metals is the lightest: gold, lead or platinum?

10 What, during WW1, were Camels and Pups?

11 Graphology is the study of what?

12 What is vulcanology?

13 What very light metal was discovered in 1827 by Hans Christian Oersted?

14 What is Kevlar?

15 With which weapon is the physicist Robert Oppenheimer connected?

ANSWERS

1. Mars. 2. Wind speed. 3. A warm, dry wind from the Rocky Mountains. 4. The opposite of transparent. 5. No difference at all. They both mean 'able to burn'. 6. Bacteriology. 7. A ballistic missile fired from a submarine. 8. Iron. 9. Lead. 10. Famous fighter planes built by Sopwith. 11. Handwriting. 12. The scientific study of volcanoes. 13. Aluminium. 14. A light but strong man-made material. 15. Atomic bomb.

NATURAL HISTORY

1. What is a group of kangaroos called?

2. What is a group of chickens called?

3. What kind of animal is said to chatter?

4. Can a porcupine shoot its quills?

5. How fast can a racehorse run in miles per hour; (a) 50 (b) 60 (c) 70?

6. What are animals without backbones called?

7. A male horse aged four or under is called a what?

8. What is unusual about the wings of a baby hoatzin bird?

9. What kind of animal could be described as a Tamworth?

10. The smell of skunk's fluid can be detected half a mile away. True or false?

11. What does the word 'hippopotamus' mean?

12. What is a gillyflower?

13. What is a katydid?

14. What is another name for the pumpkin?

15. The gooseberry is a plant relative of the saxifrage. True or false?

ANSWERS

1. A mob. 2. A brood. 3. A jay. 4. No. 5. (a) About 50 miles per hour. 6. Invertebrates. 7. A colt. 8. They have three clawed fingers on each. 9. A breed of pig. 10. True. 11. River-horse. 12. A flower which smells like cloves. 13. An American insect like a grasshopper which makes a sound like its name. 14. Squash. 15. True.

GEOGRAPHY

1 Where would you find Bow Bells?

2 Where is the Bull Ring in England?

3 It is extremely difficult to see Big Ben in London. Why?

4 'Erin' was a poetic name for which country?

5 To which country do the Faroe Islands belong?

6 Which city is on the River Elbe?

7 Which cities are on the River Arno?

8 How many hills was Rome believed to be built on?

9 Where did liquorice originate?

10 What is the village of Hambledon, in Hampshire, famed for?

11 In which English city would you find Parkway railway station?

12 Which is the world's smallest republic?

13 On which stretch of water does Toronto stand?

14 In which city would you find King's Cross railway station?

15 Where is the Cathedral of Notre Dame?

1. In the City of London, at St Mary-le-Bow Church. Not the East London district of Bow. 2. Birmingham. It's a shopping centre. 3. Because 'Big Ben' is the bell inside the clock tower. 4. Ireland. 5. Denmark. 6. Hamburg. 7. Florence and Pisa. 8. Seven. 9. Egypt. 10. Being the birthplace of cricket. 11. Bristol. 12. Nauru (5,261 acres). 13. Lake Ontario. 14. London. 15. In Paris. Its full title is 'Notre-Dame de Paris' (Our Lady of Paris).

ENGLISH LANGUAGE

1 What is an 'agony aunt'?

2 What do the initials UFO stand for?

3 What is the wife of an earl called?

4 What is the meaning of 'defunct'?

5 What, in an American bank, is a 'teller'?

6 What does the word 'Mart' mean?

7 Can you name a word, beginning with Q, that can mean extract or excerpt?

8 In cockney rhyming slang what does 'tit-for-tat' mean?

9 What is your derrière?

10 What's the difference between eminent and imminent?

11 What one word means both, 'a type of crop' and 'a horny, sore place on the foot'?

12 What politician's name is an anagram of 'that great charmer'?

13 What was a 'Dolly Varden'?

14 What does 'prolix' mean?

15 What is, or was, a 'bimbo'?

SPORT

1 Which football team plays their home games at 'The New Den'?

2 What is the accepted length of a field hockey pitch?

3 What do the initials TCCB stand for?

4 Which sporting archive was established at Cooperstown, New York State, in 1934?

5 With which sport do you associate Michael Whitaker?

6 Which sport is descended from Byerly Turk, Darley Arabian and Godolphin Arabian?

7 What did Belgian Joseph Merlin invent in 1760, which was improved on 100 years later by American Everett Plimpton, which today is the basis for several leisure sports?

8 How many disciplines are there in a Women's international gymnastics event?

9 In Olympic athletics, how long is a steeplechase?

10 This sport first became popular in the 13th Century. Its first purpose-built playing area was opened in Southampton in 1299. Its rules were unified in the 19th century, although different variations still prevail in the North of England. What is it?

11 Which football team play their home games at Ewood Park?

12 Which Brazilian won the Formula One World Drivers Championships in 1981, 1983 and 1987?

13 How high is a table tennis net; 4ins, 5ins, 6ins, or 7ins?

14 What sport do the Sacramento Kings play?

15 How long is a quarter in Water Polo?

HISTORY

1. Who was Georges Pompidou?

2. Where, in London, is the Queen forbidden entry?

3. What drastic measure against illegal parking was introduced in May, 1983?

4. When was the royal fortress of Bastille stormed by French workers?

5. What was called 'Dad's Army'?

6. In which century did the Vikings start their raids on Britain?

7. On which mountain climb did eight men lose their lives in May, 1996?

8. Who came to power in Japan in 1926?

9. Who was William Howard Taft?

10. What event was televised in June, 1953?

11. What is meant by the Third Reich?

12. Whose last words were: "Let not poor Nelly starve"?

13. Who dismissed 5,000 employees in East London in February, 1986?

14. Which important building connected with the law was opened on 27th February, 1907?

15. In Chicago, the St Valentine's Day Massacre took place. Who was involved?

CINEMA AND TV

1 Who starred in the film *The Cruel Sea*?

2 Who were Petra and Goldie?

3 Who starred in the spoof film *Dracula: Dead And Loving It*?

4 Who was originally considered to star in *The Wizard of Oz*?

5 Which Disney film was re-made as a live action film starring Glenn Close as the villain?

6 Which well-known actor played himself in *The Love Lottery*?

7 Which well-known actor played himself in *Starlift*?

8 Who starred in the film *Shane*?

9 Which black actor starred in *Jackie Brown* and *Eve's Bayou*?

10 Who starred in the film *The Quatermass Experiment*?

11 'In space, no one can hear you scream' was the slogan for which series of sci-fi horror films?

12 Which disaster movie starred Steve McQueen, Paul Newman, Fred Astaire, O.J. Simpson, Robert Wagner and Richard Chamberlain?

13 Who starred in the film *I'm All Right Jack*?

14 What sitcom did Wilfred Bramble and Harry H. Corbett star in?

15 Which US comic played Ace Ventura in several films?

POPULAR MUSIC

1 Which Mel & Kim reached number one at Christmas 1987?

2 In 1981, Starsound, had hits with 'Stars on 45' volume 1 and 2 What nationality were Starsound?

3 Who recorded the album Architecture and Morality?

4 Which US/German act had number ones with 'The Power' and 'Rhythm is a dancer'?

5 Who is the lead singer of Eurythmics?

6 Which former Radio one DJ had top ten hits including 'Everyone's Gone To The Moon', 'Loop di Love' and 'Una Paloma Blanca'?

7 With which movie and TV theme did Irene Cara, reach number one in 1982?

8 What is the link between, Mark Lamarr, BBC2 and 'What Do I Get'?

9 In 1993, with whom did Frank Sinatra record 'I've Got You Under My Skin'?

10 Which movie theme song did Boy George record in 1992?

11 With which US female singer did BoyZ II Men record 'One Sweet Day ' in 1995?

12 Which group of recording artists, designed to appeal to young Labour voters during the 1992 Election Campaign, featured Billy Bragg?

13 Boy George recorded which cover version to register his only solo number one to date?

14 Celine Dion has never had a UK number one hit. True or false?

15 Who is the lead singer/guitarist with Dire Straits?

LITERATURE

1 What have Marple, Mason and Morse in common?

2 The character 'King Rudolf' appears in which famous book?

3 Who wrote *The Book of Nonsense*?

4 'You are old, Father William,' the young man said': begins a poem by whom?

5 Complete the proverb: 'Don't empty the baby out...'

6 Which English author was regarded as the most popular 'thriller' writer of all time?

7 Who wrote *Cider With Rosie*?

8 Who was 'Biggles'?

9 Who created the fictional detective, 'John Appleby'?

10 Which of the following is not a play; *The Laughing Cavalier, The Faerie Queene, Vanity Fair*?

11 Who wrote *A Town Like Alice*?

12 Who created the first blind fictional detective 'Max Carrados'?

13 Who was Algernon Blackwood?

14 On being told that her people had no bread, Marie-Antoinette replied: Qu'ils mangent de la brioche. What does this mean?

15 Who wrote *The Vicar of Wakefield*?

ANSWERS

1. The are the surnames of fictional detectives. 2. *The Prisoner of Zenda*. 3. Edward Lear. 4. Lewis Carroll. 5. '...with the bathwater'. 6. Edgar Wallace. 7. Laurie Lee. 8. A heroic British airman with the full name, Major James Bigglesworth. 9. Michael Innes. 10. None at all! 11. Nevil Shute. 12. Ernest Bramah. 13. Novelist and short-story writer. 14. Let them eat cake! 15. Oliver Goldsmith.

GENERAL KNOWLEDGE

1 If you asked for a 'biscuit' in the United States, what would you get?

2 What did American Express introduce in 1891?

3 What has been estimated at 50 million farenheit?

4 Who was the first 'Supermac'?

5 And which tennis player was the second 'Supermac'?

6 Who is Old Nick?

7 According to the 'language of flowers', what does the nasturtium signify?

8 What animal is grouped in packs?

9 If your surname is 'Martin', what might your nickname be?

10 In a pack of cards, which way does the King of Diamonds look, to his left, or to his right?

11 What is stingo?

12 What is smörgåsbord?

13 What is a ragout?

14 Whalebone isn't the bone of a whale. What is it?

15 In card-playing, how did the word 'trump' come into being?

812

SCIENCE

1 Photophobia is (a) fear of light or (b) fear of being photographed?

2 What device for long-distance speech was invented in 1876?

3 What is a stethoscope used for?

4 From which plant do we obtain linseed oil?

5 How many pounds are there in a hundredweight?

6 What is porcelain?

7 Who discovered the circulation of the blood?

8 Desdemona is a satellite of which planet?

9 Spectacles were first reported in use in which century?

10 A day on Mars lasts only 40 minutes longer than on Earth. True or false?

11 What communications system was laid between England and France in 1891?

12 The wreck of which famous liner was found in 1985?

13 What was scientist Theodore Maimam famous for building?

14 The clavicle is another name for which bone?

15 What is a pantograph?

ANSWERS

1. Fear of light. 2. The telephone. 3. To hear sounds in the body, such as the heartbeat. 4. Flax. 5. 112. 6. A fine, white, thin, translucent earthenware. 7. William Harvey. 8. Uranus. 9. 13th century AD. 10. True. 11. The telephone cable. 12. The Titanic. 13. The first working laser. 14. The collar-bone. 15. A drawing instrument for tracing, by which means to enlarge or reduce a drawing.

NATURAL HISTORY

1 An ant-eating mammal in South Africa has a name meaning 'earth-pig'. Can you name it?

2 What is a kumquat?

3 How fast can an ostrich run? (a) 40 mph. (b) 50 mph. (c) 60 mph.

4 What sort of animal is a Pekingese?

5 What are the names for a male and a female goat?

6 A camel can go without water for up to ten days. True or false?

7 What kind of animal could be described as a Dorset Horn?

8 The okapi is the closest relative to which tall mammal?

9 Are bats really blind?

10 What is cowslip?

11 What is a cockle?

12 What is an elver?

13 What sort of animal is a Friesian?

14 The woolly mammoth was a kind of hairy, prehistoric example of what modern-day creature?

15 What kind of animal could be described as a Merino?

ANSWERS

1. The aardvark or ant-bear. 2. A small kind of orange. 3. 50 m.p.h. 4. A breed of dog. 5. A billy-goat and a nanny-goat. 6. True. 7. A breed of sheep. 8. The giraffe. 9. Some have very poor vision, but none is known to be totally blind. 10. A species of wild primrose with yellow, densely-tufted flowers. 11. A shell-fish, highly-prized by Londoners not so long ago. 12. A young eel. 13. A breed of cattle. 14. Elephant. 15. A breed of sheep.

GEOGRAPHY

1   What record does Mount Whitney hold?

2   Where, and what, is the 'Windy City'?

3   Between which two cities did the original Orient Express train run?

4   'Pompey' is the nickname for which English city?

5   What is the capital of Ghana?

6   In which county in the New Forest?

7   Where is Lizard Point?

8   What is the capital of Malta?

9   What is the capital of New Zealand?

10 Where in the World is the highest waterfall found?

11 To which country does the Pacific island of Guam belong?

12 'The Big Apple' is a colloquial name for where?

13 What is the Sargasso Sea?

14 Vectis was the name given by the Romans to what?

15 Whereabouts in the world would you find New England?

1. It's the highest peak in the continental USA. 2. The city of Chicago, USA. 3. Paris to Istanbul. 4. Portsmouth. 5. Accra. 6. In Hampshire. 7. A peninsula in Cornwall, the most southerly point in England. 8. Valletta. 9. Wellington. 10. Salto Angel, Venezuela, 3,212 feet. 11. The United States. 12. New York City. 13. An area in the Atlantic with a vast accumulation of gulfweed. 14. The Isle of Wight. 15. In the north east of the United States.

ENGLISH LANGUAGE

1 Can you name two words, sounding alike, which mean the same as this pair: flesh for food/to encounter?

2 What is 'hyperbole'?

3 What were 'bluestockings'?

4 What is a rhetorical question?

5 What does the phrase, 'In days of yore' mean?

6 What word, beginning with A, means false or synthetic?

7 What is the name for someone who studies insects?

8 If you had a white elephant (figuratively!) what in fact would you have?

9 Gypsies were so called because of what?

10 What do the initials, DOA stand for?

11 Which one word can mean both, 'a large furry animal' and 'to carry'?

12 If your surname is Martin, you might be nicknamed what?

13 What is the British equivalent of the American 'drug store'?

14 What is the female version of 'abbot'?

15 What word, beginning with C, means chat or talk?

1. Meat/meet. 2. A figure of speech: exaggeration for emphasis, such as 'tons of money'. 3. Literary or studious women. 4. One that does not require an answer. 5. In ancient times, in times past. 6. Artificial. 7. Entomologist. 8. Something which was more of a nuisance than of value. 9. Because it was thought that they came from Egypt. 10. Dead On Arrival. 11. Bear. 12. Pincher. 13. A chemist's. 14. Abbess. 15. Conversation.

SPORT

1 What makes Sculls different to conventional rowing?

2 In 1990 Hale Irwin won the US Open Golf Championship. What record did he set in doing this?

3 What nationality is Tennis star Anna Kournikova?

4 With which sport do you associate Dennis Rodman?

5 Who set the world 100m record of 9.84 seconds at the 1996 Olympics?

6 Which World Cup hero was knighted in the 1998 Queens Birthday honours list?

7 Name New York's AFC American Football team?

8 In Martial Arts such as Judo and Karate, what name is given to the ritual exercises that develop technique, and physical and mental strength?

9 In horse racing, by what name is a male horse less than four years old referred to?

10 Where did the sport of Polo originate?

11 How long is the Service Court in Tennis; 19ft, 20ft, 21ft, or 22ft?

12 Who succeeded Sean Fitzpatrick in 1998 as captain of the All Blacks?

13 What offence was supposed to have meant an automatic sending off during the 1998 World Cup?

14 In Polo, with what do you hit the ball?

15 In a Motorcycle Grand Prix, how many points are awarded for first place?

ANSWERS

1. In Sculls, each oarsman has two oars, in Rowing they have one.
2. Oldest player to win the tournament. 3. Russian. 4. Basketball.
5. Donovan Bailey. 6. Sir Geoff Hurst. 7. The Jets. 8. Kata. 9. A Colt.
10. Persia (Iran). 11. 21ft. 12. Taine Randell. 13. A tackle from behind. 14. A mallet. 15. Twenty.

HISTORY

1 What flag was first adopted in Britian in 1606?

2 The Witan was the name for a parliament held by which early people in Britain?

3 Who was the first of the Plantagenet kings?

4 In which year did Japan invaded Manchuria?

5 Where did Italy invade in 1935?

6 Who became Empress of Russia in succession to Peter the Great in 1725?

7 Who were the Incas?

8 On the 11th April, 1689, which two people were crowned together?

9 In Whitechapel, East London, in 1888, many prostitues were murdered. Who was held responsible?

10 In the House of Lords, on what does the Lord Chancellor sit?

11 In religious terms, what was the Great Schism?

12 What did Russia sell to the United States in 1867?

13 Before the reign of King Henry VIII, how were monarchs addressed?

14 After seven months of resistance, the South African town of Mafeking was relieved by troops under the command of which military figure?

15 Who and what were the Spartacists?

ANSWERS

1. The Union Flag (popularly called the Union Jack). 2. The Saxons. 3. King Henry II (1154-1189). 4. 1931. 5. Ethiopia. 6. Catherine I. 7. The original and native people of ancient Peru. 8. William III and Mary II. 9. Jack the Ripper. 10. The Woolsack. 11. The split in the 14th century between two rival Catholic groups, each with a different Pope. 12. Alaska. 13. As 'Your Highness'. 14. Col. Robert Baden-Powell. 15. A German radical socialist group from 1915, including Rosa Luxemburg and Karl Liebknecht.

CINEMA AND TV

1. What was the name of the toy astronaut in the film Toy Story?

2. From which film did the song 'My Kind of Town' come?

3. Who starred in the film The Magnificent Ambersons?

4. Who played the country vicar in the film The Holly and the Ivy in 1952?

5. With which war was the film The Deerhunter concerned?

6. Which spoof sci-fi film was directed by Tim Burton and included Tom Jones in its cast?

7. Which actor was a former member of the IRA?

8. In which film did Dudley Moore play a 'chief elf' in Santa Claus's workshop?

9. What was Michael Caine's occupation before acting?

10. Who starred in the 1927 silent film The General?

11. What was the name of the sequel to The Blues Brothers?

12. In the film Peter's Friends, who played Peter?

13. Who starred in the film Gone With the Wind?

14. Who starred in the film Mrs Doubtfire?

15. What was the name of Blackadder's loyal but dopey servant?

1. Buzz Lightyear. 2. Robin and the Seven Hoods. 3. Joseph Cotten. 4. Ralph Richardson. 5. The Vietnam War. 6. Mars Attacks! 7. George Brent. 8. Santa Claus, made in 1985. 9. He was a meat porter in Smithfield Market. 10. Buster Keaton. 11. Blues Brothers 2000. 12. Stephen Fry. 13. Clark Gable, Vivien Leigh. 14. Robin Williams, Sally Field. 15. Baldric.

POPULAR MUSIC

1   In which year did Elvis Presley die?

2   Which singer started her career as lead singer with The GoGo's?

3   True or false, Bananarama had five UK number 1's?

4   Canadian singer Terry Jacks reached number one in 1974 with which song?

5   Which football team do the Gallagher brothers support?

6   Who recorded the album 'The Lodger'?

7   Which group included Levon Helm, Rick Danko and Robbie Robertson?

8   Who fronts the group Radiohead?

9   Which band included the dancer and 'vibes manager' Bez?

10 In 1956 who reached number three with 'I'm Walking Backwards For Christmas/Bluebottle Blues'?

11 Who had hits in 1982/83 with 'I Don't Wanna Dance' and 'Electric Avenue'?

12 Which musician, the inspiration behind the band, Nine Inch Nails, also wrote the acclaimed sountrack to Oliver Stone's film, Natural Born Killers.

13 Singer Michelle Gayle was better known to BBC viewers as which character?

14 In 1990 Lindisfarne recorded 'Fog On The Tyne (revisited)'. Which footballer was credited on the record?

15 Warren G and Nate Dogg had a top ten hit with 'What's Love Got To Do With It'. Who had previously had a top ten hit with this song?

ANSWERS

1. 1977. 2. Belinda Carlisle. 3. False. 4. 'Seasons In The Sun'.
5. Manchester City. 6. David Bowie. 7. The Band. 8. Thom Yorke.
9. Happy Mondays. 10. The Goons. 11. Eddie Grant. 12. Trent Reznor.
13. Hattie from Eastenders. 14. Paul Gascoigne (Gazza). 15. Tina Turner.

LITERATURE

1   What 10,000 word tale of a seagull, first published in 1970, sold 7 million copies within five years?

2   'Sir Andrew Aguecheek' appears in which play by Shakespeare?

3   What, according to Karl Marx, was the 'opium of the people'?

4   Which author wrote under the name 'James Bridie'?

5   Who wrote The Satanic Verses?

6   Who wrote Brave New World?

7   In which play does 'Jack Worthing' appear?

8   Complete Wellington's sentence: 'I don't know what effect they will have on the enemy...'

9   Who wrote Crime and Punishment?

10 Who wrote the children's books Jackanapes and The Brownies, and Other Tales?

11 Who is the leading character in Thomas Hardy's Far From the Madding Crowd?

12 Complete the proverb: 'Don't cross a bridge...'

13 Who wrote Adam Bede?

14 'I come from haunts of coot and hern' is the beginning of a poem by whom?

15 Complete this line by Thomas Gray: 'For many a flower is born...'

ANSWERS

1. Jonathan Livingston Seagull. 2. Twelfth Night. 3. Religion. 4. Osborne Henry Mavor. 5. Salman Rushdie. 6. Aldous Huxley. 7. The Importance of Being Earnest. 8. 'But by God, they frighten me'. 9. Dostoevsky. 10. Julia Horatia Ewing. 11. 'Bathsheba Everdene'. 12. '...until you come to it'. 13. George Eliot. 14. Lord Tennyson. 15. '...to blush unseen.'

GENERAL KNOWLEDGE

1 What is 'Murphy's Law'?

2 What are duchesse potatoes?

3 What is laverbread?

4 What is a rissole?

5 What is a group of chickens called?

6 What is biltong?

7 Who was the 'Bouncing Czech'?

8 What did the S. stand for in the name of Harry S. Truman?

9 What is the Naval equivalent of a Field Marshal?

10 What is the London Palladium?

11 What word, beginning with ante- means 'before midday'?

12 What was Dr. Who's time machine called?

13 What is charlotte russe?

14 According to the 'language of flowers', what does the foxglove signify?

15 What is halva?

ANSWERS

1. Briefly, it says that 'what can go wrong, will go wrong. 2. Mashed potato, baked with butter, milk and egg-yolk. 3. Fronds of the porphyra seaweed, dipped in oatmeal and fried. 4. A fried meat ball or cake. 5. A brood. 6. Strips of dried lean meat from South Africa. 7. Robert Maxwell. 8. Nothing at all! 9. Admiral of the Fleet. 10. A famous theatre where top performers have appeared. 11. Ante meridian. 12. The TARDIS. 13. A sponge-cake containing cream, biscuit and flavourings. 14. Insincerity. 15. A sweet made with sesame seeds and honey.

SCIENCE

1 What is zoophobia?

2 What colour is the peridot stone?

3 The cotton gin, for separating the seeds from the fibres, was invented in the US in 1793 by whom?

4 Perspex is a trade name for what?

5 If something is 'extraterrestrial', where would it be found?

6 Hero of Alexandria invented the aeolipile in AD 100. What was it?

7 Apart from being a young horse, what else is called a colt?

8 Who was Jean-François Champollion?

9 What's the record for someone being struck by lightning (and surviving)? (a) 4 times (b) 10 times (c) 7 times

10 What is odontology?

11 KLM is what?

12 What is a triangle with three different sides called?

13 A machine for altering the voltage of alternating current is called what?

14 What colour is an emerald?

15 Alexander Parkes invented a well-known early plastic (very inflammable) in 1855. Name?

ANSWERS

1. A fear of animals. 2. Green. 3. Eli Whitney. 4. Transparent plastic, used instead of glass. 5. Outside, or beyond the Earth. 6. A primitive kind of steam turbine. 7. A revolver. 8. French decipherer of the Rosetta Stone. 9. (c) 7 times: Roy Sullivan of Virginia, USA. 10. The science and study of the teeth. 11. The Dutch national airline. 12. Scalene. 13. A transformer. 14. Green. 15. Celluloid.

NATURAL HISTORY

1. What is edelweiss?

2. A dolphin is a mammal related to the whale. True or false?

3. What is a death-watch beetle?

4. What kind of animal could be described as a Black Suffolk?

5. Which bird lays the largest eggs?

6. Which bird lays the smallest eggs?

7. What kind of bird is said to boom?

8. Are there lizards which can fly?

9. Broccoli is plant relative of the cabbage. Yes or no?

10. The tomato is a member of the nightshade family. Yes or no?

11. Another name for the sea cow is what?

12. White ants are not ants at all. What are they?

13. What is a group of beavers called?

14. What kind of animal could be called a shire?

15. Which animal lives in a 'lodge'?

GEOGRAPHY

1 What was the Boulder Dam, on the Colorado River, renamed?

2 Which is the world's largest active volcano?

3 Albany is the capital city of which American state?

4 What is the capital of Egypt?

5 Where, not far from Paris, would you find the Hall of Mirrors?

6 Which famous church clock in London has only one hand?

7 What is the main city of Transvaal, South Africa?

8 The Friendly Islands is another name for which country?

9 What is the capital of Tunisia?

10 To which country does Puerto Rico belong?

11 What country's capital city is Quito?

12 Which is the world's largest freshwater lake?

13 Madrid is the capital of which country?

14 Which important Polish city stands on the Vistula river?

15 If you were standing in Ueno Park, which city would you be visiting?

1. The Hoover Dam. 2. Mauna Loa, Hawaii, 13,680 feet high. 3. New York State. 4. Cairo. 5. At the Palace of Versailles. 6. The clock of Westminster Abbey. 7. Johannesburg. 8. Tonga. 9. Tunis. 10. The United States. 11. Ecuador. 12. Lake Superior, North America, 31,800 sq.m. 13. Spain. 14. Warsaw. 15. Tokyo.

ENGLISH LANGUAGE

1 What is an 'archaism'?

2 If you were a cockney, where would you wear your 'almond rocks'?

3 What would you find at a carnival in the United States?

4 Which of these words has the same vowel sound as 'show': cough, nought, furlough?

5 What's wrong with this sentence: 'Mum was angry with the mess in the kitchen.'?

6 Can you name two words, sounding alike, which mean the same as this pair: market for goods/wind-catcher?

7 What word, beginning with A, means assign or designate?

8 What is the meaning of the word 'omniscient'?

9 If you wanted the equivalent of a solicitor in the US, you would go to whom?

10 Who were the 'blackshirts'?

11 What does 'à la mode' mean?

12 What does 'à la mode' mean in the United States?

13 What is a 'quango'?

14 What is the meaning of 'omnipotent'?

15 What substance used to be known as 'Coal oil'?

ANSWERS

1. The use of out-of-date words like peradventure, albeit, quoth. 2. On your feet. It means 'socks'. 3. It would be the equivalent of a fair in Britain, with roundabouts, swings, etc. 4. Furlough. 5. It should read: Mum was angry at the mess in the kitchen. 6. Sale/sail. 7. Appoint. 8. All-knowing. 9. An attorney. 10. Followers of Oswald Mosley in the Fascist party. 11. It simply means 'in fashion'. 12. Something served with ice-cream. 13. A Quasi Autonomous Non-Governmental Organisation. 14. All-powerful. 15. Kerosene or paraffin.

SPORT

1   What is the premier UK Rally event?

2   Which British Racing driver came second in the Monte Carlo Rally in 1952, second at Le Mans in 1956, as well as winning 36 Grand Prix?

3   Which sport was invented by American William G. Morgan, a physical training instructor from Holyoke, Massachusetts, involves 2 teams of 6 players, held its first world championship in 1949, and has accepted as an Olympic sport in 1964?

4   In which sport would you compete for the Federation Cup?

5   What sport do the Denver Nuggets play?

6   In m.p.h., how fast is a Knot?

7   In which 1982 event did Mark Thatcher get lost?

8   Which British Formula One driver was nicknamed 'The Shunt'?

9   Which sports does the FINA organisation preside over?

10 In which sport do you aim to get a ringer but sometimes get a leaner whilst standing in the pitching box?

11 For which sport is Bo Jackson famous?

12 Who was born in Hong Kong in 1943, named Lee Yuen Kan, became a master of Wing Chun, before developing his own, Jeet Kune Do, style of fighting, before dying in mysterious circumstances in 1973?

13 What is the first event in a Heptathlon?

14 With which sport do you associate Lanfranco 'Frankie' Dettori?

15 In show jumping, how many faults are given for, 'a foot in the water', at the water jump?

ANSWERS

1. The Lombard RAC Rally. 2. Stirling Moss. 3. Volleyball. 4. Tennis.
5. Basketball. 6. 1.15mph. 7. The Paris-Dakar Rally. 8. James Hunt.
9. Swimming, Waterpolo and Diving. 10. Horseshoe Pitching. 11. American Football.
12. Bruce Lee. 13. 100m hurdles. 14. Horse racing. 15. Four.

HISTORY

1 Whose last words were "Et tu, Brute"?

2 Who was the last monarch of France?

3 Albania was invaded by which country in 1939?

4 What was a suffragette?

5 Joseph Paxton completed what 600-yard-long building in Hyde Park in 1851?

6 Who entered Havana in triumph in January, 1959?

7 What were Bevin Boys?

8 In 1900, in China, what was the Boxer Rebellion?

9 The Charge of the Light Brigade took place during which war?

10 Which British novelist and statesman was a friend of Queen Victoria?

11 What were the supporters of the royal House of Stuart called?

12 What was destroyed by fire in Hong Kong harbour on 9th January, 1972?

13 What has Cleopatra's Needle to do with Cleopatra?

14 Who was Edward Longshanks?

15 Which national leaders took part in the Yalta Conference in 1945?

1. Julius Caesar's. 2. Louis-Philippe (1830-1848). 3. Italy. 4. A woman campaigner for women's right to vote. 5. The Crystal Palace. 6. Fidel Castro. 7. Young men who were called up to work in the mines. 8. An uprising of peasants. 9. The Crimean. 10. Benjamin Disraeli, Earl of Beaconsfield. 11. Jacobites. 12. The liner, Queen Elizabeth. 13. Nothing at all. It is dedicated to the pharaoh Thothmes III. 14. King Edward I. 15. Churchill, Roosevelt and Stalin.

CINEMA AND TV

1   Name four regulars who starred in the Carry On films.

2   Which actor starred in both *Trainspotting* and *The Full Monty*?

3   Whose life was the basis of the film *Funny Girl*?

4   Who is Tula Ellice Funklea?

5   What were the real names of the Marx Brothers?

6   Who's haunting music was adopted for the film *The Exorcist*?

7   Who plays Frasier in the TV show of the same name?

8   Who starred in the 1995 film *Jumanji*?

9   Morgan Freeman plays the President in which recent disaster movie?

10 Name the film which became a TV series centred on the New York School Of Performing Arts?

11 Which film starred Martin Clunes as a bridegroom left stranded on a remote island?

12 Which film used the slogan 'Size Does Matter' and starred Matthew Broderick and Jean Reno?

13 Rex Harrison and Eddie Murphy have both starred in what role?

14 Which film starred Wynona Ryder and Christian Slater as two murderous teenagers?

15 Whose last words were, 'I should never have switched from Scotch to Martinis'?

POPULAR MUSIC

1 With which female singer did the Pogues record, 'Fairy Tale Of New York'?

2 Who reached number 1 in January 1959 with, 'Smoke Gets In Your Eyes'?

3 What was Donny Osmonds' first UK number 1?

4 Who recorded the album, 'Diamonds and Pearls'?

5 Complete the trio, Keith Emerson, Greg Lake and ...?

6 What comic band have radio DJ, Mark Radcliffe and ex-Fall musician, Marc 'Lard' Riley formed?

7 With which Prince song did Sinead O'Connor reach number 1 in January 1990?

8 Marvin Gaye had his only UK number 1, 'I Heard It Through The Grapevine' in 1969. Who previously recorded the song in 1967?

9 Which Beatles album cover featured the band walking across a zebra crossing?

10 Who recorded the albums, 'Leisure' and 'Parklife'?

11 Boris Gardner hit number 1 in 1986 with, 'I Want To Wake Up With You'. What nationality is he?

12 Who recorded the album, 'For Those Who Are About To Rock'?

13 Which instrument does Kenny G play?

14 With whom did Peter Gabriel record his top ten hit, 'Don't give up'?

15 Which blues guitarist was described by Eric Clapton as the 'greatest' guitarist alive'?

LITERATURE

1 'The splendour falls on castle walls/And snowy summits old in story' is the beginning of a poem by whom?

2 Who wrote *The Picture of Dorian Gray*?

3 Complete the proverb: 'Better be an old man's darling...'

4 'I remember, I remember,/The house where I was born,' is the beginning of a poem by whom?

5 'Carter Dickson' and 'Carr Dickson' were pseudonyms of which American writer?

6 In which book does the character 'Tinker Bell' appear?

7 The character 'Scrooge' appears in which story by Charles Dickens?

8 A.A. Milne wrote: 'Hush! Hush! Whisper who dares!'   How did he continue?

9 The character 'Rikki Tikki Tavi' appears in which famous book?

10 In which Shakespeare play does 'Cordelia' appear?

11 'Tread softly,' says WB Yeats, because......

12 Who wrote *A Connecticut Yankee in King Arthur's Court*?

13 The *Fortunes of Philippa* was the first book by the most prolific of girls' story writers. Who?

14 Complete the proverb: 'The devil is not so black...'

15 Which American author and journalist wrote *The Old Man And The Sea* and was famous for doing much of his writing standing up?

ANSWERS

1. Lord Tennyson. 2. Oscar Wilde. 3. '...than a young man's slave'. 4. Thomas Hood. 5. John Dickson Carr. 6. *Peter Pan*. 7. *A Christmas Carol*. 8. 'Christopher Robin is saying his prayers.' 9. *The Jungle Book*. 10. *King Lear*. 11. 'Because you tread on my dreams'. 12. Mark Twain. 13. Angela Brazil. 14. '...as he is painted'. 15. Ernest Hemmingway.

GENERAL KNOWLEDGE

1 Jews who in early times settled in Poland and Germany are called what?

2 The Archer represents which sign of the Zodiac?

3 Who's catchphrases included 'Nay, nay and thrice, nay'?

4 Who is the patron saint of tailors?

5 What was a 'penny gaff'?

6 The Isle of Portland, Dorset is not an island. What is it?

7 St Barbara is the patron saint of whom?

8 St Andrew is the patron saint of where?

9 What is perry?

10 What is a Bath bun?

11 Saturday is named after Saturn, the Roman god of culture and vegetation. True or false?

12 Which artist was renowned for his paintings of horses?

13 Which Dutch liqueur is sometimes called 'egg brandy'?

14 St Christopher is the patron saint of whom?

15 What word, beginning with ante-, means 'before birth'?

ANSWERS

1. Ashkenazim. 2. Sagittarius. 3. English comedian, Frankie Howerd. 4. St Homobonus. 5. In Victorian times, a cheap, low-class music hall. 6. A peninsula. 7. Miners. 8. Scotland. 9. A drink made from fermented pear juice. 10. A rich, rather sweet, bun. 11. True. 12. George Stubbs. 13. Advocaat. 14. Travellers. 15. Antenatal.

SCIENCE

1   Who invented the vacuum flask?

2   What is limnology?

3   Two Germans, Wilhelm Maybach and Gottlieb Daimler, invented what vehicle?

4   What can be seen through something translucent?

5   At what temperature does water boil?

6   Aluminium is so called because it takes its name from the chemical alum. True or false?

7   What is acrophobia?

8   What is the hardest of all natural substances?

9   What is the name of the planet Pluto's satellite?

10 Nitric acid is also known as what?

11 What is beri-beri?

12 Who invented the gramophone?

13 What object in the sky is called Titan, and is 3,200 miles in diameter?

14 Blaise Pascal made a calculator in 1642, which was the ancestor of what?

15 What are Phobos and Deimos?

ANSWERS

1. James Dewar in 1885. 2. The scientific study of lakes and freshwater sites. 3. The motor-cycle, in 1885. 4. Light. 5. 100 degrees centigrade. 6. True. 7. Fear of heights. 8. Diamond. 9. Charon. 10. Aqua fortis, or strong water'. 11. A disease caused by a lack of vitamin B. 12. Thomas Edison (actually, he called it the 'phonograph'). 13. It is Saturn's largest moon. 14. The modern calculating machine. 15. The moons of Mars.

NATURAL HISTORY

1 If a racehorse and a greyhound raced, which would win?

2 The marsupial wolf is not a wolf at all, but is believed extinct in its home country of...?

3 What sort of animal is a whippet?

4 What was the name of Tarzan's chimpanzee?

5 What sort of animal is a liger?

6 What is a canary?

7 Maize is really a special kind of grass. True or false?

8 What ox-like creature, found now only in zoos, once roamed wild in Europe?

9 Asparagus comes from the lily family of plants. Yes or no?

10 A duiker is an antelope found in South America. True or false?

11 What is a terrapin?

12 What is goldenrod?

13 The gibbon is the smallest of which group of animals?

14 The goliath beetle is found in the tropics, and holds what record?

15 What sort of animal is a ridgeback?

ANSWERS

1. The racehorse. 2. Tasmania. It's also called the Tasmanian wolf. 3. A breed of dog like a small greyhound. 4. Cheta. 5. A cross between a lion and female tiger. 6. A yellow cage-bird with a wonderful song, its home being the Canary Islands. 7. True. 8. The bison. 9. Yes. 10. False. It's found in South Africa. 11. A water-tortoise. 12. A perennial herb of the aster family with a woody stem and with yellow spray-shaped flowers. 13. The apes. 14. At over four inches, it's the world's largest insect. 15. A breed of dog.

GEOGRAPHY

1 Siam is the old name for where?

2 In what country would you find the Temple of the Sun and the Temple of the Moon?

3 Where is the Giant's Causeway?

4 Where and what is Chesil Bank?

5 If you landed at Orly Airport, where would you be?

6 Sumatra is an island, part of which country?

7 The official name 'Nippon' refers to which country?

8 In which city would you find Lime Street railway station?

9 The official term 'Hrvatska' refers to which country?

10 In what country would you be if your currency was in Drachma?

11 The Topkapi Palace and museum is in what city?

12 What should one do at the Trevi Fountain in Rome?

13 What countries does 'Scandinavia' include?

14 Where in the world would you find a Fleming?

15 'Salop' is another name for which county?

1. Thailand. 2. Mexico. 3. Northern Ireland. 4. A long ridge of shingle off the Dorset coast. 5. Just outside Paris. 6. Indonesia. 7. Japan. 8. Liverpool. 9. Croatia. 10. Greece. 11. Istanbul. 12. Throw in coins and wish. 13. Norway, Sweden, Denmark, Finland and Iceland. 14. Belgium. 15. Shropshire.

ENGLISH LANGUAGE

1   What is the meaning of 'garrulous'?

2   Complete the following phrase: 'ready, willing and....'

3   What word, beginning with R, means agent or delegate?

4   What do Britons call an American 'closet'?

5   A quean is; (a) a fallen woman (b) a wooden quoit (c) a rare kind of African deer?

6   What is another word for deluge or engulf?

7   What is the female equivalent of 'marquis'?

8   What were 'beatniks'?

9   What is the name for someone who studies poisons?

10   What is a lady's handbag called in the United States?

11   What is meant by the *crème de la crème*?

12   What do the initials, GPO stand for?

13   What is meant by The Fourth Estate?

14   What does it mean if a meeting is held 'in camera'?

15   If an American were to spank his child, what would he call it?

1. Talkative. 2. Able. 3. Representative. 4. Cupboard. 5. (a) a fallen woman.
6. Flood. 7. Marchioness. 8. Nonconforming young people in the 1950 and 1960s.
9. Toxicologist. 10. A purse. 11. The very, very best. 12. General Post Office.
13. The Press. 14. It's held in secret. 15. Paddling.

SPORT

1   In Baseball which player wears the most protective clothing?

2   What did Frenchman, Baron Pierre de Courbetin, do in the late 19th Century that would provide a whole new focus for the sporting world?

3   Which Rugby Union club plays its home games at Welford Road?

4   With which sport, other than football, do you associate Jack Charlton?

5   What is the term used in Golf to describe two over par at a hole?

6   Which sport holds its main British events at Santa Pod?

7   Which American event, first run in 1911, requires competitors to cover 200 laps of a 2.5 mile circuit?

8   Which sport does the ITTF govern?

9   True or false. In Netball, only 2 players on each team are allowed to score goals?

10 Which sport did the All England Croquet Club take responsibility for in 1874, asking the Marylebone Cricket Club to write the rules?

11 For major Water Polo matches, what is the minimum depth of the pool; 18m, 20m, 21m or 23m?

12 For which Premiership club did Colin Hendry play before joining Glasgow Rangers?

13 Which country has more Polo Clubs than any other?

14 In which country is Lacrosse said to have originated?

15 In which year was the FA Cup first held; 1862, 1870, 1871 or 1872?

ANSWERS

1. The Catcher. 2. Resurrected the Olympic Games. 3. Leicester. 4. Fishing. 5. Double Bogey. 6. Drag Racing. 7. Indianapolis 500. 8. Table Tennis. 9. True. 10. Lawn Tennis. 11. 1.8m. 12. Blackburn Rovers. 13. Argentina. 14. Canada. 15. 1872.

HISTORY

1   Which king of England was crowned on the battlefield?

2   Two men were hanged at Newgate, London, in 186 8
    What was notable about this?

3   The pedal cycle was perfected in 1839 by whom?

4   To whom was Princess Mary of Teck married?

5   The 'five-and-ten-cent-store' which opened in Utica, New York in
    1879 was so successful that it spread throughout the United
    States and into Britain. Can you name the famous store?

6   Which Bohemian prince commanded the Royalist cavalry during
    the English Civil War?

7   Where in England was the first Roman colony?

8   To which English king did the Pope award the title 'Defender of
    the Faith'?

9   Following the deaths of Kaisers Frederick III and Wilhelm I, who
    became the German Kaiser on 15th June, 1888?

10 Which great institution celebrated its 900th anniversary in
    December, 1965?

11 What happened in Krakatoa island in August, 1883?

12 Which wars took place in England starting in 1455 and ending in
    1471?

13 On which day does the Orthodox Church celebrate Christmas?

14 Which famous British aircraft-carrier was sunk off Gibraltar on
    12th November, 1941?

15 What is the purpose of this: Willy, Willy, Harry, Steve Harry,
    Dicky, John, Harry Three?

ANSWERS

1. King Henry VII in 1485. 2. It was the last public hanging in Britain.
3. Kirkpatrick Macmillan. 4. King George V. 5. Woolworths. 6. Prince Rupert.
7. Colchester. 8. King Henry VIII. 9. Wilhelm II. 10. Westminster Abbey. 11. The island
exploded via an enormous volcanic eruption, killing 36,380 people. 12. The Wars of
the Roses. 13. 7th January. 14. HMS Ark Royal. 15. A device for remembering the
first eight English kings after the Norman Conquest.

CINEMA AND TV

1 Which playwright has had his works filmed more than any other?

2 Which composer often provides the music for Steven Spielberg films?

3 Who plays Scully in *The X-Files*?

4 Who co-wrote *Fawlty Towers* with her husband, John Cleese?

5 Which director made the films *Taxi Driver* and *Raging Bull*?

6 What was the first film in Cinemascope?

7 Who starred in the film *Love Story*?

8 Who played the female lead in *Personal Services* and *Educating Rita*?

9 Which British film, scripted by Colin Welland, won the 1981 Best Picture Oscar?

10 What does a key grip do on a film set?

11 Which TV soap is based around the lives of the people on Ramsey Street?

12 Who directed the film *Midnight Cowboy*?

13 Who claimed to go nearly mad making a film alongside a cartoon rabbit?

14 Who directed the 1935 film *The Informer*?

15 Yogi Bear's partner was Boo Boo, but who was his girlfriend?

ANSWERS

1. William Shakespeare. 2. John Williams II. 3. Gillian Anderson. 4. Connie Booth. 5. Martin Scorsese. 6. *The Robe*, 1953. 7. Ryan O'Neal and Ali McGraw. 8. Julie Walters. 9. *Chariots Of Fire*. 10. He's in charge of the grips who look after construction and production equipment. 11. Neighbours. 12. John Schlesinger. 13. Bob Hoskins during the making of *Who Framed Roger Rabbit*. 14. John Ford. 15. Cindy.

POPULAR MUSIC

1 In which TV show did Ant and Dec start their show business careers?

2 In which James Bond film did singer Grace Jones play a villain?

3 TV presenter Cheryl Baker was formerly with which chart-topping group?

4 Who won the 1976 Eurovision Song Contest with 'Save All Your Kisses For Me'?

5 Which group became synonymous with flying pigs over Battersea Power Station?

6 Name Little Jimmy Osmond's debut single which reached number one In 1972?

7 What was Oasis' first single release?

8 In which year did Mark Morrison reach number one with 'Return of the Mack'; 1993, 1995, 1996 or 1997?

9 In 1981 Ennio Morricone reached number 2 in the UK chart with, Chi Mai', the theme from which TV series?

10 Who reached number 3 in 1988 with, 'I Don't Want To Talk About It'?

11 Who was the lead singer with the Electric Light Orchestra?

12 With whom did Olivia Newton John record Xanadu in 1980?

13 What instrument did Duane Eddy play?

14 Which TV show's theme tune was the Ian Dury and the Blockheads' song, 'Profoundly in love with Pandora?

15 Who had top ten hits with, 'Straight Up', 'Rush Rush' and 'Opposites Attract'?

840

LITERATURE

1   What line follows 'The curfew tolls the knell of parting day'?

2   Who was Robert Bridges?

3   Which famous children's book did Hugh Lofting write?

4   'Mrs Bardell' appears in which book by Charles Dickens?

5   Who created the fictional Chinese detective 'Charlie Chan'?

6   Who wrote *The Story of an African Farm*?

7   In which book does 'Raffles' appear?

8   In which children's comic did 'Desperate Dan' appear?

9   Who wrote the original *Jaws* novel?

10 What fictional character did Francis Durbridge create?

11 Complete the proverb: 'A constant guest...'

12 Who wrote *Five Children – and It*, and *The Phoenix and the Carpet*?

13 Who wrote *Cranford*?

14 Complete the proverb: 'Absence makes...'

15 Which was Shakespeare's first play?

ANSWERS

1. The lowing herd wind slowly o'er the lea'. 2. Poet Laureate and phoneticist. 3. *The Story of Doctor Dolittle*. 4. *Pickwick Papers*. 5. Earl Derr Biggers. 6. Olive Schreiner. 7. Several stories by E.W. Hornung, 'Raffles' was a gentleman burglar. 8. *The Dandy*. 9. Peter Benchley. 10. Paul Temple. 11. ... is never welcome. 12. E. Nesbit. 13. Mrs Elizabeth Gaskell. 14. '...the heart grow fonder'. 15. *The Two Gentlemen of Verona*.

GENERAL KNOWLEDGE

1   What is béchamel?

2   What is fascism?

3   What, to a soldier, is a redcap?

4   Who was known as, 'the fifth Beatle'?

5   Turkeys didn't come from Turkey. Where did they originally come from?

6   The 'Abominable Snowman' is also known as?

7   What word, beginning with ante-, means 'before the existence of the world'?

8   Who is Allah?

9   Where did the orange originate?

10 What is gumbo?

11 St Joseph is the patron saint of whom?

12 What were Lyons' Corner Houses?

13 Heracles is another name for Hercules. True or false?

14 What word, beginning with ante- means 'before, in time or place'?

15 What had Queen Victoria and Harpo Marx in common?

SCIENCE

1   What is measured by the quire?

2   What is an asteroid?

3   Aeroflot is what?

4   What kind of military vehicle is an APC?

5   What is an anaesthetic?

6   What is an ingot?

7   Sir Isaac Newton built the first of a kind of optical instrument in 1668. What was it?

8   A pump using what kind of power was invented in 1698 by Thomas Savery?

9   The branch of science which deals with the study and application of electron devices is called?

10 What is the term for a mixture of solid particles floating in a liquid or gas?

11 How many sides has a hexagon?

12 What makes up 21% of air?

13 What metric weight is equal to 0.04 ounces?

14 What is German silver?

15 The cranium is another name for what?

NATURAL HISTORY

1   What is wrong with this statement, 'Crowds of wombats flew up as we passed'?

2   What is a group of oysters called?

3   A group of gorillas is called a gang, a tree or a band?

4   What is a group of caterpillars called?

5   What is flax?

6   A peccary is; (a) a kind of wild horse (b) a kind of wild pig (c) a kind of wild cat?

7   Eland is; (a) a small island off Scilly Isles (b) a kind of antelope (c) a kind of frog?

8   The banana is a member of the same plant family as ginger. True or false?

9   What is a group of apes called?

10 The lilac is a member of the olive family. Yes or no?

11 Which British wild mammal digs a home called a 'set'?

12 How many different kinds of beetle are there; (a) 50,000 (b) 100,000 (c) 250,000?

13 What is henna?

14 How long is Britain's longest centipede?

15 The average house-fly lives; (a) about 20 days (b) about one day (c) about a week?

ANSWERS

1. A wombat is a non-flying marsupial. 2. A bed. 3. A band. 4. An army. 5. The fibres of the Linum plant, from which linen is made. 6. (b) A kind of wild pig. 7. (b) A kind of antelope. 8. True. 9. A shrewdness. 10. Yes. 11. A badger. 12. (c) 250,000. 13. A reddish-orange pigment made from a shrub of the same name. 14. About three inches. 15. (a) About 20 days.

GEOGRAPHY

1 What is the capital of Chile?

2 Which five counties were included in the ancient Wessex?

3 In which country does 23% of the World's population live?

4 Where and what is Snowdon?

5 What is the capital of the Republic of Ireland?

6 What country's capital city is La Paz?

7 Who (or what) is the Old Lady of Threadneedle Street?

8 If a foreign car displayed the letters JA, what would its country of origin be?

9 Where and what is Liechtenstein?

10 Where in England is The Lake District?

11 By what name were these five towns known in medieval times: Hastings, Sandwich, Dover, Romney and Hythe?

12 The Little St Bernard Pass runs between which two countries?

13 The republic, Slovenia was formerly part of which country?

14 In which country do they speak Shona?

15 How many Channel Isles are there?

ENGLISH LANGUAGE

1 What word is both a pain and a type of newspaper column?

2 Complete this simile: 'Look like a dying duck in a...'

3 A spanner in the USA is a what?

4 What is a 'bobby'?

5 What slang word has been used to describe teeth, billiard balls and piano keys?

6 What's the difference between illegible and eligible?

7 What is 'Betwixt' an old way of saying?

8 If you 'hid your light under a bushel' what would it mean?

9 How did the word 'mob' arise?

10 Can you quote a famous proverb, meaning the opposite of 'More haste, less speed'.

11 What's wrong with this: Offered a choice between beef and lamb, Fred chose the first?

12 What is an 'anecdote'?

13 What is a 'busby'?

14 What is the American term for the corridor in a train?

15 Which word, beginning with C means infantile or juvenile?

1. Agony. 2. '...thunderstorm'. 3. A wrench. 4. A policeman. 5. Ivories. 6. Illegible means 'unreadable' and eligible means 'fit to be chosen'. 7. Between. 8. That you were being very modest about your true talents. 9. It comes from the Latin, 'mobile vulgus', 'the fickle crowd'. 10. 'He who hesitates is lost'. 11. It should read: Offered a choice between beef, pork and lamb, Fred chose the former. 12. A brief, entertaining account of some incident. 13. A tall fur hat worn by guardsmen. 14. The aisle. 15. Childish.

SPORT

1 Which sport do the Hawthorn Hawks play?

2 In Rugby Union, how far must the ball travel from the kick off?

3 In 1921 the Fédération Equestre Internationale laid down the rules for which sport?

4 In which year was the first 'Modern' Olympic Games held in Athens?

5 How long is the wire on a hammer in Athletics; 0.9m, 12m, 15m or 19m?

6 What was introduced into America in 1644 by Colonel Richard Nicholls, Commander of the English Forces?

7 What nationality is sprinter Frankie Fredericks?

8 Who took over as Chairman of Newcastle United after his son resigned amid controversy?

9 What does the word 'Karate' mean in Japanese?

10 With which sport do you associate Jonah Barrington and Susan Devoy?

11 Name Houston's NBA Basketball team?

12 What first took place in 1829, is 4 miles and 74 yards long, involves 18 competitors in 2 teams and is held once a year in London?

13 Which football team plays its home games at Portman Road?

14 With which sport do you associate Greg Louganis?

15 In which sport would you stand on the Hack Stay behind the Hogline, aiming for the tee at the centre of the house?

ANSWERS

1. Australian Rules Football. 2. 10 yards. 3. Dressage. 4. 1896. 5. 1.2m. 6. Horse Racing (Flat Racing). 7. Namibian. 8. Sir John Hall. 9. Empty Hand. 10. Squash. 11. Rockets. 12. The University Boat Race 13. Ipswich Town. 14. Diving. 15. Curling.

HISTORY

1 Which Chinese dynasty ruled between 1368 and 1644?

2 What would a country be called if it was ruled entirely by its wealthy class?

3 What was the Marshall Plan?

4 Who were the Anzacs?

5 Where and what was Byzantium?

6 Which Chinese leader died on 9th September, 1976?

7 Which religion was officially re-established in Britain in September, 1850?

8 Who set sail aboard HMS *Beagle* to South America in December, 1831?

9 Who was the first monarch to be crowned in Westminster Abbey?

10 Who was George Blake, who escaped from Wormwood Scrubs in 1966?

11 Who were the Janissaries?

12 What was Sir Francis Drake doing when the Spanish Armada was sighted?

13 Who is George Herbert Walker Bush?

14 In what year did clothes rationing end?

15 Who attended schools in Cheam, Surrey, Gordonstoun, Scotland, and Timbertop, Australia?

1. The Ming Dynasty. 2. A plutocracy. 3. A US economic aid programme to help nations recover from WWII. 4. The Australian and New Zealand soldiers in World War 1. 5. It was an early name for Constantinople, which later became Istanbul. 6. Mao Tse-tung. 7. Roman Catholicism. 8. Charles Darwin. 9. William the Conqueror. 10. A traitor and spy. 11. The army of the Ottoman Empire. 12. Playing bowls. 13. He was the 41st American president. 14. 1949. 15. Prince Charles.

CINEMA AND TV

1 Which famous Disney film used spare scenes and footage from *Pinocchio* and was released in 1942?

2 Which film used a Boeing 707 to generate some of the high winds necessary for the plot?

3 Who played David McCallum's agent partner in the TV programme The Men From U.N.C.L.E.?

4 Who directed the Beatles' film *A Hard Day's Night*?

5 Which actress starred along Richard Gere in *Pretty Woman*?

6 Which film actress's name was given to a lifejacket?

7 Hawkeye, Hotlips and Klinger were characters in which popular TV show?

8 Who won a Best Actor Oscar for his role in the film *My Left Foot*?

9 In which film did Goldie Hawn join the army?

10 In which film did Jack Nicholson and Meryl Streep star as tramps?

11 Who were the husband and wife team who created the programmes *Stingray* and *Thunderbirds*?

12 Who was the 'Peekaboo Girl'?

13 Who was the 'Last of the Red Hot Mamas'?

14 Who directed the film *Reds*?

15 What's the gaffer in charge of on a film set?

1. *Bambi*. 2. *Twister*. 3. Robert Vaughn. 4. Richard Lester. 5. Julia Roberts. 6. Mae West. 7. *M.A.S.H.* 8. Daniel Day-Lewis. 9. *Private Benjamin*. 10. *Ironweed*. 11. Gerry and Sylvia Anderson. 12. Veronica Lake. 13. Sophie Tucker. 14. Warren Beatty. 15. All the electrical equipment.

POPULAR MUSIC

1 With whom did the Smurfs record their first hit, 'The Smurf Song'?

2 Who recorded the album, 'The Wall'?

3 Who had top ten hits with, 'So Macho', 'Toy Boy' and 'Cross My Broken Heart'?

4 In which year did Sister Sledge reach number 1 with, 'Frankie'; 1983, 1984 or 1982?

5 The Shamen had a string of hits in the early 1990's. What is a Shamen?

6 Who's 1998 album was titled, 'Hello Nasty'?

7 Who recorded the, 'Free Wheelin', album in 1963?

8 What is Boy George's real name?

9 Who did singer Barbara Streisand marry in 1998?

10 Who is the lead singer with Blur?

11 Rock and roll suicide was the final show for which of David Bowie's creations?

12 Which actors were the original Blues Brothers?

13 Which 1980 film starred singer, Hazel O'Connor?

14 Who recorded the album, 'First Of A Million Kisses'?

15 Who sang the theme song to, 'The Spy Who Loved Me'?

LITERATURE

1   Who published the first issue of the magazine *Answers* in 1888?

2   What was the fictional creation of the Rev. W.V. Awdry?

3   Who wrote the original 'James Bond' novels?

4   Complete the proverb: 'All cats are...'

5   Complete Dorothy Parker's line: 'Men seldom make passes...'

6   Who wrote *Uncle Tom's Cabin*?

7   Which Australian poet was nicknamed 'Banjo'?

8   Whose children were named Hamnet, Judith and Sussanah?

9   What was Paddington Bear's favourite food?

10 Which famous children's book did Mary Norton write?

11 What was Oscar Wilde describing when he said 'The unspeakable in pursuit of the uneatable'?

12 Who wrote *A Clockwork Orange*?

13 Who wrote *The Cruel Sea*?

14 In which book does the villainous 'Simon Legree' appear?

15 Who wrote *The Prime of Miss Jean Brodie*?

ANSWERS

1. Alfred Charles Harmsworth, later Lord Northcliffe. 2. Thomas the Tank Engine. 3. Ian Fleming. 4. ...grey in the dark. 5. '...At girls who wear glasses'. 6. Harriet Beecher Stowe. 7. Andrew Barton Paterson. 8. Shakespeare's. 9. Marmalade. 10. *The Borrowers*. 11. Foxhunting. 12. Anthony Burgess. 13. Nicholas Monsarrat. 14. *Uncle Tom's Cabin*. 15. Muriel Spark.

GENERAL KNOWLEDGE

1   What word, beginning with post-, means 'to put off until a future time?'

2   Who in the world would be called a Canuck?

3   According to the 'language of flowers', what does the bluebell signify?

4   What is cock-a-leekie?

5   Who was Sir Malcolm Campbell?

6   How long have playing-cards been known in England; (a) 400 years (b) 500 years (c) 200 years?

7   In what place do Muslim people worship?

8   What group of people are referred to as a troupe?

9   Which English Admiral saw off the Spanish Armada?

10 Scorpions are immune to their own poison. True or false?

11 In a pack of cards, which way does the Queen of Hearts look, to her left, or to her right?

12 What is chop suey?

13 What is pumpernickel?

14 What are *crêpes suzettes*?

15 In Britain, we had the game ninepins. The Americans have tenpins. Why?

1. Postpone. 2. A Canadian. 3. Constancy. 4. A soup made from a fowl and leeks. 5. Land-speed and water-speed record holder. 6. (a) 400 years. 7. A mosque. 8. Actors, acrobats, dancers, minstrels. 9. Sir Francis Drake. 10. False. 11. To her right. 12. A US-invented Chinese dish usually containing beansprouts. 13. A coarse, malted rye bread. 14. Thin, hot pancakes with lemons or oranges. 15. Ninepins was banned in America. Using the extra pin got around the law.

SCIENCE

1   Helium takes its name from the Greek word helios, meaning the Sun. True or false?

2   New York would be quite different without William Le Baron Jenney's idea. What was it?

3   How many pints in an imperial gallon?

4   What food-processing system was invented in 1812 by Brian Donkin?

5   Ernest Swinton, in 1914, invented which monstrous engine of war?

6   Chester Carlson's idea was copied many times. What was it?

7   What object in the sky is called Europa, and is 1,950 miles in diameter?

8   What aerial event did Henri Giffard undertake in 1852?

9   What is oology?

10 What is the diameter of Saturn's widest ring? (a) 200,000 miles (b) 170,000 miles.

11 The French chemist Charles Gerhardt made acetylsalicylic acid in 1853. What is it now widely used as?

12 What is air?

13 Nitrous oxide is better known as what?

14 In Roman numerals, what is C?

15 Osmium is (a) a rare metal (b) a tropical plant (c) an Asian country.

1. True. 2. The skyscraper. 3. Eight. 4. The canning of food. 5. The tank. 6. Xerography, or the copying machine. 7. It is Jupiter's fourth-largest moon. 8. The first balloon flight with powered propulsion. 9. The science or study of birds' eggs. 10. (b) 170,000 miles. 11. Aspirin. 12. A mixture of 78% nitrogen, 21% oxygen and traces of argon and carbon dioxide. 13. Laughing gas. 14. 100. 15. (a) A rare metal.

NATURAL HISTORY

1 How old is the oldest living tree; (a) 1,500 years (b) 25,000 years (c) 12,000 years?

2 The glass snake is not a snake. What is it?

3 The aubergine is a member of the nightshade family. Yes or no?

4 Which land animal is the heaviest of all?

5 What is a silver birch?

6 A shoat is a young pig. True or false?

7 Which is the only bird in the world that can fly backwards?

8 What is ambergris?

9 The carrot is a plant relative of the poisonous plant, hemlock. True or false?

10 What is a group of bees called?

11 A marsupial which lives in trees and is similar to a bat is called what?

12 What is a chow chow?

13 The plum is a member of the rose family. Yes or no?

14 What kind of animal is said to screech?

15 What sort of animal is an Airedale?

GEOGRAPHY

1 In what country do some of the people speak Romansch?

2 Which ancient city was on the River Euphrates?

3 What did Sir Stamford Raffles found in 1819?

4 What was once called 'the Dark Continent'?

5 Tasmania is named after the discoverer of New Zealand. What was his name?

6 Mesopotamia is the old name for where?

7 The Collegiate Church of St Peter is the correct name for which famous building in London?

8 In which county would you find the River Medway?

9 Where is Patagonia?

10 In what country would you find the cities of Amoy and Foochow?

11 Persia is a country now called what?

12 Which is the largest sea?

13 On which river does Vienna stand?

14 Where is Sherwood Forest?

15 Where and what is Pearl Harbor?

ANSWERS

1. Switzerland. 2. Babylon. 3. The settlement of Singapore. 4. Africa. 5. Abel Tasman. 6. Iraq. 7. Westminster Abbey. 8. Kent. 9. It's at the southern end of South America. 10. China. 11. Iran. 12. The South China Sea, 1,148,500 sq.m. 13. The Danube. 14. Mainly in Nottinghamshire. 15. The US naval base at Hawaii.

ENGLISH LANGUAGE

1   What is the difference between a homonym and a homophone?

2   What, in earlier times, was a 'hackney'?

3   What was a 'clippie'?

4   Some languages use a cedilla. What exactly is that?

5   What is the name for someone who studies the meaning of words?

6   What is a 'quack'?

7   What is an 'aigrette'?

8   Can you give a word starting with M, meaning 'numskull' or 'simpleton'?

9   What is the name for words derived from someone's name, like 'braille', 'sandwich', 'wellingtons'?

10 What do the initials CPU stand for in computing?

11 What does 'incandescent' mean?

12 What does an American mean by 'banana-oil'?

13 What is the name for someone who studies and makes maps?

14 Which armed service is sometimes referred to as 'the Andrew'?

15 What is, or was, a Sloane Ranger?

SPORT

1   In Snooker, how many points is the blue ball worth?

2   Name Tampa Bay's American football team?

3   Which County Cricket team does Andrew Flintoff play for?

4   Which football club has the nickname the 'Eagles'?

5   With which sport do you associate Kirk Stevens?

6   What is the nationality of cricketer David Boon?

7   Who are the only father and son ever to both win the Formula One Drivers World Championship?

8   Which sport competes for the Bledisloe Cup?

9   What nationality is racing driver, Thierry Boutson?

10   With which sport do you associate David Broom?

11   Which sport celebrates Cowes Week?

12   Who won the 1998 US Masters golf title?

13   Which football club plays its home games at Elland Road?

14   Which county captain of Middlesex became an England selector in the 1990s?

15   Which football team started at the Goldstone Ground, played away, and are now at home at the Withdean Stadium?

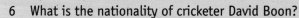

ANSWERS

1. Five. 2. Buccaneers 3. Lancashire. 4. Crystal Palace. 5. Snooker.
6. Australian. 7. Graham and Damon Hill. 8. Rugby Union. 9. Belgian.
10. Show Jumping. 11. Sailing. 12. Mark O'Meara. 13. Leeds United.
14. Mike Gatting. 15. Brighton and Hove Albion

HISTORY

1   What was the R101 and what happened to it?

2   Wroclaw, Poland, was the former German city of what?

3   How many King James have there been in Scotland?

4   By winning the Battle of Plassey in India, 1757, what did the British commander, Robert Clive achieve?

5   Who made the first telephone call on 11th March, 1876?

6   Which British monarch reigned longest?

7   What political activity were Roman Catholics in Britain first allowed to do in 1829?

8   Who was Ernesto 'Che' Guevara?

9   The first 'Peelers' appeared on the streets of London in 182 9 What were they?

10   Which famous British motor-car company was founded in 1904?

11   How does a Member of Parliament resign?

12   Who was Ulysses S. Grant?

13   Which former British King died in Paris in 1972?

14   The Prussian city of Danzig is now called what?

15   In what year was the introduction of the Penny Post in Britain?

CINEMA AND TV

1 Where and when did the first commercial radio station in Britain open?

2 What TV show featured a band whose first names were Mickey, Peter, Mike and Davey?

3 Which famous film director's first film was *The Pleasure Garden* in 1925?

4 In the film *Bugsy Malone*, which star's singing was dubbed?

5 Ian Fleming wanted his cousin to play the role of *Dr No* in the Bond film of the same name. Who was the actor?

6 For which role were a staggering 1400 actresses auditioned?

7 Who was Dominic Felix Amici?

8 How many extras were used in the film, Ghandi; (a) 3000 (b) 30,000 (c) 300,000?

9 From which musical play comes the song 'Big Spender'?

10 Who starred as a butler in the film *The Remains Of The Day*?

11 Which film actor's real name is Allen Stewart Konigsberg?

12 Who was the Jersey Lily?

13 Which Carradine had a brother called Keith?

14 Who was Satchmo?

15 Was the horse's head featured in *The Godfather* real or fake?

ANSWERS

1. 1964, on the Isle of Man. 2. The Monkees. 3. Alfred Hitchcock. 4. Jodie Foster. 5. Christopher Lee. 6. Scarlet O'Hara in Gone With the Wind. 7. The film actor Don Ameche. 8. (c) 300,000. 9. Sweet Charity. 10. Anthony Hopkins. 11. Woody Allen. 12. Lily Langtry, actress. 13. David Carradine. 14. Louis Armstrong. 15. Real.

POPULAR MUSIC

1. Who sang Britain's 1991 Eurovision song contest entry, 'A Message To Your Heart'?

2. What ended Jan and Dean's, recording career?

3. With which song did Jazzy Jeff and the Fresh Prince reach number 1 in 1993?

4. Godley and Crème reached number 3 in 1981 with, 'Under Your Thumb'. Which band were the duo previously part of?

5. Which artist has recorded more weeks on the UK chart than any other?

6. Which artist has recorded duets with, Dionne Warwick, Cliff Richard, Luciano Pavarotti and Kiki Dee?

7. Who was George Michael's partner in Wham?

8. In 1979, who sang, ' The silicon chip inside her head is switched to overload'?

9. Who went straight in at number 1 in 1991 with, 'The Fly'?

10. What do Al Martino, Whigfield, Robson & Jerome and Babylon Zoo, have in common?

11. What do the songs, 'Can't Help Falling In Love', 'Dizzy', 'I Believe' and 'Living Doll', have in common?

12. With which 1970s glam band was Les Gray the lead singer?

13. What do A-ha, Shirley Bassey, Nancy Sinatra and Sheena Easton, have in common?

14. Roger Taylor was the drummer with which group?

15. Who had hits in the 1970's with, 'Don't Take Away The Music', 'Whodunnit' and 'More Than A Woman'?

ANSWERS

1. Samantha Janus. 2. A car crash. 3. Boom! Shake the room. 4. 10cc. 5. Elvis Presley. 6. Elton John. 7. Andrew Ridgley. 8. The Boomtown Rats (Bob Geldof). 9. U2. 10. Their debut singles have gone straight in at number one. 11. All have been number 1 in 2 separate versions. 12. Mud. 13. All have recorded Bond Themes. 14. Queen. 15. Tavares.

LITERATURE

1 Who wrote the story *The Murders in the Rue Morgue*?

2 In which book is 'Toad' a leading character?

3 Who is reputed to have said, 'A verbal contract is not worth the paper it's written on'?

4 Who wrote *Sanders of the River* and its sequels?

5 The magazine *Punch* carried this line in 1845: 'Advice to persons about to marry.' How did it continue?

6 Who wrote *Of Human Bondage*?

7 Who wrote *The History of the World* while imprisoned in the Tower of London?

8 What is the actual name of the Count in *The Count of Monte Cristo*?

9 Complete Benjamin Franklin's advice: 'We must all hang together or...'

10 Who were Frank Richards, Martin Clifford and Charles Hamilton?

11 Hazel, Fiver and Bigwig appear in which book?

12 In which Shakespeare play does 'Polixenes' appear?

13 Who wrote *Ulysses*?

14 'The world is so full of a number of things......' How did R.L. Stevenson continue?

15 Who wrote *Pride and Prejudice*?

ANSWERS

1. Edgar Allan Poe. 2. *The Wind in the Willows.* 3. Sam Goldwyn, Hollywood movie mogul. 4. Edgar Wallace. 5. 'Don't.' 6. W. Somerset Maugham. 7. Sir Walter Raleigh. 8. Edmond Dantes. 9. '...Most assuredly we shall all hang separately.' (he was signing the Declaration of Independence). 10. Names used by Charles Hamilton who wrote school stories of Greyfriars and St Jim's. 11. *Watership Down*, by Richard Adams. 12. *A Winter's Tale.* 13. James Joyce. 14. 'I'm sure we should all be as happy as kings.' 15. Jane Austen.

GENERAL KNOWLEDGE

1   What is blutwurst?

2   Wednesday is named after Woden, the German god of war. True or false?

3   What is a Chelsea bun?

4   What is quiche?

5   What was 'ragtime'?

6   What is chilli con carne?

7   In a pack of cards, which way does the King of Clubs look, to his left, or to his right?

8   Who was Albrecht Dürer?

9   What are 'Grape Nuts' and who invented them?

10   What does LBW stand for?

11   R. Harmenzoon van Rijn was one of the most famous of all painters. What does the R stand for?

12   St Patrick is the patron saint of what?

13   What is the Fabian Society?

14   St Amand is the patron saint of whom?

15   What type of entertainment is a 'Charleston'?

1. The German version of black pudding. 2. True. 3. A rolled bun filled with currants and raisins. 4. A shell of unsweetened pastry which can hold a savoury filling. 5. A type of very popular music which preceded jazz. 6. Minced meat, beans and chillis. 7. To his right. 8. A German painter and engraver. 9. A breakfast cereal invented by Charles Post in 1898. 10. Leg Before Wicket in cricket. 11. Rembrandt. 12. Ireland. 13. A socialist group founded in 1884. 14. Innkeepers and wine-merchants. 15. A type of dance.

SCIENCE

1 Gravity on the moon is a third, a quarter or a sixth of what it is on Earth?

2 What is osteology?

3 What is a monorail?

4 What is oneirology?

5 What does DC stand for?

6 What is alum?

7 How many moons does Neptune have (a) 2 (b) 3 (c) 4

8 What optical instrument was invented in 1608 by Hans Lippershey?

9 What is 'latex'?

10 What's it used for?

11 What metal has the chemical symbol Fe?

12 Who was Tycho Brahe?

13 What is a megalomaniac?

14 What did Mariner 10 do in 1973?

15 Radium is so called because it comes from the Latin word radius, meaning a ray. True or false?

ANSWERS

1. A sixth. 2. The study of bones. 3. A railway which uses only a single rail, rather than the twin rails on normal lines. 4. The study of dreams. 5. Direct current. 6. A chemical. It's a double sulphate of aluminium and potassium. 7. (a) 2. 8. The telescope. 9. The milky fluid given off by trees in South America and elsewhere. 10. Making rubber. 11. Iron. 12. A Danish astronomer. 13. Someone who thinks he is all-powerful and all-important. 14. It flew by Mercury and took photographs of the planet. 15. True.

NATURAL HISTORY

1 Which is the longest snake?

2 The pear is a member of the rose family. Yes or no?

3 The bobcat is a kind of wild lynx found in North America. True or false?

4 If an American found a flicker in his garden, what should he or she be looking out for?

5 The bluebell is a member of the lily family. Yes or no?

6 How much water does a koala bear drink in a day?

7 The Borzoi is; (a) a breed of dog (b) a breed of cat or (c) a breed of horse?

8 Which animal is the most flea-ridden?

9 The raspberry is a member of the rose family. Yes or no?

10 What is a dromedary?

11 What is a bullfinch?

12 What is unique about the Komodo dragon lizard?

13 Cotton is a member of the Rubia family. Yes or no?

14 What is a chrysanthemum?

15 If you were a herpetologist, what would you be expert on?

ANSWERS

1. The python. 2. Yes. 3. True. 4. Holes in his trees. It's a woodpecker. 5. Yes. 6. None. It relies on the moisture in eucalyptus leaves. 7. (a) A breed of dog. 8. Red Squirrel. 9. Yes. 10. A camel with one hump. 11. An attractive songbird, black and white with pink underparts. 12. It's the world's heaviest lizard, weighing over 360 pounds. 13. Yes. 14. A flower related to the corn marigold and ox-eye daisy. The national flower of Japan. 15. Reptiles.

GEOGRAPHY

1. To which country do the Galapagos Islands belong?

2. Where and what is the Solway Firth?

3. Walmer Castle, near Deal, was the home of which famous military leader?

4. What is the capital of Portugal?

5. The population of the world is approximately (a) 5,300 million (b) 7,400 million (c) 4,900 million?

6. How many people live in Monaco? (a) 30,500 (b) 45,100 (c) 75,300

7. Which country's capital city is Seoul?

8. On which islands in the South Atlantic are there approximately 370 sheep for every person?

9. In which country would you find the Apennnine mountain range?

10. What was meant by the North West Passage?

11. Where and what is the Old Man of Hoy?

12. How many islands comprise Tristan da Cunha?

13. Which is the largest lake in England?

14. In which city would you find 'The Royal Mile?'

15. Where and what are 'The Needles'?

ANSWERS

1. Ecuador. 2. An inlet from the Irish Sea, forming part of the border between England and Scotland. 3. The Duke of Wellington. 4. Lisbon. 5. (a) 5,300 million. 6. (a) 30,500. 7. South Korea. 8. The Falklands. 9. Italy. 10. A supposed seaway through the north-west of America. 11. It's a rock off the Orkney Islands. 12. Five. 13. Windermere. 14. Edinburgh. 15. Three sharp chalk pillars off the Isle of Wight.

ENGLISH LANGUAGE

1 An 'angel of mercy' could be described as....?

2 What's wrong with this sentence: 'The visit to Canterbury was a great treat for my sisters and I'?

3 What was formerly meant by the slang 'a pony'?

4 What is the female version of 'ram'?

5 What was a fletcher?

6 What word, beginning with I, means advise or notify?

7 Can you quote a proverb meaning the opposite of 'Many hands make light work'?

8 What is the difference in meaning between 'biennial' and 'biannual'?

9 What we call 'maize' in Britain is called what in the United States?

10 A wallet for keeping money is called what in America?

11 What do the initials MoD stand for?

12 'Eftsoons' was an old way of saying what?

13 What is an 'autocrat'?

14 If you 'put all your eggs in one basket', what would that mean?

15 What does 'bona fide' mean?

1. Someone who helps out in a desperate situation. 2. It should read: The visit to Canterbury was a great treat for my sisters and me. 3. £25. 4. Ewe. 5. A maker of arrows. 6. Inform. 7. 'Too many cooks spoil the broth'. 8. The first means 'occurring every two years', and the second 'twice a year'. 9. Corn. 10. A billfold. 11. Ministry of Defence. 12. Forthwith or often. 13. One who rules by his own power. 14. That you were risking all on one venture. 15. 'Good faith'; genuineness.

SPORT

1   Where were the 1968 Olympics held?

2   With which club side did Will Carling finish his playing career?

3   In which sport would you use a 'Trace, a 'Beaked Barb' and a 'Waggler'?

4   Who was Italy's manager/coach during France '98?

5   With which sport do you associate Kieran Fallon?

6   Up to 1998, Will Carling was the last England Captain to win a Grand Slam. True or False?

7   In Offshore Power Boat racing, the task of piloting the boat is usually shared between two people. If one steers what does the other do?

8   Who manufactured England's 1998 World Cup strip?

9   With which sport do you associate Nancy Kerrigan?

10 In Italia '90, which England player scored the winner that knocked out Belgium?

11 With which sport do you associate Serge Blanco?

12 Who resigned as Vice Chairman of the RFU in April 1998 over a dispute with the top English clubs?

13 Which racehorse owner was the inspiration behind the Godolphin Racing operation?

14 Who won the 1997 Britannic Assurance County Championship?

15 For which country does Colin Jackson run in the Commonwealth Games?

1. Mexico. 2. Harlequins. 3. Fishing. 4. Cesare Maldini. 5. Horse Racing. 6. True. 7. Controls the throttles. 8. UMBRO. 9. Ice Skating. 10. David Platt 11. Rugby Union 12. Fran Cotton. 13. Sheikh Mohammed. 14. Glamorgan. 15. Wales.

HISTORY

1 Who was 'Lord Haw Haw'?

2 Who succeeded to the British throne in 1837?

3 Britain's first prime minister was appointed in 1721. Who was he?

4 Who was killed by a terrorist bomb in a boat off Ireland in 1979?

5 Howard Carter and Earl of Carvarvon were first to see what in 1922?

6 The Queen opened which major London exhibition centre in 1982?

7 What, on the River Thames, London, was raised for the first time in 1982?

8 Which group of men first arrived in Botany Bay, Australia in 1788?

9 Which area in the British Isles received its independence in 1921?

10 Which major German battleship was sunk in December, 1943?

11 Which television channel was launched in Britain on 2nd November, 1982?

12 George Pullman died on 19th October 1897. What did he do?

13 Which patriotic song was sung for the first time on 28th September, 1745?

14 Which world-famous discoverer died in poverty in 1506?

15 Which war between Britain and the US ended on 24th December, 1814?

CINEMA AND TV

1 Were any real pigs used in the filming of *Babe*?

2 What film festival awards Golden Palms to winning films?

3 Which writer has the TV shows *The Liver Birds*, *Butterflies* and *Bread* to her credits?

4 What type of film has Hollywood made more often than any other?

5 What famous actor and director first became known for his role in the TV series *Rawhide*?

6 Who starred as the straw man in *The Wiz*, the updated version of *The Wizard Of Oz*?

7 Who played Captain Hook in the 1991 film, *Hook*?

8 What T.V. show featured the butler Hudson and the cook, Mrs Bridges?

9 With which director is the Dreamworks film studio associated?

10 Which film dealt with a plot to assassinate Winston Churchill?

11 Which film actors have played the part of Ben Hur?

12 Which film dealt with the life of Douglas Bader?

13 From which musical play comes the song, 'Hopelessly Devoted to You'?

14 On what stage play is the film *My Fair Lady* based?

15 What was Gary Cooper's job before he was discovered by film director, Henry King?

ANSWERS

1. Yes, 48 of them. 2. The Cannes film festival. 3. Carla Lane. 4. Comedy. 5. Clint Eastwood. 6. Michael Jackson. 7. Dustin Hoffman. 8. *Upstairs Downstairs*. 9. Steven Spielberg. 10. *The Eagle Has Landed*, 1977. 11. Ramon Navarro and Charlton Heston. 12. *Reach for the Sky*, 1956. 13. Grease. 14. Pygmalion. 15. Stunt man.

POPULAR MUSIC

1   Rod Stewart once recorded a song for the England football team? True or false?

2   Who were on a, 'Road To Nowhere' in 1985?

3   Who were number one in the UK chart at the end of June 1998?

4   Which Las Vagas star had minor hits in the UK during the 1950's, with, 'Unchained Melody' and 'I Don't Care'?

5   Who had top ten hits with, 'Oops Up Side Your Head' and 'Big Fun'?

6   Why did Gabrielle have a two year gap from recording between 1994 and 1996?

7   'Rage Hard' and 'Warriors (of the wasteland)', were minor hits for which chart topping band?

8   Who did Shane Fenton become in 1973, having a number one hit with, 'Jealous Mind', in 1974?

9   Who had number one hits with, 'Nights on Broadway' and 'Young Hearts Run Free', in 1976/77?

10   Who sang, 'Let Me Entertain You', in 1998?

11   Mick Hucknall is the lead singer with which group?

12   Victoria Adams is better known by what name?

13   Under what name did Jefferson Starship, reach number one with, 'Nothing's Gonna Stop Us Now'?

14   What was Elvis Presley's last UK number one?

15   How many number ones did Elton John have in the 1980s?

LITERATURE

1 Who was the author of *Stalky and Co.*?

2 Who wrote the play *A Doll's House*?

3 Who wrote *Testament of Youth*?

4 Who was the translator of the *Rubaiyát of Omar Khayyam*?

5 In which Shakespeare play does 'Orlando' appear?

6 Who wrote *The Turn of the Screw*?

7 Who wrote the play *Waiting For Godot*?

8 Who wrote *Brideshead Revisited*?

9 Who created the detective character 'Father Brown'?

10 Complete the proverb: 'Don't cut off your nose...'

11 Complete the proverb: 'Discretion is...'

12 Who was Bertold Brecht?

13 Which famous children's book did Louisa May Alcott write?

14 What line follows 'I remember, I remember' ?

15 The writer H.H. Munro, known as 'Saki', wrote: 'The cook was a good cook, as cooks go,' How did he continue?

1. Rudyard Kipling. 2. Henrik Ibsen. 3. Vera Brittain. 4. Edward FitzGerald. 5. *As You Like It.* 6. Henry James. 7. Samuel Beckett. 8. Evelyn Waugh. 9. G.K. Chesterton. 10. '...to spite your face'. 11. '...the better part of valour'. 12. A German poet and playwright. 13. *Little Women.* 14. 'The house where I was born'. 15. 'and as cooks go, she went'.

GENERAL KNOWLEDGE

1 St Anne is the patron saint of whom?

2 Who is the patron saint of shoemakers?

3 Where does the word 'patter', meaning stage 'chat', come from?

4 In a pack of cards, which way does the King of Spades look, to his left, or to his right?

5 What word, beginning with ante-, means 'in the time before the war'?

6 From an edible point of view, what are bullseyes?

7 What does ROM stand for in computing?

8 What items are called by names such as Plantin, Baskerville and Garamond?

9 What is a *tortilla*?

10 Who was Tommy Atkins?

11 St John Bosco is the patron saint of whom?

12 What year was the Battle of Britain?

13 If you were rudely called a coot, what is it likely you'll be?

14 The first public restaurant was opened in 1765 in what city?

15 Name two well-known plays by Terence Rattigan.

SCIENCE

1 How many bones does an adult human being have?

2 What is 'jet' as used in jewellery or other decorations?

3 The Jumbo Jet is a name given to which aircraft?

4 What is epistemology?

5 Who invented margarine?

6 How did we invent the word 'radar'?

7 What is trichology?

8 What are OR, NAND and NOT examples of?

9 Which anaesthetic was used for the first time in 1847?

10 What is an insulator?

11 What does AC stand for?

12 A special kind of flour was invented by Henry Jones of Bristol in 1845. What was special about it?

13 What device for making geometric patterns was invented in 1817 by Sir David Brewster?

14 If something is ferrous, what does it contain?

15 Who is widely regarded as the inventor of the bicycle?

1. 206. 2. Very hard coal, called lignite. 3. The Boeing 747. 4. The scientific study of knowledge and its acquisition. 5. Mège-Mouriès, in France, 1868. 6. From the words of its full name, radio detection and ranging. 7. The scientific study of the hair and its disorders. 8. Logic gates used in electronics. 9. Chloroform. 10. A substance which prevents the flow of electricity or heat. 11. Alternating current. 12. It was self-raising. 13. The kaleidoscope. 14. Iron. 15. Kirkpatrick MacMillan, in 1839.

NATURAL HISTORY

1 A gila monster is venomous lizard. Is this unusual?

2 Cloves are a members of the carnation family. Yes or no?

3 A cross between a male ass and a mare is called what?

4 What is a spider?

5 What is a crayfish?

6 What is the favourite food of the aardvark?

7 What sort of animal is a harrier?

8 What is an endive?

9 The cottontail is another name for the American rabbit. True or false?

10 What are glow worms?

11 What is a 'bug'?

12 What kind of animal is said to hiss?

13 Which distant relative of the camel lives in South America?

14 Caviar is obtained from a fish. Which one?

15 The turnip is a member of the cabbage family. Yes or no?

ANSWERS

1. Yes. There is only one other venomous lizard, the related bearded lizard. 2. Yes. 3. A mule. 4. A small creature with four pairs of legs, which spins a web to catch its prey. 5. A kind of edible freshwater lobster, also called a crawfish. 6. Ants and termites. It eats nothing else! 7. A breed of dog. 8. A salad plant of the chicory family. 9. True. 10. The larvae of insects, which are able to emit light or flashes. 11. An insect which infests bedding. In the USA the word means 'any insect'. 12. A goose, or a snake. 13. The llama. 14. The sturgeon. 15. Yes.

GEOGRAPHY

1 To which country do the Azores belong?

2 Where is the Blue Mosque?

3 In which city would you find the Eiffel Tower?

4 Which city is on the River Clyde?

5 Which family lived at Haworth Parsonage?

6 For what is the village of Camberley, Surrey, famed?

7 Which country's currency has 100 kobo worth one naira?

8 Which city is on the Tagus river?

9 If it's 6 pm in London, what time is it in Norway?

10 What did early travellers mean by the New World?

11 In which English city would you find New Street railway station?

12 Which is the most populous of Canada's provinces?

13 Name three other Canadian provinces.

14 What is the city of Batavia now called?

15 There are more canals in Birmingham than in Venice. True or False?

1. Portugal. 2. In Istanbul, Turkey. 3. Paris. 4. Glasgow. 5. The Brontës. 6. It is the home of the Royal Military Academy for training Army officers. 7. Nigeria. 8. Lisbon. 9. 7 p.m. 10. America. 11. Birmingham. 12. Ontario. 13. British Columbia, Alberta, Quebec, Manitoba, Nova Scotia, Saskatchewan, Prince Edward Island, Newfoundland, New Brunswick. 14. Djakarta. 15. True.

ENGLISH LANGUAGE

1 What does the phrase, 'Apple-pie order' mean?

2 What's wrong with this sentence: Our cat always licks it's paws after a meal?

3 If you were playing checkers in America, what would you be doing?

4 What is the name for someone who studies mankind?

5 What is the name for someone who studies or collects postage-stamps?

6 What is the difference between adventitious and adventurous?

7 A peon is (a) a flower (b) a labourer in Spain (c) a comedian.

8 What does 'carry a torch' mean?

9 What would it mean if you 'cast pearls before swine'?

10 A 'shambles' is a real mess, but what was it originally?

11 What modern term replaces the word, 'Methinks'?

12 What does compos mentis mean?

13 What is a 'ham', theatrically-speaking?

14 What does 'Twain' mean?

15 What is a 'chipolata'?

SPORT

1 Which female British Athlete won the New York marathon in 1991?

2 Which county does Sally Gunnell come from?

3 After completing his studies, what career did Will Carling, embark on?

4 Which British athlete was cleared of drugs charges on appeal in March 1996?

5 What's the nationality of racing driver Nelson Piquet?

6 Which snooker ball is worth six points?

7 Which sport do the Worthing Bears play?

8 For what county did BBC cricket commentator, Jonathon Agnew, play most of his cricket?

9 In racing, what does the abbreviation SP stand for?

10 The Bulls versus the Rhinos is a local derby in which county?

11 Who does Ryan Giggs play for at International level?

12 Over which race course is the Whitbread Gold Cup run?

13 Which Formula 1 racing driver, known as, 'The Professor', won the 1989 World Driver's Championship?

14 If I were wearing a, Shooting Glove, an Arm Brace, preparing to shoot an end, always aiming for Gold, what sport would I be taking part in?

15 Who managed Chelsea during the first half of the 1997/98 season?

ANSWERS

1. Liz McColgan. 2. Essex. 3. An Army Officer. 4. Diane Modahl. 5. Brazil. 6. Pink. 7. Basketball. 8. Leicestershire. 9. Starting Price. 10. Yorkshire (Rugby League). 11. Wales. 12. Sandown Park. 13. Alain Prost. 14. Archery. 15. Ruud Gullit.

HISTORY

1 £1 and 10 shilling notes were issued for the first time in Britain in what year?

2 Which islands in the Indian Ocean became a republic in 1953?

3 Which South African prime minister was assassinated in September, 1966?

4 What did The Times newspaper publish for the first time in 1966?

5 Who succeeded General Perón of Argentina as president on his death in July, 1974?

6 Which princess died in a car crash in September, 1982?

7 How was York Minster badly damaged in 1984?

8 The baby of which famous US airman was kidnapped in March, 1932?

9 By what new country name was Persia known after 1935?

10 In 1958, Imre Nagy of Hungary was executed. Who was he?

11 Which two London newspapers merged in 1960?

12 Which group of people were first allowed on to the floor of the London Stock Exchange in 1973?

13 Which Pope died in 1978 after reigning for only 33 days?

14 Who assumed the throne of Denmark in 1972?

15 What happened at Eniwetok Atoll on 6th November, 1952?

ANSWERS

1. 1914. 2. The Maldives. 3. Dr Verwoerd. 4. News on its front page. 5. His wife, Maria Estella Perón. 6. Princess Grace of Monaco. 7. By lightning. 8. Charles Lindbergh's. 9. Iran. 10. Former president. 11. The Evening News and the Star. 12. Women. 13. Pope John Paul I. 14. Queen Margrethe. 15. The US exploded the first hydrogen bomb.

CINEMA AND TV

1. What was special about the 1906 Australian film The Story of the Kelly Gang?

2. Dylan, Brian and Dougal were some of the stars of which animated show?

3. Who starred in the 1933 film She Done Him Wrong?

4. Which movie star's real name was Doris von Kappelhoff?

5. Who starred in the film Sweet Smell of Success?

6. Who directed the film Titanic?

7. What is the basic theme of the film The Exorcist?

8. Yves Montand the French singer and actor wasn't French at all. Where was he born?

9. Who directed the 1929 film Blackmail?

10. Which famous actor has a tattoo reading, 'Scotland Forever'?

11. Elizabeth Taylor is English by birth and parentage. True or false?

12. Who starred in the film The Browning Version?

13. William Friese-Greene, movie pioneer, had a grandson famed as an actor. Who?

14. Who won the best actor Oscar for his role in the film Shine?

15. Who starred in the film Cabaret?

Stick 'em up, sport.

POPULAR MUSIC

1 Holly Johnson was the lead singer with which group?

2 What links Nirvana with Garbage?

3 With which band was Morrissey the lead singer?

4 With which song did MN8 reach number Two in 1995?

5 In 1991 the Justified Ancients of Mu Mu reached number 10 with, 'It's Grim Up North'. By what other name are the group better known?

6 From which album did Michael Jackson's single, 'Rock With You', come?

7 In 1989, Curiosity Killed The Cat, changed their name to what?

8 3T are the nephews of which mega star?

9 Who first released, 'Leader Of The Pack'?

10 What was Billy Joel's first UK top ten hit?

11 Under which name did Julian Clary release, 'Leader Of The Pack', in 1988?

12 Who had a top ten hit in 1978 with, 'Airport'?

13 With whom did En Vogue have a top ten hit in 1994 with, 'Whatta Man'?

14 Who were George Michael's female backing singers, who later released singles in their own right?

15 Peaches & Herb reached number 4 in 1979 with which song?

ANSWERS

1. Frankie Goes To Hollywood. 2. Butch Vig who produced Nirvana and is part of the band, Garbage. 3. The Smiths. 4. I've Got A Little Something For You. 5. KLF. 6. Off The Wall. 7. Curiosity. 8. Michael Jackson. 9. Shang-ri-la's. 10. Uptown Girl. 11. Joan Collins Fan Club. 12. The Motors. 13. Salt-N-Pepa. 14. Pepsi & Shirley. 15. 'Reunited'.

LITERATURE

1 Complete the proverb: 'Better the devil you know...'
2 Who wrote *The Catcher in the Rye*?
3 Who was 'Lawrence of Arabia'?
4 In which story does 'The White Rabbit' appear?
5 Who wrote *The Last of the Mohicans*?
6 Henry Ford, speaking of his cars and their colour, originally said what?
7 The fictional detective 'Albert Campion' was created by whom?
8 Who wrote *The Day of the Jackal*?
9 Complete the proverb: 'All work and no play...'
10 What D.H. Lawrence book was the subject of a famous court case in the 1960s?
11 Name a play by Shakespeare in which a ghost appears.
12 'O, what can ail thee, knight at arms,/Alone and palely loitering;' is the beginning of a poem by whom?
13 What did Blind Pew give to Billy Bones in *Treasure Island*?
14 Complete the proverb: 'Cowards die many times...'
15 On which play was the musical *My Fair Lady* based?

1. '...than the devil you don't.' 2. J.D. Salinger. 3. T.E. Lawrence, soldier and writer. 4. *Alice in Wonderland*. 5. James Fenimore Cooper. 6. 'You can have it any colour you want as long as it's black.' 7. Margery Allingham. 8. Frederick Forsyth. 9. '...makes Jack a dull boy.' 10. *Lady Chatterley's Lover*. 11. *Hamlet*, *Julius Caesar*, *Macbeth*. 12. John Keats. 13. The Black Spot. 14. '...before their deaths'. 15. *Pygmalion*, by George Bernard Shaw.

GENERAL KNOWLEDGE

1   Which British exponent of jazz on radio died very recently?

2   What is chowder?

3   A magnum is a measure of wine equivalent to how many bottles?

4   What does 'kosher' mean?

5   What is the second most expensive property on a Monopoly board?

6   Why 'dead as a doornail'?

7   Who is Viscount Linley's mother?

8   St Thomas is the patron saint of whom?

9   What is a hot dog?

10   What is a fricassee?

11   What is the maximum break in snooker?

12   What is *borsht*?

13   Who is the Pope?

14   What word, beginning with ante,- means 'existing before the Great Flood'?

15   Where is the Golden Gate?

ANSWERS

1. Benny Green.   2. A thick soup made from meat or fish.   3. Two.   4. Fit to be eaten according to Jewish law.   5. Park Lane.   6. A door nail is the bit which is whacked by the knocker.   7. Princess Margaret.   8. Architects.   9. A frankfurter inside a long soft bun.   10. A dish of cut pieces of fowl or meat, cooked in a sauce.   11. 147.   12. Russian beetroot soup.   13. The head of the Roman Catholic Church.   14. Antediluvian.   15. The entrance to the bay of San Francisco.

SCIENCE

1   Acetic acid is more familiarly known as what?

2   How many days does Mercury take to orbit the sun; 88, 205, 335 or 428?

3   A triangle with all sides equal is what?

4   What is a parallelogram?

5   The mineral bauxite produces which metal?

6   Who invented the carpet-sweeper?

7   What is a propeller?

8   What are fossils?

9   What is an accumulator?

10   How long is a furlong?

11   What is kaolin?

12   Francis Crick and James Watson are linked with the discovery of what?

13   What is sodium chloride more commonly known as?

14   What is a chronometer?

15   In Roman numerals, what is L?

ANSWERS

1. Vinegar. 2. 88. 3. Equilateral. 4. A four-sided figure whose opposite sides are parallel. 5. Aluminium. 6. Melville Bissell, in 1876. 7. A kind of screw used to propel a ship or an aircraft. 8. Remains of plants and animals found in ancient rocks. 9. A rechargeable lead-acid battery. 10. 220 yards. 11. Another name for china-clay. 12. The structure of DNA. 13. Table salt. 14. A machine for the accurate measurement of time. 15. 50.

NATURAL HISTORY

1   Which animal lives in a lair?

2   What is meant by 'horsefeathers'?

3   The Jerusalem artichoke is a plant relative of the sunflower. True or false?

4   Which member of the lemur family is only 10 inches long, looks like a monkey, and lives in Madagascar?

5   How many bones does a shark have?

6   What kind of animal could be called a Clydesdale?

7   What is a fig?

8   Are there bats that suck human blood?

9   What is the name for a large rodent covered with sharp spines?

10   What sort of animal is a schipperke?

11   What is another name for the wildebeest?

12   What is a sidewinder?

13   What kind of animal is said to roar?

14   What is a titmouse?

15   What is a palomino?

ANSWERS

1. A wolf. 2. It's an American term meaning 'nonsense'. 3. True. 4. The mouse lemur. 5. None. Its skeleton is made of cartilage. 6. A breed of horse. 7. A fruit of the mulberry family which grows in warm climates. 8. Yes. The vampire bat of Central America. 9. The porcupine. 10. A breed of dog. 11. Gnu. 12. A kind of rattlesnake. 13. A lion. 14. A small bird related to the nuthatches. 15. A horse, golden-haired with a pale mane.

GEOGRAPHY

1 What happens at Oberammergau, Bavaria, every ten years?

2 Queen Street railway stations can be found in two British cities. Which?

3 Where in London is Nelson's Column?

4 Of which country is the pomegranate the national symbol?

5 What is the coldest place on record in the UK?

6 Where in the world do they speak Amharic?

7 What, exactly, was the Flying Scotsman?

8 Where are the Menai Straits?

9 Where and what is the Solent?

10 Which place in the world is often called just 'The Rock'?

11 Which country has the most land boundaries with other countries?

12 New Amsterdam was the original name for which American city?

13 What country's currency comes in bututs and dalasi?

14 Which country has the longest life expectancy for both men and women?

15 Where is the Land of the Midnight Sun?

ENGLISH LANGUAGE

1 What is the female version of 'stallion'?

2 Can you name two words, sounding alike, which mean the same as this pair: part of a sentence/brawls?

3 What does 'emeritus' mean, after someone's job title?

4 What is wrong with this sentence: 'Her words had a good affect upon me'?

5 What does infra dig. mean?

6 What is 'a wet blanket'?

7 Whose motto is 'Per Ardua ad Astra', and what does it mean?

8 Name the adjectives derived from the following: Denmark, Slav, Isle of Man.

9 What word for a kind of pottery means 'cooked earth'?

10 What's the difference between artist and artiste?

11 How many is a 'score'?

12 If you drank some rye in the United States, what would it be?

13 What does 'up the creek without a paddle' mean?

14 What is the female version of 'Indian brave'?

15 How did the word flak, meaning anti-aircraft fire, originate?

1. Mare. 2. Phrase/frays. 3. It means he or she has retired from their job. 4. The word 'affect' should read 'effect'. 5. 'Infra dignitatem': beneath one's dignity. 6. Someone whose lack of spirit spoils a party or gathering. 7. That of the RAF, meaning 'By struggle to the stars'. 8. Danish, Slavonic, Manx. 9. Terracotta. 10. The first means someone who draws or paints; the second, someone who performs. 11. 20. 12. Whisky. 13. In real trouble. 14. Squaw. 15. It's the abbreviation for the German Flugzeugabwehrkanone.

SPORT

1   Name New England's American Football Team?

2   How many players are there on a 'Bandy' team?

3   How long is a 'Period' in an NBA basketball match?

4   The husband of Princess Caroline of Monaco, Stefano Cariraghi, died in 1990 taking part in which sport?

5   What nationality is footballer Davor Suker?

6   Which four-man event was accepted into the Olympic Games when it was held at Chamonix, France, in 1924?

7   Which sport, governed by the ICF, was introduced into the Calgary Olympics as a demonstration sport in 1988?

8   If you were playing 14:1 continuous play rules, what game would you be taking part in?

9   In '3 Position' target shooting events, what are the 3 positions?

10 Which sport held its first professional world championships in 1978, now held annually, at the Lakeside Club in Camberley?

11 Which sport was included in the 1900 Olympic games, was dropped after 1920, then re-introduced in 1972?

12 Actor Brian Glover was formerly a professional sportsman at which sport?

13 Vladimir Smirnov died in a tragic accident whilst defending his Olympic Gold Medal in which sport?

14 With which sport do you associate Clive Woodward?

15 What nationality is footballer Torre Andre Flo?

ANSWERS

1. Patriots 2. Eleven. 3. Twelve minutes. 4. Power Boat Racing.
5. Croatian. 6. Bobsleigh. 7. Curling. 8. Pool. 9. Prone, kneeling and standing.
10. Darts. 11. Archery. 12. Wrestling. 13. Fencing. 14. Rugby Union.
15. Norwegian.

HISTORY

1. Which well-known priest was excommunicated by the Roman Catholic Church in 1521?

2. The German National Socialist Party was formed in 1919 in Munich. Who became its leader?

3. What did Frank Hornby patent in 1901?

4. Which English monarch died at Richmond Palace in 1603?

5. What nation-wide service came into operation on 10th January, 1840?

6. The first London telephone directory appeared with 250 names. True or false?

7. In which year did the 1p (decimal) coin first appear?

8. Who became the first Kaiser of a newly united Germany in 1871?

9. Who was stabbed to death in the Senate House in Rome in 44BC?

10. Rationing of what commodity ended on 15 March 1949?

11. Which famous Australian bridge opened on 19th March, 1932?

12. Which famous sporting trophy was stolen in 1966?

13. The Italian Fascist party was founded by whom in 1919?

14. The US Navy was formed in 1794. True or false?

15. Which notorious American outlaw was shot by his own gang in 1882?

CINEMA AND TV

1 What film featured Richard Dreyfuss sculpting a mountain out of mash potato?

2 What nationality was the film star Greta Garbo?

3 Who was Olivia de Havilland's film-star sister?

4 Which film featured a group of transvestites travelling through the Australian outback on a dilapidated bus?

5 Which Monty Python star now travels the world?

6 *The Big Lebowski* was largely set around what sort of entertainment?

7 Who or what is 'Auntie'?

8 Kevin Costner's scenes were completely cut out of what famous film?

9 What type of animal was a star in both *A Private Function* and *Babe*?

10 In what film did the number 'Springtime for Hitler' occur?

11 Who wrote the song *There's No Business Like Show Business*?

12 The many films of Frankenstein were based on a book by which author?

13 Joan Collins starred in which TV soap?

14 Name the actress in the famous shower scene in *Psycho*?

15 The film *Yankee Doodle Dandy* was based on whose life?

ANSWERS

1. *Close Encounters Of the Third Kind.* 2. Swedish. 3. Joan Fontaine. 4. *Priscilla - Queen Of The Desert.* 5. Michael Palin. 6. Ten-pin bowling. 7. The BBC. 8. *The Big Chill.* 9. A pig. 10. *The Producers.* 11. Irving Berlin. 12. Mary Shelley. 13. *Dynasty.* 14. Janet Leigh. 15. George M. Cohan's.

POPULAR MUSIC

1 Who had hits with 'Hooked on Can Can' and 'Hooked on Classics' in 1982?

2 On Meatloaf's, 'Dead Ringer For Love', who features, but is not credited on the label?

3 Who recorded the song, 'Sound Of The Suburbs' in 1979?

4 Mark Owen was formerly a member with which band?

5 What was Sting's first UK hit?

6 Who released the album 'Like a Prayer'?

7 Who's first hit single was 'I Only Want To Be With You' in 1963?

8 What do the initials OMD stand for?

9 Which Irish, all-girl band, had top ten hits with, 'I'm In The Mood For Dancing' and 'Attention To Me'?

10 In 1984, Foreigner reached number one in the UK and number two in the US, with which ballad?

11 What was the Glitter Band's first hit without Gary?

12 Who was the entrepreneurial master-mind who managed the Sex Pistols?

13 Which Goon reached number fourteen in 1965 with a re-working of the Beatles' 'Hard Days Night'?

14 How many were in the band Showaddywaddy?

15 Who recorded the album 'Diamond Life'?

1. Royal Philharmonic Orchestra. 2. Cher. 3. The Members. 4. Take That. 5. 'Spread A Little Happiness'. 6. Madonna. 7. Dusty Springfield. 8. Orchestral Manoeuvres in the Dark. 9. The Nolans. 10. 'I Want To Know What Love Is'. 11. 'Angel Face'. 12. Malcolm Mclaren. 13. Peter Sellers. 14. Eight. 15. Sade.

LITERATURE

1   Who's dead business partner, Jacob Marley, returns to haunt him and teach him to be charitable and kind?

2   Charles Wesley had an older brother called?

3   Who wrote the play, *Blithe Spirit*?

4   Reputedly, what did the Austrian governor Gessler instruct William Tell to do?

5   In which pantomime would you find the character 'Buttons'?

6   Which British author wrote *The Magus*?

7   In what novel do the characters, 'Professor Van Helsing', 'Jonathan Harker' and 'Lucy Westernra' appear?

8   Exactly what was 'Chitty-Chitty Bang-Bang'?

9   Who wrote the story Dr Jekyll and Mr Hyde?

10 Who wrote the words for a *Policeman's Lot is Not a Happy One*?

11 What or who, is *She*?

12 What is the Boston Globe? Is it (a) a theatre (b) a sports stadium (c) a newspaper?

13 What is Gill Sans Extra Bold?

14 Who was 'Old Nick'?

15 Who was Geoffrey of Monmouth?

ANSWERS

1. Ebeneezer Scrooge. 2. John Wesley. 3. Noël Coward. 4. Shoot an apple placed upon his son's head. 5. Cinderella. 6. John Fowles. 7. Dracula. 8. A flying motor-car. 9. Robert Louis Stevenson. 10. Sir William Schwenck Gilbert. 11. It's two things! First, a monthly women's magazine, and second, a novel by Rider Haggard. 12. It's an American newspaper. 13. The name of a typeface used by printers. 14. The devil. 15. An English chronicler, who lived between 1100 and 1154.

GENERAL KNOWLEDGE

1   On which radio programme would you find CMJ, Blowers and Fred?

2   St Vincent Ferrer is the patron saint of whom?

3   What is housed at Hertford House in London?

4   What is risotto?

5   Which musician was known as 'Flash Harry'?

6   Rule by an hereditary monarch in his or her own right is called what?

7   St George is the patron saint of where?

8   How does the Archbishop of Canterbury sign himself?

9   What kind of food item comes from Kendal?

10 What's the connection between baloney and polony?

11 What did athlete Darren Campbell win in the 1998 European Championships?

12 What are a Manhattan and a Screwdriver?

13 The titmouse isn't a mouse. What is it?

14 Who is the patron saint of scientists?

15 What are 'petits fours'?

1. Test Match Special. 2. Builders. 3. The Wallace Collection. 4. Rice cooked in stock, with meat, saffron, vegetables and cheese. 5. Sir Malcolm Sargent. 6. A monarchy. 7. England. 8. His name, followed by Cantuar. 9. A mint cake. 10. From the Bologna sausage: the first means 'rubbish, nonsense', and the second is the sausage (US version). 11. A Gold Medal in the 100m. 12. Cocktails. 13. A small bird. 14. St Albert. 15. Small, very fancy, biscuits or cakes.

SCIENCE

1 What colour is an amethyst?

2 Which is lighter - helium or hydrogen?

3 What is chronology?

4 Captain Albert Berry, in 1912, did what from an aircraft for the first time?

5 What is a magneto?

6 The mandible is another name for which bone?

7 What did Clarence Birdseye invent in 1925?

8 What vehicle was first launched in 1981?

9 Iron pyrites has a golden colour, and is sometimes called what?

10 What is arboriculture?

11 Does a concave mirror or lens bend inwards or outwards?

12 What kind of engine did Richard Trevithick invent in 1804?

13 What's the record for snowfall in Britain? (a) 60 inches (b) 40 inches (c) 84 inches.

14 What is egomania?

15 Carbon takes its name from the Latin word carbo, meaning charcoal. True or false?

ANSWERS

1. Violet or purple. 2. Hydrogen. 3. The science of computing time.
4. Made a parachute jump. 5. A simple electrical generator. 6. The lower jawbone.
7. The frozen food process. 8. The Space Shuttle. 9. Fool's gold. 10. Forestry and the study of trees. 11. Inwards. 12. The steam locomotive. 13. (a) 60 inches, in Yorkshire and Wales, 1947. 14. The belief that one is of enormous importance.
15. True.

NATURAL HISTORY

1 What is a dingo?

2 Who or what was the Yeti?

3 The strawberry is a member of the rose family. Yes or no?

4 An animal with a bill like a duck, four webbed feet and covered in soft fur is called what?

5 Britain's largest dragonfly is about (a) 2 inches long (b) 3 inches long (c) 4 inches long.

6 Where are an earthworm's eyes?

7 What kind of animal is said to mew?

8 What is ebony?

9 What kind of animal is said to twitter?

10 What is clover?

11 Which dinosaur had a series of heavy plates along its back?

12 What sort of animal is called a Hereford?

13 What is a mallow?

14 Which animal lives in a 'set'?

15 What is salsify?

GEOGRAPHY

1 Pomona is the main island of which group?

2 Which is the most southerly point in England?

3 Which town in Belgium is famed for its lace-making?

4 The official name Côte d'Ivoire refers to which country?

5 In which country is Europe's highest waterfall?

6 What is the name of the London Underground line usually shown by the colour green?

7 In which country would you find Montevideo?

8 What are a people or tribe if they are said to be nomadic?

9 Where is the EPCOT centre?

10 Which city is known as The Granite City?

11 Bechuanaland is the old name for which country?

12 Malaga is a popular holiday destination in which country?

13 The U-Bahn in Berlin is what, exactly?

14 Where would you find Copacabana beach?

15 To which country does Guadeloupe belong?

ANSWERS

1. The Orkneys. 2. The Lizard, Cornwall. 3. Brugges. 4. The Ivory Coast. 5. Norway. 6. The District Line. 7. Uruguay. 8. They have no fixed home but wander around a region. 9. Orlando, Florida, USA. 10. Aberdeen. 11. Botswana. 12. Spain. 13. An underground railway. 14. Brazil. 15. France.

ENGLISH LANGUAGE

1. What word can mean attorney or barrister?

2. What one word means both 'a large, flat dish' and 'an officer's horse'?

3. Can you name two words, sounding alike, which mean the same as this pair: layer of gold/sinfulness?

4. What's wrong with this sentence: 'Dad was able to get a large amount of people into his car'?

5. What's the difference between 'ferment' and 'foment'?

6. A dragoman was: (a) an Eastern guide (b) a slave-driver (c) a fanciful bogeyman?

7. What do the initials, TUC stand for?

8. What is 'parsimony'?

9. To what type of conveyance did Lord Brougham gave his name?

10. What did 'Burgess' mean in earlier times?

11. What would you be, if you were a *goy*?

12. What is it called when sentences or phrases have words all starting with the same letter?

13. What does 'ersatz' mean?

14. What is a 'troglodyte'?

15. Can you give a word starting with D, meaning 'loathe' or 'scorn'?

1. Lawyer. 2. Charger. 3. Gilt/guilt. 4. It should read: Dad was able to get a large number of people into his car. 5. 'Ferment' means 'to boil up something'; 'foment' means 'to stir up trouble. 6. (a) an Eastern guide. 7. Trades Union Congress. 8. Stinginess. 9. A kind of horse-drawn carriage. 10. Citizen. 11. Not Jewish. It's a Hebrew term for a gentile. 12. Alliteration. As in Sister Susie's sewing shirts for soldiers. 13. Substitute, usually an imitation. 14. A cave-dweller. 15. Despise.

SPORT

1 Name Baltimore's Major League baseball team?

2 At which football club's ground would you find the Stretford End?

3 Which sport do the Barcelona Dragons play?

4 Who or what are Goldie and Isis?

5 Which Rugby Union club does British Lion and Army officer, Tim Rodber, play for?

6 What is the total width of a Badminton court. 18ft, 20ft, 22ft or 26ft?

7 Who won an incredible six World Snooker Championships in the 1980s?

8 How many players are there on a Basketball court at any one time?

9 Name the three Olympic athletic field events that are still men-only?

10 What is the minimum weight of a tennis ball; 55g, 55.9g, 56.3g or 56.7g?

11 In which year was women's Shooting introduced to the Olympic Games?

12 Which Motor Sport did Barry Sheene take up, after he retired from Motor Cycling?

13 Which football team plays its home games at St James' Park?

14 In America, what do the initials NCAA, stand for?

15 In Cricket, how do you commonly describe 'out first ball'?

ANSWERS

1. Orioles. 2. Manchester United. 3. American Football. 4. Oxford and Cambridge Number Two Crews. 5. Northampton. 6. 20 ft. 7. Steve Davis. 8. Ten. 9. Triple Jump, Hammer and Pole Vault. 10. 56.7g. 11. 1984. 12. Truck Racing 13. Newcastle United. 14. National Collegiate Athletic Association 15. A Golden Duck.

HISTORY

1. Who was knighted aboard his ship, the Golden Hind, in 1581?

2. In April, 1909, a US Naval officer was the first to reach the North Pole. Who was he?

3. What did Dr Samuel Johnston publish in 1755?

4. What was permitted in the Serpentine for the first time in 1930?

5. What did Charles Macintosh patent in 1823?

6. What did John Cabot discover in 1497?

7. Joseph Smith and his brother were killed in a US jail in 184 4 For what were they famed?

8. In what year did the 999 telephone emergency service begin?

9. A rally held by William Booth in Whitechapel founded what in 1865?

10. Which Russian socialist died in 1883, and was buried in Highgate Cemetery, London?

11. What happened to Sir Thomas More in 1535 when he refused to swear allegiance to Henry VIII as Head of the Church of England?

12. The first underground trains in Paris started in 1900, 1905 or 1910?

13. Who did Henry VIII marry on 12th July, 1543?

14. In 1865, Edward Whymper made the first ascent of what?

15. Europe's first banknotes were issued in 1661 in which country; (a) England (b) Scotland (c) Sweden?

ANSWERS

1. Francis Drake. 2. Robert Perry. 3. His English dictionary. 4. Mixed bathing. 5. Waterproof cloth. 6. Newfoundland. 7. Founding the Mormon Church. 8. 1937. 9. The Salvation Army. 10. Karl Marx. 11. He was beheaded. 12. 1900. 13. Catherine Parr. 14. The Matterhorn. 15. Sweden.

CINEMA AND TV

1 The Noël Coward play *Still Life* was made into a film under what title?

2 What film featured dozens of skydiving Elvis Presley impersonators?

3 What film featured a famous soundtrack from the Australian group The Bee Gees?

4 Ambridge is the fictional setting for which long-running radio drama?

5 From which musical play comes the song 'Anything You Can Do'?

6 Who won an Oscar for directing *Forrest Gump*?

7 The Christopher Isherwood play *I Am a Camera* was made into a film under what title?

8 Who created the cartoon character 'Bugs Bunny'?

9 'I Wanna Be Like You' and 'Bear Necessities' are songs from which film?

10 'Be Careful Out There' was a catchphrase of which American TV cop show?

11 Who was the female lead in the Alan Parker film, Evita?

12 What is Equity?

13 Who was married to Humphrey Bogart and Jason Robards?

14 Who was the first Director-General of the BBC?

15 Which Disney cartoon tells the story of a princess in America in the 17th Century?

1. *Brief Encounter*. 2. *Honeymoon In Las Vegas*. 3. *Saturday Night Fever*. 4. *The Archers*. 5. *Annie Get Your Gun*. 6. Robert Zemeckis. 7. *Cabaret*. 8. Chuck Jones. 9. *Jungle Book*. 10. *Hill Street Blues*. 11. Madonna. 12. The actors' trade union. 13. Lauren Bacall. 14. John Reith. 15. *Pocahontas*.

POPULAR MUSIC

1   Which 1979 film starred the Sex Pistols?

2   Name Prince's 1984 semi-autobiographical film?

3   With which children's TV theme did Mike Oldfield reach number 19 in 1979?

4   Ocean Colour Scene's guitarist Steve Craddock played keyboards on Paul Weller's first solo album. True or false?

5   'Use It Up And Wear It Out' was number one in 1980 for which US group?

6   Which singer starred in the film, Blue Hawaii?

7   Who reached number one in 1979 with 'Brass In Pocket'?

8   Name Supergrass's debut album?

9   Which artist along with The Luvvers, reached number seven in 1964 with 'Shout'?

10 Name David Bowie's band who had minor hits between 1989 and 1991 including 'You Belong In Rock and Roll?

11 Who was the lead singer with Tenpole Tudor?

12 Which band joined Vic Reeves to have a number one with the song, 'Dizzy'?

13 Who was the lead singer of punk band X-Ray Spex?

14 With whom did Stevie Wonder record 'Ebony And Ivory'?

15 Which bearded band gave us the songs, 'Gimme All Your Lovin' in 1983 and 'Viva Las Vegas' in 1992?

LITERATURE

1 Who was Christopher Plantin?

2 What was the *City Press,* which first appeared in 1857?

3 Who wrote 'Was this the face which launch'd a thousand ships?'

4 Who wrote the book *Eyeless in Gaza* in 1936?

5 Whose stock phrase was 'Now here's a funny thing...'?

6 What does 'kick the bucket' mean?

7 Who, or what, were Pip, Squeak and Wilfred?

8 What D.H. Lawrence novel was originally entitled Paul Morel?

9 The American poet Ezra Pound was the nephew of which very famous poet?

10 What have W.H. Auden, Dylan Thomas and Edith Sitwell in common?

11 What is alliteration?

12 Who wrote Watership Down?

13 What is a 'malapropism'?

14 Who were the 'Famous Five'?

15 Who were 'Janet and John'?

ANSWERS

1. A French printer who worked in 16th-century Antwerp. 2. The first local newspaper for the City of London. 3. Christopher Marlowe. 4. Aldous Huxley. 5. Max Miller. 6. To die. 7. Children's cartoon characters which appeared in the *Daily Mirror* from 1920. 8. *Sons and Lovers.* 9. Longfellow. 10. They were all poets. 11. Two or more words in a sentence, each starting with the same letter. 12. Richard Adams. 13. A word or phrase used wrongly due to ignorance or carelessness. 14. There were two lots! The Greyfriars Famous Five (Wharton, Nugent, Cherry, Bull and Hurree Singh), and Enid Blyton's: Julian, Dick, Anne and Georgina. 15. Characters from reading-books for children issued from 1949.

GENERAL KNOWLEDGE

1   What is cassata?

2   What is poker?

3   What anniversary does a
    diamond wedding celebrate?

4   What word, beginning with
    ante- means 'going before, in
    time'?

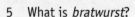

5   What is *bratwurst*?

6   The Water Carrier represents which sign of the Zodiac?

7   What is a *Bar Mitzvah*?

8   St Michael is the patron saint of whom?

9   Whose motto is: '*E Pluribus Unum*'?

10   Chips with Everything was a successful play by which author?

11   What is *Yom Kippur*?

12   What were Pioneer, Galileo and Magellan?

13   A stitch in time will save how many?

14   St Boniface is the patron saint of what?

15   The impresario Lewis Winogradsky is better known as whom?

SCIENCE

1   What is the chemical symbol for sodium?

2   What colour is a turquoise?

3   What does a Geiger counter measure?

4   Sulphuric, hydrochloric and nitric are the three what?

5   The study of the action of forces on bodies is called what?

6   What is guano?

7   What is the object in space called Saturn?

8   What was a Sten?

9   After 1865, what needed to precede any 'horseless carriage' in the streets of Britain?

10 What kind of unusual car engine was introduced by Felix Wankel in 1957?

11 What is horology?

12 Reginald Booth, in 1901, invented which now-essential household device?

13 Ebb and flow is the regular movement of what?

14 In Roman numerals, what is XV?

15 The pelvis is another name for which bone?

1. Na. 2. Blue. 3. Radiation. 4. Main mineral acids. 5. Mechanics. 6. A natural fertiliser, formed from bird droppings on the Peruvian islands. 7. One of the nine planets. 8. A sub-machine gun. 9. A man with a red flag. 10. The rotary petrol engine. 11. The science of measuring time. 12. The vacuum cleaner. 13. The sea. 14. Fifteen. 15. The hip-bone.

NATURAL HISTORY

1 What part of the vegetable okra is eaten?

2 What is a colugo?

3 What is a gerenuk?

4 What is fenugreek?

5 From which area does the chameleon come?

6 Where do blueberries come from?

7 What is an ibex?

8 What are caraway seeds used for?

9 What is a macaque?

10 What endangered animal rarely mates, eats largely only bamboo shoots, and estimates state that there are only 500 of them in the wild?

11 The watercress is from the Nasturtium family. True or false?

12 What is the difference between a marten and a martin?

13 What part of a soya is eaten?

14 What is a narwhal?

15 Where did the kiwi fruit originate?

1. The pods and seeds. 2. A monkey-like animal, also called the flying lemur. 3. A kind of African antelope. 4. A spice whose seeds are used in cooking. 5. Asia, Africa, part of Europe. 6. North America. 7. A large-horned mountain goat. 8. As a spice and ingredient. 9. A kind of monkey. 10. Giant Panda. 11. True. 12. A marten is an animal like a weasel and the martin is a bird. 13. The beans. 14. A kind of whale with a large, projecting tusk. 15. China.

GEOGRAPHY

1　Where would you find the republic of San Marino?

2　In which county would you find the Mendip Hills?

3　Where is the language Romany spoken?

4　Where would you expect to find 'Number Ten'?

5　What is the national language of Mexico?

6　The length of the River Thames is; (a) about 160 miles (b) about 200 miles (c) about 90 miles?

7　Where in the world is there a giant statue of Christ on a high mountain?

8　If you were changing your money into ore and krona, where would you be going?

9　King Jigme Singye Wangchuk is the ruler of which country?

10　In which English town would you find 'The Pantiles'?

11　Cambridge is on the River Cam. What is the river also called?

12　In which country is the Yellow River?

13　Stalagtites and Stalagmites: which go up?

14　Excluding Alaska, which is the largest state in the USA?

15　In which city would you find The Gorbals?

ANSWERS

1. In Northern Italy. 2. Somerset. 3. Wherever there are true Gypsies. 4. In Downing Street, London. 5. Spanish. 6. (a) about 160 miles. 7. Above Rio de Janeiro, Brazil. 8. Sweden. 9. Bhutan. 10. Tunbridge Wells. 11. The Granta. 12. China. 13. Stalagmites. 14. Texas. 15. Glasgow.

ENGLISH LANGUAGE

1 What do the initials, RAAF stand for?

2 Can you name two words, sounding alike, which mean the same as this pair: revenge or punish/smoke or smell?

3 A moonraker was: (a) a cheesemonger (b) a man from Wiltshire (c) a kind of male witch?

4 A kulak is: (a) a rich Russian peasant (b) a two-wheeled pony-cart (c) a wild ass?

5 What do Americans mean by the game called 'tic tac toe'?

6 What does the phrase 'volte-face' mean?

7 Re-arrange these three single-word anagrams: Angle, pirates, telegraph.

8 What does 'above-board' mean?

9 What is a 'Yippie'?

10 'Trusty' was an old way of saying what?

11 A bodger is (a) a travelling artisan or salesperson (b) a small dagger (c) an implement for making holes.

12 What is a ménage a trois?

13 What, in earlier times, did 'varlet' mean?

14 If you 'washed up' in the United States, what would it mean?

15 What is a 'daguerreotype'?

SPORT

1 In American football, how many points are awarded for a field goal?

2 In which sport are you not allowed to refer to females as women, but always as ladies?

3 What are a jockey's Silks?

4 Whilst Cardiff Arms Park was being renovated, where did the Welsh Rugby Union team play their home games?

5 Where is the British Grand Prix currently held?

6 Which football club did Brian Robson manage in the 1997/98 football season?

7 True or false. Tim Henman and Greg Rusedski have the same birthday?

8 Name Britain's top woman Boxer who became the first woman to be granted a Licence by the British Boxing Board of Control?

9 Who were the main sponsors of the Jordan Formula One team during the 1998 season?

10 Which professional sport does the WPBSA preside over?

11 Where does the National Rifle Association of Great Britain hold its prestigious annual Championships?

12 In Archery, what are the feathers on an arrow called?

13 Who scored England's last goal in open play during the 1990 World Cup?

14 In American football, what is the name of the line between the two teams on which the ball is placed?

15 In which year did Board Sailing become an Olympic sport?

HISTORY

1   The foundation stone of which London Cathedral was laid in 1675?

2   What did New Hampshire elect to become in 1788?

3   In 1900, the Wallace Collection was opened. Where is it based?

4   Burgess and Maclean were two diplomats. What did they do in 1951?

5   In 1812, Napoleon's armies began the invasion of which country?

6   What took place aboard the Russian battleship Potemkin in 1905?

7   Which theatre in London burned down in 1613?

8   In what year was the pillory abolished; 1820, 1837 or 1890?

9   What happened to James Garfield, US President, in 1881?

10 Over whom was Saladin victorious in 1187?

11 What notorious legal institution was abolished in 1641?

12 What coin was issued for the first time in 1817?

13 What racing circuit was opened in 1907?

14 Which Glasgow exhibition hall was destroyed by fire in 1925?

15 What was the verdict in the famous case of Madeleine Smith in Edinburgh, 1857?

ANSWERS

1. St Paul's. 2. The 9th state of the United States. 3. In London. 4. Fled to the USSR. 5. Russia. 6. A mutiny. 7. Shakespeare's Globe. 8. 1837. 9. He was shot, and later, died from those wounds. 10. The Crusaders. 11. The Star Chamber. 12. The gold sovereign. 13. Brooklands. 14. Kelvin Hall. 15. 'Not proven'.

CINEMA AND TV

1 What connects Ishtar, *The Adventures Of Baron Munchausen* and *Heaven's Gate*?

2 Which long-running TV show was hosted for many years by presenters, William Woollard and Raymond Baxter?

3 In what film did Bruce Willis provide the voice of a baby?

4 Who wrote the music 'The Entertainer'?

5 From which musical play comes the song 'It Ain't Necesarily So'?

6 In what film did Dennis Hopper, Jack Nicholson and Peter Fonda star?

7 Who provided the voices for the animated films starring Wallace and Gromit?

8 What film featured Rick Moranis reducing the size of his family?

9 What Disney film mixed cartoon and live action and featured a magical bed?

10 Percy Thrower and Alan Titchmarsh have both hosted TV programmes on what subject?

11 Who directed the films *The Big Chill* and *Grand Canyon*?

12 Where does the expression: 'May the force be with you' come from?

13 What role did David Niven play just once and Timothy Dalton twice?

14 Who play the hit men in the film *Pulp Fiction*?

15 Who played the character 'Virgil Tibbs'?

POPULAR MUSIC

1   By what name were the band 'The Who' originally known?

2   Which band backed Cliff Richard in the 1960s?

3   On the Specials single 'A Message To You Rudi' who played the trombone?

4   Who was the lead singer with the Communards?

5   Who reached number one in 1978 with 'Three Times A Lady'?

6   Who released the 'Velvet Rope' album in 1998?

7   Who had top ten hits with, 'System Addict', 'Find The Time' and 'The Slightest Touch'?

8   What was Brian Ferry's first solo top ten hit?

9   Which TV Series's theme tune was the song, 'Suicide Is Painless'?

10 Which TV characters reached number 5 in 1994, with 'Them Girls, Them Girls'?

11 Rita Coolidge performed this Tim Rice-composed song as the theme to the Bond film Octopussy. Can you name it?

12 Who reached number 5 in May 1981 with, 'Ossie's Dream'?

13 Who was the lead singer with The Style Council?

14 Who had top ten hits with 'Simon Smith And His Amazing Dancing Bear' and 'Jarrow Song'?

15 Who was 'Leavin' On A Jet Plane' in 1970?

1. High Numbers. 2. The Shadows. 3. Rico. 4. Jimmy Sommerville. 5. Commodores. 6. Janet Jackson. 7. Five Star. 8. 'A Hard Rain's Gonna Fall'. 9. M.A.S.H. 10. Zig and Zag. 11. 'All Time High' (Octopussy). 12. Tottenham Hotspur F.A. Cup final squad. 13. Paul Weller. 14. Alan Price. 15. Peter, Paul and Mary.

LITERATURE

1   What H.G. Wells novel was originally called *The Chronic Argonauts*?

2   Who was Rumpelstiltskin?

3   In Kipling's story, what was Kim's real name?

4   Who wrote *A Connecticut Yankee at King Arthur's Court*?

5   Who was the author of *The Cloister and the Hearth*?

6   How many lines are there in Chaucer's Canterbury Tales; 2,000, 8,000 or 17,000?

7   What famous book did Walter Pater write in 1885?

8   Who wrote the play *Street Scene* in 1929?

9   Who wrote *The Decameron*, in 1351?

10   'Mr Bumble' appears in which Dickens novel?

11   The clown 'Touchstone' appears in which Shakespeare play?

12   *The Daisy Chain* was a novel for young people written in 1856 by whom?

13   What kind of novels did Bret Harte write?

14   Who is the narrator of the story in *Treasure Island*?

15   Who wrote the novel *Phineas Finn*?

ANSWERS

1. The Time Machine. 2. A character in fairy stories by the brothers, Grimm. 3. Kimball O'Hara. 4. Mark Twain. 5. Charles Reade. 6. 17,000. 7. *Marius the Epicurean*. 8. Elmer Rice. 9. Giovanni Boccaccio. 10. *Oliver Twist*. 11. *As You Like It*. 12. Charlotte M. Yonge. 13. Westerns. 14. Jim Hawkins. 15. Anthony Trollope.

GENERAL KNOWLEDGE

1 What does 'to bellyache' mean?

2 Where did the Flintstones live?

3 What does 'beef up' mean?

4 What is an ampersand?

5 What does the expression 'in the can' mean?

6 What were 'Teddy Boys'?

7 What is a 'Hooray Henry'?

8 What does 'in the buff' mean?

9 What is a 'sleuth'?

10 What is a 'shemozzle'?

11 If you went by Shanks's pony, how would you be travelling?

12 What is 'plonk'?

13 What is an 'Oscar'?

14 If someone asked you to be QUEBEC UNIFORM INDIA ECHO TANGO what would you have to do?

15 What does 'above board' mean?

SCIENCE

1 What is carbon dioxide?

2 What is a Sea-King?

3 Brimstone is an old name for which chemical?

4 What are the primary colours?

5 What was a Thompson?

6 Who invented the concertina?

7 How much salt is there in seawater? (a) 3% (b) 6% (c) 10%.

8 What is theomania?

9 What are the pointed arms on an anchor called?

10 What is an antenna?

11 Who built the Rocket railway locomotive?

12 What is the difference between wolfram and tungsten?

13 Epsom salts is another name for what?

14 What is bibliomania?

15 A lump or swelling on the big toe is called a what?

NATURAL HISTORY

1 What are Manx cats missing?

2 What unusual feature does the tuatara have?

3 What is a deciduous tree?

4 What is a clementine?

5 A condor is a bird of prey. True or false?

6 What is the common stinkhorn?

7 A phalarope is a shore-bird. Yes or no?

8 Where did the lychee originate?

9 What is a skink?

10 What is the most common vegetable grown in British gardens?

11 A drongo is; (a) a foolish fellow (b) a songbird (c) a fish?

12 What is a tinamou?

13 Where did bamboo originate?

14 What is a wolverine?

15 What speedy bird has been timed at over 105mph?

1.Their tails. 2. It's a reptile with a third eye in its forehead. 3. One which sheds its leaves periodically. 4. A small orange from the Mediterranean region. 5. True. 6. An edible mushroom. 7. Yes. 8. China. 9. A tree-dwelling reptile. 10. Beetroot. 11. (b) a songbird. 12. A South American flightless bird. 13. America. 14. A kind of mountain cat of North America. 15. Spinetail Swift.

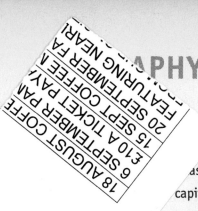

...APHY

...ted country; Macao, Monaco or

... aster Island called?

... capital cities, depending on the

... the world's oldest zoo?

... ulation of Pitcairn Island; (a) 104 (b) 55 (c) 277?

... down from the air and observed the Royal Albert
... on, what shape would you see?

... was the North West Frontier?

8   ... re, in London, is the original 'Oranges and Lemons' church?

9   Where and what is the 'Moulin Rouge'?

10   What is the capital of Australia?

11   What part of the United States is nicknamed The Lone Star
     State?

12   Which country has the longest total coastline?

13   In which country is the Ganges river?

14   Which major Russian city stands on the Neva river?

15   Which is the world's largest land gorge?

ANSWERS

1. Macao with over 68,000 people per sq. mile. 2. Hanga Roa. 3. South Africa;
Pretoria, Cape Town or Bloemfontein. 4. Vienna. 5. (b) 55. 6. An oval, or ellipse.
7. Between Afghanistan and India. 8. St Clement Danes, in the Strand. 9. A theatre
night-club in Paris. 10. Canberra. 11. Texas. 12. Canada. 13. India.
14. St Petersburg. 15. The Grand Canyon, Arizona, 277 miles long.

ENGLISH LANGUAGE

1   What does an American mean by a 'nickel'?

2   What is the name for someone who studies living things?

3   In cockney rhyming slang, what does 'Rosie Lee' mean?

4   In America, you take an elevator to the upper floors. In Britain, what would we take?

5   What does the Latin 'ad nauseam' mean?

6   What does q.v. stand for?

7   What does 'acme' mean?

8   What does an American housewife mean by 'drapes'?

9   What does the A.D. stand for in '1998 A.D.'?

10 What object would you have, 'to grind', if you had something on your mind?

11 What did 'Ere' mean?

12 What word, beginning with S, means caustic or sardonic?

13 What is the female version of 'bachelor'

14 What one word means, 'The covering of tree trunks' and 'the cry of a dog'?

15 What is the meaning of 'itinerant'?

SPORT

1 Which winter sport does ex-England Cricket Captain David Gower regularly take part in at St Moritz?

2 Which football team plays its home games at Goodison Park?

3 With which sport do you associate Brian Johnston?

4 Name the American football team based in Dallas?

5 In Formula One, what change in the rules led to the running of two separate Grand Prix Championships in the mid 1980's?

6 In Water Polo, what happens to a player who commits three personal faults in one match?

7 In which year was Canoeing introduced into the Olympic Games; 1920, 1924, 1932 or 1936?

8 Footballer Ian Rush was granted a Soccer scholarship, by a US university. True or false?

9 What did swimmer Captain Matthew Webb achieve in 1875?

10 How many balls are there on a Billiards Table?

11 Which English football team has the nickname the Magpies?

12 Why in Tennis does the scoring follow the pattern - 15, 30, 40 and Game?

13 In which city is the San Siro Stadium?

14 Name Philadelphia's American football team?

15 With which Formula One team did Michael Schumacher win his first World Driver's Championship?

ANSWERS

1. Tobogganing (Skeleton). 2. Everton 3. Cricket. 4. The Cowboys 5. The banning of Turbo Chargers. 6. Banned for the rest of the game. 7. 1936. 8. False. 9. First person to swim the English Channel. 10. Three 11. Newcastle United. 12. Quarters of the clock (40 was originally 45, and Game was 60). 13. Milan. 14. Eagles. 15. Benetton

HISTORY

1 What set sail from Spain to England in 1588?

2 Who did Charlotte Corday murder in 1793?

3 The Crusaders were successful in capturing what in 1099?

4 What was adopted by the French as their national anthem in 1795?

5 Jacques Cartier landed in North America, in 1534 and claimed it for France. What area of North America?

6 Whom did Philip of Spain marry in 1554?

7 What status did New York assume in 1788?

8 What city in South Australia was founded in 1836?

9 Parliament granted a 12-year charter to which bank in 1694?

10 Peru declared its independence from which country in 1821?

11 Which great liner was launched at Birkenhead in 1938?

12 Kurt von Schuschnigg became Chancellor of which country in 1934?

13 Le Morte D'Arthur, by Thomas Mallory, was published by whom in 1485?

14 What kind of tax duties were first introduced and imposed in 1894?

15 Which opera house in Milan was opened in 1778?

ANSWERS

1. The Spanish Armada. 2. Paul Marat. 3. Jerusalem. 4. La Marseillaise. 5. Canada. 6. Queen Mary I of England. 7. It became the 11th of the United States. 8. Adelaide. 9. The Bank of England. 10. Spain. 11. The Mauritania. 12. Austria. 13. William Caxton. 14. Death duties. 15. La Scala.

CINEMA AND TV

1   Who starred in the 1994 movie *Bullets Over Broadway*?

2   Who played the leading role in *The Madness of King George*?

3   How many Oscars did the film *The English Patient* receive in 1996?

4   Judy Garland played 'Dorothy Gale' in which film?

5   'Andy Hardy' was played by whom?

6   Dustin Hoffman and Tom Cruise are together in this story of an autistic brother. Title?

7   Gene Hackman stars with whom in the 1995 film *Get Shorty*?

8   Who starred in *Blue Sky*, made in 1995?

9   In *Yankee Doodle Dandy*, what part does James Cagney play?

10 A car salesman gets his wife kidnapped in order to swindle her father. Title of the 1996 movie?

11 Kevin Costner, a US Civil War soldier, communes with the Indians and becomes one of them. Title?

12 What character was played in the movies by **Sean Connery, David Niven, George Lazenby, Roger Moore, Timothy Dalton and Pierce Brosnan**?

13 This 1996 Australian movie is about a young dysfunctional piano prodigy. Lynn Redgrave and John Gielgud appear. What is the name of the film?

14 Which character was played by both Peter Sellers and Alan Arkin?

15 Who played opposite Henry Fonda in *On Golden Pond*?

POPULAR MUSIC

1   Which singer married footballer Jamie Redknapp in 1998?

2   Which former Eastender had hits with 'Someone To Love' and, 'Good Day'?

3   Name one of the two bands Trevor Horn has been a member of?

4   Who is the lead singer of The Fall?

5   Up until 1998, which act has had the most UK hits without ever entering the top ten?

6   Who recorded 'Matchstalk Men And Matchstalk Cats And Dogs?

7   In which film did Art Garfunkel's, 'Bright Eyes' appear?

8   Which, Bond theme was recorded by Matt Munroe in 1963?

9   Who sang the theme to the first Ghostbusters movie?

10 Who was 'Forever In Blue Jeans', in 1979?

11 Who had hits in the 1960s and 1970s with 'Wouldn't It Be Nice', 'Sloop John B' and 'Good Vibrations'?

12 Which tartan-clad lads, kept on dancing, gave a little love and said, bye bye baby?

13 Who recorded the theme to the Bond film, Goldfinger?

14 Which group was Lynsey De Paul a quarter of?

15   Name Abba's, semi auto-biographical film?

1. Louise. 2. Sean Maguire. 3. Yes, The Buggles. 4. Mark E. Smith. 5. AC/DC. 6. Brian And Michael. 7. Watership Down. 8. From Russia With Love. 9. Ray Parker Jnr. 10. Neil Diamond. 11. The Beach Boys. 12. The Bay City Rollers. 13. Shirley Bassey. 14. The New Seekers. 15. ABBA The Movie.

LITERATURE

1   What was the *Book of the Dead*?

2   What are dead languages?

3   What was the magical land portrayed in *The Lion, The Witch And The Wardrobe*?

4   Complete the line: 'Now is the time for all good men...'

5   Solomon Grundy was born on Monday. What happened to him on Friday?

6   According to the *Communist Manifesto*, what are workers of the world expected to do?

7   Lucy Locket lost her pocket. How much was in it?

8   According to the BBC motto, what should nations do?

9   Who wrote *The Shining*, *Carrie* and *Bag Of Bones*?

10 Which Jane was concerned with aspects of human pride and prejudice?

11 Which William was famous for his odes to the lakes?

12 Which William was renowned for his *Vanity Fair*?

13 Which James probably never wanted to grow up?

14 Which sci-fi author wrote *Rendezvous With Rama*?

15 Who wrote the influential ecology book, *Small Is Beautiful*?

1. A collection of Ancient Egyptian texts. 2. Languages, like Latin, which are no longer spoken regularly. 3. Narnia. 4. '...to come to the aid of the party'. 5. He died. 6. Unite! 7. Not a penny. 8. Speak peace unto nations. 9. Stephen King. 10. Austen. 11. Wordsworth. 12. Thackeray. 13. Barrie. 14. Arthur C. Clarke. 15. E.F. Schumacher.

GENERAL KNOWLEDGE

1   What, according to the old schoolboys' joke, is the meaning of *coup de grâce*?

2   What, to a British soldier, was 'Blighty'?

3   If you were 'in the altogether', what would you be?

4   If you asked the price, and were told 'gratis', what would you pay?

5   Who made the phrase, 'Clunk, Click - Every Trip' famous?

6   Which comic featured the characters, Biffa Bacon, Billy The Fish and Black Bag?

7   In American English, what is a 'rubberneck'?

8   What is, or was, a spoonerism?

9   What is a busker?

10   If you were in the Army, and 'got a rocket', what would have happened?

11   What is 'Adam's ale'?

12   What does the symbol © mean?

13   What is an 'oik'?

14   If, in the Navy, the captain gave the order 'splice the mainbrace', what would happen?

15   What's a 'Walter Mitty'?

ANSWERS

1. A lawn-mower. 2. Home. 3. Naked. 4. Nothing! 5. Jimmy Savile. 6. *Viz.* 7. Someone who stares and gawps. 8. A habit of transposing initial letters of words, as 'shoving leopard' for 'loving shepherd'. 9. A street singer or performer. 10. You would have received a severe telling-off. 11. Water. 12. Copyright. 13. An ignorant lout. 14. All sailors received an extra tot of rum. 15. A day-dreaming fantasist.

SCIENCE

1   The maxilla is another name for which bone?

2   The scientific study of drugs is called what?

3   What is the name given to a structure built to check the flow of water?

4   The study of heredity and mutation is called?

5   What is the name given to a solid figure with six square sides?

6   What is constantan?

7   Photogravure, lithography and letterpress are different methods of what?

8   We'd have a bumpy time in a vehicle without John Boyd Dunlop's invention of 1888. What was it?

9   What is caffeine?

10   Which of the planets is farthest from the Sun?

11   You taste lactic acid when you drink what?

12   A Bessemer converter used to make what?

13   A human being has how many chromosomes?

14   'Yin' and 'yang' are expressions used in what kind of treatment?

15   The Sea of Tranquility is near the South Pole. True or false?

ANSWERS

1. The upper jawbone. 2. Pharmacology. 3. A dam. 4. Genetics. 5. A cube. 6. An alloy of 40% nickel and 60% copper. 7. Printing. 8. The pneumatic tyre. 9. A stimulant drug found in tea and coffee. 10. Pluto. 11. Sour milk. 12. Steel. 13. 46. 14. Acupuncture. 15. False. It's an area on the Moon.

NATURAL HISTORY

1 What is a rhea?

2 What is a black widow?

3 Exactly what is a 'ship of the desert'?

4 What sort of creature is a Portuguese man of war?

5 What sort of an animal would be feline?

6 In which countries does the bowerbird live?

7 How far can a flying-fish fly: hundreds of feet, hundreds of yards, or even miles?

8 A flamingo is a water-bird. Yes or no?

9 What sort of animal is a carnivore?

10 What sort of animal is a teal?

11 Which bird was originally called the apteryx?

12 A group of eggs, all laid at one time, is called what?

13 What animal has the heaviest brain?

14 What kind of tree grows dates?

15 Crabs, lobsters and shrimps all have the same number of legs. How many?

1. A flightless bird found on the plains of South America. 2. A poisonous spider. 3. A camel. 4. A jellyfish. 5. A cat. 6. Australia and New Guinea. 7. Several hundred yards. 8. Yes. 9. One that eats meat. 10. A freshwater duck. 11. The kiwi. 12. A clutch. 13. The sperm whale. 14. A date palm. 15. Ten.

GEOGRAPHY

1   What is the capital of Malaysia?

2   What, in Australia, is a billabong?

3   What is the Troposphere?

4   Middlesex Street in London is a street market, better known as?

5   Hibernia was the name given by the Romans to where?

6   The official name 'Helvetica' refers to which country?

7   What is a native of the county of Shropshire called?

8   What body of water does the American city Tampa border?

9   Where are the Tivoli Gardens?

10 Albion was the name given by the Romans to where?

11 Which city is on the Garonne river?

12 Which is the world's loneliest inhabited island?

13 Anglesey is an island, part of which country?

14 Where in the world is Swaziland?

15 British Honduras is the old name for where?

ANSWERS

1. Kuala Lumpur. 2. A waterhole. 3. The lowest region of the atmosphere.
4. Petticoat Lane. 5. Ireland. 6. Switzerland. 7. A Salopian. 8. Gulf of Mexico.
9. Copenhagen. 10. Britain. 11. Bordeaux. 12. Tristan da Cunha. 13. Wales.
14. Southern Africa. 15. Belize.

ENGLISH LANGUAGE

1　What is the meaning of 'acquiesce'?

2　What does 'R.I.P.' stand for?

3　Can you name two words, sounding alike, which mean the same as this pair: plaited binding/cried like an ass?

4　A Wend is: (a) A German of Slav descent (b) a letter in the Runic alphabet (c) an ear infection?

5　What is wrong with this sentence: It is over a year ago since we met?

6　What, in the US is a 'victrola'?

7　What do 'toothbrush' and 'walrus' have in common?

8　'Beaver' was old slang for what male appendage?

9　What is a 'flying buttress'?

10　What is a rasp?

11　What is a spiritual?

12　What, in US showbiz talk, is a 'boffo'?

13　What kind of amphibian is not an animal at all?

14　What does 'larceny' mean?

15　A cataract is (a) a waterfall (b) a malfunction of the eye?

1. To rest satisfied, to agree. 2. 'Requiescat in pace': Rest In Peace. 3. Braid/brayed. 4. (a) A German of Slav descent. 5. The use of both 'ago' and 'since' is wrong. Omit 'since' or say It is over a year ago that we met. 6. A record-player. 7. They are both kinds of moustache. 8. A beard. 9. A bar of masonry from a pier or arch. 10. A kind of heavy file. 11. A kind of religious song. 12. A box-office hit. 13. A vehicle which can travel on land or in water. 14. Stealing. 15. It's both!

SPORT

1   What is the diameter of a Basketball hoop; 30cm, 40cm, 45cm or 50cm?

2   How long is an Olympic-sized swimming pool?

3   Which ski's are narrower - Cross Country (Nordic) or Downhill?

4   What material is the tip of a Snooker Cue made from?

5   Who won the Men's Singles at Wimbledon in 1997?

6   With which sport do you associate Iwan Thomas?

7   In international swimming events, how warm must the water be; 20°C, 22°C, 24°C or 26°C?

8   Which team scored in injury time in all three of its group matches in France '98?

9   With which sport do you associate James Wattana?

10 Which football team play their home games at the Nou Camp Stadium?

11 Name Los Angeles' NFC American football team?

12 Name Britain's Ladies tennis number 1 who reached the 4th round of Wimbledon in 1998?

13 In Australian Rules Football, how many points are scored by putting the ball between the opposition's goal posts?

14 In Rugby Union, which player is at the back of the scrum?

15 In which sport do men compete for the King George V Gold Cup at the Birmingham NEC?

ANSWERS

1. 45cm. 2. 50m. 3. Downhill. 4. Leather. 5. Pete Sampras. 6. Athletics (400m). 7. 24°C. 8. Austria. 9. Snooker. 10. Barcelona. 11. Rams. 12. Sam Smith 13. Six. 14. Number Eight. 15. Show Jumping.

HISTORY

1 What social practice was abolished in Turkey in 1924?

2 Which famous London hotel opened in 1889?

3 By what name was Bytown known when it became capital of Canada in 1858?

4 Why is Adelaide, Australia, sometimes called the, 'City of Light'?

5 What was founded in 1864 by Jean-Henri Dunant, and granted international immunity?

6 What Atlantic communication was completed in 1858 by Cyrus Field?

7 The Austrians and English defeated whom at Blenheim in 1704?

8 Which island in the Atlantic was annexed to Britain in 1816?

9 Which cathedral, started in 1248, was completed in 1880?

10 Which Zulu chief was received by Queen Victoria in 1882?

11 Which religious group was founded in 1534 by Ignatius de Loyola?

12 What took place at St Peter's Field, Manchester, 1819?

13 What was the Peterloo Massacre?

14 Which London art gallery was opened in 1897?

15 Which Mediterranean island became an independent republic in 1960?

CINEMA AND TV

1 Name two English stars in this 1995 remake of *Sense and Sensibility*?

2 What was the title of the film which featured a group of young New Yorkers going on a cattle drive led by Jack Palance?

3 *Nobody's Fool* (1994) stars which seasoned film actor?

4 What is the name of Superman's girl-friend?

5 Who played the lead role in the film *Barbarella*?

6 Which of these three British sitcoms was NOT made into a feature film; *Porridge, Are You Being Served, Birds Of A Feather*?

7 Who starred in the 1992 movie *Scent of a Woman*?

8 Meryl Streep and Robert Redford stared in this epic true story about Africa. What was the title of this film?

9 What TV sitcom starred Neil Morrissey and Martin Clunes?

10 The 1993 film *The Piano* tells of a woman arriving in New Zealand, to do what?

11 Who is Popeye's great enemy?

12 Who starred with Patrick Swayze and Demi Moore in *Ghost* (1990)?

13 What was the Disney cartoon which told the story of a lion cub in the jungle?

14 *Leaving Las Vegas* tells the story of which two kinds of lonely people?

15 In which film did the character 'Harry Lime' appear?

ANSWERS

1. Emma Thompson, Alan Rickman, Hugh Grant, Robert Hardy. 2. City Slickers. 3. Paul Newman. 4. Lois Lane. 5. Jane Fonda. 6. *Birds Of A Feather*. 7. Al Pacino. 8. *Out of Africa*. 9. *Men Behaving Badly*. 10. Get married to an local man. 11. Bluto. 12. Whoopi Goldberg. 13. *The Lion King*. 14. An alcoholic and a hooker. 15. *The Third Man*.

POPULAR MUSIC

1   Whose albums include 'Siamese Dream' and 'Gish'?

2   Who recorded the album, 'Raintown' in 1988?

3   Who reached number 1 in 1969 with, 'The Israelites'?

4   Who recorded the album, 'Hello I Must Be Going' in 1982?

5   Whose music is used througout the 1968 film, 'The Graduate'?

6   Which Australian band recorded the, 'Business As Usual' album in 1982?

7   Who recorded the album, 'Running in the family' in 1987?

8   Who had top ten hits with, '2-4-6-8 Motorway' and 'War Baby'?

9   Who recorded the 'Invisible touch' album in 1986?

10 Which John Lennon and Yoko Ono album featured 'Woman' and 'Beautiful Boy'?

11 Celine Dion, although Canadian at birth, won the Eurovision song contest for which country?

12 Whose song, 'Come on Eileen' won best single at the 1983, 'Brits'?

13 Who is the lead singer of The Divine Comedy?

14 With whom did The Fat Boys reach number 2 in 1987, with, 'Wipeout'?

15 Who reached number one in 1991 with, 'The Stonk'?

1. Smashing Pumpkins. 2. Deacon Blue. 3. Desmond Dekker and the Aces. 4. Phil Collins. 5. Simon & Garfunkel. 6. Men at Work. 7. Level 42. 8. Tom Robinson (Band). 9. Genesis. 10. Double Fantasy. 11. Switzerland. 12. Dexy's Midnight Runners. 13. Neil Hannon. 14. The Beach Boys. 15. Hale & Pace (and the Stonkers).

LITERATURE

1 How much did Charley Barley sell his wife for?

2 Who wrote a series of humorous books featuring the butler, Jeeves?

3 Who wrote *Three Men In A Boat*?

4 Complete this proverb: 'If you were born to be hanged, you'll never be...'

5 Which science fiction writer was the author of the Foundation trilogy?

6 Which author's books include *The Coup, Rabbit Run* and *Couples*?

7 Complete this proverb: 'There's no so blind as...'

8 Which author whose works include Idoru and Neuromancer is known as the, 'father of Cyberpunk'?

9 Complete the proverb: 'Blessed is he who expect nothing...'

10 Who wrote the novel, *100 Years of Solitude*?

11 Complete the proverb: 'Those whom the Gods love...'

12 Who wrote *The Water-Babies*?

13 Which Booker prize-winning novel by Kazuo Ishiguro was made into a feature film starring Anthony Hopkins as the butler, 'Stevens'?

14 Which satirical magazine has been edited by Richard Ingrams and Ian Hislop?

15 The First Baron Tweedsmuir was a novelist better known as?

GENERAL KNOWLEDGE

1 What does 'naff' mean?

2 If someone sent you an invitation marked R.S.V.P., what should you do?

3 Why were the first London policemen called 'peelers'?

4 What does AWOL stand for?

5 What does 'schmaltz' mean?

6 What was nicknamed 'The Thunderer'?

7 What did the Owl and the Pussycat go to sea in?

8 What is The Observer?

9 By what name is Robert Louis Stevenson's novel, *The Sea Cook* better known?

10 In the 1930s, a child could buy *The Rainbow*. What was it?

11 Who was the first author to have his novels serialised?

12 Who wrote *Kane and Abel*?

13 Who was Hans Christian Andersen?

14 What famous character did Richmal Crompton create?

15 Who has written well over 500 romantic novels?

SCIENCE

1   In diving, what does the acronym 'scuba' stand for?

2   Which home entertainment system needs woofers and tweeters?

3   What does the chemical symbol C signify?

4   What are hydraulic machines driven by?

5   How many lines does a British television set use?

6   Nacre is another name for what?

7   What was tested for the first time by a Dutchman on the Thames in 1620?

8   What does a compositor do?

9   How many units in a score?

10 What colour does litmus paper become when immersed in acid?

11 What is the difference between a 'corpse' and a 'carcass'?

12 What was Betamax?

13 Which electronic systems use hardware and software?

14 As a measurement, how many links are there in a chain?

15 What proportion of air is nitrogen?

ANSWERS

1. Self-contained Underwater Breathing Apparatus. 2. Hi-fi. 3. Carbon.
4. Liquid pressure. 5. 625. 6. Mother of pearl. 7. The world's first submarine. 8. He sets printing type. 9. 20. 10. Red. 11. A corpse is a dead human body; a carcass a dead animal body. 12. A system of video recording which was superceded by VHS.
13. Computers. 14. 100. s15. Four-fifths.

NATURAL HISTORY

1 What is the name for the nostril of a whale?

2 Which animal may defend itself by squirting blood from its eyes?

3 How fast can a mallard duck fly?

4 What is the present name for what used to be called the camelopard?

5 For how many days is a cow pregnant?

6 What is the true name of the bird called the 'laughing jackass'?

7 The dragonfly has one sense better developed than any other insect. Which?

8 Which tree is sometimes called the 'Scots mahogany'?

9 How much of an egg's weight is taken up by shell?

10 Which fruit has the largest amount of calories?

11 'White ants' is another name for what creatures?

12 Dogs are canine, cats are feline. What are bears?

13 Nowadays 'Chinese gooseberries' are better known as what?

14 What colour is a cornflower?

15 What to a British person is what an American would call a 'chickadee'?

1. Blowhole. 2. The American horned toad. 3. 65mph. 4. The giraffe.
5. About 280. 6. The kookaburra. 7. Its eyesight. 8. The alder. 9. Twelve percent.
10. The avocado. 11. Termites. 12. Ursine. 13. Kiwi fruit.
14. Blue. 15. The bird called a 'tit' or 'titmouse'.

GEOGRAPHY

1 What, exactly, was the Golden Arrow?

2 Whereabouts is Holy Island, or Lindisfarne?

3 On which sea is British Honduras situated?

4 What is the capital of Bulgaria?

5 What is the present name of what was called South-West Africa?

6 Where in the world do they speak Latin?

7 A native of Sardinia is not called a Sardine. What is he or she called?

8 Where is known as the 'Eternal City'?

9 In which London park is 'Speakers' Corner'?

10 In which countries is Mont Blanc situated?

11 Brussels is the capital of which country?

12 What is the Savoy, London?

13 Which is the most populous city in Africa?

14 Edinburgh is the capital of which country?.

15 In St Paul's Cathedral the following inscription is above a tomb: *Lector, sic momumentum requiris, circumspice* (Reader, if thou seekest his monument, look around). Who is buried beneath?

ANSWERS

1. An express train that ran between London and Paris. 2. Off the Northumberland coast. 3. The Caribbean. 4. Sofia. 5. Namibia. 6. It is still used to some extent in the Vatican City. 7. A Sard. 8. Rome. 9. Hyde Park. 10. France, Italy and Switzerland. 11. Belgium. 12. A famous hotel, built on the the site of the Savoy Palace. 13. Cairo. 14. Scotland. 15. Sir Christopher Wren.

ENGLISH LANGUAGE

1 What part of the body is the maxilla?

2 The tower and spire of a church is called what?

3 In films, what is the 'best boy'?

4 What is a Klieg light?

5 If someone out of hospital told you he'd had a shunt, what would it mean?

6 What in WW1 army slang, was an 'army banjo'?

7 What is a duffel coat?

8 In 'cat' terminology, what is a queen?

9 What is a quagmire?

10 What is a copse?

11 What is a young whale called?

12 What is a campanella?

13 What do the initials WHO stand for?

14 'Digital', in human terms, refers to what?

15 What does 'English bond' refer to?

SPORT

1   In Athletics, how high is a Steeplechase Hurdle; 2ft 6ins, 2ft 9ins, 3ft 0ins or 3ft 6ins?

2   In Rugby Union, which players form part of the back row on each side of the scrum?

3   Which County Cricket team plays the majority of their home matches at Chester-le-Street?

4   Who kept goal for Scotland in the 1998 World Cup finals, after Andy Goram returned home amid allegations concerning his personal life?

5   Which wood is a cricket bat traditionally made from?

6   Which sport do the Richmond Tigers play?

7   Which football team play their home games at Craven Cottage?

8   How many players are there in a Lacrosse team?

9   For which British Touring Car Championship Team did TV presenter Mike Smith drive?

10 With which team did Nigel Mansell win the Formula One World Driver's Championships?

11 Who won the 1998 Women's French Open Tennis Championships?

12 Which County Cricket Team play some home games at Ilford?

13 Which cricketer holds the record for the highest individual test score?

14 Which football team play their home games at Filbert Street?

15 Name the Rugby Union player in the middle of the front row of the scrum?

937

ANSWERS

1. 3ft 0ins. 2. Flanker (Wing Forward). 3. Durham 4. Jim Leighton 5. Willow. 6. Australian Rules Football. 7. Fulham. 8. Ten. 9. BMW. 10. Williams. 11. Arantxa Sanchez Vicario. 12. Essex. 13. Brian Lara. 14. Leicester City. 15. Hooker.

HISTORY

1 What important social registry was begun in 1836?

2 What was discovered in Klondyke, Canada, in 1896?

3 What did the town of Long Beach, California, buy from Britain in 1967?

4 What wartime position did General Montgomery assume in 1942?

5 What began operating at Calder Hall in 1956?

6 What famous painting was stolen from the Louvre in Paris in 1911?

7 What status did Hawaii assume in 1959?

8 What nation-wide event took place in England, starting in 1642?

9 Hong Kong was taken by the British in which year?

10 In which year did the Blitz on London start?

11 What happened to the cities of Pompeii and Herculaneum in AD79?

12 What did Matthew Webb, the swimmer, achieve in 1875?

13 A raid on London resulted in eight deaths in 1916. What caused them?

14 In 1940, the RAF made the first raid on which city?

15 Which Roman landed in Britain in 55 BC?

CINEMA AND TV

1 What were the better-known names of Arthur Stanley Jefferson and Norvell Hardy?

2 Who starred in the film *Breakfast at Tiffany's*?

3 In which film featured an epic chariot race?

4 Name the 1994 film starring Brad Pitt as a wild son being raised in Montana?

5 Name two stars from the film *Four Weddings and a Funeral*.

6 Who played the lead role in the TV series *The Fugitive*?

7 What was the historic film about William Wallace, starring Mel Gibson and Patrick McGoohan?

8 Who played 'Harry Callahan' in such movies as *Magnum Force*?

9 Actress Mira Sorvino won an Oscar for her role in which film?

10 Who has received the most actor or actress Oscar nominations?

11 Five known criminals are put in a police line-up for a crime they didn't do. Can you name the title of the film?

12 What was the purpose of Schindler's List?

13 Who played 'Adenoid Hynkel' in *The Great Dictator*?

14 Name the film starring Gene Hackman and Clint Eastwood in a story of an ageing desperado returning for one last gunfight?

15 Who starred in the 1991 movie *The Silence of the Lambs*?

POPULAR MUSIC

1   Ex Happy Monday's frontman, Shaun Ryder, went on to further success with which band?

2   Which major U.S. city is home to 'Fun Loving Criminals'?

3   Who was 'Going for Gold' in 1996?

4   Name the 1992 Manic Street Preachers album featuring 'You Love Us' and 'Motorcycle Emptiness'

5   Billy MacKenzie was the lead singer of which 1980's group?

6   Which group's first hit was 'What you need' in 1985?

7   Which 1980's three piece group had hits including 'Doctor, Doctor' and 'Hold me now'?

8   'Dub be good to me' was a hit for which group featuring Norman Cook?

9   Stuart Adamson of Big Country was formerly a member of which late 1970's band?

10 What is the name of the original drummer in the super group The Who?

11 Who had hits with 'White lines (Don't do it) with Melle Mel and 'The message' with The Furious Fire?

12 Which group had a hit with 'The only one I know' in 1990?

13 David McAlmont teamed up with which ex-Suede member on the 1995 hit 'Yes'?

14 Who had a hit in 1993 with 'Boom Shack-a-lak'?

15 What was the B-side to Neil, from the Young one's, hit 'Hole in my shoe'?

LITERATURE

1 Which author dropped the Onions when he changed his name?

2 Who wrote the early play, *Every Man in His Humour*, performed with Shakespeare in the cast?

3 Which early writer compiled *Chronicles of Britain* in 1577?

4 Who wrote the novel *Porgy*, which was later dramatised into the musical, *Porgy and Bess*?

5 Who were Gilbert and Pamela Frankau?

6 Which pop music singer and songwriter published a collection of his words with the title *Tarantula*?

7 Whose epic poem, *Endymion* was published when he was only 23 years old?

8 Which author and novelist named Korzeniowski became famed as a writer of English novels under another name?

9 Which newspaper correspondent, taken prisoner during the Boer War, became British Prime Minister?

10 Who wrote *The Pit And The Pendulum*?

11 What was Arnold Bennett's first name?

12 Who wrote the novel *Gentlemen Prefer Blondes*?

13 Which Poet Laureate started life as a sailor and only took up writing due to ill-health?

14 Which daily newspaper formerly bore the slogan on its masthead, 'Forward with the People'?

15 Which 'Goon' wrote *Puckoon* and a series of autobiographies about his time in the Second World War and after?

ANSWERS

1. George Oliver Onions, who became plain George Oliver. 2. Ben Jonson in 1598. 3. Holinshed. 4. Du Bose Heywood. 5. Novelists, father and daughter. 6. Stephen Foster. 7. John Keats. 8. Josef Conrad. 9. Winston Churchill. 10. Edgar Allen Poe. 11. Enoch. 12. Anita Loos. 13. John Masefield. 14. *The Mirror*. 15. Spike Milligan.

GENERAL KNOWLEDGE

1 Who, or what, is Stanley Gibbons?

2 Where and what was Dixieland?

3 What was a 'Tin Lizzie'?

4 What does 'carry coals to Newcastle' mean?

5 What is the *Reader's Digest*?

6 Who created 'Tarzan'?

7 What is *Private Eye*?

8 What is the *Frankfurter Allgemeine Zeitung*? Is it (a) a newpaper (b) a sausage (c) a secret society?

9 What famous book did A.A. Milne write?

10 Which country was the home of Dracula?

11 Who was Robert Browning?

12 What is the *Melody Maker*?

13 Who was Geoffrey Chaucer?

14 What was the surname of the family of writers whose first names were Osbert, Sacheverell and Edith?

15 Who was the author of the Noddy books?

SCIENCE

1   How many lines does an American television set use; 325, 525, 625 or 675?

2   How many hundredweights are there in a ton?

3   What did Sir Frederick Banting and and J.J.R. MacLeod discover in 1922?

4   What is the chemical symbol for Zinc?

5   When did the first cable car come into use?

6   What was the name given in early times, to people who thought they could transmute base metals into gold?

7   The first commercial typewriter was made by an armaments firm. True or false?

8   How many pecks are there in a bushel?

9   Geometrically speaking, how many surfaces does a cone have?

10   If you had a cutaneous infection, what would be troubling you?

11   What is your oesophagus?

12   What was the name of the space-traveller aboard Sputnik 2 in 1967?

13   What do veins do in the human body?

14   What do arteries do in the human body?

15   What day was known to the Romans as *Dies Mercurii*?

NATURAL HISTORY

1 Which bird is able to swim fastest?

2 Which monkey has the longest nose?

3 The old word emmet meant which insect?

4 What can substances called 'gums' do which 'resins' can't?

5 Why is the pilot fish so called?

6 Why would you have difficulty in identifying a female blackbird?

7 What sort of fruit would you find on an arbutus?

8 Rabies has another name, too. What is it?

9 On which part of the body would you find your tarsus?

10 What is a fingerling?

11 Which is fastest, a greyhound, a red deer or a bluefish tuna?

12 What is a pangolin?

13 The budgerigar is an Australian parakeet. True or false?

14 Which is the tallest and thickest kind of grass?

15 What exactly is a poult?

ANSWERS

1. The penguin. 2. The proboscis monkey. 3. The ant. 4. Dissolve in water. 5. Because it tends to swim alongside ships and even with sharks. 6. Because it's brown, not black. 7. Strawberries. 8. Hydrophobia. 9. On your foot. It's the ankle-bone. 10. A very small fish, such as a baby salmon. 11. Bluefish tuna, with a top speed of 44mph. 12. Another name for the scaly anteater. 13. True. 14. Bamboo. 15. A young turkey or other domestic fowl.

GEOGRAPHY

1 At which London cemetery is Karl Marx buried?

2 Which city is to host the 2000 Olympic Games?

3 In which island would you find Montego Bay?

4 Where would you find the lost city of Machu Picchu?

5 What region includes the islands Tahiti and Bora-Bora?

6 What does ACT stand for?

7 Which country is the greatest consumer of baked beans ahead of Sweden, in second place?

8 Which island is split into contested Greek and Turkish areas?

9 What is the largest lake in Africa?

10 What two continents does the Drake Passage separate?

11 Name three of North America's Great Lakes?

12 Which country has a larger population; Indonesia, Brazil or Japan?

13 How many provinces are in Canada?

14 Which African country has Mogadishu as its capital city?

15 Which country, bordering India and China, contains much of the Himalaya range of mountains?

ANSWERS

1. Highgate. 2. Sydney. 3. Jamaica. 4. Peru. 5. French Polynesia. 6. Australian Capital Territory. 7. United Kingdom. 8. Cyprus. 9. Lake Victoria. 10. South America and Antarctica. 11. Lake Ontario, Lake Huron, Lake Superior, Lake Michigan, Lake Erie. 12. Indonesia. 13. Ten. 14. Somalia. 15. Nepal.

ENGLISH LANGUAGE

1   What is a 'salto'?

2   What does the latin, '*ad valorem*' mean?

3   What is an 'alcazar'?

4   What is a caricature?

5   If something is cooked 'à la king' what does it mean?

6   How many items are in a gross?

7   How long is a league?

8   What is phagomania a fear of?

9   What is a testator?

10   What is a psalter?

11   What is georgette?

12   What do the initials, BAA stand for?

13   What is a 'parapet'?

14   Can you give two meanings for the word, 'sorrel'?

15   What is 'bran'?

ANSWERS

1. A daring or dangerous leap. 2. In proportion to the estimated value. 3. A Spanish castle. 4. A drawing which exaggerates features to make fun of them. 5. In mushrooms with a cream sauce and pimentos. 6. 144. 7. Three miles. 8. Food. 9. Someone who makes a will. 10. A book of psalms. 11. A crepe-like fabric similar to chiffon. 12. British Airports Authority. 13. A long wall along a balcony. 14. (a) an acid-tasting plant (b) a reddish-brown colour. 15. The husks of grain.

SPORT

1 When England and Australia play for the Ashes, the contents of the urn are reputed to be what?

2 How many crew are there in a Tornado Sailing Boat?

3 In Judo, which is the higher grade, White Belt, Yellow Belt or Blue Belt?

4 Which sport usually uses the larger pitch, Rugby League or Rugby Union?

5 What is the maximum number of players permitted in a Rounders Team?

6 Who won the 1996/97 Carling Premiership?

7 Which of Horse racing's classics is the oldest?

8 Who was John Mcenroe's normal doubles partner?

9 Which one of these golf courses is the odd one out: Birkdale, Troon, Gleneagles, Carnoustie?

10 In what sport might you catch a crab?

11 Who was Britain's first million pound footballer?

12 What was Billy Jean King's maiden name?

13 With which team did James Hunt begin his career?

14 With which sport would you associate Jens Weissflog?

15 In which U.S. city would you see the Sea Hawks play?

ANSWERS

1. Ashes of a burnt cricket ball. 2. Two. 3. Blue Belt. 4. Rugby Union. 5. Nine 6. Manchester United. 7. St. Leger. 8. Peter Fleming. 9. Birkdale - others are in Scotland. 10. Rowing. 11. Trevor Francis. 12. Moffat. 13. Hesketh. 14. Ski-jumping. 15. Seattle.

HISTORY

1 King Edward III defeated which fleet at Winchelsea in 1350?

2 Henry Cecil Booth patented which household appliance in 1901?

3 Who was found dead in Whitechapel, London, in 1888?

4 What was the Cape of Good Hope first to issue in 1853?

5 What did Flight-Lieut. W. Leefe Robinson achieve following an air raid on London in 1916?

6 What youth organisation held its first rally at Crystal Palace, London, in 1909?

7 Which European Queen abdicated in 1948 in favour of her daughter?

8 King Carol of Romania abdicated in 1940 in favour of whom?

9 Brazil became independent of whom in 1822?

10 Which large South African city was founded in 1886?

11 What aerial menace first reached London in 1944?

12 What object was erected on the Thames Embankment in 1878?

13 What status did New York achieve in 1788?

14 Alexander Kerensky, in 1917, proclaimed what status for Russia?

15 The Commonwealth of Australia was formed from how many colonies?

1. The Spaniards. 2. The vacuum cleaner. 3. The first victim of Jack the Ripper. 4. The world's first triangular postage stamps. 5. He was the first to shoot down a Zeppelin airship. 6. The Boy Scouts. 7. Queen Wilhelmina of the Netherlands. 8. His son, Michael. 9. Portugal. 10. Johannesburg. 11. The V2 flying bombs. 12. 'Cleopatra's Needle'. 13. It became the capital of the newly-formed United States. 14. A republic. 15. Six.

CINEMA AND TV

1 'Hi-yo Silver, Away!' was the catchphrase or which TV hero?

2 'Mary the Mole' from *Thumbelina*, received what award in 1994?

3 What 1994 father-and-son story starred Jeff Bridges and Edward Furlong?

4 Who's first feature film was *Take The Money And Run*?

5 Peter O'Toole starred as the sympathetic Scot advising a very young Chinese ruler in what film?

6 Sophia Abuza was an American vaudeville star famed in Britain as a popular singer. By what name was she better known as?

7 Who starred in the cop shows, *The Sweeney* and *Inspector Morse*?

8 What was missing from the series of Batman films in the 1980s and 1990s?

9 Which Hungarian-born US pioneer founded the company which became Paramount Pictures?

10 Which sexy, bawdy American woman wrote and performed her own material in the 1930s?

11 Who directed the 1951 film *A Streetcar Named Desire*?

12 Dino and Pebbles are characters in which popular cartoon series?

13 Who wrote the play *Chicken Soup with Barley* in 1959?

14 For what production was music lyricist Alan Jay Lerner mainly famed?

15 Laszlo Loewenstein, and actor who played 'Mr Moto', is better known as what?

ANSWERS

1. The Lone Ranger. 2. Worst Song Of The Year. 3. *American Heart*.
4. Woody Allen. 5. *The Last Emperor*. 6 Sophie Tucker. 7. John Thaw.
8. Batman's sidekick, Robin, the boy wonder. 9. Adolph Zukor. 10. Mae West.
11. Elia Kazan. 12. *The Flintstones*. 13. Arnold Wesker. 14. *My Fair Lady*. 15. Peter Lorre.

POPULAR MUSIC

1 Which American four piece band had a hit album called 'Pocket full of kryptonite'?

2 Which Seventies Bond singer joined fellow Welshmen, Propellorheads in their 1998 hit?

3 What made the 'Magical mystery tour' different from the other Beatles' films.

4 What was the inspiration for Midnight Oil's 'Beds are burning'?

5 How much cash did the KLF burn?

6 Who is the link between The Bangles, Chakka Khan and Sinead O'Connor.

7 What's the name of Kid Creole's backing singers?

8 Name the 1980's TV pop show hosted by Jools Holland?

9 Where is Massive Attack's home town?

10 Who recommended that the BBC should ban the Frankie Goes To Hollywood hit 'Relax'?

11 Who was dancing on the ceiling?

12 Which female artist guested on Massive Attack's hit 'Protection'?

13 Who was the mastermind behind the hit singles by the Wombles?

14 Which star of the movie 'Armaggedon' sang 'Under the boardwalk'?

15 PuffDaddy's 1998 hit featured a guitarist from which 1970's super group?

LITERATURE

1   Which famous book by a famous Irish author, was described by a critic as 'the foulest book ever printed?

2   Who was Sir Henry Morton Stanley?

3   Which American author wrote *Of Mice and Men*?

4   Who wrote a series of essays called *Virginibus Puerisque*?

5   Which Ancient Greek thinker wrote *Republic* and *Phaedo*?

6   Which famous thriller writer died in debt, but paid this off after his death?

7   Who wrote the novel *My Brother Jonathan* in 1928?

8   Who was Israel Zangwill?

9   Who was Daisy Ashford?

10   What was very unusual about the book, *The Young Visitors*?

11   Who wrote *Moll Flanders*?

12   Who wrote *The Tenant of Wildfell Hall* in 1848?

13   Under what name was Manfred Bennington Lee better known?

14   For which great historical work was Edward Gibbon famed?

15   Who wrote *Erewhon* and *Erewhon Revisited*?

ANSWERS

1. *Ulysses* by James Joyce. 2. The explorer and journalist who went to Africa in search of David Livingstone. 3. John Steinbeck. 4. Robert Louis Stevenson. 5. Plato. 6. Edgar Wallace, whose huge royalties only accrued after he died. 7. Francis Brett Young. 8 Novelist and playwright, son of Russian-Jewish refugees, but born in London, 1864. 9. An author at the age of nine, she wrote *The Young Visiters*. 10. It was printed exactly as she wrote it, spelling and grammatical errors and all. 11. Daniel Defoe. 12. Anne Brontë. 13. As 'Ellery Queen' with his cousin, Frederic Dannay. 14. *The Decline and Fall of the Roman Empire*. 15. Samuel Butler, in 1872 and 1901.

CHILDREN'S SECTION

LEVEL 1

1 What alcoholic drink is made from crushed grapes?

2 What is the name for the stick carried by a British policeman or woman?

3 What transport machine has forks, gears and a chainwheel?

4 What stately home in Britain is famous for its maze?

5 Who is the cartoon and comic strip sailor who loves spinach?

6 What is a male elephant called?

7 How many letters are there in the alphabet?

8 Is a great bustard an old-fashioned gun, a bird or a type of drink?

9 What are a sombrero and a deerstalker examples of?

10 In which city would you find the shop Harrods?

LEVEL 1

1   How many weeks are there in a year?

2   Red sky at night is whose delight?

3   From which country does lasagne and spaghetti come?

4   Where are coffins buried?

5   What relation is Prince Charles to Prince Philip?

6   How many tens are there in a thousand?

7   How many television channels for all viewers does the BBC fund?

8   What part of the coffee plant is harvested to make the drink?

9   Which buildings have blue lamps outside them in Britain?

10   Which is longer a foot or a yard?

ANSWERS

1. 52 2. Shepherds' 3. Italy 4. In a graveyard 5. Son 6. 100 7. Two 8. The beans 9. Police stations 10. A yard

LEVEL 1

1 How many lungs does the human body contain?

2 What phone number is usually dialled for the emergency services in Britain?

3 What are the three emergency services?

4 In cockney rhyming slang, what does "apples and pears" mean?

5 Where would you find woofers and tweeters?

6 If you were born on March 7, what would your star sign be?

7 Can you give the first name of Victoria and David Beckham's son?

8 What are Danish blue, Brie and Gouda examples of?

9 What colour was the Beatles' submarine?

10 Which soap has a pub called the *Rovers Return*?

LEVEL 1

1   Which precious stone is red?

2   Pikachu is a character in which cartoon series?

3   How many five pences in a pound?

4   What is a winklepicker: a bird, a type of hunting knife or a shoe?

5   If you were using split shot on a line tied with a size 16 hook, what would you be doing?

6   Is a minidisk: a way of storing computer information or music?

7   Name the board game that you would be playing if you landed on Mayfair?

8   What is the ninth letter of the alphabet?

9   How many sevens are there in 35?

10   How many sides does a dice have?

ANSWERS

1. The ruby 2. Pokémon 3. Twenty 4. A shoe 5. Fishing (angling) 6. Music 7. Monopoly 8. I 9. Five 10. Six

LEVEL 1

1   What is 1.25 as a fraction?

2   What is the key ingredient of an omelette?

3   Which boyband includes lead singer Ronan Keating?

4   What is the national airline of Canada?

5   Used in World War II, what sort of device were U-boats?

6   With what films do you associate Darth Maul and Darth Vader?

7   What does the French word "Bonjour" mean?

8   How many days in the month of April?

9   Would you fish with, eat or kick a melon ball?

10 How many 10 pence pieces are there in twenty pounds?

LEVEL 1

1 What does the Roman numeral V equal?

2 Which is the higher belt in Judo: black or yellow?

3 Beetle, Golf and Polo are all made by which motor manufacturer?

4 How many hours in two days?

5 In what structure would Clark Kent visit to change into Superman?

6 How many years have a couple been married if they're celebrating their silver wedding?

7 What colour is the gemstone ruby?

8 Which popular author is the sister of actress Joan Collins?

9 Emulsion and enamel are types of what?

10 How many eighths are there in a half?

LEVEL 1

1 What word, beginning with K, is the correct term for tomato sauce?

2 What device currently orbiting Earth was named after the astronomer Edwin Hubble?

3 Are Airbus aircraft made by a group of American, European or Asian companies?

4 Did Alex Ferguson become manager of Manchester United in 1986, 1993 or 1996?

5 St Clare is the patron saint of television – true or false?

6 What is 0.75 as a fraction?

7 What are bourbon, digestive and malted milk examples of?

8 What colour has shades known as scarlet and vermilion?

9 How many threes are there in 63?

10 In paints, what two colours do you mix together to get green?

LEVEL 1

1 What sort of animal was often killed by a harpoon?

2 What do the initials NHS stand for?

3 Is A6 paper bigger than A5?

4 Which science fiction film starred Ewan McGregor as a Jedi Knight?

5 What is a museum of the stars called?

6 What sort of animal is a pug?

7 In a pack of cards, does the queen of clubs look to her left or right?

8 How can you tell that a car has a learner driver in it?

9 What colour is the bird, the canary?

10 If you walk up something do you ascend or descend?

ANSWERS

1. A whale 2. National Health Service 3. No, it is half the size of A5 4. *Star Wars Episode 1: The Phantom Menace* 5. Planetarium 6. A dog 7. Left 8. By the L-plate sign displayed on the car 9. Yellow 10. Ascend

LEVEL 1

1 What year was the last ever Five Nations rugby union tournament played?

2 What are the two red suits in a pack of cards?

3 What fruit, beginning with A, is shaped like a small peach?

4 Which tennis tournament is famous for strawberries and cream and its Centre Court?

5 Does the word "amplify" mean to make sound louder or quieter?

6 What British mammal lives in a sett and has a distinctive black and white striped head?

7 If you "bottle up" your feelings, what do you do with them?

8 Is the first book of the Bible, Exodus, Genesis or Psalms?

9 How many edge sides does a 50 pence piece have?

10 What is the past tense of the word drink?

LEVEL 1

1 Who sells houses and other properties?

2 Around what part of your body might you wear a dicky bow?

3 What is the opposite of temporary: infinite, enormous or permanent?

4 Were tea bags invented in the 1420s, the 1620s or the 1920s?

5 Which country does Liebfraumilch wine come from?

6 Are the Prodigy a dance music act, a comedy sketch team or an American basketball team?

7 What relation is the brother of your father to you?

8 Which national side has Colin Hendry played football for?

9 What are the largest of all plants: seaweed, trees or cacti?

10 Where would you find a meteorite: underwater, in a desert or in space?

ANSWERS

1. An estate agent 2. Your neck 3. Permanent 4. 1920s 5. Germany 6. A dance music act 7. Your uncle 8. Scotland 9. Trees 10. In space

LEVEL 1

1 How many sides has a 20 pence piece?

2 If you fixed water pipes in a house, what would your job title be?

3 Poodles were once used as hunting dogs – true or false?

4 Who were the first people to live in New Zealand: the Maoris, the Aborigines or the Spanish?

5 How do Americans spell grey?

6 How many strings does a violin have?

7 What two paint colours would you mix to make purple?

8 If you serve a double fault, what sport are you playing?

9 What word means a small downpour of rain and also a bathroom spraying device?

10 In which continent is the country Togo situated?

LEVEL 1

ales

associated with?

4   Who was born Elizabeth Alexandra Mary of
    Windsor?

5   Were the Velvet Underground a pop music band, a
    terrorist group or a group of modern artists?

6   What body part are biceps and triceps?

7   What is 0.5 of 11?

8   What is someone who sells fruit and vegetables
    called?

9   What foodstuff can come in UHT, condensed and
    semi-skimmed?

10 What is 20% of 200?

ANSWERS

LEVEL 1

1. In which James Bond film did the character of Oddjob appear?

2. What is the name of the headquarters of the Metropolitan Police Force?

3. Which fish makes spectacular leaps upstream to return to its birthplace?

4. Who was the first Frenchman to manage Arsenal football club?

5. What are the horns of a stag called?

6. If someone is Oxbridge-educated, which university other than Oxford may they have attended?

7. What are *Pravda*, the *Washington Post* and the *Miami Herald*?

8. In which athletics event did Steve Backley once hold the world record?

9. Which European country has the continent's only active volcanoes?

10. What garden creature, beginning with F, starts life as a tadpole?

LEVEL 1

1 What are the Himalayas, the Alps and Pyrenees examples of?

2 Which is the biggest land animal?

3 What is the opposite of above?

4 Where is the Antarctic?

5 Is the Sun a star?

6 Who was Cleopatra?

7 What does to lose your nerve mean?

8 What is an igloo?

9 In which American city would you find Central Park?

10 What shape has three sides?

ANSWERS

1. Mountain ranges 2. The African elephant 3. Below 4. At the South Pole 5. Yes 6. The last queen of Egypt 7. To become afraid 8. An Inuit house built of ice blocks 9. New York 10. A triangle

LEVEL 1

1 Are all snakes poisonous?

2 What is an iceberg?

3 What is in the nick of time?

4 Which came first, the Stone Age or the Bronze Age?

5 What is the world's biggest ocean?

6 Who were the first people in Australia?

7 Which black and white striped animal looks like the horse?

8 What do we call the U–shaped plate nailed to a horse's hoof?

9 Does the Earth travel round the Sun?

10 Which bear has a white coat?

1. No 2. A large block of ice that floats in the sea 3. At the last possible moment 4. The Stone Age 5. The Pacific 6. The Aborigines 7. The zebra 8. A horseshoe 9. Yes (once a year) 10. The polar bear

LEVEL 1

1 How many hours are there in a day?

2 What is meant by the saying look before you leap?

3 Which joint lets you bend your arm?

4 Which precious stone is red?

5 Which bird pecks holes in trees?

6 What is the capital of the United Kingdom?

7 Who was the first woman prime minister of Great Britain?

8 What is the opposite of lazy?

9 Sneezy, Doc, Grumpy, Happy, Bashful, Dopey. Who else?

10 Does the Moonhave any air?

1. 24 2. Think carefully before you act 3. Your elbow 4. The ruby 5. The woodpecker 6. London 7. Margaret Thatcher 8. Hard-working 9. Sleepy 10. No. It has no wind or weather either

LEVEL 1

1 Who was the German leader during World War II?

2 Which is the world's highest mountain?

3 Which is the largest bird?

4 What is the capital of France?

5 What is meant by the saying many hands make light work?

6 Where are your taste buds?

7 Heads of United States presidents are carved into which mountain?

8 Which saint is Santa Claus called after?

9 What is the rough outside of a tree called?

10 What was Cinderella's coach made from?

LEVEL 1

1   What grows in paddy fields?

2   Which children's story tells of a wooden puppet that comes to life?

3   Where is the Eiffel Tower?

4   Who won the race between the hare and the tortoise?

5   Which filmstar wore a bowler hat and carried a cane in his films?

6   Which ancient people first built pyramids?

7   Where does gold come from?

8   What is the main ingredient of ketchup?

9   What is the next number in this sequence: 4·5, 5, 5·5, 6?

10   Which animal is king of the beasts?

LEVEL 1

1 Which famous general gave his name to the Wellington boot?

2 What is a Tam o' Shanter?

3 Where is Mount Snowdon?

4 Complete this saying: As dry as a...

5 What does a caterpillar turn into?

6 Which sport is associated with Wimbledon?

7 Is a spider an insect?

8 Do camels store water in their humps?

9 Which parts of the Earth have the longest summer days?

10 What do we use our lungs for?

LEVEL 1

1   What is the opposite of soft?

2   In which sea does the island of Malta lie?

3   What country did Pelé play for?

4   Which girl walked along the Yellow Brick Road?

5   Where does a mole live?

6   Which is the Earth's only natural satellite?

7   What is the capital of Russia?

8   Which bear did A.A. Milne write about?

9   What is a young cow called?

10 Do all birds fly?

LEVEL 2

1 Who was the captain of the England rugby team in the 1999 World Cup?

2 An American quarter is worth how many cents?

3 What is the Japanese art of Bonsai?

4 In which country was a wok originally used for cooking?

5 Which chain of stores use the brand name *St Michael*?

6 What sort of food is a courgette?

7 What colour are taxis in New York?

8 What part of a bishop's clothing is his mitre?

9 Are all metals magnetic?

10 When were the Olympics last held in Britain?

1. Martin Johnson 2. 25 3. Growing miniature tree 4. China 5. Marks and Spencer 6. A vegetable 7. Yellow 8. His hat 9. No 10. 1948

LEVEL 2

1 What was the first name of the composer Beethoven?

2 Which charity runs Red Nose Day?

3 With what sport is Nick Skelton associated?

4 What sort of creature is a tarantula?

5 Who plays the lead in *The Vicar of Dibley*?

6 What is the fastest airliner in the world?

7 What car-maker's previous models include the Capri and the Anglia?

8 What street features the prime minister's official London residence?

9 In which country is the world's longest wall?

10 How many English kings have been named Edward?

LEVEL 2

1 In which city would you find Madison Square Gardens?

2 Which airline sponsored the London Eye ride in London?

3 Was the Spanish Main in the Caribbean, Red or Mediterranean Sea?

4 How many make up a baker's dozen?

5 Who wore togas?

6 Which British city sits on the River Lagan?

7 What is 1 and $3/5$ in decimal numbers?

8 Who led the knights of the round table?

9 What tree gives its name to the syrup poured over pancakes?

10 In which TV soap did Dirty Den, Arthur Fowler and Angie once appear?

ANSWERS

1. New York 2. British Airways 3. Caribbean 4. 13 5. Romans 6. Belfast 7. 1.6 8. King Arthur 9. Maple 10. *EastEnders*

LEVEL 2

1 In cockney rhyming slang, what is a "trouble and strife"?

2 What are granny, reef and sheepshank examples of?

3 What boyband did Robbie Williams used to be in?

4 Where would you be most likely to find an alternator?

5 What was the name of the sheep in *Wallace and Gromit*?

6 Lord Baden Powell founded which movement?

7 In the Bible, how many apostles did Jesus have?

8 An early version of what machine was called a "boneshaker"?

9 What substance makes bread rise?

10 With what sort of drink is the campaign group CAMRA associated?

ANSWERS

1. A wife 2. Knots 3. Take That 4. In a car engine 5. Shaun 6. Scouts 7. Twelve 8. Bicycle 9. Yeast 10. Real ale (beer)

LEVEL 2

1   Is oxtail soup really made from ox's tail?

2   What is the real-life name of the lady who plays Pauline Fowler in *EastEnders*?

3   Which country was once ruled by tsars?

4   What does the French word "oeuf" mean in English?

5   Which Michael Jackson video was the most expensive ever made?

6   In cockney rhyming slang, what is a "frog and toad"?

7   Which was the first Boeing jet airliner?

8   How old is a centenarian?

9   Was Westlife, Point Break or Boyzone number one in the 1999 Christmas charts?

10 If you were at a bureau de change what would you be doing?

LEVEL 2

1 According to folklore, what does the sandman help children to do?

2 Who hosted the TV show *Blind Date*?

3 Which Greek philosopher was made to commit suicide by drinking hemlock?

4 What does the phrase "Parlez vous Anglais" mean in English?

5 In which European country is the port of Antwerp?

6 Which TV show has been hosted by Johnny Vaughan, Mark Little, Peter Kay and Chris Evans?

7 Which English king was killed at the Battle of Bosworth in 1485?

8 What can be divided into stanzas: time, food or poetry?

9 The moons Oberon and Miranda orbit which planet?

10 Which language was invented to be a universal language?

ANSWERS

1. Go to sleep 2. Cilla Black 3. Socrates 4. Do you speak English 5. Belgium 6. *The Big Breakfast* 7. Richard III 8. Poetry 9. Uranus 10. Esperanto

LEVEL 2

1 Is a sole a freshwater or saltwater fish?

2 How many years have a couple been married if they are celebrating their golden wedding?

3 Which Spice Girl sang on a hit single with Bryan Adams?

4 In the nursery rhyme, which town was Dr Foster heading to: Towcester, Gloucester or Worcester?

5 What trade did Jesus learn?

6 If you were born in February, what gem would be your birthstone?

7 What sort of clothing item is a homburg?

8 Which cartoon pirate has an enemy called Black Jake?

9 In French it is "jeudi", in German it is "Donnerstag"; what day of the week is it in English?

10 In imperial measurements, how many pints equal a UK gallon?

LEVEL 2

1 How many years have a couple been married if they are celebrating their diamond wedding?

2 Which female singer was with the Fugees before having solo success?

3 In Roman numerals, what number is represented by CXIII?

4 What are the first names of the two Geordie lads who host *SMTV* on Saturday mornings?

5 What was the stage name of the pair when they were a singing duo?

6 If you were born in January, what gem would be your birthstone?

7 Is the currency of China: the Yuan, the Yen or the Yinni?

8 How many people usually make up a jury in England and Wales?

9 What kind of food comes from Bakewell?

10 What word is both a harbour and a socket on the back of a personal computer?

ANSWERS

1. 60 2. Lauryn Hill 3. 113 4. Ant and Dec 5. PJ and Duncan 6. Garnet 7. Yuan 8. 12 9. A tart 10. Port

LEVEL 2

1 What does "in the buff" mean?

2 What animal represents the star sign Taurus?

3 Which ex-American president was nicknamed "Tricky Dicky"?

4 In the nursery rhyme, what could Jack Sprat's wife not eat?

5 Who wrote and directed the *Star Wars* films?

6 What sort of aircraft were the Lancaster and the Stirling?

7 What instrument are Gibson, Les Paul and Fender famous for making?

8 What flavour is the drink crΩème de menthe?

9 Chiropody is the treatment of what part of your body?

10 What is the square root of 64?

LEVEL 2

1 Is a cor anglais a woodwind, stringed or percussion instrument?

2 What name is given to a small round beetle with black spots on its red wings?

3 What are you if you are laid-back?

4 What sort of drink is Adam's ale?

5 What is the largest stringed instrument?

6 What subject is the quiz show *They Think It's All Over* about?

7 Is the tale of Daniel and the lions in the Old or New Testament of the Bible?

8 What creature represents the star sign, Capricorn?

9 How old do you have to be to hold a full driving licence in Britain?

10 Where is the sting of a scorpion situated?

LEVEL 2

1 Who, in the Bible, was swallowed alive by a whale?

2 Does the musical term adagio mean fast, bass or very slow?

3 If you were born in April, what gem would be your birthstone?

4 What is the name of a building used to store aircraft?

5 What do the initials VAT stand for?

6 What creature would you be eating if you were served calimari?

7 What food, made from a stuffed sheep's stomach, is often eaten on Burn's Night?

8 What does the word "utterly" mean?

9 What day of the week is called "Mittwoch" in German?

10 If you are wily, are you: tall and thin, rude or cunning?

1. Jonah 2. Very slow 3. Diamond 4. Hangar 5. Value Added Tax 6. Squid 7. Haggis 8. Completely 9. Wednesday 10. Cunning

LEVEL 2

1   According to the grammatical rule, what letter comes before e except after c?

2   If you cook food slowly in a covered pan are you braising it, flash-frying it or blanching it?

3   In the Vietnam War, did the United States join the side of the South or North Vietnam forces?

4   David Trimble is a politician in which part of the United Kingdom?

5   What nationality was the composer Richard Wagner?

6   Was Caligula: a Viking warlord, a Saxon king or a Roman emperor?

7   Is hypothermia when your body gets very hot, very cold or lacking water?

8   Which melon has pink flesh and lots of large black seeds?

9   What is the world's most popular sport?

10 What name is given to a fertile place in a desert?

ANSWERS

1. I 2. Braising 3. South Vietnam 4. Ulster (Northern Ireland) 5. German 6. Roman emperor 7. Very cold 8. Watermelon 9. Football 10. Oasis

LEVEL 2

1 What is a noun?

2 Which brass instrument has a sliding section?

3 What is the capital of Northern Ireland?

4 What is created when a meteorite hits a planet?

5 What do we do when we have a nap?

6 What did David use to kill Goliath?

7 Why do you sneeze?

8 Which was the biggest dinosaur?

9 Which bird has big, round eyes at the front of its head?

10 What is another name for the Netherlands?

LEVEL 2

1 Which flower commemorates the war dead?

2 What is another word for begin?

3 How many bones are in the human body?

4 Which rugby team is called the All-Blacks?

5 Who built the Sphinx?

6 What are Scottish lakes called?

7 What is irrigation?

8 Who wrote Twelfth Night, Hamlet, and Macbeth?

9 Which book told the adventures of Toad of Toad Hall?

10 Where is the Amazon rainforest?

ANSWERS

1. The poppy 2. Start or commence 3. 206 4. The New Zealand team 5. The ancient Egyptians 6. Lochs 7. The supply of water for crops 8. William Shakespeare 9. 'Wind in the Willows' 10. In South America (mainly in Brazil)

LEVEL 2

1 Punch and Judy are what?

2 Who lived in Sherwood Forest?

3 Which American animal sprays out a foul-smelling fluid to defend itself?

4 Who was the first black president of South Africa?

5 If I have 36 bananas, how many people can I give three to?

6 Which garden pest is related to the snail?

7 Who was Winnie the Pooh's donkey friend?

8 What is the Indy 500?

9 On which British coin can you see a portcullis?

10 What happens to your eyes when you sneeze?

1. Puppets 2. Robin Hood 3. The skunk 4. Nelson Mandela 5. 12 people 6. The slug 7. Eeyore 8. A motor-racing event 9. On the penny 10. They close

LEVEL 2

1 Which island is at the toe of Italy?

2 Who are the infantry?

3 The Chinese were making ice cream some 5,000 years ago. True or false?

4 Which people wrote in hieroglyphics?

5 Which creature did St George slay?

6 What is the capital of Germany?

7 What is another word for unite?

8 Is alcohol a drug?

9 What is a cylinder?

10 What is kelp?

ANSWERS

1. Sicily 2. Soldiers who fight on foot 3. True 4. The ancient Egyptians 5. A dragon 6. Berlin 7. Join 8. Yes 9. It is a tube shaped like a can of beans 10. Seaweed

LEVEL 2

1 Which game is played in a four-walled court with a small rubber ball?

2 In which country was tea first grown?

3 Which is the fastest passenger aircraft?

4 Which is the wealthiest nation?

5 What is the shape of one side of a cube?

6 Who led Britain through World War II?

7 How often are the Olympic Games held?

8 What is another word for suspend?

9 Which animal is said to have nine lives?

10 What is the name for the imaginary line around the middle of the Earth?

LEVEL 2

1 What is the masculine of goose?

2 Which country has a military force called the Foreign Legion?

3 What colours are the jerseys of the Newcastle United football team?

4 Which sea does the river Nile flow into?

5 What is the national emblem of Wales?

6 What is the popular name for the Boeing 747?

7 Why is it dark at night?

8 A Triceratops was what?

9 What was the bombing of London called during World War II?

10 Which is the tallest animal?

LEVEL 2

1 What is another word for difficult?

2 Which forbidden fruit did Adam and Eve eat?

3 What is the plural of mother-in-law?

4 How many sides has an octagon?

5 Who is the heir apparent to Britain's throne?

6 Which plant contains nicotine?

7 Which is the world's biggest animal?

8 What powers London's underground trains?

9 What was the Luftwaffe?

10 What is the Great Barrier Reef in Australia made of?

LEVEL 2

1 What do too many cooks do?

2 What are back, breast, and crawl?

3 What were zeppelins?

4 What's behind your ribs?

5 Where are the Crown Jewels?

6 Which country is famous for canals, windmills and bulb fields?

7 How many sides does a cube have?

8 How many people play or sing in a quartet?

9 What sank the SS Titanic?

10 Where is Fujiyama?

LEVEL 3

1 An American dime is worth how many cents?

2 Which record company announced a merger with Time-Warner in 2000?

3 Who was captain of the England cricket team before Nasser Hussein?

4 Ash Wednesday is the first day of which religious period?

5 Which is the most easterly country: Norway, Sweden or Finland?

6 Who wrote the play *Troilus and Cressida*?

7 What do we call the time that a baby spends inside its mother's womb?

8 Who was selected as Labour Party candidate for Mayor of London in 2000?

9 If you were born on April 5, what star sign would you be?

10 On what part of the body do cowboys wear chaps?

1. Ten 2. EMI 3. Alec Stewart 4. Lent 5. Norway 6. Shakespeare 7. Gestation period or pregnancy 8. Frank Dobson 9. Aries 10. Legs

LEVEL 3

1 What is measured in firkins?

2 Which band played a New Year's Eve night concert at Cardiff's Millennium Stadium?

3 Whose assembly line revolutionized car-making in the early 20th century?

4 What is the connection between *Wayne's World* and *Austin Powers: International Man of Mystery*?

5 How many make up a score?

6 Who was the most famous marshall of the wild west town of Tombstone?

7 What is the name for the regular rise and fall of the sea?

8 Which athletics commentator hosted *A Question of Sport* before Sue Barker?

9 What year did the great storm cause much damage and destroy many trees in southern England?

10 How many birth signs are there in the Zodiac?

LEVEL 3

1   What does a numismatist study?

2   Which player aimed a kung-fu kick at a Crystal Palace supporter and was banned?

3   Who is the quiz master on *Countdown*?

4   What is the first letter of the Greek alphabet?

5   What vegetable is sauerkraut made from?

6   What does simultaneously mean?

7   What is the square root of 121?

8   In which city were houses first given numbers?

9   Which language is described as Hispanic?

10 Which European city is famous for its Oktoberfest?

LEVEL 3

1 According to the old phrase, what did curiosity do the cat?

2 What daytime quiz show does Carol Vorderman star in?

3 If you were born on December 27, what would your star sign be?

4 If you were performing a cascade or shower, what pastime would you be taking part in?

5 What name did the ancient Greeks give to a supposed large island west of Gibraltar?

6 What number does the Roman numeral M equal?

7 What is the last letter of the Greek alphabet?

8 What is mulligatawny?

9 In which film did Tommy Lee Jones and Will Smith fight aliens?

10 Chelsea, Spode and Royal Doulton are types of what?

ANSWERS

1. Kill it 2. *Countdown* 3. Capricorn 4. Juggling 5. Atlantis 6. 1,000 7. Omega 8. A soup 9. *Men in Black* 10. Porcelain

LEVEL 3

1   Who wrote tales about Flopsy, Mopsy and Cottontail?

2   What is a chow?

3   Which national radio station does Chris Evans present on?

4   What word means a type of pig meat and an amateur radio operator?

5   What building traditionally has three balls displayed outside?

6   Who had a hit with *No Scrubs* in 1999?

7   What is the national airline of Indonesia?

8   Was the Battle of Inkerman in the Crimean, Boer or Falklands War?

9   In which city did Anne Frank live?

10 In which month does the grouse shooting season start in Britain?

LEVEL 3

1 What do the initials AWOL stand for in the military?

2 What year in the 20th century was the bikini invented?

3 What unusual pet did the Roman, Julius Caesar, have?

4 Nick Park is behind which popular animated characters made of modelling clay?

5 Is Ezra a book of the Old or New Testament?

6 The astrological sign Cancer is shown as what type of creature?

7 What day of the week does the German word Dienstag refer to?

8 Who is the lead singer of the Manic Street Preachers?

9 In which country is Vesuvius found?

10 What word means to "invent" and "cosmetics"?

ANSWERS

1. Absent With Out Leave 2. 1946 3. Giraffe 4. Wallace and Gromit 5. Old Testament 6. A crab 7. Tuesday 8. James Dean Bradfield 9. Italy 10. Make up

LEVEL 3

1   On what date did the Chinese New Year of 2000 fall?

2   What number do people dial in the United States to get their emergency services?

3   In Roman numerals, what number is represented by CXXXVII?

4   What TV show launched the career of actor/singer Will Smith?

5   What British building traditionally has a red and white striped pole displayed outside?

6   Who is the quiz master on *University Challenge*?

7   Where is the Prime Meridian situated?

8   The *Niña*, the *Pinta* and the *Santa Maria* were the three ships in the voyage commanded by what famous explorer?

9   What is the main vegetable ingredient of the Russian soup, borscht?

10   Where would you find derailleur gears?

1000

LEVEL 3

1 According to Chinese tradition, is the year 2000 the year of the cat, the monkey or the dragon?

2 If you were born on the October 1, what star sign would you be?

3 In Roman numerals, what number is represented by XIX?

4 Which TV soap did singer Adam Ricketts used to star in?

5 In which English county would you find Matlock?

6 What date is St Stephen's feast day?

7 In computing, what does USB stand for?

8 What is the currency of Pakistan?

9 In which Dutch city does the International Court of Justice sit?

10 The Asian country of Cambodia was formerly known as what?

ANSWERS

1. Year of the dragon 2. Libra 3. 19 4. *Coronation Street* 5. Derbyshire 6. December 26 7. Universal Serial Bus 8. Rupee 9. The Hague 10. Kampuchea

LEVEL 3

1 If you had MP3 files running through a player, what would you be doing?

2 What is the more commonly used name for the musical instrument, the timpani?

3 What is the chemical symbol for chlorine?

4 What word, beginning with H, means New Year's Eve in Scotland?

5 What is the highest female voice?

6 How many revolutions per minute did an old-fashioned LP used to turn at?

7 St Bona is the patron saint of air hostesses – true or false?

8 What name is given to a creature which lives on another animal and gets its food from it?

9 The World War II Battle of the Leyte Gulf was between Japan and which other country?

10 "Slick Willie" is the nickname of which United States president?

LEVEL 3

1 In Greek mythology, who was set twelve labours?

2 In Roman numerals, what number is represented by XXXIX?

3 What word, beginning with F, means accidental success?

4 Which country did Albert Einstein become a citizen of in 1901?

5 Is a leveret a young rabbit, hare or ferret?

6 What is the largest brass instrument?

7 Juno and Gold Beaches were landing points for which World War II invasion?

8 How many American senators are elected from each US state?

9 Name the first of the Wallace and Gromit films?

10 Is the Sun a thousand, a million or 100 million times bigger than Earth?

1003

1. Hercules 2. 39 3. Fluke 4. Switzerland 5. A young hare 6. The tuba 7. D-Day (Normandy landings) 8. Two 9. A Grand Day Out 10. A million

LEVEL 3

1 Is contralto the highest or lowest female voice?

2 What Moroccan port gives its name to the fruit, the tangerine?

3 What subject is the quiz show *Never Mind the Buzzcocks* about?

4 Riga is the capital of Latvia, Lithuania or Estonia?

5 The TV show *Stars in Their Eyes* is hosted by which Kelly: Lorraine, Gene or Matthew?

6 If you were born in May, what gem would be your birthstone?

7 Sir Alf Ramsey managed which English sports team in the 1960s?

8 Nassau is the capital of Bermuda, the Bahamas or Trinidad and Tobago?

9 If you were born on June 18, what would be your star sign?

10 If you cook something in a case of pastry, would your dish be: en croute, al fresco or pot au feu?

LEVEL 3

1 Anne of Burgundy was the first woman to receive what sign of an impending marriage?

2 How old was Sir Stanley Matthews when he stopped playing professional football?

3 How old was he when he died in February 2000?

4 What was the last record the Beatles made: *Sgt Pepper's Lonely Hearts Club Band*, *Abbey Road* or *Let It Be*?

5 What name is given to a law judge's small wooden hammer?

6 What London Underground line is coloured brown on a map?

7 In what year did Margaret Thatcher become British prime minister?

8 Was she the first ever British female prime minister?

9 What are progeny: fragments of Moon rock, a class of virus or children?

10 What's the official language of Haiti?

ANSWERS

1. A diamond engagement ring 2. 50 3. 85 4. *Let It Be* 5. A gavel 6. Bakerloo 7. 1979 8. Yes 9. Children 10. French

LEVEL 3

1 What are the uprights of cricket wickets called?

2 How many fiddlers had Old King Cole?

3 Who wore a coat of many colours?

4 Iceberg and Cos are types of what?

5 Where is the bow of a ship?

6 Which bird lays the largest egg?

7 Which is larger: 8 x 14 or 14 x 8?

8 What did Guy Fawkes try to blow up?

9 What are Catherine Wheels and Roman Candles examples of?

10 Where is Venice?

LEVEL 3

1 What is the opposite of the word brave?

2 The date is 10th May. What will the date be in two weeks' time?

3 What does a greengrocer sell?

4 What is a quarter of a half?

5 Which island lies just south of Hampshire?

6 What is the plural of sheep?

7 Frog spawn, tadpole. What comes next?

8 What is the name for a moving staircase?

9 What were German submarines called?

10 For which sport would you practise on nursery slopes?

ANSWERS

1. Cowardly 2. 24th May 3. Fruit and vegetables 4. An eighth 5. The Isle of Wight 6. Sheep 7. Frog 8. An escalator 9. U-boats 10. Skiing

LEVEL 3

1 Does air have weight?

2 What is the capital of the USA?

3 Which queen ruled Britain for 64 years?

4 How many 4s are there in 56?

5 If today is Tuesday, what was the day before yesterday?

6 What word do we use for a book of maps?

7 How many metres are there in 4.5 km?

8 Munich, Berlin and Hamburg are in which country?

9 Which of these animals is a carnivore: squirrel, leopard, rabbit, or giraffe?

10 What is the opposite of generous?

ANSWERS

1. Yes 2. Washington DC 3. Queen Victoria 4. 14 5. Sunday 6. An atlas 7. 4,500 8. Germany 9. The leopard 10. Mean or stingy

LEVEL 3

1 In which country is the Costa del Sol?

2 In which game is a shuttlecock used?

3 What is the plural of mouse?

4 In which century is 1314?

5 Where is Ayers Rock?

6 What do you call a barrier that holds back water?

7 Which aircraft carries the most passengers?

8 Where are your incisors?

9 How many wives did Henry VIII have?

10 What is the past tense of eat?

ANSWERS

1. Spain 2. Badminton 3. Mice 4. 14th 5. Australia 6. A dam 7. Jumbo jet 8. In your mouth (they are teeth) 9. 6 10. Ate

LEVEL 3

1 A river flows towards the sea. True or false?

2 How many grams are there in a kilogram?

3 What kind of fruit does a vine produce?

4 What did the dish run away with?

5 Which Indian leader lead his country in peaceful resistance?

6 On a compass, which direction is 90 degrees anticlockwise of East?

7 If a king abdicates, what does he do?

8 Napoleon Bonaparte was a leader of which country?

9 Which sea lies between Africa and Europe?

10 What is lightning?

LEVEL 3

1　Which flying machine has a rotor and a propeller?

2　How can you tell if a shape is symmetrical?

3　Which is the odd one out: Asia, Australia, China, North America?

4　Which Australian marsupial looks like a bear?

5　What is the plural of knife?

6　Who killed Cock Robin?

7　What is a young deer called?

8　Where was William the Conqueror from?

9　In which country would you find the towns of Nice and Marseilles?

10　Which of these numbers are exactly divisible by 3: 6, 8, 12, 24?

1. A helicopter 2. One fold gives 2 identical halves 3. China (the others are continents) 4. The koala 5. Knives 6. The sparrow 7. A fawn 8. Normandy in France 9. France 10. 6, 12, 24

LEVEL 3

1 What work did the Seven Dwarfs do?

2 What is mutton?

3 Where is Bombay?

4 What colour are British fire engines?

5 What emerged from Aladdin's lamp?

6 What are cirrus and cumulus examples of?

7 What is chocolate made from?

8 What does temperature measure?

9 What is the modern name of the Roman port of Londinium?

10 How many metres are there in half a kilometre?

ANSWERS

1. They worked in a mine 2. Meat from sheep over one year old 3. India 4. Red 5. A genie 6. Clouds 7. Cocoa beans 8. Heat 9. London 10. 500

LEVEL 3

1 What does Popeye eat for strength?

2 Which part of an aeroplane is the fuselage?

3 How many blackbirds were baked in the pie?

4 Which limbs of the Venus de Milo are missing?

5 Which animal is usually ridden in the desert?

6 Can you ride on African elephants?

7 Which of these numbers can be divided by both 3 and 4: 9, 12, 15, 16?

8 In which English city was there a great fire in 1666?

9 A recipe needs 80 grams of butter, I have 55 grams. How much do I need?

10 With which colour is Robin Hood associated?

1. Spinach 2. The body 3. 24 4. The arms 5. The camel 6. No, only on Indian elephants 7. 12 8. London 9. 25 grams 10. Green

LEVEL 3

1 Which American president was assassinated in Dallas, Texas?

2 What is the usual number of kidneys humans have?

3 What is the main language spoken in Turkey?

4 What are Sleeping Beauty, Giselle, and Swan Lake?

5 Which bridge in London can be lifted?

6 Where is the pupil in your eye?

7 Tyrannosaurus was what?

8 Where did gladiators originally come from?

9 What is to pull the wool over someone's eyes?

10 Which is the most common disease?